Joseph Boylan

Leaving
ertificate

Discovering Maths 3

ORDINARY LEVEL

Revised euro edition

FOLENS *Oliver Murphy*

ACKNOWLEDGEMENTS

I would like to thank the many people who helped me produce this book: Ed Guiney, Gerry Barry and Brendan MacGuill, for their work in de-bugging the text; Eleanor Mangan, Áine Clarke and Margaret Leen of St Mary's Secondary School in Moyderwell, Tralee for their advice in the drafting of this new version; editor Margaret Burns, and typesetter and designer Liz Murphy.

I would like to dedicate this book to every student I have taught over the years. Thanks to all of you.

Editor
Margaret Burns

Design & Layout
Liz Murphy

Artwork
Aidan MacCreary, John Sweeney

Folens Publishers,
Hibernian Industrial Estate,
Greenhills Road,
Tallaght,
Dublin 24.

ISBN 0 86 121 497 8

Produced in Ireland by Folens Publishers

CONTENTS

PREFACE

This new edition of *Discovering Maths 3* replaces the Irish pound with the Euro. Other changes have been introduced, based on comments received from teachers nationwide who used the first edition.

The new Leaving Certificate Ordinary Level Mathematics course has been up-and-running for several years. The examinations have put great emphasis on certain aspects of the new course and less emphasis on others. This book reflects exactly these emphases. It stresses what is important, and only touches on what is less important. It prepares students for precisely the kind of tasks which they will be asked to perform in the Leaving Certificate examinations.

The early chapters of this book cover the basics, where, as every teacher knows, students can be weak. At the same time, every chapter contains questions similar to the questions which have appeared in Leaving Certificate examinations to date. Towards the end of each chapter, there is a *Revision Exercise* which consists of eight or ten questions. These are modelled on examination questions, with an easy part (a), a standard part (b) and a more challenging part (c).

This book is up to date. The latest calculators can add fractions and perform some probability functions. This book shows students how to make the most of their calculators and hence do better in their exams.

This book is designed to be user-friendly for both student and teacher. For the student, the explanations are in clear and simple language, even when difficult material is covered. For example, the proofs of the theorems are very easy to follow. There are plenty of worked examples, not just of easy questions, but of harder ones as well. There is a *Summary of Important Points* at the end of each chapter, which contains the important formulae, points to remember, mnemonics and tips. For the teacher, the book is very carefully structured to introduce the difficulties of the course gradually. Each exercise is graded and contains plenty of questions for the regular student as well as a few challenging questions to stretch the more advanced student. The answers to most questions are at the back of the book, except where the answer requires only one step: (e.g. 'Write down the range and period of the given function').

This book contains the entire core as well as all four options, of which students must study at least one.

I hope that students and teachers find this book both practical and enjoyable in their work.

Oliver Murphy

Chapter 1

Arithmetic

One of the most common problems which students have with Mathematics is this: they mix up the rules for addition/subtraction with the rules for multiplication/division. Let's iron out this problem from the start.

Addition/Subtraction

Think of going up and down a lift, starting at the ground floor (zero).

Plus is up; minus is down.

$-8+2=-6$ [Down 8, up 2 is -6]

$-8-2=-10$ [Down 8, down 2 is -10]

Multiplication/Division

Like signs give plus.

Unlike signs give minus.

$(-8)\times(-2)=+16$ [Like signs give plus]

$(-8)\div 2=-4$ [Unlike signs give minus]

If you want to get a negative number, say -11.7 on a calculator, press 11.7 [+/–]. The number -11.7 should come up on the screen. So, to do the calculation $(-11.7)\times(-30)$, you should press 11.7 [+/–] × 30 [+/–] =. The answer 351 should appear.

Exercise 1.A

Evaluate:

1. $-5-3$	**11.** $(-8)\div(-4)$	**21.** $(-1.2)\times(-7)$	**31.** $(-1)\times(-2)\times(-3)$
2. $-5+3$	**12.** $(8)\div(-4)$	**22.** $-1.2-7$	**32.** $-10+2$
3. $(-5)\times(-3)$	**13.** $-15+3$	**23.** 50×1.4	**33.** $(-10)\div(+2)$
4. $(-12)\div(-4)$	**14.** $-15-3$	**24.** $50\times(-1.4)$	**34.** $(-10)\times(+2)$
5. $-12-4$	**15.** $(-15)\div(-3)$	**25.** $50\div 2.5$	**35.** $(-10)\div(-2)$
6. $(-12)\times(-4)$	**16.** $(-15)\div 3$	**26.** $50\div(-2.5)$	**36.** $-10-2$
7. $-12+4$	**17.** $(-15)\times 3$	**27.** $(-1)\times(-1)$	**37.** $(-10)\times(-2)$
8. $8-4$	**18.** $15\div(-3)$	**28.** $-1-1$	**38.** $(-4)\times(-3)\times(-2)$
9. $-8-4$	**19.** $-2-3$	**29.** $(-1)\div(-1)$	**39.** $-4-3-2$
10. $(-8)\times(-4)$	**20.** $(-2)\times(-3)$	**30.** $-1-2-3$	**40.** $4-3-2$

BRACKETS

In Mathematics, we put brackets around the operation which must be done ***first***. For example, to evaluate $3 \times (4 + 7)$, we do what's in the brackets first. So,

$$3 \times (4 + 7) = 3 \times 11 = 33$$

If no operation is indicated, it is understood that multiplication is the required operation. Hence, the above evaluation could be written $3(4 + 7)$ instead of $3 \times (4 + 7)$.

Similarly, $(-5)(-7)$ is a short way of writing $(-5) \times (-7)$. Hence, $(-5)(-7) = 35$.

DOUBLE NEGATIVES

In English, when we say that a film was ***not un***interesting, we mean that it was interesting. If we feel ***not dis***contented, we are contented. If a task is ***not im***possible, it is possible. So, a double negative is really positive.

It is the same with Maths. A double negative is positive. Here are five examples:

$-(-4) = +4$

$-(-1) = +1$

$5 - (-2) = 5 + 2 = 7$

$-5 - (-2) = -5 + 2 = -3$

$(7 - 1) - (2 - 10) = (6) - (-8) = 6 + 8 = 14$

INDICES AND ROOTS

2^3 means $2 \times 2 \times 2 = 8$. The number three is called the ***index*** or ***power***. The plural of index is ***indices***.

$(-3)^4$ means $(-3)(-3)(-3)(-3) = 81$

$(-1)^5$ means $(-1)(-1)(-1)(-1)(-1) = -1$

$\sqrt{25} = 5$ [the number which you square to get 25]

$\sqrt[3]{8} = 2$ [the number which you multiply by itself three times to get 8]

$\sqrt[3]{125} = 5$ [the number which you multiply by itself three times to get 125]

To get 2^3 on a calculator, press the four buttons [2] [x^y] [3] [=]. The answer 8 will appear.

To get $\sqrt{25}$ on a calculator, press [$\sqrt{\ }$] [2] [5] [=]. The answer 5 will appear.

To get $\sqrt[3]{125}$ on a calculator, press [$\sqrt[3]{\ }$] [1] [2] [5] [=]. The answer 5 will appear.

THE HIERARCHY OF MATHS

In Maths it is important to do the operations in the right order. If you do them in the wrong order, you will get the wrong answer. Here is the correct order in which to do them:

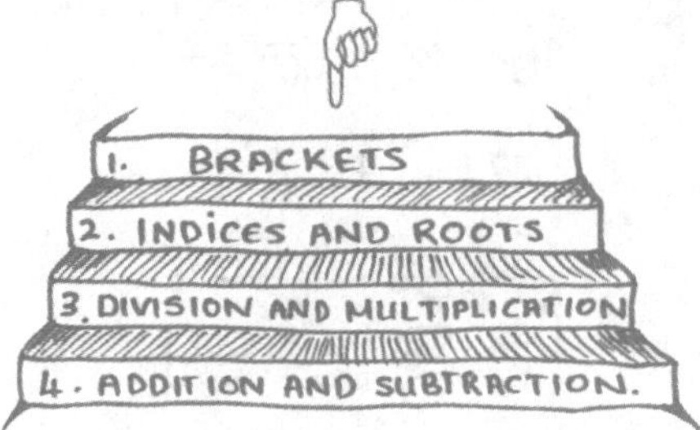

1. BRACKETS
2. INDICES AND ROOTS
3. DIVISION AND MULTIPLICATION
4. ADDITION AND SUBTRACTION.

This is an extension of the BOMDAS rules which you may have learned in Primary School. The new word to remember is **BIRDMAS**, which stands for ***b***rackets, ***i***ndices, ***r***oots, ***d***ivision, ***m***ultiplication, ***a***ddition, ***s***ubtraction.

Example 1: Evaluate (i) $5 + 3 \times 4$ (ii) $2 + 3(4 + 5)$

(iii) $30 - 2\sqrt{49}$ (iv) $1 + 3(5 - 1)^2$

Solution:

(i) $5 + 3 \times 4 = 5 + 12$ [Doing the multiplication first]

$= 17$ [Doing the addition next]

(ii) $2 + 3(4 + 5) = 2 + 3(9)$ [Doing what's in the bracket first]

$= 2 + 27$ [Doing the multiplication next]

$= 29$ [Doing the addition next]

(iii) $30 - 2\sqrt{49} = 30 - 2(7)$ [Doing the square root first]

$= 30 - 14$ [Doing the multiplication next]

$= 16$ [Doing the addition next]

(iv) $1 + 3(5 - 1)^2 = 1 + 3(4)^2$ [Doing what's in the bracket first]

$= 1 + 3(16)$ [Doing the index next]

$= 1 + 48$ [Doing the multiplication next]

$= 49$ [Doing the addition next]

Exercise 1.B

Evaluate the following:

1. $3+4\times 10$
2. $2+3\times 7$
3. $20+2\times 3$
4. $2(10-7)$
5. $3(1+4)$
6. $5(11-7)$
7. $1+2(3+3)$
8. $3+5(4-2)$
9. $4+3(11-8)$
10. $20-2(3+2)$
11. $(2+3)^2$
12. $2+(3)^2$
13. $(4+2)^2$
14. $4+2^2$
15. $(2+1)^3$
16. $2+(1)^3$
17. $1+(2+1)^2$
18. $4(3+2)^2$
19. $5(2+1)^3$
20. $2+3(7-5)^3$
21. $3\sqrt{36}$
22. $2\sqrt{9}+1$
23. $2\sqrt{25}-3$
24. $3\sqrt{4}+10$
25. $\sqrt[3]{27}$
26. $2+\sqrt{36}$
27. $\sqrt[3]{1000}+2$
28. $2\sqrt{49}+2$
29. $\sqrt{64}-5$
30. $2\sqrt{100}-4$
31. $3\sqrt{100}-14$
32. $10(\sqrt[3]{27})-5$
33. $3(1+\sqrt{49})$
34. $2(3+2\sqrt{25})$
35. $10(3\sqrt{4}+1)$
36. $4(\sqrt[3]{1000}-7)$
37. $\sqrt{64}-\sqrt[3]{64}$
38. $2(\sqrt{9}+1)^2$
39. $4(\sqrt{16}+\sqrt{1})^2$
40. $1+2(\sqrt{81}+1)^2$
41. $(\sqrt{4}+1)(\sqrt{4}-1)$
42. $(1+\sqrt{121})(3^2+1)$
43. $\sqrt[4]{16}+10$
44. $\sqrt[4]{16}+\sqrt{16}$
45. $(1+\sqrt{9})^2(\sqrt{4}+1)$
46. $2\sqrt{144}-2\sqrt[3]{125}$
47. $(\sqrt{36}-1)(\sqrt{25}-1)$
48. $10-3(1-\sqrt[3]{8})^3$
49. $11+3(11-\sqrt{64})^2$
50. $1-3(5-8)^3$

FRACTIONS

For those who hate fractions, here is some good news: your calculator will work out all calculations involving fractions – as long as you know how to use it!

To write 4½ press [4] [a b/c] [1] [a b/c] [2]. You will get 4 ⌐ 1 ⌐ 2 on the screen. This is the number 4½ in calculator-language.

So, to evaluate $3\frac{1}{2} \times 5\frac{2}{7}$, press

[3] [a b/c] [1] [a b/c] [2] [X] [5] [a b/c] [2] [a b/c] [7] [=].

The answer 18½ comes up on the screen (in the form 18 ⌐ 1 ⌐ 2, of course!)

AUTOMATIC BRACKETS

Sometimes, brackets are not written, but are ***understood*** to be there, nonetheless. Here are two examples:

$\sqrt{5+4}$ really means $\sqrt{(5+4)}$. We must do what's in the bracket first.

$\therefore\ \sqrt{(5+4)} = \sqrt{9} = 3$

$\frac{3+5}{5-1}$ really means $\frac{(3+5)}{(5-1)} = (3+5) \div (5-1) = 8 \div 4 = 2$

Exercise 1.C

Evaluate:

1. $\sqrt{3+1}$

2. $\sqrt{4+12}$

3. $\sqrt{3^2+7}$

4. $\sqrt{3(7)+4}$

5. $\sqrt{6^2+8^2}$

6. $5\frac{1}{4}+1\frac{2}{3}$

7. $6\frac{1}{4}+1\frac{2}{5}$

8. $2\frac{5}{8} \div 1\frac{1}{4}$

9. $2\frac{1}{2}+5\frac{5}{8}$

10. $5\frac{1}{2}+3\frac{5}{6}$

11. $\frac{13+5}{5+1}$

12. $\frac{36-3}{5+6}$

13. $\frac{5^2-1^2}{2^3}$

14. $\frac{3(4+5)}{3^2}$

15. $\sqrt{1+2^3}$

16. $\frac{\sqrt{3+13}}{7-5}$

17. $\frac{4^2-1}{4-1}$

18. $\frac{\sqrt{3^3+3^2}}{3^2-3}$

19. $\sqrt{\frac{4^2+3^2}{2^2}}$

20. $\sqrt{\frac{5^2+2}{2^2-1}}$

21. $\sqrt[3]{4^2+3^2+2}$

22. $\sqrt[3]{(3+4+1)^2}$

23. $\sqrt{\frac{4^3-1}{2^3-1}}$

24. $\sqrt[4]{3^3-3^2-2}$

25. $\sqrt{\frac{1+7^2}{2}}$

PROBLEMS INVOLVING FRACTIONS

Example 1: Write 45 cent as a fraction of €1.20.

Solution: This question means 'If 45 cent is the same as ☐ of 120 cent, what fraction goes in the box?'

The fraction= $^{45}/_{120}$ = $^{9}/_{24}$ = $^{3}/_{8}$: ***Answer***

Example 2: If ¾ of my money is €60, how much have I?

Solution: Use the 'three–step' method, known as the 'Unitary method'.

I ¾ of my money = €60

II ∴ ¼ of my money = €20

III ∴ $^{4}/_{4}$ of my money = €80 ***Answer***: €80

Exercise 1.D

1. Write 25 cent as a fraction of €1.
2. Write 75 cent as a fraction of €1.
3. Write 40 cent as a fraction of €1.20.
4. Write 35 cent as a fraction of €1.
5. Write €1.20 as a fraction of €6.
6. Write €1.50 as a fraction of €12.
7. Find ¾ of €7.
8. Find $^{4}/_{5}$ of €9.
9. Find ½ of ½ of €44.
10. Find ¾ of ¾ of €8.
11. If $^{2}/_{3}$ of my money is €20, how much have I?
12. If $^{4}/_{7}$ of my money is €120, how much have I?
13. If $^{2}/_{5}$ of my money is €100, how much have I?
14. I spent ½ of my money on a cinema ticket. I spent ¼ of what was left on popcorn. I have €3 left. How much did I start with?
15. A woman left half of her land to her brother. The remainder is to be divided equally amongst her eight grand-children. If each grand-child got 20 hectares, how much land was left?
16. A building site has area 7½ hectares. Each house requires an area of $^{3}/_{8}$ of a hectare. How many houses can be built on the site?
17. I spent $^{3}/_{8}$ of my money on a sandwich. I then spent $^{3}/_{10}$ of what was left on a can. I have €1.40 left. How much did the sandwich cost?

DECIMALS

Some evaluations do not work out exactly. In such cases, you may be asked to give the answer correct to a number of decimal places. In such cases, you should start counting after the decimal point and look at one ***extra*** digit. If the extra digit is 0, 1, 2, 3 or 4, then the decimal stays as it is. If the extra digit is 5, 6, 7, 8, or 9, the previous digit goes up by one.

For example, $\pi = 3.1415927654$ ... (a decimal number which goes on forever)

Correct to ***one*** decimal place, $\pi = 3.1$

Correct to ***two*** decimal places, $\pi = 3.14$

Correct to ***three*** decimal places, $\pi = 3.142$

Correct to ***four*** decimal places, $\pi = 3.1416$

Correct to ***five*** decimal places, $\pi =$ – well, what do you think?

Correct to ***six*** decimal places, $\pi =$ – again, what do you think?

Correct to ***seven*** decimal places, $\pi =$ – what do you think? And finally…

…correct to ***eight*** decimal places, $\pi =$

SIGNIFICANT FIGURES

As we saw, when we count decimal places, we start counting the digits after the decimal point.

But when we count significant figures, we count ***all*** digits, except zeros at the beginning or at the end.

Example 1:

(i) Evaluate $\dfrac{3+17}{3+10}$ correct to three significant figures.

(ii) Evaluate $\sqrt{3^2+11^2}$ correct to five significant figures.

(iii) Evaluate $\dfrac{1}{3^2+10^2}$ correct to two significant figures.

(iv) Evaluate 93.6×31.7 correct to one significant figure.

Solution: (i) $\frac{3+17}{3+10} = \frac{20}{13}$ $= 20 \div 13 = 1.538461538 = 1.54$ (correct to 3 sig. figs.)

(ii) $\sqrt{3^2 + 11^2} = \sqrt{9+121} = \sqrt{130} = 11.40175425$

$= 11.402$ (to 5 sig. figs)

(iii) $\frac{1}{3^2 + 10^2} = \frac{1}{9+100} = \frac{1}{109} = 1 \div 109$

$= 0.00917431 = 0.0092$ (to 2 sig. figs.)

(iv) $93.6 \times 31.7 = 2967.12 = 3000$ (correct to one sig. fig.)

Exercise 1.E

1. Write 4.1382
- (i) correct to one decimal place,
- (ii) correct to two decimal places,
- (iii) correct to three decimal places.

2. Write the number 51.2835
- (i) correct one decimal place,
- (ii) correct to two decimal places,
- (iii) correct to three decimal places.

3. Write the number 5.216
- (i) correct to two decimal places,
- (ii) correct to two significant figures.

4. Write the number 52.426
- (i) correct to three significant figures,
- (ii) correct to four significant figures,
- (iii) correct to two significant figures.

5. Write the number 34.6175
- (i) correct to four significant figures,
- (ii) correct to five significant figures,
- (iii) correct to two significant figures.

6. Write the number 3.9713
- (i) correct to three decimal places,
- (ii) correct to three significant figures,
- (iii) correct to two decimal places,
- (iv) correct to two significant figures.

7. Write the number 4927 correct to one significant figure.

8. Write 21 807 correct to two significant figures.

9. Evaluate $^2/_7$ correct to
- (i) three decimal places,
- (ii) two decimal places.

10. Evaluate $3/11$ correct to three decimal places.

11. Evaluate $\frac{3+10}{6}$ correct to three significant figures.

12. Write $\sqrt{2}$ correct to four significant figures.

13. Write $1+\sqrt{5}$ correct to three significant figures.

14. Write $5+\sqrt{130}$ correct to five significant figures.

15. Evaluate $\frac{3+\sqrt{13}}{2}$ correct to three decimal places.

16. Evaluate $\sqrt{1+3^2}$ correct to two significant figures.

17. Evaluate $\frac{1}{1+5^2}$ correct to three significant figures.

18. Evaluate $\frac{1}{2^2+5^3}$ correct to two significant figures.

19. Evaluate 4^6 correct to two significant figures.

THE WORD "OF"

The word 'of', when applied to Mathematics, means 'multiplied by'.
To get $5/8$ of 96, you get $5/8 \times 96 = 60$
To get 0.4 of €24, you get 0.4 × €24 = €9.60

RATIO AND PROPORTION

Example 1: Divide €40 between two people in the ratio 5 : 3.

Solution:

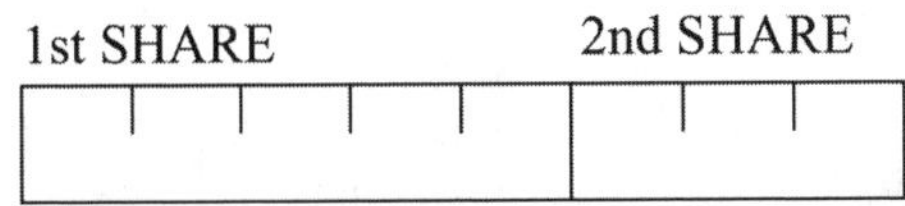

We can see from the diagram that the first person will get $5/8$ of the money $= 5/8$ of €40 = €25.
The other person will get $3/8$ of the money $= 3/8$ of €40 = €15.

Example 2: When €1 = 8.5 Norwegian krone,

(i) find the value in krone of €7.20,

(ii) find the value, to the nearest cent, of 100 krone.

Solution:

(i) €1 = 8.5 krone

$\therefore$ €7.20 = (8.5 × 7.20) = 61.2 krone

(ii) 8.5 krone = €1

$\therefore$ 1 krone = €$\frac{1}{8.5}$

$\therefore$ 100 krone = €100 x $\frac{1}{8.5}$ = €$\frac{100}{8.5}$ = €11.76 : ***Answer***

The method used to solve the above example is called the ***unitary method***. When the answer is in krone, you put the krone ***last*** in the first line. When the answer is euro, put the euro ***last*** in the first line.

Example 3:

The headmistress of a school agrees to contribute 20 cent to a fund for every €1 which the students in the school can raise.

(i) In the first week, the students raise €94.75. How much will the headmistress contribute?

(ii) In the second week, the total money collected (including the headmistress's contribution) amounts to €153. How much of this money did the students raise?

Solution:

(i) The students and the headmistress contribute money in the ratio 100 cent : 20 cent = 5 : 1
The contribution of the headmistress
= $^1/_5$ of €94.75 = €18.95 : ***Answer***

(ii) The students and the headmistress contribute money in the ratio 5 : 1

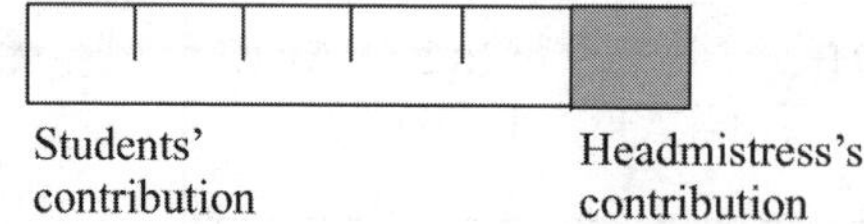

You can see from the diagram that the students contribute $^5/_6$ of the total. They contribute $^5/_6$ of €153 = €127.50 : ***Answer***

Example 4:

If x : 15 = 4 : 5, find the value of x.

Solution:

Since 15 is three times greater than 5, x must be three times greater than 4.

$\therefore \quad x = 12$: ***Answer***

Exercise 1.F

1. Divide €24 in the ratio 7 : 1.
2. Divide €21 in the ratio 4 : 3.
3. Divide €105 in the ratio 2 : 1.
4. Divide €88 in the ratio 8 : 3.
5. Divide 85 cent between two brothers in the ratio 4 : 1.
6. Divide €42 between three people in the ratio 4 : 2 : 1.
7. Divide $91 between three people in the ratio 8 : 3 : 2.
8. Divide prize-money of €1200 into three parts in the ratio 3 : 2 : 1.
9. Divide €3000 into four prizes in the ratio 4 : 3 : 2 : 1.
10. Divide prize-money of €700 into three parts so that the first prize is twice the second prize and the second prize is twice the third prize.
11. Divide 72 sweets between three children, so that the first child gets three times as much as the second, and the second gets twice as much as the third.
12. Divide 120 hectares of land between a woman and her three children, so that she gets three times as much as each child, but the children get equal shares.
13. Divide €10 000 between a man and his three sons, so that the sons get equal shares, but he gets twice as much as each son.
14. Divide 270 hectares between a woman and her five children, so that the children get equal shares, each getting a quarter of what the mother gets.
15. If $x : 3 = 20 : 15$, find x.
16. If $18 : 12 = 3 : x$, find x.
17. If $30 : 24 = 5 : y$, find y.
18. If $42 : 35 = k : 5$, find k.
19. If $100 : x = 5 : 2$, find x.
20. If $21 : 49 = 3 : x$, find x.
21. If $4\frac{1}{2} : 1\frac{1}{2} = 3 : x$, find x.
22. If €1 = 8 Norwegian krone, find
    (i) the value of €50 in krone,
    (ii) the value of 100 krone in €.
23. If €1 = 3 Polish zloty, find
    (i) the value of €40 in zloty,
    (ii) the value of 45 zloty in €.
24. When a euro is worth 200 Japanese yen, find
    (i) the value in yen of €250,
    (ii) the value in euro of a million yen.
25. When 1 euro is worth 1.8 dollars, find the value of
    (i) 50 euro in dollars,
    (ii) 450 dollars in euro.
26. A woman has $200 which she wants to convert to euro. At the time, the exchange rate is €1 = $1.6. The bank charges €5 per transaction. How many euro will the woman end up with?
27. A tourist from Australia wants to change 300 Australian dollars into euro. The exchange rate at a certain Bureau de Change is 1 euro = 2.5 Australian dollars. The Bureau de Change charges 10 euro per transaction. How many euro will the tourist get into the hand?

28. The 'Green World Company' pays €1 for every 50 cans. The pupils of a school collect 1400 cans. How much money will they get?

29. 5 miles = 8 kilometres.
   (i) Convert 100 miles to kilometres.
   (ii) Convert 100 kilometres to miles.

30. 1 kilogram = 2.2 lbs.
   (i) Convert 7 kilograms to pounds.
   (ii) Convert 11 lbs to kilograms.

31. A cookery book gives the following instructions for working out the length of time for cooking a turkey: 'Fifteen minutes to the pound plus 30 minutes extra'.
   (i) For how many hours should a 14-pound turkey remain in the oven?
   (ii) A turkey cooks for six hours. What is its weight in pounds?

32. Annie and Bertie live in two towns which are 12 kilometres apart. They agree to meet. They walk towards each other. Annie goes three times as fast as Bertie. How far from Annie's home town will they meet?

33. Divide €54.40 between three people in the ratio 10 : 5 : 2

34. When €1 = 9 krone, a man exchanges 315 krone for €32.50. There is a charge for this transaction. What is the charge?

35. Three people (X, Y and Z) contribute 45 cent, 30 cent and 25 cent towards a raffle ticket. They win a prize of €300. How much should each get, if they divide the prize proportionally?

36. Kylie is 8 years old and Lennie is 12 years old. They get a joint present of $100 from their aunt in California. They agree to divide it in proportion to their ages. How much does each of them get?

37. The headmaster of a school agrees to contribute 10 cent to a charity, for every €1 which the students can raise.
   (i) If the students raise €225 in the first week, how much will the headmaster contribute?
   (ii) If the headmaster has to contribute €17 in the second week, how much did the students raise in this week?
   (iii) In the third week, the combined sum for students and headmaster is €165. How much of this did the students raise?

38. When a sum of money is divided between two people in the ratio 4 : 3, the smaller share was €5 less than the greater share. How much was the original sum?

39. When a farm is divided between three children in the ratio 7 : 5 : 2, the smallest share was 100 hectares smaller than the greatest share. How many hectares were there on the farm?

REVISION EXERCISE 1.G

1. (a) Evaluate 3 – 4 – 5 – 6.
(b) Evaluate $\sqrt{12^2 + 5^2}$.
(c) Divide €350 between two people in the ratio 3 : 4.

2. (a) Evaluate $2^5 - 5^2$.
(b) Write $^1/_{13}$ as a decimal
(i) correct to three decimal places,
(ii) correct to three significant figures.
(c) When the exchange rate is \$1 = 9 Hong Kong dollars (HKD), find
(i) the value of \$50 in HKD,
(ii) the value in \$s of 50 HKD to the nearest cent.

3. (a) Evaluate $\sqrt{\dfrac{7^2 + 1}{1^2 + 1}}$.
(b) John is 13 years old. Jane is 17 years old. Divide €60 between John and Jane in proportion to their ages.
(c) A prize fund of €900 is divided in the following way: The first prize is three times as big as the second. The second prize is twice as big as the third. How much is each prize worth?
(d) A woman leaves her farmland to her five children. The eldest gets ½ of the land. The second eldest gets $^1/_3$ of the remainder. The other three children will get equal shares of what is left. What fraction of the land does each of these three children get?

4. (a) Write $\sqrt{7}$ correct to
(i) 2 decimal places,
(ii) 2 significant figures.
(b) Evaluate $4\frac{1}{2} \times 7^2/_3$.
(c) 5 miles = 8 kilometres.
(i) Convert 40 miles to kilometres,
(ii) Convert 40 kilometres to miles.

5. (a) Evaluate $3^4 - 4^3$.
(b) Evaluate $3\frac{3}{7} \times \left(2\frac{2}{5} + 1\frac{1}{10}\right)$.
(c) Members of a club had two weeks to raise money for their club. The President of the club agrees to contribute an extra
5 cent for every euro raised by the members.
(i) In the first week, the members raised €2700. How much did the President add to this in the first week?
(ii) In the second week, the total money raised by the members and the President was €3675.
How much did the members raise in the second week?

6. (a) If 36 : 45 = 4 : x, find x.
(b) Find $^3/_4$ of $1^3/_5$.
(c) A prize fund of €1000 is divided up between the first three winners in such a way that the first prize is twice the second prize and the second prize is three times the third. Find the value of each prize.

7. (a) If 1 : 3 = $3^1/_2$: y, find the value of y.
(b) Write $^8/_7$ as a decimal, correct to three decimal places.
(c) When the exchange rate is 1 euro = 230 Japanese yen, find the value of
(i) 250 euro in yen,
(ii) 25 000 yen, to the nearest euro.

8. (a) Write the number 53.1695
(i) correct to three decimal places,
(ii) correct to three significant figures.

(b) Evaluate $2 + 5\sqrt{17^2 - 15^2}$.

(c) A woman has 500 Swiss francs which she wants to convert into euro. The exchange rate is €1 = 2.2 Swiss francs. The bank charges €5 for the transaction. How much will the woman get, correct to the nearest euro?

9. (a) Evaluate $4 + \sqrt{4^3}$.

(b) If $3\frac{1}{4} : x = 13 : 4$, find x.

(c) Three people (A, B and C) contribute 55 cent, 40 cent and 5 cent, towards a lottery ticket, which costs €1. They win a prize of €220. How much will each of them get if they divide the prize-money proportionally?

10. (a) Evaluate $(3 - 5) - (11 - 4)$.

(b) Evaluate $\frac{5}{6} \times 5\frac{1}{4} + 5\frac{1}{2}$.

(c) To make an alloy of bronze, copper and tin are mixed in the ratio 9 : 1.
(i) If 270 grams of copper are used, how many grams of tin are needed?
(ii) If 500 grams of bronze is required, how many grams of copper and how many of tin will be needed?

1. **Addition and subtraction:** Plus is up, minus is down.

   Multiplication and division: Same signs give plus, different signs give minus.

2. The order in which to carry out operations is given by the ***BIRDMAS*** rule:
   brackets, ***i***ndices, ***r***oots, ***d***ivision, ***m***ultiplication, ***a***ddition, ***s***ubtraction.

3. **Decimal places:** start counting after the decimal point.

4. **Significant figures:** start counting at the first non-zero digit.

Chapter 2

Algebra

When we are solving Mathematical problems, we are often hunting for a mystery number. We usually let the mystery number be represented by a ***letter*** of the alphabet. So, we might let x represent grandfather's age, or let y represent the number of tickets sold for a concert, or v represent the velocity of a car. And so on. When we use letters to represent unknown numbers, we have entered the field of ***algebra***.

The rules for dealing with such mystery numbers are the same as those which we learned in Chapter 1 for real numbers. In other words, the rules for algebra are based on the rules for arithmetic.

In **algebra**, we write $2y$ as shorthand for $2 \times y$.
Similarly, $7k$ really means $7 \times k$.
And again, ab is the same as $a \times b$.
d^2 means $d \times d$.
And, p^3 is the same as $p \times p \times p$.
And $3ab^2$ means $3 \times a \times b \times b$.
Finally, here are two that cause much confusion:
$-x$ really means $-1x$ and, similarly, $-b^2$ means $-1b^2 = -1 \times b \times b$.

Example 1: If $x = 5$, find the value of

(i) $2x - 7$ (ii) $1 + 10x$ (iii) x^2 (iv) $3x^2$ (v) $10 + 12x - 2x^2$

Solution:

(i) $2x - 7 = 2(5) - 7 = 10 - 7 = 3$

(ii) $1 + 10x = 1 + 10(5) = 1 + 50 = 51$

(iii) $x^2 = (5)^2 = 25$

(iv) $3x^2 = 3(5)^2 = 3(25) = 75$

[Remember ***BIRDMAS***! Do the **i**ndex before the **m**ultiplication!]

(v) $10 + 12x - 2x^2 = 10 + 12(5) - 2(5)^2$
$= 10 + 12(5) - 2(25)$ [Indices first]
$= 10 + 60 - 50$ [Multiplications next]
$= 20$ [Additions and subtractions last]

Example 2: If $y = -3$ and $z = 4$, find the value of

(i) $5y + z$ (ii) $2yz$ (iii) $(y - z)^2$ (iv) $-z^3$ (v) $\frac{5y^2 - 1}{3z - 1}$

Solution:

(i) $5y + z = 5(-3) + 4 = -15 + 4 = -11$

(ii) $2yz = 2(-3)(4) = (-6)(4) = -24$

(iii) $(y - z)^2 = (-3 - 4)^2 = (-7)^2 = 49$

(iv) $-z^3 = -1z^3 = (-1)(4)^3 = (-1)(64) = -64$

(v) $\frac{5y^2 - 1}{3z - 1} = \frac{5(-3)^2 - 1}{3(4) - 1} = \frac{5(9) - 1}{3(4) - 1} = \frac{45 - 1}{12 - 1} = \frac{44}{11} = 4$

Exercise 2.A

1. If $x = 3$, find the value of

(i) $5x + 2$
(ii) $7x - 1$
(iii) $x - 7$
(iv) x^2
(v) $x + 11$
(vi) $2x^2$
(vii) $5x^2$
(viii) $10x^2 + 9$
(ix) $3x^3 + 10$
(x) $13 + 5x$

2. If $x = 2$, and $y = 5$, evaluate

(i) $x + y$
(ii) $y - x$
(iii) $x - y$
(iv) xy
(v) $3x^2$
(vi) xy^2
(vii) x^2y
(viii) $x^2 + y^2$
(ix) $3xy - 11$
(x) $(x + y)^2$

3. If $a = 6$ and $b = 4$, evaluate

(i) $2a + b$
(ii) ab
(iii) b^2
(iv) ab^2
(v) $(a + b)^2$
(vi) $a^2 + b^2$
(vii) $(a - b)^3$
(viii) $7a + 3a$
(ix) $11a - a$
(x) $a + 14a - 5a$

4. If $p = -2$ and $q = 3$, evaluate

(i) $p + q$
(ii) $p - q$
(iii) $q - p$
(iv) pq
(v) $-pq$
(vi) $q^2 + pq - q$
(vii) $10p - 2q$
(viii) p^3
(ix) p^2q
(x) $17p + 3p$

5. If $x = -5$ and $y = 2$, evaluate

(i) $x + y$
(ii) $x - y$
(iii) $y - x$
(iv) $3y^2$
(v) $4y^2 - y^2$
(vi) $y^2 + 2y^2$
(vii) $x^2 + xy + 3x$
(viii) $(x + 2y)^2$
(ix) $(x + 5y) - (x + 3y)$
(x) $y^2 + y^3$

6. If $m = -4$, find the value of

(i) $m + 1$
(ii) $m - 1$
(iii) $2m + 8$
(iv) $m^2 + 4m$
(v) $m(m + 4)$
(vi) $(m + 7)^2$
(vii) $m^2 + 49$
(viii) $3 - 5m$
(ix) $(m - 3) - (m + 7)$
(x) $m^3 + 4m^2$

7. Insert = or > or < between each of these pairs of expressions, where $x = 3$:

(i) $x + x$ ..... $2x$
(ii) $2x^2$ ..... $(2x)^2$
(iii) $(x + 1)^2$ ..... $x^2 + 1$
(iv) $13x - 3x$ ..... $10x$
(v) x ..... $x^3 - x^2$

8. If $a = 6$, insert <, >, or = between each pair of expressions:

(i) $5a$ ..... $6a - a$
(ii) $(a + 2)^2$ ..... $a^2 + 4$
(iii) $\frac{1}{2}a$ ..... $\frac{a}{2}$
(iv) $(a + 1)^2$ .... $a^2 + 2a + 1$
(v) $\left(\frac{1}{2}a\right)^2$ ..... $\frac{1}{2}a^2$

9. If $x = -1$ and $y = -2$, find the value of

(i) $x + y$
(ii) $x - y$
(iii) $2x - y$
(iv) xy
(v) $5xy$
(vi) $y - x$
(vii) $3x + 4y$
(viii) $3(x - 2y)$
(ix) $3(x - 2y)^2$
(x) $3(x - 2y)^3$

10. If $b = -3$, evaluate, $\dfrac{5b - 1}{b - 1}$

11. If $k = -7$, find the value of $\dfrac{k^2 - 1}{k - 1}$

12. If $x = 8$, find the value of $\sqrt{\dfrac{3x + 1}{2x}}$

13. If $y = -3$, evaluate $\sqrt{\dfrac{10 - 2y}{1 - y}}$

14. If $x = 5$ and $y = -2$, evaluate

$$\sqrt{\frac{x - 2y}{2(2x + y)}}$$

15. If $a = 4$ and $b = -7$, evaluate, $\sqrt[3]{5a - b}$

16. If $y = 6$, evaluate $\sqrt{\dfrac{3y - 1}{y + 4}}$ correct to three decimal places.

ADDING AND SUBTRACTING

You have surely noticed by now that $2x + 5x = 7x$, no matter what value x has.

Similarly $3x + 8x = 11x$.

And $9a - 2a = 7a$.

Also, $10t + t = 11t$.

And, $2x^2 + 3x^2 = 5x^2$.

Finally $x^2 + 7x^2 = 8x^2$.

Terms with the same letters, to the same powers are called ***like*** terms.
For example, $3ab$ and $7ab$ are two ***like*** terms.

$11xy^2$ and $-2xy^2$ are also ***like*** terms.
These three terms are also ***like*** terms: a, $5a$, and $-20a$.

But $3a^2b$ and $4ab^2$ are ***unlike***. Why? You answer!
It is very important to remember that you may add (or subtract) like terms, but you may not add (or subtract) unlike terms.

Example 1: Simplify:

(i) $2x + x - 11x$
(ii) $2p^2 + 3p - p$
(iii) $2a + 3b - a + 11b$
(iv) $y^2 + y^3$

Solution:

(i) $2x + x - 11x = -8x$
(ii) $2p^2 + 3p - p = 2p^2 + 2p$ [Only the like terms may be combined]
(iii) $2a + 3b - a + 11b = a + 14b$
(iv) $y^2 + y^3$: This ***cannot*** be simplified, as the terms are unlike.

Example 2: Simplify:

(i) $2xy + x^2 - 11xy - 3x^2$
(ii) $2p^2 + 3pq - p - 4pq + 4$
(iii) $3x^2y + 4xy^2$

Solution:

(i) $2xy + x^2 - 11xy - 3x^2 = -9xy - 2x^2$
(ii) $2p^2 + 3pq - p - 4pq + 4 = 2p^2 - pq - p + 4$
(iii) $3x^2y + 4xy^2$: No simplifications can be done here as the two terms are ***unlike***.

Exercise 2.B

1. Simplify the following:

(i) $2a + 5a$

(ii) $11b - 6b$

(iii) $7c - c$

(iv) $10d - d + 3d$

(v) $3x - 5x$

(vi) $y - 7y$

(vii) $2k + 2k - 3k$

(viii) $p + 4p - 6p$

(ix) $100x - 12x - 4x$

(x) $-3y + y$

2. Simplify the following:

(i) $11c - 2c$

(ii) $14b - b - 5b$

(iii) $3b - 11b - b$

(iv) $a - 8a$

(v) $99x - 100x$

(vi) $3y - y - 9y$

(vii) $12x - 25x$

(viii) $-10x + 17x + x$

(ix) $-4x - 5x$

(x) $-p - 2p$

3. Simplify the following:

(i) $-21c - 2c - c$

(ii) $4b - b - 5b - b$

(iii) $b - b - b$

(iv) $a - a + a$

(v) $9p - 21p$

(vi) $33y - y - 9y$

(vii) $-12x - 25x - 2x$

(viii) $-12k + 11k + k$

(ix) $-4x - 5x + 9x$

(x) $-p - 2p - 3p$

4. Simplify the following:

(i) $2a + 3b + 4a + 5b$

(ii) $3x + y + x + 5y$

(iii) $3b + 4c - b - c$

(iv) $a + 8a + 5b - b$

(v) $9x + 10y + x - y$

(vi) $3y - y + 4x - x + y$

(vii) $12x - 3y - 5x - y$

(viii) $-10x + 7z + x - z$

(ix) $-14x + 4y - 5x - 11y$

(x) $p + 10q - q - 2p$

5. Simplify the following:

(i) $11a + b - 2a - 3b + 3a$

(ii) $3x + 2xy + 4x + 10xy$

(iii) $3b + 11b^2 - b + 2b^2$

(iv) $a + 8a^2 + 2a + 3a^2$

(v) $9x^2 + x + 3x^2 + 10x$

(vi) $3y - 4 + 9y + 10$

(vii) $12x + 5 - 2x - 25$

(viii) $10x + 17 + x - 11$

(ix) $-4x + 13 - x - 5 + 6x$

(x) $-y + 11 - 2y - 13 + 8y$

6. Simplify the following:

(i) $11ab + 6 + 4ab - 2$

(ii) $7xy + 4 + 10xy - 9$

(iii) $8b^2 + 11b^2 - b + 2b$

(iv) $20 + 6a^2 - 2 - 3a^2$

(v) $9x^2 + xy + 7 + 3x^2 + 10xy - 5$

(vi) $11y + 4y + y + 10z - z$

(vii) $12x^2 + 5x - 8 - x^2 - 2x - 5$

(viii) $x^2 + 4x - 5 + 17x + x^2 - 11$

(ix) $3x^2 - 4x + 13 - x^2 - 15 + 11x$

(x) $y^2 + 11x^2 - 2xy - 13x^2 + 8xy + y^2$

7. Simplify: $4xy - y + 3xy - y - xy$

8. Simplify: $6xy - y^2 + 3xy - y - y^2$

9. Simplify: $y^2 + 3x^2 - x^2 - y^2$

10. Simplify: $6y^2 - y^2 + 3xy - xy + 5y^2$

11. Simplify: $x^2 + x^3 + 4x^2 + x^3$

12. Simplify: $a - a^2 + 2a + 2a^2$

13. Simplify: $3a^3 - a^2 + 12a + 12a^2 + 5$

14. Simplify these, if possible:

(i) $ab + 2ab + 3ab$

(ii) $3x^2 + 2x^2$

(iii) $3x^2 + 2x^3$

15. Simplify these, if possible:

(i) $ab^2 + 2a^2b + 3ab^2$

(ii) $3x^2 + 2x + 4$

(iii) $3x^2 + 2x^3 + 5x^3$

16. Simplify these, if possible:

(i) $11xy - xy$

(ii) $11x^2 - x^2$

(iii) $11x^2 - x^3$

17. Simplify these, if possible:

(i) $x^2 + x + 1$

(ii) $x^2 + 2x^2 - 3x^2$

(iii) $x^2 + 2x^2 - 3x^3$

18. Simplify these, where possible:

(i) $x^2 + x^3 + x^4$

(ii) $2x + 3x + 4x$

(iii) $2x^2 + 3x^2 + 4x^2$

19. Simplify: $1 + x^2 + 3x - 2x - x^2 - x - 1$

20. Simplify: $a + 2b^2 - 3a - 4b^2 - 5 + 6b$

MULTIPLYING TERMS

We have seen that we may add (or subtract) only terms which are ***like***. This is not true of multiplication. Indeed, we may multiply ***any*** terms.

When you multiply two algebraic terms, remember the rule of indices:

$$a^m \times a^n = a^{m+n}$$

When you multiply terms, start by multiplying the coefficients (the number parts), then multiply the letters in alphabetical order.

Example 1: Multiply these:

(i) $3p^2 \times 7p^3$ (ii) $2a^4b^2 \times 5a^3b^7$ (iii) $(10xy^2z^3)(-2x^2y)$

(iv) $(2xy)(3x^2y)(5y^4)$ (v) $(2a)(3b)(10c)$ (vi) $(10x)^3$

Solution: (i) $3p^2 \times 7p^3 = 21p^5$

[Since $3 \times 7 = 21$ and $p^2 \times p^3 = p^{2+3} = p^5$]

(ii) $2a^4b \times 5a^3b^7 = 10a^7b^8$

[Since $2 \times 5 = 10$, $a^4 \times a^3 = a^7$ and $b \times b^7 = b^8$]

(iii) $(10xy^2z^3)(-2x^2y) = -20x^3y^3z^3$

(iv) $(2xy)(3x^2y)(5y^4) = (6x^3y^2)(5y^4) = 30x^3y^6$

(v) $(2a)(3b)(10c) = (6ab)(10c) = 60abc$

(vi) $(10x)^3 = (10x)(10x)(10x) = (100x^2)(10x) = 1000x^3$

Exercise 2.C

1. Multiply these, using the rule $a^m \times a^n = a^{m+n}$

(i) $a^2 \times a^4$

(ii) $a^3 \times a^7$

(iii) $a^5 \times a^2$

(iv) $p^4 \times p^{10}$

(v) $y^2 \times y^3 \times y^7$

2. Multiply these terms:

(i) $2a^5 \times 3a^2$

(ii) $6b^3 \times 4b^7$

(iii) $5c \times 3c^2$

(iv) $10d^3 \times 6d^2$

(v) $4e \times 5e$

3. Multiply these terms:

(i) $6a^4 \times 3a^5$

(ii) $b^2 \times 4b^2$

(iii) $10c^4 \times 3c$

(iv) $2d^7 \times 8d^5$

(v) $9e^5 \times 3e^4$

4. Multiply these terms:

(i) $(2a)(7a^2)$

(ii) $(16b^5)(2b^6)$

(iii) $(5c)(3c)(2c)$

(iv) $(10d)(6d^2)$

(v) $(4e)(11e)(e)$

5. Multiply these terms:

(i) $(2ab)(10a^2b)$

(ii) $(6a^3b^5)(2a^2b^6)$

(iii) $(5ac)(3a^5c^2)$

(iv) $(2xy)(6xy^2)$

(v) $(4pq^3)(2pq)$

6. Multiply these terms:

(i) $(3ab)(7ab)$

(ii) $(2a^{10}b^2)(9ab^{11})$

(iii) $(5abc)(4abc)$

(iv) $(2xy)(3xy)(4xy)$

(v) $(7pq)(2p)(10q)$

7. Multiply these terms:

(i) $(-2a)(7a)$

(ii) $(-3b)(-2b)$

(iii) $(-5c)(-3c)$

(iv) $(-6p)(6q)$

(v) $(4x)(-7x)(-y)$

8. Multiply these terms:

(i) $(-2a)(-a)$

(ii) $(-b^2)(-2b^6)$

(iii) $(-c)(-c)(-c)(-c)$

(iv) $(4d)(-9d^2)$

(v) $(-e)(-2e)(-3e)$

9. Multiply out the following:

(i) $(12a)(12a)$

(ii) $(3b)^2$

(iii) $(5c)^2$

(iv) $(10d)^2$

(v) $(4e)^2$

10. Multiply out the following:

(i) $(11a)^2$

(ii) $(2b)^3$

(iii) $(5c)^3$

(iv) $(10d)^3$

(v) $(3e)^3$

11. Multiply out the following:

(i) $(2a)^4$

(ii) $(-2b)^3$

(iii) $(4c)^3$

(iv) $(10d)^4$

(v) $(3e)^4$

12. Multiply out the following:

(i) $(-2a)^5$

(ii) $(-4b)^3$

(iii) $(4x)^3(2y)^2$

(iv) $(3m^2)^3$

(v) $(-2k^2)^2$

BRACKETS

When we want to double or subtract or square a whole expression, we put it inside a bracket.

Example 1: Simplify the following:

(i) $2(3a+4b-c+11)$

(ii) $3(a-6b)-2(6a-3b)$

(iii) $(6x^2+3x+7)-(x^2-8x+5)$

(iv) $2x(x+1)-(2x^2-3x-10)$

Solution: (i) $2(3a + 4b - c + 11) = 6a + 8b - 2c + 22$ [Multiplying ***every*** term by 2]

(ii) $3(a - 6b) - 2(6a - 3b) = 3a - 18b - 12a + 6b$ [Note! $-2 \times -3b = +6b$]

$= -9a - 12b$ [Adding the like terms]

(iii) $(6x^2 + 3x + 7) - (x^2 - 8x + 5)$ [Subtract **every** term in the bracket...

$= (6x^2 + 3x + 7) - 1(x^2 - 8x + 5)$ ... by multiplying them by – 1 ...

$= 6x^2 + 3x + 7 - 1x^2 + 8x - 5$ ...**very** carefully!]

$= 5x^2 + 11x + 2$ [Adding the like terms]

(iv) $2x(x + 1) - (2x^2 - 3x - 10)$

$= 2x^2 + 2x - 2x^2 + 3x + 10$

$= 5x + 10$

Exercise 2.D

Simplify the following:

1. $2(3a + 4b)$

2. $3(4a + 10b)$

3. $4(3x - 2y)$

4. $6(x + 2y + 3z)$

5. $-2(2x + 5y)$

6. $-3(10x - 2y)$

7. $-10(4p - 6q)$

8. $-(x - 2y - 7z)$

9. $x(3x + 4)$

10. $3a(5a - 2b)$

11. $2b(3b^2 + 6b - 11)$

12. $2(x + 3y) + 3(2x + y)$

13. $6(m + 3n) + 7(m + n)$

14. $9(a - b - 1) + 3(2a - 6b + 5)$

15. $2(4x^2 + x + 3) + 3(x^2 - 4x - 7)$

16. $2(3t + k) - 4(t + 2k)$

17. $5(x - y) - 3(x + y)$

18. $3(x + 2y - 6) - 2(x - 10y - 7)$

19. $4(2x^2 - x - 1) - 3(x^2 + 3x - 5)$

20. $2x(x - 8) + x(x - 7)$

21. $(3a + 6b) - (2a + b)$

22. $(4a - 7b) - (a - 3b)$

23. $(a - 11b) - (6a - 2b)$

24. $(6x - 5y + 6) - (x - 11y + 8)$

25. $(14a^2 - 17b^2) - (5a^2 + 9b^2)$

26. $2(10a - 3b - 1) - (15a - 6b + 20)$

27. $x(3x - 1) - (3x^2 - x - 11)$

28. $a(4a - 7b) - 2a(2a - 3b)$

29. $2x(3x^2 + x + 1) - x(5x^2 + x - 3)$

30. $(x^2(10x - 3) - 9x(x^2 - x + 11))$

31. $\frac{1}{2}(6x - 8y + 4) - (3x - 4y + 2)$

MULTIPLYING EXPRESSIONS

There is one thing to be careful about when you are asked to multiply two expressions like $(3x+4)(4x+5)$: make sure that you multiply **every** term in the first bracket by **every** term in the second bracket. Then add together any like terms. Multiplying out two (or more) expressions is sometimes described as 'expanding'.

Example 1: Expand

(i) $(3x+4)(4x+5)$ (ii) $(2x-5y)(x-9y)$

(iii) $(2x+1)^2$ (iv) $(2x+1)^3$

Solution:

(i)
$$\begin{aligned}(3x+4)(4x+5) &= 3x(4x+5)+4(4x+5)\\ &= 12x^2+15x+16x+20\\ &= 12x^2+31x+20\end{aligned}$$

(ii)
$$\begin{aligned}(2x-5y)(x-9y) &= 2x(x-9y)-5y(x-9y)\\ &= 2x^2-18xy-5xy+45y^2\\ &= 2x^2-23xy+45y^2\end{aligned}$$

(iii)
$$\begin{aligned}(2x+1)^2 &= (2x+1)(2x+1)\\ &= 2x(2x+1)+1(2x+1)\\ &= 4x^2+2x+2x+1\\ &= 4x^2+4x+1\end{aligned}$$

[A **very** common mistake is to say that $(2x+1)^2 = 4x^2+1$ which you can see is ***wrong***!]

(iv)
$$\begin{aligned}(2x+1)^3 &= (2x+1)(2x+1)(2x+1)\\ &= (4x^2+4x+1)(2x+1) \quad \text{[Using the result from (iii) above]}\\ &= 4x^2(2x+1)+4x(2x+1)+1(2x+1)\\ &= 8x^3+4x^2+8x^2+4x+2x+1\\ &= 8x^3+12x^2+6x+1\end{aligned}$$

Remember:

Never write $(2x+1)^3 = 8x^3+1$.
This is commonly done by students,
but it is simply ***wrong***!

Exercise 2.E

Expand the following:

1. $(x+1)(x+5)$
2. $(x+2)(x+4)$
3. $(x+10)(x+4)$
4. $(y+2)(y+7)$
5. $(a+3)(a+2)$
6. $(a+2)^2$
7. $(x-6)(x+11)$
8. $(a+5)(a-8)$
9. $(y+8)(y-3)$
10. $(k+1)(k-7)$
11. $(x-2)(x-3)$
12. $(x-9)(x-2)$
13. $(2x+1)(3x+5)$
14. $(5x+2)(x+4)$
15. $(3x-7)(5x+2)$
16. $(2a+4)(2a+4)$
17. $(3y+2)^2$
18. $(10a+1)^2$
19. $(4y-1)^2$
20. $(7x-2)^2$
21. $x(x+2)(x+3)$
22. $x(x+1)(x-5)$
23. $2x(x+1)(x+5)$
24. $(x+1)(x-1)(x+2)$
25. $(x+1)^3$
26. $(x-2)(x^2+2x+4)$
27. $(2x+3)(4x^2-6x+9)$
28. $(2x-3)^3$

DIVIDING TERMS

The best way to do divisions is to think of dividing as multiplying in reverse. Ask 'What do I multiply the bottom by to get the top?' Remember the law of indices:

$$\frac{a^m}{a^n} = a^{m-n}$$

For example $\frac{45}{9} = 5$ ['What do we multiply 9 by to get 45?' Answer: 5]

Similarly, $\frac{35x^2y^3}{7xy} = 5xy^2$ ['What do we multiply $7xy$ by to get $35x^2y^3$?' Answer: $5xy^2$]

Finally, $\frac{-12x^8}{2x^2} = -6x^6$ [Since $\frac{-12}{2} = -6$ and $\frac{x^8}{x^2} = x^{8-2} = x^6$]

Exercise 2.F

Divide the following:

1. $\frac{a^7}{a^3}$
2. $\frac{a^{10}}{a^7}$
3. $\frac{a^{11}}{a^5}$
4. $\frac{a^{12}}{a^3}$
5. $\frac{14a^5}{2a^3}$
6. $\frac{6a^5}{2a^5}$
7. $\frac{20a^{12}}{4a^7}$
8. $\frac{16a^5}{2a^4}$
9. $\frac{6a^2}{2a}$
10. $\frac{10a^{10}}{5a^5}$
11. $\frac{6a^6}{2a^2}$
12. $\frac{15a^3b^2}{3ab}$
13. $\frac{25a^6b^3}{5ab^2}$
14. $\frac{18a^2b^2}{6ab}$
15. $\frac{21ab^2}{3ab}$
16. $\frac{27b^2}{3b}$
17. $\frac{-21x^{11}}{7x^7}$
18. $\frac{-24x^7}{-4x^5}$
19. $\frac{-12x^3}{-4x}$
20. $\frac{-2x^2}{x}$
21. $\frac{-6x^2}{-2x}$
22. $\frac{-2x^2y^3}{-xy}$
23. $\frac{-22x^2y}{-11x}$
24. $\frac{42x^7y^6}{6x^3y^4}$
25. $\frac{54x^{11}y^3}{6x^9y^2}$
26. $\frac{64x^4y^5z^7}{8x^3y^2z^5}$
27. $\frac{144xy^4z^5}{12xy^2z^5}$
28. $\frac{-14x^2y^9z^4}{-2xy^2z}$
29. $\frac{(3xy)(12x^2)}{6xy}$
30. $\frac{(4xy)(6xy^2)}{-2xy^2}$
31. $\frac{(12x^4y)(4xy^3)}{(2xy)^3}$
32. $\frac{(3p^4q^2)^2(10pq)}{(5pq)(3pq^2)}$

DIVIDING EXPRESSIONS BY A SINGLE TERM

$3x^2$, $-5a^2b$ and $11x^2y^3$ are called ***terms***. When terms are added together, we have an ***expression***. For example : $3x^2 + 5x^2y$ is an ***expression***. Similarly, here are some more expressions: $5x^2 + 2x - 7$, $2x - 9$, $3x^3 - 4x^2y - 11xy^2 + 4y^3$.

To divide an ***expression*** by a single ***term*** is easy: just divide each term in the expression, one by one.

For example: $\dfrac{12x^3 - 8x^2 + 6x}{2x} = 6x^2 - 4x + 3$ [Dividing the top, term by term]

Similarly, $\dfrac{9x - 6}{-3} = -3x + 2$ [Being ***very*** careful with the signs]

Exercise 2.G

Divide these expressions by the given term:

1. $\dfrac{2a + 4b}{2}$
2. $\dfrac{12a + 15b}{3}$
3. $\dfrac{22a + 14}{2}$
4. $\dfrac{2a^2 + 4a - 6}{2}$
5. $\dfrac{12a^2 + 54a - 6}{6}$
6. $\dfrac{21i - 14}{7}$
7. $\dfrac{12x^2 + 8x}{2x}$
8. $\dfrac{9x^2 + 18x}{3x}$
9. $\dfrac{10x^2 - 15x}{5x}$
10. $\dfrac{12x^3 + 18x^2 - 30x}{6x}$
11. $\dfrac{22x^3 - 88x^2 - 33x}{11x}$
12. $\dfrac{32x^3 + 8x^2 - 64x}{8x}$
13. $\dfrac{2x^4 + 6x^3 - 8x^2 - 10x}{-2x}$
14. $\dfrac{12x^4 + 16x^3 - 80x^2}{4x^2}$
15. $\dfrac{20x^4 + 15x^3 - 35x^2}{5x^2}$
16. $\dfrac{9x^4 + 6x^3}{3x^3}$
17. $\dfrac{14x^3 - 8x^2}{-2x^2}$
18. $\dfrac{4x^3y - 18x^2y^2}{2xy}$
19. $\dfrac{27x^3y^2 - 81x^2y^3}{9x^2y^2}$
20. $\dfrac{144x^3y^3 - 48x^2y^4 - 108xy^5}{-12xy^2}$

DIVIDING EXPRESSIONS BY EXPRESSIONS: LONG DIVISION

When we are asked to divide an expression by another ***expression*** (not just a single ***term***), we must use the method of 'long division'. This is very like the method of long division which you learnt in Primary school, for doing questions like $1197 \div 21$.

Example 1: Divide: $\dfrac{10x^2 + 11x + 3}{2x + 1}$

Solution:

$$\begin{array}{r|l} & 5x + 3 \\ 2x + 1 & 10x^2 + 11x + 3 \\ & \underline{10x^2 + 5x} \\ & \quad\quad 6x + 3 \\ & \quad\quad \underline{6x + 3} \\ & \quad\quad\quad 0 \end{array}$$

[$10x^2 \div (2x) = 5x$, so put $5x$ up]
[$5x(2x + 1) = 10x^2 + 5x$]
[Subtract and bring down 3]
[$3(2x + 1) = 6x + 3$]
[The remainder is zero]

***Answer*:** $5x + 3$

Example 2: Divide: $\dfrac{2x^3 + 11x^2 + 22x + 21}{x + 3}$

Solution:

$$\begin{array}{r|l} & 2x^2 + 5x + 7 \\ x + 3 & 2x^3 + 11x^2 + 22x + 21 \\ & \underline{2x^3 + 6x^2} \\ & \quad\quad 5x^2 + 22x \\ & \quad\quad \underline{5x^2 + 15x} \\ & \quad\quad\quad\quad 7x + 21 \\ & \quad\quad\quad\quad \underline{7x + 21} \\ & \quad\quad\quad\quad\quad 0 \end{array}$$

[$2x^3 \div x = 2x^2$, so put $2x^2$ up]
[$2x^2(x + 3) = 2x^3 + 6x^2$]
[Subtract and bring down $22x$]
[$5x(x + 3) = 5x^2 + 15x$]
[Subtract and bring down 21]
[$7(x + 3) = 7x + 21$]
[The remainder is zero]

***Answer*:** $2x^2 + 5x + 7$

When either expression involves ***negative*** terms, great care must be taken with the ***signs***. The best way to subtract is to 'change the sign on the bottom line and add'.

Example 3: Divide: $\dfrac{2x^3 - 7x^2 - 4x + 15}{2x - 3}$

Solution:

$$\begin{array}{rll}
 & x^2 - 2x - 5 & \\
2x - 3 \,) & 2x^3 - 7x^2 - 4x + 15 & [2x^3 \div 2x = x^2, \text{ so put } x^2 \text{ up}] \\
 & \underline{2x^3 - 3x^2} & [2x^2(2x - 3) = 2x^3 - 3x^2] \\
 & -4x^2 - 4x & [-7x^2 - (-3x^2) = -4x^2] \\
 & \underline{-4x^2 + 6x} & [-2x(2x - 3) = -4x^2 + 6x] \\
 & -10x + 15 & [-4x - (6x) = -10x] \\
 & \underline{-10x + 15} & [-5(2x - 3) = -10x + 15] \\
 & 0 & [\text{The remainder is zero}]
\end{array}$$

***Answer*:** $x^2 - 2x - 5$

Example 4: Divide: $\dfrac{x^3 + x + 10}{x + 2}$

Solution: In this case, there is ***no*** term in x^2. So we write the numerator as $x^3 + \underline{\mathbf{0x^2}} + x + 10$.

$$\begin{array}{rll}
 & x^2 - 2x + 5 & \\
x + 2 \,) & x^3 + 0x^2 + x + 10 & [x^3 \div x = x^2, \text{ so put } x^2 \text{ up}] \\
 & \underline{x^3 + 2x^2} & [x^2(x + 2) = x^3 + 2x^2] \\
 & -2x^2 + x & [0x^2 - (2x^2) = -2x^2] \\
 & \underline{-2x^2 - 4x} & [-2x(x + 2) = -2x^2 - 4x] \\
 & 5x + 10 & [x - (-4x) = 5x] \\
 & \underline{5x + 10} & [5(x + 2) = 5x + 10] \\
 & 0 & [\text{The remainder is zero}]
\end{array}$$

***Answer*:** $x^2 - 2x + 5$

Exercise 2.H

Perform these divisions:

1. $\dfrac{x^2+7x+10}{x+2}$

2. $\dfrac{x^2+8x+15}{x+5}$

3. $\dfrac{x^2+10x+21}{x+3}$

4. $\dfrac{x^2+6x+8}{x+4}$

5. $\dfrac{x^2+11x+30}{x+6}$

6. $\dfrac{2x^2+9x+10}{x+2}$

7. $\dfrac{3x^2+19x+28}{x+4}$

8. $\dfrac{2x^2+15x+27}{2x+9}$

9. $\dfrac{4x^2+12x+5}{2x+1}$

10. $\dfrac{x^2-2x-15}{x-5}$

11. $\dfrac{x^2+2x-24}{x+6}$

12. $\dfrac{x^2+4x-32}{x-4}$

13. $\dfrac{x^2-4x-60}{x+6}$

14. $\dfrac{x^2-14x+48}{x-8}$

15. $\dfrac{x^2-11x+24}{x-3}$

16. $\dfrac{10x^2+19x-15}{2x+5}$

17. $\dfrac{6x^2-13x-28}{2x-7}$

18. $\dfrac{10x^2-31x-14}{2x+7}$

19. $\dfrac{6x^2-7+2}{2x-1}$

20. $\dfrac{22x^2+13x+1}{11x-1}$

21. $\dfrac{x^3+3x^2+5x+3}{x+1}$

22. $\dfrac{x^3+5x^2+13x+14}{x+2}$

23. $\dfrac{x^3+5x^2+11x+15}{x+3}$

24. $\dfrac{2x^3+5x^2+6x+8}{x+2}$

25. $\dfrac{x^3+2x^2+2x+40}{x+4}$
[Take great care with signs]

26. $\dfrac{x^3+2x^2-9x-18}{x-3}$

27. $\dfrac{2x^3-6x^2+11x-7}{x-1}$

28. $\dfrac{x^3+2x^2-2x-3}{x+1}$

29. $\dfrac{x^3+2x^2-6x+3}{x-1}$

30. $\dfrac{x^3-8x+3}{x+3}$
[Remember to write the numerator as x^3+0x^2-8x+3]

31. $\dfrac{5x^3 - 19x + 2}{x + 2}$

32. $\dfrac{x^3 - 3x^2 + 20}{x + 2}$

[Write the numerator as $x^3 - 3x^2 + 0x + 20$]

33. $\dfrac{6x^3 + 19x^2 - 25}{3x + 5}$

34. $\dfrac{48x^3 - 11x - 12}{4x - 3}$

35. $\dfrac{x^3 - 1}{x - 1}$

36. $\dfrac{x^3 + 125}{x + 5}$

REVISION EXERCISE 2.I

1. (a) If $x = 6$, find the value of

(i) $2x + 11$

(ii) $1 - 5x$

(iii) $2x^2$

(b) Simplify $(2x^2 - x + 9) - (x^2 - 3x - 11)$

(c) Divide: $\dfrac{4x^2 + 18x}{2x}$

2. (a) If $x = -3$, find the value of

(i) $10x$

(ii) $21 - 7x$

(iii) $10x^2$

(iv) $(10x)^2$

(b) Multiply out:

(i) $(2x + 9)(3x - 1)$

(ii) $(2x + 9)^2$

(c) Divide: $\dfrac{6x^3 - 33x^2 + 18x}{3x}$

3. (a) If $x = 4$ and $y = 7$, find the value of

(i) $2x + y$

(ii) $2x^2 - 5x - 12$

(iii) $(x - y)^2$

(iv) $100 - 2xy$

(b) Simplify $2(2x^2 - x + 9) - (2x - 1)^2$

(c) If $x = 11$, evaluate:

(i) $\sqrt{9x + 1}$

(ii) $\dfrac{3x - 1}{x - 3}$

4. (a) If $x = 4$, evaluate $x^3 - 2x^2 - 3x - 20$

(b) Simplify $(3a + 2)^2 - (9a^2 + 4)$

(c) If $x = -7$, evaluate:

(i) $\sqrt{72 + 9x}$

(ii) $\dfrac{3x^2 - 3}{x + 16}$

5. (a) If $x = -3$, evaluate $x^3 - x^2 - 8x + 12$

(b) Simplify $(a - 1)^2 + (a + 1)^2$

(c) Multiply out $2(x - 7)^2$

6. (a) If $x = -2$, evaluate $x^3 - 5x^2 + 10x + 50$

(b) Simplify $(a + 5)^2 - (a - 5)^2$

(c) Multiply out $(x + 10)^3$

7. (a) If $x = 2$, evaluate $4x^3 - 10x^2 - x + 2$

(b) If $a = -7$ and $b = 3$, evaluate

(i) $b + a$

(ii) $b - a$

(iii) $(b + a)(b - a)$

(iv) $b^2 - a^2$

(c) Divide: $\dfrac{x^2 + 7x + 12}{x + 3}$

8. (a) If $x = -5$, evaluate $x^3 + 5x^2 - x - 6$

(b) If $a = 4$ and $b = 3$, evaluate

(i) $b^2 + a^2$

(ii) $\sqrt{b^2 + a^2}$

Investigate if $\sqrt{b^2 + a^2} = b + a$

(c) Divide: $\dfrac{x^2 - 2x - 35}{x - 7}$

9. (a) If $x = 8$, evaluate $\sqrt[3]{x^2}$.

(b) If $x = 2$ and $y = 5$, investigate if

$\dfrac{1}{x} + \dfrac{1}{y} = \dfrac{1}{x + y}$

(c) Do this long division:

$\dfrac{x^3 + 4x^2 + 8x + 15}{x + 3}$

10. (a) If $p = -2$ and $q = -8$, find the value of

(i) $p + q$

(ii) $p - q$

(iii) $\sqrt{pq}$

(b) Simplify:

(i) $(x - 3)^2 - 3(3 - x)$

(ii) $(x + 3)^3 - (x - 3)^3$

(iii) $(a^2)(a^3) + a^5$

(c) Divide:

(i) $\dfrac{2x^3 - 5x^2 + x + 3}{2x - 3}$

(ii) $\dfrac{27x^3 + 8}{3x + 2}$

1. $3x$, $4xy$, $-5x^3$ are examples of ***terms***.

2. An ***expression*** consists of some terms added together:
$3x + 4xy - 5x^3$.

3. Terms with the ***same*** letters to the ***same*** powers are called ***like*** terms.
For example, $3xy$ and $5xy$ are ***like*** terms.
$3ab^2$ and $5a^2b$ are ***unlike*** terms.

4. Only ***like*** terms may be added or subtracted. ***Any*** terms may be multiplied or divided.

5. $a^m \times a^n = a^{m+n}$

6. $\dfrac{a^m}{a^n} = a^{m-n}$

Chapter 3

Linear Equations and Inequalities

LINEAR EQUATIONS

Any equation in which the highest power of x is one, is called a ***linear*** equation. There are no squares, or cubes, or higher powers in a linear equation.

Here are some examples.

Example 1: Solve for x: $5x + 7 = 52$

Solution:

$$\begin{aligned} 5x + 7 &= 52 \\ \therefore \quad 5x + 7 - 7 &= 52 - 7 && \text{[Subtracting 7 from both sides]} \\ \therefore \quad 5x &= 45 && \text{[Simplifying]} \\ \therefore \quad x &= 9 && \text{[Dividing both sides by 5]} \end{aligned}$$

Example 2: Solve for x: $3x + 11 = 7x - 1$

Solution: When there are xs on both sides, get rid of the ***lesser number*** of xs, by subtracting that number of xs from both sides.

$$\begin{aligned} 3x + 11 &= 7x - 1 && \text{[}3x\text{ is the lesser number of }x\text{s]} \\ \therefore \quad 3x + 11 - 3x &= 7x - 1 - 3x && \text{[Subtracting }3x\text{ from both sides]} \\ \therefore \quad 11 &= 4x - 1 && \text{[Simplifying]} \\ \therefore \quad 11 + 1 &= 4x - 1 + 1 && \text{[Adding 1 to both sides]} \\ \therefore \quad 12 &= 4x && \text{[Simplifying]} \\ \therefore \quad 3 &= x && \text{[Dividing both sides by 4]} \end{aligned}$$

Example 3: Solve for x: $2(x + 10) = 11 - 3(x - 7)$

Solution:

$$\begin{aligned} 2(x + 10) &= 11 - 3(x - 7) \\ \therefore \quad 2x + 20 &= 11 - 3x + 21 && \text{[Getting rid of brackets]} \\ \therefore \quad 2x + 20 &= 32 - 3x && \text{[Simplifying]} \\ \therefore \quad 2x + 20 + 3x &= 32 - 3x + 3x && \text{[Adding }3x\text{ to both sides]} \\ \therefore \quad 5x + 20 &= 32 && \text{[Simplifying]} \\ \therefore \quad 5x &= 12 && \text{[Subtracting 20 from both sides]} \\ \therefore \quad \frac{5x}{5} &= \frac{12}{5} && \text{[Dividing both sides by 5]} \\ \therefore \quad x &= \frac{12}{5} && \text{[Simplifying]} \end{aligned}$$

[In line four of this solution, we got rid of the $-3x$, since -3 is a lower number than $+2$. In general, we always get rid of the term with the lower number of xs.]

Exercise 3.A

Solve these equations:

1. $2x + 5 = 11$

2. $3x + 6 = 21$

3. $7x + 1 = 43$

4. $12x + 5 = 41$

5. $2x - 5 = 7$

6. $8x - 5 = 19$

7. $11x - 7 = 81$

8. $5 = 2x - 11$

9. $21 = 3x - 6$

10. $4x + 7 = -1$

11. $2x + 15 = 9$

12. $x + 5 = -11$

13. $2x + 3 = x + 11$

14. $3x + 1 = x + 15$

15. $7x - 1 = 3x + 15$

16. $10x + 1 = x + 46$

17. $9x + 8 = 6x + 20$

18. $x + 1 = 7 - x$

19. $2x + 1 = 8x - 53$

20. $5x + 7 = 9x - 5$

21. $15x - 1 = 9x - 19$

22. $x + 17 = 27 - 9x$

23. $5(x + 7) = 25(x - 1)$

24. $8(x + 3) = 5(x + 6)$

25. $5(x + 1) + 1 = 12(x - 3)$

26. $4(x + 7) = 5(2 - x)$

27. $2(3x + 7) = 7(4x - 1) - 1$

28. $11(x + 7) = 4 - 10(x - 1)$

29. $9(2x - 3) = 25(x - 1) + 5$

30. $3(x - 2) = 7(x + 5) - 1$

31. $2(x + 7) - 5(x - 1) = 13$

32. $3(4x - 6) + 25(x + 2) = x - 4$

Some of the solutions here will not be whole numbers.

33. $3(x - 1) = x + 2$

34. $3(2x - 1) = 4x$

35. $4(x - 1) = 2x + 3$

36. $8(2x - 1) = 4x - 5$

37. $5(x - 1) = 2(x + 2) - x$

38. $5(7x + 3) = 2(3 - x) - 3 + x$

39. $5x - 1 - 2(x + 2) = x$

40. $11 = 7(x + 1) - 2(3 - 8x) - 3x$

41. Find the value of y which satisfies the equation $3(y - 1) = 1 + 4y$ and verify your solution.

42. Find the value of k which satisfies the equation $11 - k = 3(2 - k) + 1$ and verify your solution

43. Find the value of p which satisfies the equation $9(3 - p) + 1 + 4p = -p$ and verify your solution.

44. Find the value of z which satisfies the equation $11z - 2 = 5(z - 2) - 2z$ and verify your solution.

45. Find the value of y which satisfies the equation $2 - 3(y + 5) = 1 + 4y$ and verify your solution.

EQUATIONS WITH FRACTIONS

When an equation contains fractions, we multiply both sides by the lowest common denominator. This will see an end to the fractions.

Example 1: Solve $\frac{x+1}{5} = 1 + \frac{x-7}{2}$

Solution: The lowest common denominator is 10, so we will multiply ***all three*** parts by 10.

$$\frac{10(x+1)}{5} = 10(1) + \frac{10(x-7)}{2}$$

$$\therefore\ 2(x+1) = 10 + 5(x-7)$$

$$\therefore\ 2x+2 = 10 + 5x - 35$$

$$\therefore\ 2x+2 = 5x - 25$$

$$\therefore\ 2x+2-2x = 5x - 25 - 2x$$

$$\therefore\ 2 = 3x - 25$$

$$\therefore\ 27 = 3x$$

$$\therefore\ 9 = x$$

Example 2: Solve for x: $\frac{2}{3}(x+1) = \frac{1}{2}(x-5) + 5$

Solution: The lowest common denominator is 6, so we will multiply all parts by 6.

$$6\left(\frac{2}{3}\right)(x+1) = 6\left(\frac{1}{2}\right)(x-5) + 6(5)$$

$$\therefore\ 4(x+1) = 3(x-5) + 30$$

$$\therefore\ 4x+4 = 3x - 15 + 30$$

$$\therefore\ 4x+4 = 3x + 15$$

$$\therefore\ 4x - 3x + 4 = 15$$

$$\therefore\ x + 4 = 15$$

$$\therefore\ x = 15 - 4$$

$$\therefore\ x = 11$$

Exercise 3.B

Solve these equations:

1. $\frac{x+1}{3} = \frac{x}{2}$

2. $\frac{x+4}{3} = \frac{x+1}{2}$

3. $\frac{x+1}{4} = \frac{x-1}{3}$

4. $\frac{x+1}{5} = \frac{x}{3} - 1$

5. $\frac{2x-1}{3} = x - 4$

6. $\frac{5x+1}{3} = \frac{x+1}{2} + 8$

7. $\frac{5x-1}{7} = \frac{(x+2)}{2} + 1$

8. $\frac{4x+1}{5} + 1 = x$

9. $\frac{11x+1}{10} + 3 = x + \frac{x-1}{2}$

10. $\frac{2x-1}{5} = \frac{x+2}{3}$

11. $\frac{1}{2}x + \frac{1}{3}x = 5$

12. $\frac{1}{3}x - \frac{1}{4}x = 2$

13. $\frac{1}{2}x + \frac{1}{3}x - \frac{1}{4}x = 7$

14. $\frac{1}{2}(x-4) - \frac{1}{3}(x-3) = 5$

15. $\frac{x+1}{5} - \frac{x+9}{4} = 1 - \frac{x+19}{6}$

16. $\frac{1}{6}x - \frac{2}{5}(x+1) = \frac{5}{2}(x-10)$

17. $\frac{x-1}{3} - \frac{x+2}{6} - \frac{x-6}{4} = 0$

18. $\frac{1}{3}(x+13) - \frac{1}{7}(x+9) = x - 1$

19. $\frac{1}{4}(5x+1) - \frac{4x-7}{3} = 1\frac{5}{12}$

20. $\frac{1}{7}(6x-1) + \frac{1}{6}(2x+5) = 1 - \frac{3}{14}(x+8)$

21. $\frac{x-3}{5} - \frac{x-2}{6} = \frac{x+2}{10} - 1$

22. $2 = \frac{3x-7}{7} - \frac{5x-4}{2} - \frac{x-3}{3}$

MAKING UP MATHEMATICAL EXPRESSIONS

How many days are there in 5 weeks? The answer is $7 \times 5 = 35$.
How many days are there in y weeks? The answer is $7 \times y = 7y$.
How many months are there in 3 years and 7 months? The answer is $12 \times 3 + 7 = 43$.
How many months are there in n years and m months? The answer is $12 \times n + m = 12n + m$.
Anne is 16 years old and her mother is three times as old. How old will the mother be in 5 years' time? The answer is $3 \times 16 + 5 = 48 + 5 = 53$.
Anne is x years old and her mother is three times as old. How old will the mother be in 5 years' time? The answer is $3 \times x + 5 = 3x + 5$.

Exercise 3.C

1. (i) How many days are there in 10 weeks?
   (ii) How many days are there in x weeks?
2. (i) How many months are there in 5 years?
   (ii) How many months are there in x years?
3. (i) How many minutes are there in 2 hours?
   (ii) How many minutes are there in x hours?
4. (i) How many days are there in 4 weeks and 2 days?
   (ii) How many days are there in x weeks and y days?
5. (i) How many points does a hurling team get for 3 goals and 10 points? [1 goal = 3 points]
   (ii) How many points does a hurling team get for x goals and y points?
6. (i) Barry is 22 years old. How old will he be in 4 years' time?
   (ii) Carol is x years old. How old will she be in 4 years' time?
7. (i) Deirdre is 18 years old. Her father is three times as old. How old is her father?
   (ii) Emer is y years old. Her father is three times as old. How old is her father?
8. (i) Fred is 27 years old. His mother is twice as old. How old will his mother be in 10 years' time?
   (ii) Gus is x years old. His father is twice as old. How old will his father be in 10 years' time?
9. (i) Harry is 80 years old. His son is half as old. How old was his son three years ago?
   (ii) Ivan is x years old. His son is half as old. How old was his son three years ago?
10. (i) Sally is 75 years old. Her grandson is one third as old. How old was her grandson 10 years ago?
    (ii) Theresa is x years old. Her granddaughter is one third as old. How old was her granddaughter 10 years ago?
11. (i) There are 100 books on a shelf. If 75 of them are paperbacks, how many are hardbacks?
    (ii) There are 100 books on a shelf. If x of them are paperbacks, how many are hardbacks?
12. (i) There are 29 students in a class. If 17 of them are girls, how many are boys?
    (ii) There are 29 students in a class. If x of them are girls, how many are boys?
13. There are 44 people in a room. If n of them are adults, how many are children?
14. There are 53 people in a room. x of them are children. The adults are divided equally into male and female. Write down an expression for the number of female adults in the room
15. A woman leaves €1000 to her four children. €x is for the eldest. The rest is to be divided equally amongst the other three (who are triplets). How much does each triplet get?
16. A rectangular field has length x metres and width y metres. Write down an expression for
    (i) the area of the field,
    (ii) the perimeter of the field.
17. There are n people in a town. Two-fifths of them are female. Two hundred males leave the town. How many males remain?
18. I bought n tapes for €x each and m CDs for €y each. How much change will I get from €z?

PROBLEMS LEADING TO A LINEAR EQUATION

Here are the steps which you should take, when solving problems.

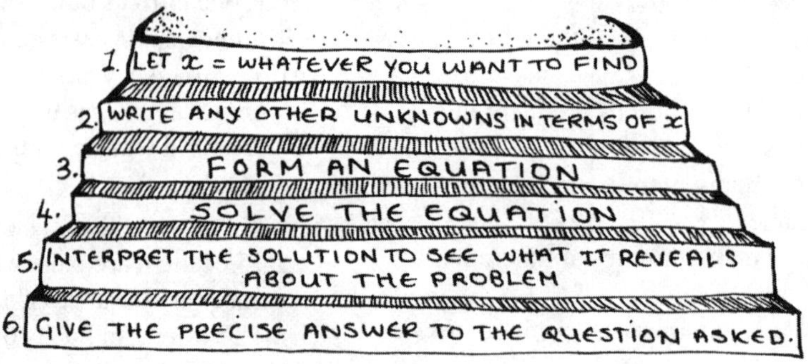

1. LET x = WHATEVER YOU WANT TO FIND
2. WRITE ANY OTHER UNKNOWNS IN TERMS OF x
3. FORM AN EQUATION
4. SOLVE THE EQUATION
5. INTERPRET THE SOLUTION TO SEE WHAT IT REVEALS ABOUT THE PROBLEM
6. GIVE THE PRECISE ANSWER TO THE QUESTION ASKED.

Never guess the answer, or use trial-and-error until you chance upon the solution! This is a Mathematics course, not a good-guessers guide book.

Example 1: James is one year older than Kevin. Leah is twice as old as James. The total of their ages is 47. How old are they?

Solution: Let x = Kevin's age. [It is a good idea to let x = the youngest's age]

$\therefore \quad x + 1 = \text{James' age.}$

$\therefore \quad 2(x + 1) = \text{Leah's age.}$

The sum of their ages = 47

$\therefore \quad x + (x + 1) + 2(x + 1) = 47$

$\therefore \quad x + x + 1 + 2x + 2 = 47$

$\therefore \quad 4x + 3 = 47$

$\therefore \quad 4x = 44$

$\therefore \quad x = 11$

$\therefore$ Kevin's age = 11, James' age = 11 + 1 = 12, Leah's age = 2(12) = 24

Example 2: There are 80 seats in a cinema. Some are de luxe (costing €3 each) and the rest are ordinary (costing €2 each). When the cinema is full, the takings amount to €185. How many of each type of seat are there?

Solution: Let x = the number of de luxe seats.

$\therefore$ $80 - x$ = the number of ordinary seats.

The total sum of the takings = 185

$\therefore \quad 3x + 2(80 - x) = 185$

$\therefore \quad 3x + 160 - 2x = 185$

$\therefore \quad x + 160 = 185$

$\therefore \quad x = 25$

$\therefore$ There are 25 de luxe seats and 80 – 25 = 55 ordinary seats.

Exercise 3.D

1. When you double a number and add 17, the result is 35. Find the number.
2. When I add three to a certain number and double the result, I get 62. What is the number?
3. When a number is trebled and 7 is taken away, the result is 26. Find the number.
4. When I multiply a number by 12 and add 37, the result is 325. Find the number.
5. When a number is trebled, the result is the same as when 14 is added to the number. What is the number?
6. Find two consecutive natural numbers whose sum is 83. [Hint: Let the numbers be n and $(n + 1)$].
7. Find two consecutive natural numbers such that eight times the first is 1 less than seven times the second.
8. Find three consecutive natural numbers such that five times the first is 24 more than the sum of the other two.
9. Annie is y years old. Her sister is twice as old as her. Their mother is 25 years older than Annie's sister. The total of all their ages is 80. How old is Annie?
10. There are 100 seats in a cinema. Some are luxury seats, costing €2 each; the rest are ordinary seats, costing €1 each. When the cinema is full, the takings come to a total of €170. How many of the seats are 'luxury'?
11. Find two consecutive ***even*** numbers such that six times the first is equal to five times the second. [Hint: Let the numbers be n and $(n + 2)$]
12. Find two consecutive ***odd*** numbers such that seven times the smaller is 12 more than five times the bigger.
13. Emily's age is x. Frances is three years older. Their father's age is twice the sum of their ages. If their three ages add up to 93, find their ages.
14. Marie is x years old. Her brother, Ned, is 5 years older. Oliver, their father, is three times as old as Ned. The sum total of their three ages is 95. How old is Marie?
15. Graham is x years old. Hilda is three times as old. In four years' time, Hilda's age will be twice Graham's age. How old are they now?
16. Darren is five times as old as his little sister, Stacey. In five years' time, Darren will be three times as old as Stacey. How old is Stacey now?
17. I have 20 coins. All of them are either 1 euro coins or 50 cent coins. They are worth €11. How many euro coins and how many 50 cent coins do I have? [Hint: Let x = the number of 1 euro coins and let $(20 - x)$ = the number of 50 cent coins.]
18. Divide 34 into two parts so that two-thirds of one part is equal to three-quarters of the other.
19. Find three consecutive numbers such that the sum of one-half of the smallest, one-fifth of the middle one and one-quarter of the largest is equal to 14.
20. I have 12 coins in my pocket. All of them are either 10 cent coins or 50 cent coins. They are worth €2.40. How many 10 cent coins and how many 50 cent coins do I have?
21. A blender mixes 2 kg of Kenyan tea, worth 30 cent per kg with x kg of Indian tea worth 24 cent per kg. The mixture is worth 26 cent per kg. Find x.
22. I mix 6 kg of Brazilian coffee, which costs 81 cent per kg with x kg of Colombian coffee, which costs 86 cent per kg. The mixture costs 84 cent per kg. Find the value of x.
23. $^{2}/_{3}$ of a number is 10 more than $^{3}/_{7}$ of the number. What is the number?

SIMULTANEOUS EQUATIONS

We will now show how to solve a pair of simultaneous equations. These are two equations (in x and y) which must be simultaneously satisfied by particular values of x and y. For example: $2x + y = 11$, $3x - 2y = 6$.

Here are the steps to follow:

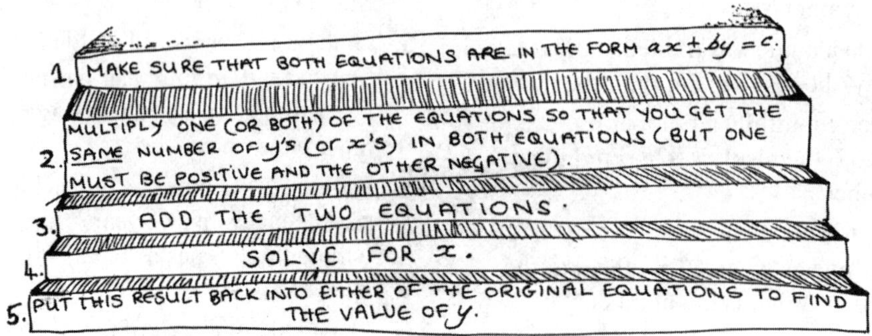

1. MAKE SURE THAT BOTH EQUATIONS ARE IN THE FORM $ax \pm by = c$.
2. MULTIPLY ONE (OR BOTH) OF THE EQUATIONS SO THAT YOU GET THE SAME NUMBER OF y'S (or x'S) IN BOTH EQUATIONS (BUT ONE MUST BE POSITIVE AND THE OTHER NEGATIVE).
3. ADD THE TWO EQUATIONS.
4. SOLVE FOR x.
5. PUT THIS RESULT BACK INTO EITHER OF THE ORIGINAL EQUATIONS TO FIND THE VALUE OF y.

Example 1: Solve the simultaneous equations: $2x + y = 11$, $3x - 2y = 6$.

Solution: We will multiply the first equation by 2 so that we will get $+2y$ in the first equation and $-2y$ in the other.

$2 \times$ I:	$4x + 2y = 22$	
II:	$3x - 2y = 6$	
Add!	$7x = 28$	
$\therefore$	$x = 4$	
But	$2x + y = 11$	[Taking either of the original equations]
$\therefore$	$2(4) + y = 11$	[Since we have found that $x = 4$]
$\therefore$	$8 + y = 11$	
$\therefore$	$y = 3$	

Answer: $x = 4$ and $y = 3$. This can be written as (4, 3).

Example 2: Solve the simultaneous equations:

$5x + 3y - 19 = 0$.

$$\frac{2x - y}{4} - \frac{x + y}{3} = 2$$

Solution: We will write the first equation like this: $5x + 3y = 19$.

We will multiply the second equation by 12 (the lowest common denominator):

$$\frac{12(2x - y)}{4} - \frac{12(x + y)}{3} = 12(2)$$

$$\therefore \quad 3(2x - y) - 4(x + y) = 24$$

$$\therefore \quad 6x - 3y - 4x - 4y = 24$$

$$\therefore \quad 2x - 7y = 24$$

We will multiply the first equation by 7 and the second by 3, so that we will get $+21y$ in one and $-21y$ in the other.

$7 \times$ I:	$35x + 21y$	$=$	133
$3 \times$ II:	$6x - 21y$	$=$	72
Add!	$41x$	$=$	205
$\therefore$	x	$=$	5
But	$5x + 3y$	$=$	19 [Taking either of the original equations]
$\therefore$	$5(5) + 3y$	$=$	19 [Since we have found that $x = 5$]
$\therefore$	$25 + 3y$	$=$	19
$\therefore$	$3y$	$=$	-6
$\therefore$	y	$=$	-2

Answer: $x = 5$ and $y = -2$. This can be written as $(5, -2)$.

Exercise 3.E

Solve these simultaneous equations:

1. $x + 3y = 7$
$2x - y = 0$

2. $2x + y = 7$
$x - 2y = 1$

3. $x + y = 8$
$2x - y = 7$

4. $5x + y = 9$
$4x - y = 0$

5. $2x + 3y = 25$
$4x - y = 1$

6. $x + y = 10$
$x - y = 4$

7. $x + 3y = 2$
$2x + y = 9$

8. $x + y = 1$
$2x + y = -1$

9. $10x + 3y = 1$
$x - 2y = 7$

10. $5x - 3y = 1$
$2x - y = 0$

11. $x - 3y = 4$
$5x - 2y = 7$

12. $2x - 3y = 2$
$6x + y = 16$

13. $x - y = 1$
$3x + 5y = 7$

14. $5x - 3y = 1$
$x - y = 0$

15. $5x - 3y - 11 = 0$
$3x + 10y + 17 = 0$

16. $2x - 3y - 2 = 0$
$3x + 8y - 3 = 0$

17. $x + 3(y - 1) = 5$
$5x + 13 - y = 5$

18. $4(x - 3) + 3(y + 1) = 10$
$6(x - 4) + 5y = 5$

19. $\frac{x}{2} + \frac{y}{5} = 4$
$\frac{x}{4} + \frac{y}{2} = 6$

20. $\frac{x}{2} + y = 13$
$\frac{x}{7} - \frac{y}{3} = 0$

21. $\frac{x+y}{5} + \frac{y-x}{2} = 5$
$\frac{x+2y}{9} = 2$

22. $5x - 12y - 17 = 0$
$\frac{1}{9}(x + 2) - (y + 1) + \frac{3}{2} = 0$

PROBLEMS LEADING TO SIMULTANEOUS EQUATIONS

Example 1: The sum of the ages of A and B is 63. Nine years ago, A was twice as old as B. How old are they now?

Solution:

Let $x = A$'s age now.

Let $y = B$'s age now.

$\therefore$ $(x-9) = A$'s age nine years ago.

and $(y-9) = B$'s age nine years ago.

I: $x + y = 63$ [The sum of their ages is 63]

II: $(x-9) = 2(y-9)$ [A's age was twice B's age, nine years ago]

$\therefore$ $x - 9 = 2y - 18$

$\therefore$ $x - 2y = -9$

I: $x + y = 63$

$-1 \times$ II: $-x + 2y = 9$

Add! $3y = 72$

$\therefore$ $y = 24$

But $x + y = 63$

$\therefore$ $x + 24 = 63$

$\therefore$ $x = 63 - 24 = 39$

Answer: A is 39 years old and B is 24 years old.

Exercise 3.F

In each of these problems, use simultaneous equations to find the solution:

1. The sum of two numbers is 14. The first is 4 greater than the second. Find the numbers.
2. The sum of two numbers is 45. The first is 11 greater than the second. Find the numbers.
3. The sum of two numbers is 21. Twice the first number added to three times the other is equal to 52. Find the numbers.
4. Find two numbers, such that seven times the first is 1 more than twice the second, and twice the first added to three times the second gives 36.
5. Two apples and an orange cost 32 cent. Three apples and five oranges cost 90 cent. Find the cost of an apple and the cost of an orange.
6. A 'Stikky' bar costs 4 cent less than a 'Chewit'. Five Stikky bars cost the same as four Chewits. Find the cost of each.
7. A Gaelic football team scored 11 times during a match. Their total is 17 points. How many goals and how many points did they score? [1 goal = 3 points] [Hint: Let x = number of goals, and let y = number of points.]

8. I mix x kg of Kenyan tea (which costs €3 per kg) with y kg of China tea (which costs €4 per kg). I get a total of 10 kg of a blend, which costs €3.70 per kg. Find the values of x and y.

9. A coffee company blends two kinds of coffee. Each day, they mix x kilogrammes of Colombian coffee, which costs €2 per kg with y kg of Brazilian coffee which costs €1.50 per kg. They produce, each day, 100 kg of blend which is worth €1.90 per kg. Find the value of x and y.

10. 150 children have to go on a school tour. They can use minibuses, which carry x pupils each, or cars which carry y pupils each. The Mathematics teacher works out that they could just manage with 10 minibuses and 6 cars, or with 5 minibuses and 18 cars. Write down two equations and hence find the value of x and y.

11. A guest-house has 10 rooms to let. Some of these sleep 2 people and some sleep 3 people. On a certain day all rooms are taken and full. There are 23 people in the guest-house that day. How many of each kind of room are there?

12. Barbara gets €1.50 for her pocket money each week. One week she spends all of her pocket money on 9 toffees and 3 ice-pops. The next week she spends it all on 5 toffees and 10 ice-pops. Find the cost of each.

13. One-half of a number is one more than double another. Two-thirds of the first is one less than three times the second. Find the two numbers.

14. One-third of a number is four more than one-half of another number. The first number is one more than twice the second. Find the two numbers.

THE FOUR SETS N, Z, *Q* AND R

There are four important infinite sets which you must know about. Here they are:

N = the ***natural numbers*** = {0, 1, 2, 3, 4, … }.

Z = the ***integers*** = { … –3, –2, –1, 0, 1, 2, 3, …}.

Q = the ***rational numbers*** = $\{ \frac{a}{b} \mid a \in Z, b \in Z\}$

= {Any number which can be written as a fraction of integers}.

R = the ***real numbers***

= {Any number which can be written as a decimal number}.

$-4 \notin N$ since N contains only positive whole numbers.

$\frac{3}{7} \notin Z$ since Z contains only whole numbers.

$0.9 \in Q$ since 0.9 can be written as $\frac{9}{10}$.

$\frac{11}{8} \in R$ since $\frac{11}{8}$ can be written as 1.375

$\sqrt{2} \in R$ since $\sqrt{2}$ can be written as the decimal number 1.41421356 ...

$\sqrt{2} \notin Q$ since $\sqrt{2}$ cannot be written as a fraction of integers.

Exercise 3.G

1. State whether these are true or false:

(i) $-6 \in N$
(ii) $-6 \in Z$
(iii) $\frac{1}{4} \in N$
(iv) $0.7 \in R$
(v) $\frac{3}{5} \in Z$
(vi) $\frac{3}{5} \in R$
(vii) $0.6 \in Q$
(viii) $\sqrt{9} \in N$
(ix) $\sqrt{5} \in Z$
(x) $\sqrt{3} \in R$

2. Write down one element in each of these sets:
[Note: A \ B means the set of elements which are in *A* but ***not*** in *B*]

(i) $Z \setminus N$
(ii) $Q \setminus Z$
(iii) $R \setminus Q$

3. Write these numbers in the form $\frac{a}{b}$, where $a \in Z$ and $b \in Z$.

(i) 0.8
(ii) −0.3
(iii) $0.\dot{3}$ (i.e. 0.33333...)
(iv) $-2\frac{1}{7}$

LINEAR INEQUALITIES

$x > 3$ means 'x is greater than 3'.
$x < 3$ means 'x is less than 3'.
$x \geq 5$ means 'x is greater than or equal to 5'.
$x \leq 7$ means 'x is less than or equal to 7'.
$-1 < x < 4$ means 'x lies between −1 and 4 (exclusive)'.
$3 \leq x \leq 11$ means 'x lies between 3 and 11 (inclusive)'.

Inequalities are very like equations. You may add or subtract both sides by the same number. You may multiply (or divide) both sides by any ***positive*** number. But when you multiply (or divide) both sides by a ***negative*** number, you must turn the inequality sign around.

For example, if $-2x > -6$, then $x < 3$ [Dividing both sides by −2]

Similarly, if $-x \leq 7$, then $x \geq -7$ [Multiplying both sides by −1]

Example 1: Show on the number line the solution set of $7-2x>1,\ x\in R$.

Solution:

$$7-2x > 1$$

$\therefore\quad 7-2x-7 > 1-7$ [Subtracting 7 from both sides]

$\therefore\quad -2x > -6$ [Simplifying]

$\therefore\quad 2x < 6$ [Multiplying by –1 and turning > around]

$\therefore\quad x < 3$ [Dividing by 2]

Here is the set on the number line:

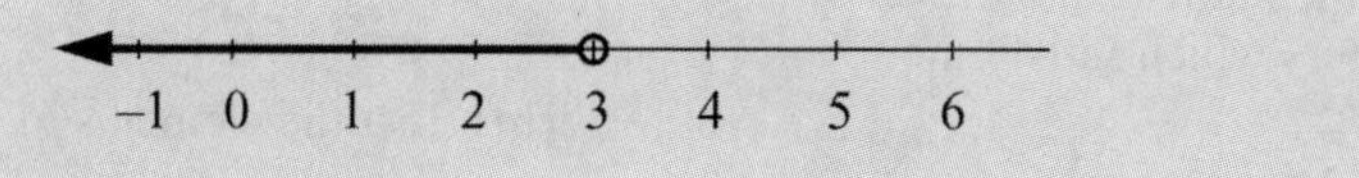

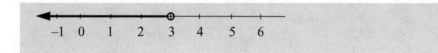

Example 2: (i) Find the solution set E of $3x+1\le 10,\ x\in Z$.

(ii) Find the solution set F of $1-2x\le 5,\ x\in Z$.

(iii) List the elements of $E\cap F$.

Solution:

(i) $3x+1\le 10$

$\therefore\quad 3x\le 9$

$\therefore\quad x\le 3$

The solution set is $E=\{\ldots -4,-3,-2,-1,0,1,2,3\}$.

(ii) $1-2x\le 5$

$\therefore\quad -2x\le 4$

$\therefore\quad 2x\ge -4$

$\therefore\quad x\ge -2$

The solution set is $F=\{-2,-1,0,1,2,3,4,5,\ldots\}$

(iii) $E\cap F=\{-2,-1,0,1,2,3\}$ [The elements common to both E and F.]

Exercise 3.H

1. List the elements of N which satisfy the inequality: $2x < 8$

2. List the elements of N which satisfy the inequality: $x + 3 \leq 8$.

3. List the elements of N which satisfy the inequality: $2x + 1 \leq 7$.

4. List the elements of N which satisfy the inequality: $5x - 3 \leq 28$.

5. List the elements of the set $\{x \mid 13 - 2x > 3, x \in N\}$.

6. Show on the number line the set of real numbers which satisfy the inequality:
$4x + 1 > 13$

7. Show on the number line the set of real numbers which satisfy the inequality: $2x - 1 > 13$

8. Show on the number line the set of real numbers which satisfy the inequality: $5x + 7 \leq 27$

9. Show on a number line the solution set of the inequality:
$3 - 2x > 7, x \in R$

10. Show on a number line the solution set of the inequality:
$13 - 5x > -7, x \in R$

11. Show on a number line the solution set of the inequality:
$3 + 3x < x + 11, x \in R$

12. Show on a number line the solution set of the inequality:
$8 - 2x \leq x - 7, x \in R$

13. Show on a number line the solution set of the inequality:
$1 - 12x \geq 10x - 76 , x \in R$

14. Show on a number line the solution set of the inequality:
$8(x - 3) \leq x + 4, x \in R$

15. (i) Find the solution set E of $2x - 1 \leq 13 , x \in Z$
(ii) Find the solution set F of $1 - 2x \leq 3, x \in Z$
(iii) List the elements of $E \cap F$

16. (i) Find the solution set E of $4x - 1 \leq 13 , x \in Z$
(ii) Find the solution set F of $1 - 3x \leq 7 , x \in Z$
(iii) List the elements of $E \cap F$

17. Show on three separate number lines the following sets
(i) $A = \{x \mid 6x + 2 < 20, x \varepsilon R\}$
(ii) $B = \{x \mid 6 - 2x < 20, x \varepsilon R\}$
(iii) $A \cap B$

18. Show on three separate number lines the following sets
(i) $E = \{x \mid 3 - 2x \geq 1, x \varepsilon N\}$
(ii) $F = \{x \mid {}^{1}/_{2}x - {}^{2}/_{3} \leq {}^{5}/_{6}, x \varepsilon N\}$
(iii) $F \setminus E$

19. Show on three separate number lines the following sets
(i) $A = \{x \mid -2 < x < 5, x \varepsilon R\}$
(ii) $B = \{x \mid 6 - 2x > 2, x \varepsilon R\}$
(iii) $A \cap B$

20. Show on three separate number lines the following sets
(i) $E = \{x \mid 15 - 4x \geq - 1, x \varepsilon N\}$
(ii) $F = \{x \mid \dfrac{2x + 1}{2} - \dfrac{x + 2}{3} \leq 1, x \varepsilon N\}$
(iii) $E \cap F$

MANIPULATING FORMULAE

We have seen how, when we are evaluating an expression, we follow the ***BIRDMAS*** hierarchy:

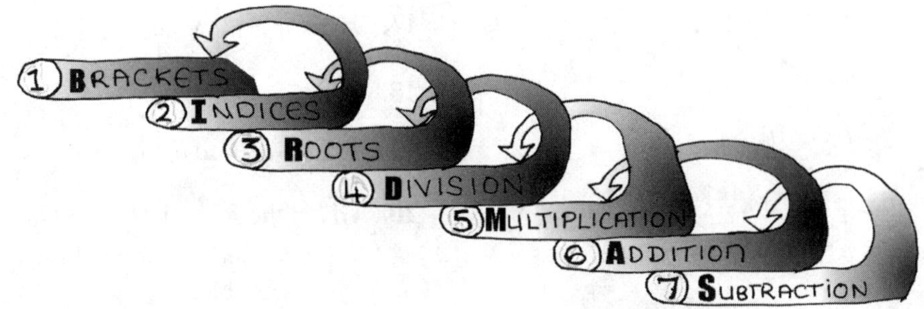

When we are manipulating a formula, we go through the ***BIRDMAS*** hierarchy in reverse order!

Example 1: Make x the subject of the formula: $y = mx + c$

Solution:

$$y = mx + c$$

$\therefore \quad mx + c = y$ [Switching sides]

$\therefore \quad mx + c - c = y - c$ [Subtracting c from both sides]

$\therefore \quad mx = y - c$ [Simplifying]

$\therefore \quad \dfrac{mx}{m} = \dfrac{y-c}{m}$ [Dividing both sides by m]

$\therefore \quad x = \dfrac{y-c}{m}$

[Note how we got rid of c (which was added) before m (which was multiplied), using the ***BIRDMAS*** hierarchy in reverse order.]

Example 2: Given $\dfrac{2a+b}{3c-d} = y$, write c in terms of the other variables.

Solution: There are two 'automatic brackets' lurking here. Let's put them in.

$$\frac{(2a+b)}{(3c-d)} = y$$

$\therefore \quad \dfrac{(3c-d)(2a+b)}{(3c-d)} = (3c-d)y$ [Multiplying both sides by $(3c-d)$]

$\therefore \quad (2a+b) = (3c-d)y$ [Simplifying]

$\therefore \quad 2a + b = 3cy - dy$ [Getting rid of brackets]

$\therefore \quad 2a + b + dy = 3cy$ [Adding dy to both sides]

$\therefore \quad \dfrac{2a+b+dy}{3y} = c$ [Dividing both sides by $3y$]

Exercise 3.I

In each case, write the variable in the square bracket in terms of the other variables:

1. $y = mx + c$ $[m]$
2. $y = pq - t$ $[q]$
3. $p = tv$ $[t]$
4. $v = u + at$ $[a]$
5. $v = u + at$ $[u]$
6. $ax + by + c = 0$ $[a]$
7. $z = 2(4x - y)$ $[x]$
8. $t = a + (n - 1)d$ $[a]$
9. $t = a + (n - 1)d$ $[d]$
10. $t = a + (n - 1)d$ $[n]$
11. $A = 2\pi rh$ $[r]$
12. $A = 2\pi rh + 2\pi r^2$ $[h]$
13. $2(s - 3t) = q$ $[t]$
14. $V = \frac{1}{3}\pi r^2 h$ $[h]$
15. $s = ut + \frac{1}{2}at^2$ $[a]$
16. $v^2 = u^2 + 2as$ $[a]$
17. $v^2 = u^2 + 2as$ $[u]$
18. $v^2 = u^2 + 2as$ $[s]$
19. $v(2 - 3a) = u(b - c)$ $[c]$
20. Given the formula $V = \pi r^2 h$
    (i) Write h in terms of the other variables.
    (ii) Write r in terms of the other variables.
21. Given the formula $\frac{2a - b}{3x} = c$
    (i) Write a in terms of the other variables.
    (ii) Find the value of a if $x = 3$, $b = 5$ and $c = 7$.
22. Given the formula $\frac{3x - y}{a + b} = k$
    (i) Write x in terms of the other variables.
    (ii) Write y in terms of the other variables.
23. Given the formula $S = \frac{a}{1 - r}$
    (i) Write r in terms of the other variables.
    (ii) Find the value of r if $a = 10$ and $S = 40$.

DOUBLE-TROUBLE

When the variable which you are trying to isolate appears ***twice***, you should bring the two terms in which it appears to one side of the equation, and the other terms to the other side of the equation. Then take out the ***common factor*** and proceed as before.

Example 1: Given $\frac{2x-y}{x} = k$, write x in terms of the other variables.

Solution:

$$\frac{2x-y}{x} = k$$

$\therefore \quad \frac{x(2x-y)}{x} = kx$ [Multiplying both sides by x]

$\therefore \quad 2x - y = kx$ [Simplifying]

$\therefore \quad 2x - kx = y$ [Bringing the two terms in x to one side]

$\therefore \quad x(2-k) = y$ [Taking out the common factor]

$\therefore \quad \frac{x(2-k)}{(2-k)} = \frac{y}{(2-k)}$ [Dividing both sides by $(2-k)$]

$\therefore \quad x = \frac{y}{2-k}$ [Simplifying]

Exercise 3.J

Isolate the variable in the square bracket:

1. $ax = bx + c$ $[x]$

2. $ax = c - kx$ $[x]$

3. $pq = c + rq$ $[q]$

4. $r - 1 = rs + c$ $[r]$

5. $a + b = bx + c$ $[b]$

6. $\frac{a-b}{k} = a$ $[a]$

7. $\frac{2(a-t)}{c} = a$ $[a]$

8. $\frac{a-3b}{b} = c$ $[b]$

9. $\frac{a-b}{b+1} = c$ $[b]$

10. Given the equation $p = \frac{2(a-p)}{b}$

(i) Write p in terms of the other variables

(ii) Find the value of p if $a = 6$ and $b = 2$

11. Given the equation $s = \frac{rl-a}{r-l}$

(i) Write l in terms of the other variables.

(ii) Write r in terms of the other variables.

(iii) Find the value of r if $s = 12$, $a = 6$ and $l = 10$

REVISION EXERCISE 3.K

1. (a) Solve: $2x - 31 = 45$

(b) Solve the simultaneous equations:

$3x + y = 10$

$x - 4y = -1$

(c) Find three consecutive natural numbers such that five times the first is equal to twice the sum of the other two.

2. (a) Solve: $2x + 3 = 7x - 42$

(b) (i) Find the solution set E to $3x + 1 < 16, x \varepsilon R$.

(ii) Find the solution set F to $1 - 4x < 17, x \varepsilon R$.

(iii) Show $E \cap F$ on a number line.

(c) Given $\dfrac{a - 5b}{c} = d$

(i) Write a in terms of the other variables.

(ii) Find the value of a if $b = -2$, $c = -1$ and $d = 3$.

3. (a) Solve the inequality $2x - 2 > 10, x \in R$.

Show your solution on a number line.

(b) Solve: $\dfrac{2x - 35}{x} = 9$

(c) Given $\dfrac{x + 7y}{x} = k$

(i) Write x in terms of the other variables.

(ii) Find the value of x if $k = -2$, and $y = 3$.

4. (a) Solve: $2(x - 3) + 1 = 21$

(b) Solve the simultaneous equations:

$7x + 2y = 17$

$x - y = 5$

Show that the solution also satisfies the equation $5x + y = 13$

(c) Jane is two years older than Liam. Their grandfather's age is three times the sum of their ages. The total sum of all three ages is 128. How old are they?

5. (a) Solve: $2(x + 1) = 7(x - 4) + 10$

(b) (i) Find the solution set E to $9x + 1 \leq 46, x \in N$

(ii) Find the solution set F to $21 - 8x \geq 5, x \in N$

(iii) List the elements of $E \setminus F$.

(c) Given $\dfrac{a - 5c}{c + 1} = d$

(i) Write c in terms of the other variables.

(ii) Find the value of c if $a = 1$ and $d = -11$.

6. (a) Solve: $12(x - 1) = 2(36 - x)$

(b) Solve the simultaneous equations:

$x + 5y = -5$

$2x + y = 8$

(c) There are 13 rooms in a guest house. Small rooms sleep two people. Large rooms sleep three people. When full, the guest-house sleeps 35 people. How many of each kind or room are there?

7. (a) Solve the inequality
$3(1-x) > 21, x \in R$
Show your solution on a number line.

(b) Solve the simultaneous equations:
$x = y + 7$
$2x + 5y = 0$

(c) Given $\frac{x+7y}{x+5} = y$
(i) Write x in terms y.
(ii) Find the value of x if $y = \frac{3}{2}$.

8. (a) State if these are true or false:
(i) $-3 \in N$
(ii) $\frac{12}{17} \in Z$
(iii) $-1.3 \in Q$
(iv) $\sqrt{11} \in R$

(b) Alan and Barbara's ages add up to 30. Three times Alan's age is 5 more than twice Barbara's age. Find their ages.

(c) Given $V = \frac{4}{3}\pi r^3$
(i) Write r in terms of V.
(ii) Find the value of r if $V = \frac{99}{7}$. [Take $\pi = \frac{22}{7}$]

9. (a) Show on a number line the set
$\{x \mid -3 \le x \le 2, x \in Z\}$

(b) Solve the equation:
$\frac{3}{4}(3x+1) = \frac{2}{3}(5x-1)-4)$

(c) Ninety-six primary school pupils have to travel to a zone final. They may travel on minibuses which carry m pupils or in cars which carry n pupils. They could just manage with 5 minibuses and one car, or with 2 minibuses and 10 cars. Find the values of m and n.

10. (a) Solve the inequality
$\frac{2}{5}x + \frac{1}{2} \le \frac{9}{10}, x \in R$
Show your solution on a number line.

(b) Solve the simultaneous equations:
$y = \frac{x+3y}{5} + 5$
$3x + 5y - 46 = 0$

(c) Given $x = \frac{2t-7}{t+8}$,
(i) write t in terms x,
(ii) find the value of t if $x = 1.8$

N = the ***natural numbers*** = {0, 1, 2, 3, 4, … }.

Z = the ***integers*** = { … –3, –2, –1, 0, 1, 2, 3, …}.

Q = the ***rational numbers*** = $\{ \frac{a}{b} \mid a \in Z, b \in Z \}$
= {Any number which can be written as a fraction of integers}.

R = the ***real numbers***
= {Any number which can be written as a decimal number}.

Chapter 4

Quadratic and Cubic Equations

QUADRATIC FACTORS

Any expression of the form $ax^2 + bx + c$ is called a ***quadratic expression***.
The best way to factorise such an expression is 'trial and error'.

Example 1: Factorise $10x^2 - x - 21$

Solution: The factors of $10x^2$ are $5x$ and $2x$ (or $10x$ and x).

The factors of -21 are -7 and 3 (or 7 and -3, or -21 and 1, or 21 and -1).

Try out different combinations of these until you hit upon the correct answer.

$$\begin{array}{r} 5x-7 \\ \times\, 2x+3 \\ \hline 10x^2+x-21 \end{array} \quad \text{Wrong!} \qquad\qquad \begin{array}{r} 5x+7 \\ \times\, 2x-3 \\ \hline 10x^2-x-21 \end{array} \quad \text{Correct!}$$

The correct factors are $(5x+7)(2x-3)$.

COMMON FACTORS

Some quadratic expressions have a common factor (i.e. a factor which divides into every term of the expression).

For example the factors of $x^2 + 6x$ are $x(x+6)$.

The factors of $2x^2 - 11x$ are $x(2x-11)$.

DIFFERENCE OF TWO SQUARES

The factors of $A^2 - B^2$ are $(A-B)(A+B)$.
The factors of $4x^2 - 49$ are $(2x-7)(2x+7)$.
The factors of $121x^2 - 36$ are $(11x-6)(11x+6)$.

Exercise 4.A

Factorise:

1. $x^2 + 8x + 15$	**6.** $x^2 - 2x - 48$
2. $x^2 + 10x + 21$	**7.** $x^2 + 3x - 10$
3. $x^2 + 7x + 10$	**8.** $x^2 - 49$
4. $x^2 + 9x + 20$	**9.** $x^2 - 100$
5. $x^2 - x - 42$	**10.** $x^2 - 144$

11. $2x^2 - 3x - 14$

12. $6x^2 + 23x + 20$

13. $x^2 + 10x$

14. $4x^2 + 7x$

15. $11x - 8x^2$

16. $9x^2 - 64$

17. $9x^2 - 64x$

18. $9x^2 - 48x + 64$

19. $36x^2 - 49$

20. $36x^2 + x$

ADDING AND SUBTRACTING ALGEBRAIC FRACTIONS

When we add (or subtract) fractions, we use a ***common denominator.***

For example: $\frac{3}{5} + \frac{2}{7} = \frac{3(7) + 2(5)}{35} = \frac{31}{35}$.

[The common denominator in this case is 35]

When we add (or subtract) fractions with algebra in them, we proceed in exactly the same way. For example,

$$\frac{3}{x+1} + \frac{2}{x+7} = \frac{3(x+7) + 2(x+1)}{(x+1)(x+7)} = \frac{3x + 21 + 2x + 2}{(x+1)(x+7)} = \frac{5x + 23}{(x+1)(x+7)}$$

When you are subtracting, be careful to ***distribute*** the minus to all terms inside the bracket!

$$\frac{1}{2x-3} - \frac{1}{7x-5} = \frac{1(7x-5) - 1(2x-3)}{(2x-3)(7x-5)} = \frac{7x - 5 - 2x + 3}{(2x-3)(7x-5)} = \frac{5x-2}{(2x-3)(7x-5)}$$

If any of the denominators have factors, you should factorise them first. Then make sure that you find the ***lowest*** common denominator.

$$\frac{7}{x^2-4} - \frac{3}{x^2+x-2} = \frac{7}{(x-2)(x+2)} - \frac{3}{(x+2)(x-1)} = \frac{7(x-1) - 3(x-2)}{(x-2)(x+2)(x-1)}$$

$$= \frac{7x - 7 - 3x + 6}{(x-2)(x+2)(x-1)} = \frac{4x-1}{(x-2)(x+2)(x-1)}$$

Exercise 4.B

Write these as ***one*** fraction:

1. $\dfrac{2}{x+1}+\dfrac{3}{x+7}$

2. $\dfrac{1}{x+5}+\dfrac{2}{x+6}$

3. $\dfrac{6}{x+1}+\dfrac{3}{x-7}$

4. $\dfrac{1}{x+10}-\dfrac{3}{6x+8}$

5. $\dfrac{2}{2x+1}-\dfrac{3}{5x-1}$

6. $\dfrac{12}{4x+1}-\dfrac{3}{x-7}$

7. $\dfrac{1}{x-9}-\dfrac{1}{x+7}$

8. $\dfrac{1}{x^2-4}+\dfrac{1}{x^2+5x+6}$

9. $\dfrac{1}{x^2-9}+\dfrac{2}{x^2+5x+6}$

10. $\dfrac{1}{x^2-1}+\dfrac{1}{x^2-x-2}$

11. $\dfrac{1}{x-4}+\dfrac{1}{x^2-2x-8}$

12. $\dfrac{1}{x-3}-\dfrac{1}{x^2+x-12}$

13. $\dfrac{x+1}{x^2-4}+\dfrac{x-3}{x^2+7x+10}$

14. $\dfrac{x+3}{x^2-36}+\dfrac{x-7}{x^2+x-30}$

MULTIPLYING AND DIVIDING ALGEBRAIC FRACTIONS

When we multiply ordinary fractions, we ***do not*** use common denominators. We simply multiply the top by the top and the bottom by the bottom.

For example: $\frac{3}{7}\times\frac{2}{5} = \frac{6}{35}$.

When we divide ordinary fractions, we turn the second fraction upside-down and then multiply. If the top and bottom have a common factor, we may divide above and below by that common factor. It is easier if you divide out common factors ***before*** multiplying.

For example: $\frac{22}{3}\div\frac{11}{12} = \frac{22}{3}\times\frac{12}{11} = \frac{2}{1}\times\frac{4}{1} = 8$

We multiply and divide algebraic fractions in the same way:

$$\frac{3}{x-1}\cdot\frac{4}{x+2} = \frac{12}{(x-1)(x+2)}$$

$$\frac{x^2-25}{x+1}\div\frac{x^2+7x+10}{x+2} = \frac{x^2-25}{x+1}\cdot\frac{x+2}{x^2+7x+10} = \frac{(x-5)(x+5)(x+2)}{(x+1)(x+5)(x+2)} = \frac{x-5}{x+1}$$

Exercise 4.C

Simplify the following:

1. $\frac{3}{x+1} \cdot \frac{5}{x-1}$
2. $\frac{10}{x+7} \cdot \frac{3}{x-2}$
3. $\frac{3x-3}{x+1} \cdot \frac{5}{x-1}$
4. $\frac{x^2-16}{x^2-1} \cdot \frac{x-1}{x+4}$
5. $\frac{x^2-9}{x^2-5x-14} \cdot \frac{x-7}{x+3}$
6. $\frac{x^2-1}{x^2-12x+20} \cdot \frac{x-10}{x+1}$
7. $\frac{x^2-4}{x^2-1} \cdot \frac{2x-2}{4x+8}$
8. $\frac{x^2+11x+28}{x^2-49} \cdot \frac{x-7}{x+4}$
9. $\frac{3}{x+1} \div \frac{5}{x+1}$
10. $\frac{10}{x} \div \frac{5}{x^2}$
11. $\frac{x-3}{x+1} \div \frac{x^2-8x+15}{x^2-1}$
12. $\frac{x^2}{x^2-16} \div \frac{x}{x+4}$
13. $\left(1+\frac{1}{x}\right) \div \left(1-\frac{1}{x}\right)$
14. $\left(1+\frac{x+8}{x+1}\right)\left(\frac{1}{4x^2-81}\right)$
15. $\left(\frac{1}{x+1}+\frac{1}{x-1}\right) \div \left(\frac{1}{x+2}+\frac{1}{x-2}\right)$
16. $\left(x-\frac{2}{1+x}\right)\left(x+\frac{1}{x+2}\right)$

THE ZERO LAW

Two numbers, when multiplied, give zero. What do you know about the numbers? You know that one of them (at least) must equal zero. This fact (which we shall call the 'Zero Law') can be very useful in solving quadratic and cubic equations, as we shall see. Here is the 'Zero Law', stated in a formal mathematical way:

If $A \times B = 0$, then either $A = 0$ or $B = 0$.

QUADRATIC EQUATIONS

Any equation, which can be written in the form $ax^2 + bx + c = 0$ is called a ***quadratic equation***. Each quadratic equation has two solutions, which are sometimes called ***roots***.

To find these solutions we follow these steps:

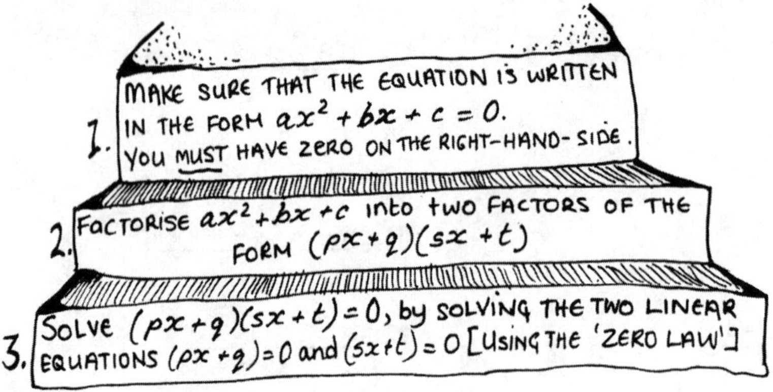

1. MAKE SURE THAT THE EQUATION IS WRITTEN IN THE FORM $ax^2+bx+c=0$.
YOU MUST HAVE ZERO ON THE RIGHT-HAND-SIDE.
2. FACTORISE ax^2+bx+c INTO TWO FACTORS OF THE FORM $(px+q)(sx+t)$
3. SOLVE $(px+q)(sx+t)=0$, BY SOLVING THE TWO LINEAR EQUATIONS $(px+q)=0$ AND $(sx+t)=0$ [USING THE 'ZERO LAW']

Example 1 Solve these quadratic equations:

(i) $x^2+5x+6 = 0$ (iii) $5x^2+2x = 0$

(ii) $2x^2 = x+10$ (iv) $4x^2-9 = 0$

Solution: (i)

$$x^2+5x+6 = 0$$

$$\therefore (x+3)(x+2) = 0 \quad \text{[Factorising]}$$

$$\therefore (x+3) = 0 \text{ or } (x+2) = 0 \quad \text{[By the Zero Law]}$$

$$\therefore x = -3 \text{ or } x = -2$$

(ii)

$$2x^2 = x+10$$

$$\therefore 2x^2-x-10 = 0 \quad \text{[Getting zero on the right]}$$

$$\therefore (2x-5)(x+2) = 0 \quad \text{[Factorising]}$$

$$\therefore (2x-5) = 0 \text{ or } (x+2) = 0 \quad \text{[By the Zero Law]}$$

$$\therefore 2x = 5 \text{ or } x = -2$$

$$\therefore x = \tfrac{5}{2} \text{ or } -2$$

(iii)

$$5x^2+2x = 0$$

$$\therefore x(5x+2) = 0 \quad \text{[Factorising a \textbf{\textit{common factor}}]}$$

$$\therefore x = 0 \text{ or } (5x+2) = 0 \quad \text{[By the Zero Law]}$$

$$\therefore x = 0 \text{ or } 5x = -2$$

$$\therefore x = 0 \text{ or } x = -\tfrac{2}{5}$$

(iv)
$$4x^2 - 9 = 0$$
$$\therefore (2x-3)(2x+3) = 0 \quad \text{[Difference of two squares]}$$
$$\therefore (2x-3) = 0 \text{ or } (2x+3) = 0$$
$$\therefore 2x = 3 \text{ or } 2x = -3$$
$$\therefore x = \frac{3}{2} \text{ or } x = -\frac{3}{2}$$

Exercise 4.D

Solve these quadratic equations:

1. $x^2 + 7x + 10 = 0$

2. $x^2 + 8x + 15 = 0$

3. $x^2 - 2x - 8 = 0$

4. $x^2 - 12x + 20 = 0$

5. $x^2 + x - 6 = 0$

6. $x^2 - 3x - 18 = 0$

7. $x^2 + 4x - 21 = 0$

8. $x^2 - 9 = 0$

9. $x^2 - 81 = 0$

10. $x^2 - 100 = 0$

11. $2x^2 + 5x - 12 = 0$

12. $2x^2 - x - 28 = 0$

13. $x^2 - 9x + 18 = 0$

14. $3x^2 + 5x - 2 = 0$

15. $3x^2 - 13x + 14 = 0$

16. $x^2 + 5x = 0$

17. $6x^2 - 5x + 1 = 0$

18. $10x^2 - 9x + 2 = 0$

19. $x^2 = 5x + 6$

20. $x^2 = x + 30$

21. $x^2 = 24 - 5x$

22. $2x^2 = 4 - 7x$

23. $x^2 = 36$

24. $x(x+1) = 72$

25. $x(3x-1) = 10$

26. $x(2x-1) = 3x$

27. $8(x-2) = x^2$

28. $(x+1)(3x-1) = 4$

29. $49x^2 = 100$

30. $5x(3x-1) = 10x + 30$

31. $(x+1)(x-1) = 24$

32. $21x^2 = x^2 - 7x + 6$

33. $(3x)^2 = 4(3x-1)$

34. $(2+x)(8-x) = 0$

35. $(2+x)(8-x) = 7$

36. $(5x-6)(2x+7) = 0$

37. $30x^2 = 13x - 1$

38. $30x^2 = 13x + 1$

39. $x(x+10) = 100(x+10)$

40. $3x^2 = 13x - 12$

THE QUADRATIC FORMULA

There are many quadratic equations (like $x^2 + 9x + 7 = 0$, for example) in which the left hand side does ***not*** have factors. If we want to solve such equations, we use a formula, known as the ***quadratic formula***. Here it is:

The solutions of the equation $ax^2 + bx + c = 0$ are given by

$$x = \frac{-b \pm \sqrt{b^2 - 4ac}}{2a}$$

This formula may be used to solve all quadratic equations.

Example 1: (i) Solve the equation $2x^2 - x - 5 = 0$, in surd (square root) form.

(ii) Deduce the solutions correct to two decimal places.

Solution: (i) In this case, $a = 2$, $b = -1$, $c = -5$ and so $4ac = 4(2)(-5) = -40$.

$$x = \frac{-b \pm \sqrt{b^2 - 4ac}}{2a}$$

$$= \frac{1 \pm \sqrt{(-1)^2 - (-40)}}{2(2)}$$

$$= \frac{1 \pm \sqrt{41}}{4}$$

$$= \frac{1 + \sqrt{41}}{4} \text{ or } \frac{1 - \sqrt{41}}{4}$$

(ii) Using a calculator, we find that $\sqrt{41} = 6.403$

$$\therefore x = \frac{1 + 6.403}{4} \text{ or } \frac{1 - 6.403}{4}$$

$$= \frac{7.403}{4} \text{ or } \frac{-5.403}{4}$$

$$= 1.85078 \text{ or } -1.35078$$

$= 1.85$ or -1.35, correct to two decimal places.

Exercise 4.E

Use the quadratic formula to solve these equations in surd form:

1. $2x^2 + 9x + 5 = 0$

2. $3x^2 + 2x - 3 = 0$

3. $x^2 - 8x + 5 = 0$

4. $2x^2 - 2x - 5 = 0$

5. $x^2 + 10x + 1 = 0$

6. $2x^2 - 11x - 7 = 0$

7. $x^2 + 12x + 10 = 0$

8. $4x^2 - x - 11 = 0$

9. $5x^2 + x - 1 = 0$

10. $10x^2 - 3x - 10 = 0$

Solve these correct to one decimal place:

11. $x^2 + 2x - 5 = 0$

12. $x^2 - 12x + 5 = 0$

13. $x^2 + x - 10 = 0$

14. $x^2 - 3x - 20 = 0$

15. $2x^2 + 2x - 1 = 0$

16. $5x^2 - 8x + 2 = 0$

17. $10x^2 = 2(x + 5)$

18. $x(x + 5) = 11$

19. $2x(x + 1) = 7$

20. $(x - 5)^2 = 13$

EQUATIONS WITH ALGEBRAIC FRACTIONS

Example 1: Solve the equation: $\frac{8}{x+2} - \frac{2}{x+3} = 1\frac{3}{5}$

Solution: Write the right hand side as a top-heavy fraction:

$\frac{8}{x+2} - \frac{2}{x+3} = \frac{8}{5}$ [Multiply each part by the L.C.D.: $5(x + 2)(x + 3)$]

$$\therefore \frac{8(5)(x+2)(x+3)}{x+2} - \frac{2(5)(x+2)(x+3)}{x+3} = \frac{8(5)(x+2)(x+3)}{5}$$

$$\therefore 40(x + 3) - 10(x + 2) = 8(x + 2)(x + 3)$$

$$\therefore 40x + 120 - 10x - 20 = 8x^2 + 40x + 48$$

$$\therefore 0 = 8x^2 + 10x - 52$$

$\therefore 0 = 4x^2 + 5x - 26$ [Dividing both sides by 2]

$$\therefore 0 = (x - 2)(4x + 13)$$

$$\therefore x = 2, x = -\frac{13}{4}$$

Exercise 4.F

Solve these equations:

1. $x = 1 + \frac{56}{x}$

2. $7 = 5x + \frac{2}{x}$

3. $\frac{3x-5}{x-1} = \frac{2x+15}{x+5}$

4. $\frac{5x+4}{2x+4} = \frac{4x+11}{x+9}$

5. $\frac{1}{x+4} + \frac{1}{x+1} = \frac{1}{2}$

6. $\frac{1}{x} + \frac{9}{x+8} = 1$

7. $\frac{3}{x-3} + \frac{2}{x-1} = 2$

8. $\frac{1}{4}(x+2)^2 = (x-2)^2$

9. $\frac{2x+3}{x+3} + \frac{x-1}{x+1} = 2$

10. $\frac{2x+1}{x-3} = 4 + \frac{x+4}{x+1}$

11. $x + 8 + \frac{7}{3x-1} = 13\frac{1}{2}$

12. $\frac{1}{2}(x+4) + \frac{9}{2x-13} - \frac{1}{4} = 0$

13. Solve $\frac{16-x}{4} - \frac{2(x-11)}{x-6} = \frac{x-4}{12}$

and verify both solutions.

14. Solve $\frac{x}{x-1} + \frac{x-1}{x} = 4$

correct to two places of decimals.

15. Solve $\frac{2x-4}{x-3} + \frac{3x-2}{x-2} = 3$

correct to three decimal places

SUBSTITUTION

In Chapter 3, we saw how to solve simultaneous equations in which both equations are ***linear*** (i.e. no squares or products). But how do we solve simultaneous equations in which one of the equations is non-linear [for example: $x + 2y = 7, x^2 + 3y^2 = 28$]? The answer is: we use a method called ***substitution***. This is similar to substitution in a football match, in which one player is removed and a new player is introduced.

Example 1: Solve the simultaneous equations: $x + 2y = 7, x^2 + 3y^2 = 28$.

Solution: This is a 'game of two halves'. Always start with the ***linear*** equation.

Manipulate this equation, until you get '$x = \dots$' or '$y = \dots$'

First half

$x + 2y = 7$

$\therefore x = 7 - 2y$

$\therefore x = (7 - 2y)$

Off! ***On!***

Second half

Now for the second half. Take the ***non-linear*** equation. In it we replace the letter x with the expression $(7-2y)$. This is the moment of substitution.

$$x^2 + 3y^2 = 28$$

$$\therefore\ (7-2y)^2 + 3y^2 = 28 \qquad \text{[Substituting]}$$

$$\therefore\ 49 - 28y + 4y^2 + 3y^2 = 28$$

$$\therefore\ 7y^2 - 28y + 21 = 0 \qquad \text{[A quadratic equation]}$$

$$\therefore\ y^2 - 4y + 3 = 0 \qquad \text{[Dividing both sides by 7]}$$

$$\therefore\ (y-1)(y-3) = 0$$

$$\therefore\ y = 1 \text{ or } y = 3$$

Extra time

It's not over yet! You must find the corresponding values of x.

Go back to the substitution formula: $x = 7-2y$

If $y = 1$, then $x = 7-2(1) = 5$. Therefore, this answer is (5, 1).

If $y = 3$, then $x = 7-2(3) = 1$. Therefore, this answer is (1, 3).

There are two sets of answers: (5, 1) and (1, 3).

Exercise 4.G

Solve these simultaneous equations:

1. $x = y+1$
$x^2 + y^2 = 13$

2. $x = y+4$
$y^2 + 3x = 16$

3. $y = x+2$
$x^2 + 2y = 12$

4. $y = x+1$
$x^2 + y^2 = 25$

5. $y = x$
$x^2 + 2y = 35$

6. $x + y = 3$
$x^2 + y^2 = 5$

7. $x - y = 4$
$y^2 + 7x = 18$

8. $x - y = 3$
$x^2 + y^2 = 17$

9. $x - 2y = 0$
$x^2 + y^2 = 5$

10. $x = 2y+1$
$x^2 - 3y^2 = 6$

11. $x + y = 1$
$x^2 + y^2 = 1$

12. $x + y = 7$
$xy = 12$

13. $x + 2y = 11$
$xy = 14$

14. $2x - y = 7$
$xy = 15$

15. $x - 2y + 1 = 0$
$x^2 - xy = 10$

16. $x + 2y = 1$
$x^2 - y^2 = 8$

17. $x + 2y = 3$
$x^2 + y^2 = 2$

18. $2x - 3y = 1$
$x^2 - 3y^2 + 2 = 0$

19. $4x - 3y = 25$
$x^2 + y^2 = 25$

20. $2x + 3y = 1$
$x^2 - xy + y^2 = 3$

PROBLEMS LEADING TO A QUADRATIC EQUATION

Example 1: Two numbers differ by three. The sum of their squares is 65. Find the numbers.

Solution: Let x = the first of the two numbers.
$\therefore\ x + 3$ = the second of the two numbers.

The sum of their squares = 65

$$\therefore \quad x^2 + (x + 3)^2 = 65$$
$$\therefore \quad x^2 + x^2 + 6x + 9 = 65$$
$$\therefore \quad 2x^2 + 6x - 56 = 0 \qquad \text{[Getting zero on the right]}$$
$$\therefore \quad x^2 + 3x - 28 = 0 \qquad \text{[Dividing by 2]}$$
$$\therefore \quad (x - 4)(x + 7) = 0 \qquad \text{[Factorising]}$$
$$\therefore \quad x = 4 \text{ or } x = -7$$

The two numbers are represented by x and $x + 3$.

If $x = 4$, then the two numbers are 4 and 7.

If $x = -7$, then the two numbers are -7 and -4.

Example 2: The perimeter of a rectangular field is 36 metres. Its area is 77 square metres. Find the dimensions of the field.

Solution: Let x = the width of the field.
Let y = the length of the field.

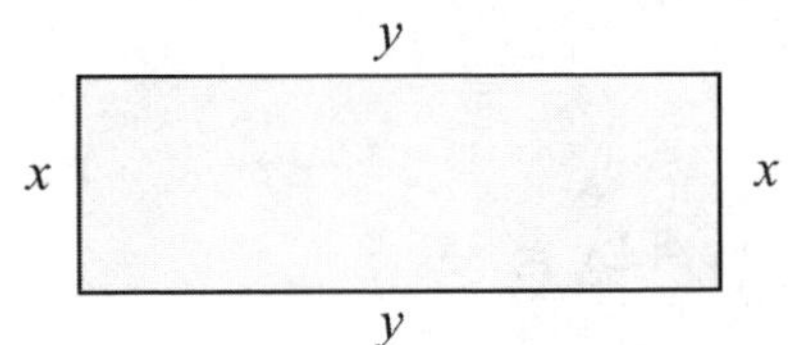

The perimeter $= 36$

$\therefore \quad 2x + 2y = 36$

$\therefore \quad x + y = 18$

$\therefore \quad y = (18 - x)$ ...***Equation I***

The area $= 77$

$\therefore \quad xy = 77$

$\therefore \quad x(18 - x) = 77$ [Substituting from ***equation I***]

$\therefore \quad 18x - x^2 = 77$

$\therefore \quad 0 = x^2 - 18x + 77$

$\therefore \quad 0 = (x - 11)(x - 7)$

$\therefore \quad x = 11 \text{ or } x = 7$

Now, $y = 18 - x$. [From equation I, above]
If $x = 11$, then $y = 18 - 11 = 7$. The dimensions are 11×7.
If $x = 7$, then $y = 18 - 7$. The dimensions are 7×11.

Exercise 4.H

Solve each of these problems by means of a quadratic equation.
Don't guess the answers!

1. Find two consecutive natural numbers, whose squares add up to 61.

2. Two numbers differ by 3. Their product is 28. Find the numbers.

3. Divide 20 into two parts, whose product is 96.

4. The square of a number is 14 more than five times the number. Find the number.

5. The square of a number is 10 less than seven times the number. Find the number.

6. There are two consecutive natural numbers, such that twice the square of the first is 34 more than the square of the second. Find the numbers.

7. Divide 15 into two parts such that the sum of their squares is 117.

8. The perimeter of a rectangular garden is 32 metres. The area is 60 square metres. Find the dimensions of the garden.

9. Find three consecutive numbers, the sum of whose squares is 50.

10. Find two consecutive ***even*** natural numbers, such that three times the square of the smaller one is 60 more than their product.
[Let the numbers be n and $(n + 2)$]

11. The sum of a number (x) and its reciprocal $\left(\frac{1}{x}\right)$ is 2.9. Find x.

12. A boat travels a distance 30 km at a speed of x km/h. It then travels 20 km at a speed of $(x + 1)$ km/h. The total time for the two journeys is 15 hours. Find x.

13. A woman cycles a distance 24 km at a speed of x km/h. She then travels 28 km at a speed of $(x - 1)$ km/h. The total time for the two journeys is 7 hours. Find x.

14. A prize fund of €300 is divided equally among the n winners. If there had been 2 more winners, each prize-winner would have got €5 less. Find the value of n.

15. A migrating bird flies 400 km at a steady rate of x km/h. If the bird increased its speed by 4 km/h, the journey would take 5 hours less. Find x.

16. Ann and Ben travel 45 km at steady speeds on their bikes. Ann travels 1 km/h faster than Ben. She finishes half an hour before Ben. Find their speeds on the journey.

THE FACTOR THEOREM

You have already seen that if the ***factors*** of a quadratic expression are, say, $(x-5)(x-9)$, then the ***roots*** of the equation $(x-5)(x-9) = 0$ are 5 and 9.

This can work the other way as well. For example, if we know that the ***roots*** of a quadratic are 7 and 2, then the ***factors*** of the quadratic are $(x-7)$ and $(x-2)$. Hence, the equation with these roots must be $(x-7)(x-2) = 0$ or $x^2-9x+14 = 0$.

This is an example of ***The Factor Theorem*** which is stated here:

> If k is a ***root*** of an expression, then $(x-k)$ is a ***factor***.

Example 1: Find the quadratic equations with these pairs of roots:

(i) 3 and 5

(ii) -9 and $\frac{1}{2}$

Solution:

(i) The ***roots*** are 3 and 5.
Therefore, the factors are $(x-3)(x-5)$.
Therefore the equation is $(x-3)(x-5) = 0$.
Therefore the equation is $x^2-8x+15 = 0$.

(ii) The ***roots*** are -9 and $\frac{1}{2}$.
Therefore the factors are $(x - -9)(x-\frac{1}{2})$.
Therefore the equation is $(x+9)(x-\frac{1}{2}) = 0$.
Therefore the equation is $(x+9)(2x-1) = 0$. [DOUBLING both sides]
Therefore the equation is $2x^2+17x-9 = 0$.

Exercise 4.I

Find the quadratic equations with these pairs of roots:

1. 2 and 6

2. 1 and 5

3. 11 and −2

4. 10 and −4

5. 5 and −7

6. −3 and −4

7. $\frac{1}{2}$ and 3

8. $\frac{1}{4}$ and 1

9. $1\frac{1}{2}$ and −3

10. $-2\frac{1}{2}$ and 5

11. $-1\frac{1}{3}$ and −2

12. $-\frac{1}{2}$ and $-\frac{1}{5}$

13. The roots of $x^2 + bx + c = 0$ are 7 and 10. Find the values of b and c.

14. The roots of $x^2 + bx + c = 0$ are −3 and 0. Find the values of b and c.

15. The roots of $2x^2 + bx + c = 0$ are $\frac{3}{2}$ and 4. Find the values of b and c.

16. The roots of $x^2 + bx + c = 0$ are 3 and 3. Find the values of b and c.

17. The roots of $x^2 + px + q = 0$ are −4 and −4. Find the values of p and q.

18. The roots of $x^2 + bx + c = 0$ are both equal to 10. Find the values of b and c.

19. The roots of $x^2 - 12x + c = 0$ are ***equal*** (i.e. both roots are the same). Find the value of c.

20. The roots of $x^2 - 10x + k = 0$ are equal. Find the value of k.

CUBIC EQUATIONS

An equation of the form $ax^3 + bx^2 + cx + d = 0$ is called a ***cubic equation***. It usually has three roots (or solutions). The search for the three roots is done in these four steps:

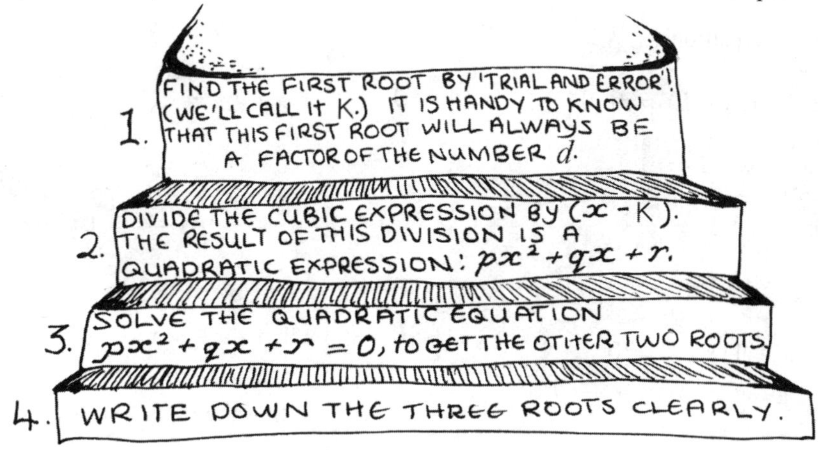

1. FIND THE FIRST ROOT BY 'TRIAL AND ERROR'! (WE'LL CALL IT K.) IT IS HANDY TO KNOW THAT THIS FIRST ROOT WILL ALWAYS BE A FACTOR OF THE NUMBER d.
2. DIVIDE THE CUBIC EXPRESSION BY $(x - K)$. THE RESULT OF THIS DIVISION IS A QUADRATIC EXPRESSION: $px^2 + qx + r$.
3. SOLVE THE QUADRATIC EQUATION $px^2 + qx + r = 0$, TO GET THE OTHER TWO ROOTS.
4. WRITE DOWN THE THREE ROOTS CLEARLY.

Example 1: Solve the cubic equation $2x^3 - 9x^2 + 7x + 6 = 0$.

Solution: We will call $f(x) = 2x^3 - 9x^2 + 7x + 6$

Step 1:

Find the first root by trial and error. The first root will be a factor of 6, so we try out 1, 2, 3, 6 and then –1, –2, –3 and –6, if necessary.

$f(1) = 2(1)^3 - 9(1)^2 + 7(1) + 6 = 2 - 9 + 7 + 6 = 6$. So, 1 is not a root.

$f(2) = 2(2)^3 - 9(2)^2 + 7(2) + 6 = 16 - 36 + 14 + 6 = 0$. So, 2 is a root.

Step 2:

Since 2 is a root, we divide by $(x - 2)$, which is a factor.

$$\begin{array}{r|l} & 2x^2 - 5x - 3 \\ \hline x - 2 & 2x^3 - 9x^2 + 7x + 6 \\ & 2x^3 - 4x^2 \\ \hline & \quad -5x^2 + 7x \\ & \quad -5x^2 + 10x \\ \hline & \qquad\quad -3x + 6 \\ & \qquad\quad -3x + 6 \\ \hline & \qquad\qquad\quad 0 \end{array}$$

Step 3:

The other two roots are found by solving the quadratic equation:

$$2x^2 - 5x - 3 = 0$$

$$\therefore \quad (2x + 1)(x - 3) = 0$$

$$\therefore \quad x = -\tfrac{1}{2} \text{ or } 3$$

Step 4:

The three roots are $2, -\frac{1}{2}$ and 3.

Exercise 4.J

Solve these cubic equations:

1. $x^3 + 2x^2 - 13x + 10 = 0$
2. $2x^3 - x^2 - 5x - 2 = 0$
3. $x^3 - 3x^2 - x + 3 = 0$
4. $x^3 + 5x^2 - 4x - 20 = 0$
5. $2x^3 + 5x^2 - 11x + 4 = 0$
6. $x^3 - 39x + 70 = 0$
7. $3x^3 + x^2 - 12x - 4 = 0$
8. $3x^3 - 13x^2 + 16x - 4 = 0$
9. $4x^3 + x^2 - 4x - 1 = 0$
10. Show that $x = 4$ is a root of $x^3 - 12x - 16 = 0$. Hence find the other two roots.

11. Show that $x = 5$ is a root of

$$2x^3 - 5x^2 - 23x - 10 = 0.$$

Hence find the other two roots.

12. Show that $x = 7$ is a root of

$$x^3 - 5x^2 - 13x - 7 = 0.$$

Hence find the other two roots.

13. Show that $x = -1$ is a root of

$$6x^3 + 5x^2 - 2x - 1 = 0.$$

Hence find the other two roots.

14. Show that $x = -2$ is a root of

$$4x^3 + 8x^2 - x - 2 = 0.$$

Hence find the other two roots.

REVISION EXERCISE 4.K

1. (a) Solve $x^2 - x - 110 = 0$.

(b) Solve the simultaneous equations:

$$x + 3y = 13$$
$$y^2 + 2x = 18$$

(c) Show that $x = 2$ is a root of the cubic equation:

$$2x^3 + 3x^2 - 11x - 6 = 0.$$

Hence find the other two roots.

2. (a) Show that $x = 6$ is a solution to

$$x^3 + x^2 - 40x - 12 = 0.$$

(b) Solve the simultaneous equations:

$$x + y = 10$$
$$x^2 + y^2 = 58$$

(c) The square of a number is 8 more than seven times the number. Find the number.

3. (a) Factorise: $12x^2 + 7x - 12$

(b) Show that $x = 5$ is a root of the cubic equation:

$$2x^3 - x^2 - 35x - 50 = 0.$$

Hence find the other two roots.

(c) Find two consecutive natural numbers, whose squares add up to 25.

4. (a) Factorise: $2x^2 - 7x - 4$ and hence solve the equation

$$2x^2 - 7x - 4 = 0.$$

(b) (i) If $x = 3$ is a root of the quadratic equation:

$7x^2 + kx - 30 = 0$, find the value of k and the other root.

(ii) Simplify:

$$\left(\frac{x^2 - 9}{x + 4}\right) \div \left(\frac{x^2 + 2x - 15}{2x + 8}\right)$$

(c) Find two consecutive natural numbers, whose cubes differ by 61.

5. (a) Solve $10x^2 = 3x + 4$

(b) Solve the simultaneous equations:

$$x + 2y = 1$$
$$x^2 + y^2 = 10$$

(c) Show that $x = -7$ is a root of the cubic equation:

$$6x^3 + 37x^2 - 34x + 7 = 0.$$

Hence find the other two roots.

6. (a) Solve $\frac{18}{x} = x + 3$.

(b) The roots of $x^2 + px + q = 0$ are -8 and 3. Find p and q.

(c) If $x = 2$ is one solution of $x^3 - 4x^2 + x + k = 0$, find the value of k and hence find the other two solutions.

7. (a) Show that $x = -2$ is a root of the equation: $x^3 + 3x^2 + x - 2 = 0$

(b) The roots of $2x^2 - px + q = 0$ are 6 and $\frac{1}{2}$. Find the values of p and q.

(c) Solve the simultaneous equations:

$2x + y = 3$

$x^2 + y^2 = 26$

and deduce two possible values of $x^3 + y^3$.

8. (a) Solve these equations:

(i) $(x - 1)(x + 1) = 99$

(ii) $(x - 1)(x + 1) = 5x + 13$

(b) The perimeter of a rectangular room is 22 metres. The area is 30 square metres. If x = the width and y = the length, write down two equations and hence find the values of x and y.

(c) Solve: $\frac{3}{x+1} + \frac{1}{x-1} = 1\frac{1}{4}$

9. (a) Factorise: $2x^2 - x - 21$ and hence solve the equations

(i) $2x^2 - x - 21 = 0$.

(ii) $2x^3 - x^2 - 21x = 0$.

(b) Simplify: $\left(\frac{1}{x} - 1\right)(x + 1)$

And hence solve the equation $(\frac{1}{x} - 1)(x + 1) = \frac{15}{4}$

(c) (i) Find the quadratic equation, both of whose roots are equal to 10.

(ii) The roots of $x^2 - kx + 49 = 0$ are ***equal***. Write down the roots and the value of k.

10. (a) Show that $x = 3$ is a root of the equation: $x^3 - 5x^2 - x + 21 = 0$ and find the other roots correct to one decimal place.

(b) Write $(\frac{2}{x} - 1)(\frac{2}{x} + 1)$ as a single fraction.

And hence solve the equation: $(\frac{2}{x} - 1)(\frac{2}{x} + 1) = 15$

(c) Solve the simultaneous equations:

$2x - 3y = 13$

$x^2 + y^2 = 13$

1. The '**Zero Law**': If $A \times B = 0$, then $A = 0$ or $B = 0$.
2. The **quadratic formula**: If $ax^2 + bx + c = 0$, then
$$x = \frac{-b \pm \sqrt{b^2 - 4ac}}{2a}$$
3. The **factor theorem**: If k is a ***root*** of a quadratic or cubic expression, then $(x - k)$ is a ***factor***.

Chapter 5

Powers and Roots

THE LAWS OF INDICES

1. $a^m \times a^n = a^{m+n}$ For example, $a^3 \times a^4 = a^{3+4} = a^7$
2. $\dfrac{a^m}{a^n} = a^{m-n}$ For example, $\dfrac{a^{11}}{a^7} = a^{11-7} = a^4$
3. $(a^m)^n = a^{mn}$ For example, $(a^3)^4 = a^{3(4)} = a^{12}$
4. $(ab)^n = a^n b^n$ For example, $(ab)^2 = a^2b^2$
5. $a^{-n} = \dfrac{1}{a^n}$ For example, $3^{-2} = \dfrac{1}{3^2} = \dfrac{1}{9}$
6. $a^0 = 1$ For example, $10^0 = 1$
7. $a^{\frac{1}{n}} = \sqrt[n]{a}$ For example, $8^{\frac{1}{3}} = \sqrt[3]{8} = 2$

Example 1: Evaluate the following:

(i) $\dfrac{2^7 \times 2^3}{(2^5)^2}$ (ii) $(2\sqrt{3})^2$ (iii) 5^{-3} (iv) $9^{\frac{1}{2}}$ (v) $8^{\frac{2}{3}}$ (vi) $\left(\dfrac{4}{9}\right)^{-\frac{1}{2}}$

Solution:

(i) $\dfrac{2^7 \times 2^3}{(2^5)^2} = \dfrac{2^{10}}{2^{10}} = 2^{10-10} = 2^0 = 1$

(ii) $(2\sqrt{3})^2 = 2^2(\sqrt{3})^2 = 4(3) = 12$

(iii) $5^{-3} = \dfrac{1}{5^3} = \dfrac{1}{125}$

(iv) $9^{\frac{1}{2}} = \sqrt[2]{9} = \sqrt{9} = 3$

(v) $8^{\frac{2}{3}} = \left(8^{\frac{1}{3}}\right)^2 = (\sqrt[3]{8})^2 = (2)^2 = 4$

(vi) $\left(\dfrac{4}{9}\right)^{-\frac{1}{2}} = \dfrac{1}{\left(\frac{4}{9}\right)^{\frac{1}{2}}} = \dfrac{1}{\sqrt{\frac{4}{9}}} = \dfrac{1}{\frac{2}{3}} = 1 \div \dfrac{2}{3} = 1 \times \dfrac{3}{2} = \dfrac{3}{2}$

Exercise 5.A

Write these as a^p, where $p \varepsilon Q$:

1. $a^3 \times a^4$
2. $a^6 \times a^2$
3. $\frac{a^5}{a^3}$
4. $\frac{a^5}{a^4}$
5. $\frac{a^6 \times a^3}{a^4}$
6. $\frac{a^3 \times a^5}{(a^2)^2}$
7. $\frac{a^4 \times a^5}{(a^4)^2}$
8. $\frac{a^6 \times a^3}{(a^3)^3}$
9. $\sqrt{a}$
10. $\sqrt[3]{a}$
11. $\frac{1}{a^4}$
12. $\frac{1}{a^9}$
13. $\frac{1}{a^5}$
14. $\frac{1}{a}$
15. $\frac{1}{a^2}$
16. $\frac{1}{\sqrt{a}}$
17. $a\sqrt{a}$
18. $a^3\sqrt{a}$
19. $(a^{11})^3$
20. Write $\sqrt{x^7}$ in the form x^n.

Evaluate the following:

21. 3^3
22. $2^3 \times 2^2$
23. $\frac{2^5}{2^3}$
24. $\frac{7^5}{7^4}$
25. $\frac{10^6}{10^4}$
26. $\frac{2^3 \times 2^5}{(2^4)^2}$
27. $\frac{5^4 \times 5^5}{(5^4)^2}$
28. $\frac{5^{10} \times 5}{(5^3)^3}$
29. $25^{\frac{1}{2}}$
30. $100^{\frac{1}{2}}$
31. $49^{\frac{1}{2}}$
32. $125^{\frac{1}{3}}$
33. $64^{\frac{1}{2}} + 64^{\frac{1}{3}}$
34. $27^{\frac{1}{3}}$
35. 10^{-2}
36. 3^{-2}

37. 4^{-1}

38. $100^{-\frac{1}{2}}$

39. $36^{-\frac{1}{2}}$

40. $16^{\frac{1}{4}}$

41. $16^{-\frac{1}{4}}$

42. $27^{\frac{2}{3}}$

43. $64^{\frac{2}{3}}$

44. $16^{\frac{3}{4}}$

45. $100^{\frac{3}{2}}$

46. $125^{\frac{2}{3}}$

47. $16^{\frac{5}{4}}$

48. $81^{\frac{3}{4}}$

49. $9^{\frac{3}{2}}$

50. $9^{-\frac{3}{2}}$

51. $81^{-\frac{3}{4}}$

52. $\left(\frac{1}{4}\right)^{\frac{1}{2}}$

53. $\left(\frac{1}{25}\right)^{\frac{1}{2}}$

54. $\left(\frac{4}{9}\right)^{\frac{1}{2}}$

55. $\left(\frac{81}{25}\right)^{\frac{1}{2}}$

56. $\left(\frac{8}{27}\right)^{\frac{1}{3}}$

57. $\left(\frac{8}{125}\right)^{\frac{1}{3}}$

58. $\left(\frac{8}{27}\right)^{-\frac{1}{3}}$

59. $\left(\frac{36}{25}\right)^{-\frac{1}{2}}$

60. $\left(\frac{4}{121}\right)^{-\frac{1}{2}}$

61. $\left(\frac{8}{125}\right)^{-\frac{1}{3}}$

62. $\left(\frac{27}{1000}\right)^{-\frac{2}{3}}$

63. $\left(\frac{125}{27}\right)^{-\frac{2}{3}}$

64. Write these in the form 2^p:
(i) 8 (ii) 16 (iii) 32 (iv) 4 (v) $^1/_2$
(vi) $^1/_4$ (vii) $\sqrt{2}$ (viii) $\sqrt[3]{2}$ (ix) $\frac{1}{\sqrt{2}}$

65. Write these in the form of 3^p:
(i) 9 (ii) 27 (iii) 81 (iv) 1 (v) $^1/_3$
(vi) $^1/_9$ (vii) $\sqrt{3}$ (viii) $\sqrt{27}$ (ix) $\frac{1}{\sqrt{3}}$

66. Write these in the form of 5^p:
(i) 25 (ii) 125 (iii) $^1/_5$ (iv) 1 (v) $^1/_{25}$
(vi) $^1/_{125}$ (vii) $\sqrt{5}$ (viii) $5\sqrt{5}$ (ix) $\frac{1}{\sqrt{5}}$

67. Write these in the form of 10^p:
(i) 100 (ii) 1000 (iii) 0.01 (iv) 10 000
(v) $^1/_{10}$ (vi) $^1/_{10\,000}$ (vii) $\sqrt{10}$
(viii) $100\sqrt{10}$ (ix) $\frac{1}{\sqrt{10}}$ (x) $\frac{\sqrt{10}}{\sqrt[3]{10}}$
(xi) $\sqrt{1000}$ (xii) $\frac{100}{\sqrt{10}}$

EQUATIONS WITH POWERS

When you are solving an equation like $4^x = \frac{8}{\sqrt{2}}$, write ***all*** numbers on both sides in the form 2^n. If the equation is $3^{2x-1} = \frac{81}{\sqrt{3}}$, write ***all*** numbers on both sides in the form 3^n. Use (and obey!) the laws of indices, with great care.

Example 1: Solve (i) $4^x = \frac{8}{\sqrt{2}}$ (ii) $3^{2x-1} = \frac{81}{\sqrt{3}}$

Solution: (i) $4 = 2^2$, $8 = 2^3$ and $\sqrt{2} = 2^{\frac{1}{2}}$ [converting all numbers to powers of 2].

$$4^x = \frac{8}{\sqrt{2}}$$

$$\therefore\ (2^2)^x = \frac{2^3}{2^{\frac{1}{2}}}$$

$$\therefore\ 2^{2x} = 2^{2\frac{1}{2}}$$

$$\therefore\ 2x = 2\tfrac{1}{2}$$

$$\therefore\ x = 1\tfrac{1}{4}$$

(ii) $81 = 3^4$ and $\sqrt{3} = 3^{\frac{1}{2}}$ [converting all numbers to powers of 3].

$$3^{2x-1} = \frac{81}{\sqrt{3}}$$

$$\therefore\ 3^{2x-1} = \frac{3^4}{3^{\frac{1}{2}}}$$

$$\therefore\ 3^{2x-1} = 3^{3\frac{1}{2}}$$

$$\therefore\ 2x - 1 = 3\tfrac{1}{2}$$

$$\therefore\ 2x = 4\tfrac{1}{2}$$

$$\therefore\ x = 2\tfrac{1}{4}$$

Exercise 5.B

Solve these equations:

1. $2^x = 8$
2. $3^x = 9$
3. $2^x = 32$
4. $10^x = 100$
5. $5^x = 25$
6. $2^x = 4\sqrt{2}$
7. $2^x = (4)^7$
8. $3^x = (27)^5$
9. $2^x = 2^7\sqrt{2}$
10. $2^x = \frac{2^7}{4}$
11. $5^x = \frac{125}{\sqrt{5}}$
12. $3^{x+1} = \frac{9}{\sqrt{3}}$
13. $10^{x-3} = \frac{\sqrt{10}}{100}$
14. $7^x = \frac{49}{\sqrt[3]{7}}$
15. $10^{2x-1} = \frac{\sqrt{1000}}{10}$
16. $4^x = \frac{32\sqrt{2}}{2}$
17. $49^x = \frac{49}{\sqrt{7}}$
18. $2^x = \left(\frac{16}{\sqrt{2}}\right)^3$
19. $7^{x^2} \cdot 7^x = (49)^3$
20. $\frac{10^{x^2}}{10^{3x}} = \frac{1}{100}$
21. Write these as 2^x:
    (i) 16
    (ii) 8
    (iii) $\sqrt{8}$

    Hence solve: $2^{2x-1} = \left(\frac{16}{\sqrt{8}}\right)^3$
22. Write these as 3^x:
    (i) 27
    (ii) $\sqrt{3}$

    Hence solve: $3^{3x-1} = \left(\frac{27}{\sqrt{3}}\right)^5$
23. Write these as 5^x:
    (i) 25
    (ii) $\sqrt{125}$
    (iii) $\sqrt[3]{5}$

    Hence solve: $25^x = \left(\frac{\sqrt{125}}{\sqrt[3]{5}}\right)^{12}$
24. Write these as 10^x:
    (i) 100
    (ii) $\sqrt{100000}$
    (iii) $\sqrt[4]{10}$

    Hence solve: $100^{2x-1} = \left(\frac{\sqrt{100000}}{\sqrt[4]{10}}\right)^2$

DEALING WITH SURDS

Square roots are often called ***surds***. Surds do not behave like ordinary numbers. For example, $\sqrt{2} + \sqrt{3} \neq \sqrt{5}$. Check this out with a calculator. Similarly, $\sqrt{7} - \sqrt{2} \neq \sqrt{5}$. So we ***cannot*** add or subtract surds.

However, the fourth law of indices states that $(ab)^n = a^n b^n$. It follows that $(ab)^{\frac{1}{2}} = a^{\frac{1}{2}} b^{\frac{1}{2}}$. Hence, we ***can*** multiply (and divide) surds. For example, $(\sqrt{2})(\sqrt{3}) = \sqrt{6}$ and $\frac{\sqrt{21}}{\sqrt{3}} = \sqrt{7}$.

Furthermore, when you square a square root, you arrive back at the number you started with: $(\sqrt{11})^2 = 11$ and $(\sqrt{29})^2 = 29$ and $(2\sqrt{7})^2 = (2)^2(\sqrt{7})^2 = (4)(7) = 28$.

Exercise 5.C

Evaluate:

1. $(\sqrt{3})^2$
2. $(\sqrt{7})^2$
3. $(\sqrt{17})^2$
4. $(\sqrt{30})^2$
5. $(2\sqrt{2})^2$
6. $(3\sqrt{5})^2$
7. $(2\sqrt{10})^2$
8. $(10\sqrt{2})^2$
9. $(\sqrt{12})(\sqrt{3})$
10. $(\sqrt{20})(\sqrt{5})$
11. $(\sqrt{2})(\sqrt{8})$
12. $\frac{\sqrt{27}}{\sqrt{3}}$
13. $\frac{\sqrt{50}}{\sqrt{2}}$
14. $\frac{\sqrt{28}}{\sqrt{7}}$
15. State if these are true or false:
    (i) $\sqrt{3} + \sqrt{5} = \sqrt{8}$
    (ii) $\sqrt{13} - \sqrt{5} = \sqrt{8}$
    (iii) $(\sqrt{3})(\sqrt{5}) = \sqrt{15}$
    (iv) $\frac{\sqrt{30}}{\sqrt{5}} = \sqrt{6}$
16. State if these are true or false:
    (i) $\sqrt{2} + \sqrt{8} = \sqrt{10}$
    (ii) $\sqrt{8} - \sqrt{2} = \sqrt{6}$
    (iii) $(\sqrt{8})(\sqrt{2}) = 4$
    (iv) $\frac{\sqrt{8}}{\sqrt{2}} = 2$
17. Insert > or < or = in the spaces:
    (i) $\sqrt{9} + \sqrt{16} \ldots \sqrt{25}$
    (ii) $\sqrt{169} - \sqrt{25} \ldots \sqrt{144}$
    (iii) $(2\sqrt{11})^2 \ldots 22$
    (iv) $\frac{\sqrt{64}}{2} \ldots \sqrt{16}$
    (v) $(\sqrt{7})^3 \ldots 7\sqrt{7}$

REDUCING SURDS

A fraction can be ***reduced*** by dividing above and below by the same number.

For example $^6/_8 = {}^3/_4$ [dividing above and below by 2].

Surds can also be reduced, but in a different way. If the number under the square root has, as a factor, a perfect square (4, 9, 16, 25, 36, ...), then we can reduce the surd by dividing out the perfect square.

In this way, $\sqrt{28} = \sqrt{4}\sqrt{7} = 2\sqrt{7}$. You can see that the number under the square root has been ***reduced***.

Similarly, $\sqrt{200} = \sqrt{100}\sqrt{2} = 10\sqrt{2}$.

Sometimes it is possible to combine surds in this way:

$\sqrt{18} + \sqrt{50} = \sqrt{9}\sqrt{2} + \sqrt{25}\sqrt{2} = 3\sqrt{2} + 5\sqrt{2} = 8\sqrt{2}$.

Finally, $\frac{\sqrt{20}}{2} = \frac{\sqrt{4}\sqrt{5}}{2} = \frac{2\sqrt{5}}{2} = \sqrt{5}$.

Exercise 5.D

Reduce these surds:

1. $\sqrt{8}$
2. $\sqrt{45}$
3. $\sqrt{300}$
4. $\sqrt{12}$
5. $\sqrt{32}$
6. $\sqrt{500}$
7. $\sqrt{27}$
8. $\sqrt{54}$
9. $\sqrt{75}$
10. $\sqrt{98}$
11. Write $\sqrt{50} + \sqrt{8}$ in the form $k\sqrt{2}$.
12. Write $\sqrt{27} + \sqrt{12}$ in the form $k\sqrt{3}$.
13. Write $\sqrt{125} + \sqrt{20}$ in the form $k\sqrt{5}$.
14. If $\sqrt{44} + \sqrt{99} = n\sqrt{11}$, find n.
15. If $\sqrt{12} + \sqrt{300} - \sqrt{3} = n\sqrt{3}$, find n.
16. If $\sqrt{54} + 2\sqrt{24} - \sqrt{6} = k\sqrt{6}$, find k.

Write these as $\sqrt{n}$, where $n \varepsilon N$:

17. $\frac{\sqrt{12}}{2}$
18. $\frac{\sqrt{45}}{3}$
19. $\frac{\sqrt{700}}{10}$
20. $\frac{\sqrt{175}}{5}$
21. $\frac{\sqrt{72}}{6}$

Use the quadratic formula to find the roots of these equations in the form $n \pm \sqrt{m}$, where $n, m \varepsilon Z$:

22. $x^2 - 4x + 1 = 0$
23. $x^2 - 12x + 34 = 0$
24. $x^2 - 2x - 6 = 0$
25. $x^2 + 6x + 4 = 0$

EQUATIONS WITH SURDS

When an equation has a surd in it which you want to get rid of, proceed as follows:

1. Isolate the surd on one side of the equation.
2. Square both sides properly, by putting a bracket around both sides and squaring them.

Example 1: Solve for x: $1 + \sqrt{x-6} = 3$

Solution:

$$1 + \sqrt{x-6} = 3$$

$\therefore$ $\sqrt{x-6} = 2$ [Isolating the surd]

$\therefore$ $(\sqrt{x-6})^2 = (2)^2$ [Squaring both sides]

$\therefore$ $x - 6 = 4$

$\therefore$ $x = 10$

Example 2: Given $T = 2\pi\sqrt{\frac{l}{g}}$, write l in terms of the other variables.

Solution:

$$T = 2\pi\sqrt{\frac{l}{g}}$$

$\therefore$ $\frac{T}{2\pi} = \sqrt{\frac{l}{g}}$ [Isolating the surd]

$\therefore$ $\left(\frac{T}{2\pi}\right)^2 = \left(\sqrt{\frac{l}{g}}\right)^2$ [Squaring both sides]

$\therefore$ $\frac{T^2}{4\pi^2} = \frac{l}{g}$

$\therefore$ $\frac{T^2 g}{4\pi^2} = l$ [Multiplying both sides by g]

Exercise 5.E

Solve for x:

1. $\sqrt{x} = 5$
2. $\sqrt{x} = 10$
3. $1 + \sqrt{x} = 4$
4. $\sqrt{x+6} = 4$
5. $\sqrt{2x+1} = 9$
6. $\sqrt{7x+1} = 6$
7. $\sqrt{2x-1} = 3$
8. $3 + \sqrt{3x+1} = 8$
9. $\sqrt{5x-1} - 3 = 4$
10. $13 - \sqrt{9x+1} = 3$
11. $20 - \sqrt{9x-8} = 12$
12. $1 + \sqrt{22x+100} = 13$
13. $\sqrt{x^2+5^2} = 13$
14. $\sqrt{x^2-6^2} = 8$
15. $\sqrt{2x^2-1} = 7$

Write x in terms of the other variables:

16. $\sqrt{x} = y$
17. $\sqrt{x+a} = y$
18. $\sqrt{x-b} = c$
19. $\sqrt{2x-y} = p$
20. $\sqrt{x} + a = b$
21. $\sqrt{x-1} = yz$
22. $T = 2\pi\sqrt{\frac{x}{mgh}}$

SCIENTIFIC NOTATION

Some numbers are very small (0.0000035, for example). Others are enormous (470 000 000, for example). Such numbers are cumbersome to deal with. We often write such numbers in ***scientific notation***. This means that the number is written as

$$a \times 10^n, \text{ where } 1 \leq a < 10, \text{ and } n \in Z$$

In scientific notation, 470 000 000 = 4.7×10^8 since you would need to multiply 4.7 by 10 eight times in order to get 470 000 000.

Similarly, 0.0000035 = 3.5×10^{-6}, since you would need to divide 3.5 by 10 six times in order to get 0.0000035

To enter 4.7×10^8 into a calculator, press the buttons:

You should get either 470 000 000 or 4.7^{08} on the screen. You must realise that 4.7^{08} is the calculator's way of representing the scientific number 4.7×10^8.

Exercise 5.F

1. Write these numbers in scientific notation:
   (i) 4500
   (ii) 57 000
   (iii) 310
   (iv) 972 000
   (v) 1 300 000
   (vi) 0.0063
   (vii) 0.0002
   (viii) 0.045
   (ix) 0.000006
   (x) 0.00385

2. Write these as decimal numbers:
   (i) 3×10^2
   (ii) 7×10^4
   (iii) 3.8×10^3
   (iv) 4.7×10^5
   (v) 9.3×10^2
   (vi) 3.6×10^{-2}
   (vii) 1.63×10^{-4}
   (viii) 7.6×10^{-3}
   (ix) 2.76×10^{-1}
   (x) 3.06×10^{-6}

3. Write these numbers in scientific notation:
   (i) 52 000 000
   (ii) 0.57
   (iii) 3570
   (iv) 0.000972
   (v) 7308
   (vi) 0.000077
   (vii) 6 000 000
   (viii) 0.4545
   (ix) 678 900
   (x) 1000

4. Write these as decimal numbers:
   (i) 3.63×10^2
   (ii) 3.3×10^{-3}
   (iii) 9.8×10^7
   (iv) 1.7×10^{-5}
   (v) 1×10^2
   (vi) 1×10^{-2}
   (vii) 1.63×10^7
   (viii) 7.612×10^{-1}
   (ix) 2.76345×10^8
   (x) 9.006×10^{-2}

5. Write $^1/_4$
   (i) as a decimal number,
   (ii) in scientific notation.

6. Write $^3/_4$
   (i) as a decimal number,
   (ii) in scientific notation.

7. Write 5 metres as a fraction of 1 kilometre, giving your answer
   (i) as a decimal number,
   (ii) in scientific notation.

8. The sun is 1.5×10^8 kilometres from the earth. Convert this distance to metres, giving your answer
   (i) in scientific notation,
   (ii) as a decimal number.

9. The moon is 384 400 000 metres from the earth. Convert this to kilometres, giving your answer
   (i) as a decimal number,
   (ii) in scientific notation.

10. Avogadro's number is 602 252 000 000 000 000 000 000. Write this in scientific notation.

OPERATIONS WITH SCIENTIFIC NOTATION

To ***add*** or ***subtract*** scientific numbers, you should convert them into decimal numbers, then add (or subtract). Convert your answer back into scientific notation, if required.

To ***multiply*** (or ***divide***) scientific numbers, do the operation in two bits:

Multiply like this: $(a \times 10^m) \times (b \times 10^n) = ab \times 10^{a+b}$

Divide like this: $\dfrac{a \times 10^m}{b \times 10^n} = \dfrac{a}{b} \times 10^{m-n}$

Example 1: Write $3.1 \times 10^3 + 2.45 \times 10^4$ in the form $a \times 10^n$, where $1 \le a < 10$, and $n \in Z$.

Solution: $3.1 \times 10^3 + 2.45 \times 10^4$

$= 3100 + 24\,500$

$= 27\,600$

$= 2.76 \times 10^4$

[With a calculator:

3 . 1 Exp 3 + 2 . 4 5 Exp 4 = 27600]

Example 2: Evaluate: $\dfrac{(1.7 \times 10^{11}) \times (2.2 \times 10^{-5})}{3.4 \times 10^8}$, giving your answer as a decimal.

Solution:

$$\frac{(1.7 \times 10^{11}) \times (2.2 \times 10^{-5})}{3.4 \times 10^8}$$

$$= \frac{(1.7 \times 2.2) \times 10^{11-5}}{3.4 \times 10^8}$$

$$= \frac{3.74 \times 10^6}{3.4 \times 10^8}$$

$$= \frac{3.74}{3.4} \times 10^{6-8}$$

$$= 1.1 \times 10^{-2}$$

$$= 0.011$$

[On a calculator: 1 . 7 Exp 1 1 X 2 . 2 Exp 5 +/- = ÷ 3 . 4 Exp 8 = 0.011]

Exercise 5.G

Write the answers to these as decimal numbers:

1. $2.1 \times 10^2 + 3.2 \times 10^3$
2. $6.7 \times 10^4 - 9.2 \times 10^3$
3. $(2.1 \times 10^2) \times (3 \times 10^3)$
4. $\dfrac{8.4 \times 10^7}{2 \times 10^4}$
5. $8.71 \times 10^1 + 1.27 \times 10^2$
6. $9.14 \times 10^5 - 1.2 \times 10^4$
7. $(1.5 \times 10^5) \times (5 \times 10^6)$
8. $\dfrac{6.3 \times 10^5}{2.1 \times 10^2}$
9. $9.66 \times 10^0 + 1.22 \times 10^1$
10. $8.7 \times 10^{-4} - 9.9 \times 10^{-5}$
11. $\dfrac{(2.1 \times 10^2) \times (3 \times 10^3)}{7 \times 10^4}$
12. $\dfrac{(2 \times 10^4) + (3 \times 10^5)}{1.6 \times 10^2}$

Write the answers to these in scientific notation: $a \times 10^n$:

13. $2.1 \times 10^2 + 3.2 \times 10^2$
14. $7.27 \times 10^4 - 9.6 \times 10^3$
15. $(2.1 \times 10^9) \times (3.1 \times 10^8)$
16. $\dfrac{8.8 \times 10^{11}}{2.2 \times 10^4}$
17. $5.5 \times 10^{-1} + 9.2 \times 10^{-2}$
18. $9.4 \times 10^{-5} - 3.2 \times 10^{-4}$
19. $\dfrac{(2.5 \times 10^5) \times (5.5 \times 10^6)}{1.25 \times 10^7}$
20. $\dfrac{8.2 \times 10^{-2}}{(3.8 \times 10^3) + (3 \times 10^2)}$
21. Write π^3
    (i) as a decimal number correct to the nearest natural number,
    (ii) in scientific notation, correct to two significant figures.
22. Write $\left(\frac{1}{\pi}\right)^4$
    (i) as a decimal number correct to three significant figures,
    (ii) in scientific notation, correct to three significant figures.
23. The mass of a hydrogen atom is 1.67×10^{-27} kilograms.
    (i) Find the mass of 55 billion such atoms. Give your answer in scientific notation. [Note: 1 billion = 10^9]
    (ii) How many atoms are there in 1 kg of hydrogen? Give your answer to 1 significant figure in scientific notation.
24. The mass of the Earth is 5.98×10^{24} kg. The mass of the Moon is 7.4×10^{22} kg. Find their combined mass in scientific notation.
25. The population of the world is 6.4 billion. Each person drinks, on average, 2.3 litres of water per day. Find, in scientific notation, the amount of water drunk by the world population
    (i) in a day,
    (ii) in a year.
26. The sun is 150 million kilometres from the Earth. Light takes 8 minutes and 20 seconds to travel from the Sun to the Earth. Find the speed of light in metres per second in scientific notation.
27. Evaluate in scientific notation, correct to four significant figures: $\dfrac{1}{(\sqrt{45} + \sqrt{55})^5}$
28. Write 0.0718 grams as a fraction of 1 kilogram. Give your answer in scientific notation.

REVISION EXERCISE 5.H

1. (a) Evaluate: $25^{\frac{1}{2}}$.

(b) Write as a power of 3:

(i) 9

(ii) $\sqrt{3}$

Hence solve the equation: $3^x = \dfrac{9}{\sqrt{3}}$

(c) If $\sqrt{8} + \sqrt{50} - \sqrt{2} = n\sqrt{2}$, find n.

2. (a) Evaluate: $64^{-\frac{1}{2}}$

(b) Write as a power of 2:

(i) 128

(ii) $\sqrt{2}$

Hence solve the equation:

$2^{2x+1} = \dfrac{128}{\sqrt{2}}$

(c) If $\sqrt{2x - y} = z$, write x in terms of the other variables.

3. (a) Express 125 m as a fraction of 1 km. Write this fraction in scientific notation.

(b) Calculate the value of

$$\frac{3.3 \times 10^6 + 1.2 \times 10^4}{3.6 \times 10^3}$$

(c) If g = 9.81, write $^1/_{g^2}$ in the form $a \times 10^n$, writing a correct to three significant figures and n as an integer.

4. (a) Evaluate: $\left(\frac{8}{27}\right)^{-\frac{1}{3}}$.

(b) Write 2 grams as a fraction of 1 kilogram, giving your answer

(i) as a decimal number,

(ii) in scientific notation.

(c) Write these as p^n:

(i) $p^4 \times p^6$

(ii) $(p^4)^6$

(iii) $\sqrt[4]{p^6}$

5. (a) Evaluate: $\left(\frac{4}{81}\right)^{-\frac{1}{2}}$

(b) Write as a power of 7:

(i) 343

(ii) $\sqrt{7}$

Hence solve the equation:

$7^{2x+1} = \dfrac{343}{(\sqrt{7})^3}$

(c) If $T = 2\pi\sqrt{\frac{l}{g}}$, write g in terms of the other variables and evaluate g if $T = 2$ and $l = 1$. Give your answer correct to one decimal place.

6. (a) Write 1 second as a fraction of a day, giving your answer

(i) as a decimal (to three significant figures),

(ii) in scientific notation (correct to three significant figures).

(b) Write as a power of 10:

(i) 100

(ii) $\sqrt{1000}$

Hence solve the equation: $10^{7x-3} = \dfrac{100}{\sqrt{1000}}$

(c) Simplify

$\left(\sqrt{x} + \frac{2}{\sqrt{x}}\right)\left(\sqrt{x} - \frac{2}{\sqrt{x}}\right)$ if $x > 0$.

Hence solve for x (where $x > 0$)

$\left(\sqrt{x} + \frac{2}{\sqrt{x}}\right)\left(\sqrt{x} - \frac{2}{\sqrt{x}}\right) = 3$

7. (a) Express $\dfrac{3}{9125}$ in scientific notation, to two significant figures.

(b) Calculate the value of

$$\sqrt{\frac{(3.63 \times 10^{11}) \times (1.2 \times 10^{-3})}{3.6 \times 10^2}}$$

(c) If $\sqrt{4x - 3y} = 5z$, write y in terms of x and z.

Hence find the value of y if $x = 28$ and $z = 2$.

8. (a) Evaluate: $\left(\frac{1000}{27}\right)^{-\frac{2}{3}}$

(b) Calculate the value of:

(i) $(3\sqrt{7})^2$

(ii) $(3\sqrt{7})^4$

(c) Find the roots of $x^2 - 3x - 6 = 0$ in surd form. Find also the sum and the product of these roots.

9. (a) Evaluate: $\left(\frac{16}{81}\right)^{-\frac{3}{4}}$

(b) Write $\sqrt{\frac{x^3}{\sqrt{x}}}$ in the form x^p.

(c) Solve for x: $\frac{100^x}{10^{1-x}} = 100\ 000$

10. (a) The mass of an atom of hydrogen is 1.67×10^{-27} kilograms. The mass of an atom of oxygen is 16 times greater. Find the mass of a ***molecule*** of water which consists of two atoms of hydrogen and one of oxygen. Write your answer in the form $a \times 10^n$, where $1 \leq a < 10$ and $n \in Z$.

(b) Write 1 day as a fraction of a year (not a leap year), giving your answer correct to three significant figures

(i) as a decimal number,

(ii) in scientific notation.

(c) The roots of $x^2 + bx + c = 0$ are $1 + \sqrt{11}$ and $1 - \sqrt{11}$. Find the values of b and c.

1. $a^m \times a^n = a^{m+n}$

2. $\frac{a^m}{a^n} = a^{m-n}$

3. $(a^m)^n = a^{mn}$

4. $(ab)^n = a^n b^n$

5. $a^{-n} = \frac{1}{a^n}$

6. $a^0 = 1$

7. $a^{\frac{1}{n}} = \sqrt[n]{a}$

8. $\sqrt{a} + \sqrt{b} \neq \sqrt{a+b}$

9. $\sqrt{a} - \sqrt{b} \neq \sqrt{a-b}$

10. $\sqrt{a} \times \sqrt{b} = \sqrt{ab}$

11. $\frac{\sqrt{a}}{\sqrt{b}} = \sqrt{\frac{a}{b}}$

12. In scientific notation, a number is written in the form $a \times 10^n$, where $1 \leq a < 10$ and $n \in Z$.

Chapter 6

Functions and Graphs

THE IDEA OF A FUNCTION

A function is like a machine. You put a number in, it is transformed by the machine, and another number emerges.

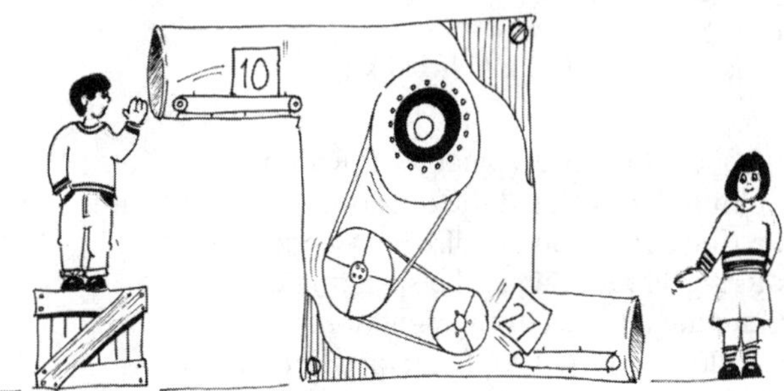

For example, the illustration shows the function $f : x \rightarrow 2x + 7$. This function has a job to do. It doubles and adds seven. Whatever number you put in will be doubled and then 7 will be added.

If you put 10 in, 27 will come out. This can be illustrated in any of three different ways: $f(10) = 27$ or (10, 27) or by plotting the point (10, 27) on a graph.
10 is called the ***first component*** (the input). 27 is called the ***second component*** (the output).

If you put 3 in, 13 will come out.
This can be written in three ways: $f(3) = 13$ or (3, 13) or by plotting the point (3, 13) on a graph. The first component is 3; the second component is 13.
If you put –6 in, –5 will come out.
This, too, can be written in three ways: $f(-6) = -5$ or (–6, –5) or by plotting (–6, –5) on a graph. The first component is –6; the second component is –5.
If you put in $(5x + 1)$, the function will double this and add 7. So, you will get out $2(5x + 1) + 7 = 10x + 9$.
We can write $f(5x + 1) = 10x + 9$.

Here, then is a graph showing the three points (10, 27), (3, 13) and (–6, –5) and linking them with a straight line.

The first components are the x–coordinates.
The second components are the y–coordinates.

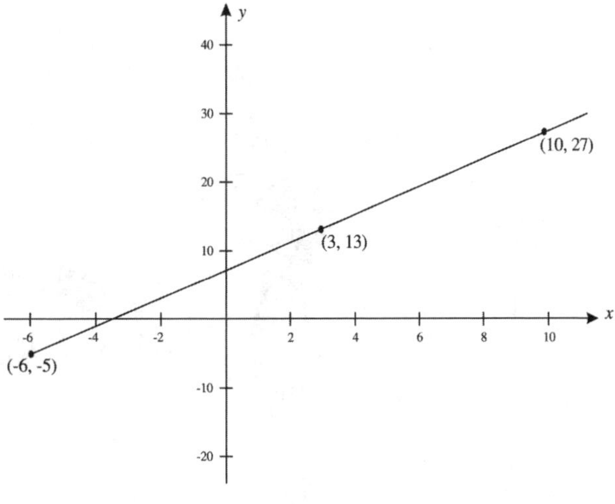

It would be wrong to think that functions are something which we meet in the field of Mathematics, but not in everyday life. On the contrary, you meet functions all throughout your normal daily life.

Your remote control for the television performs a ***function***. If you press one number, say 1, you get RTE 1. If you press another (say 5) you get BBC 1. If you press another (say 11) you get UTV. These could be represented by the set of couples:
(1, RTE 1), (5, BBC 1), (11, UTV), ...

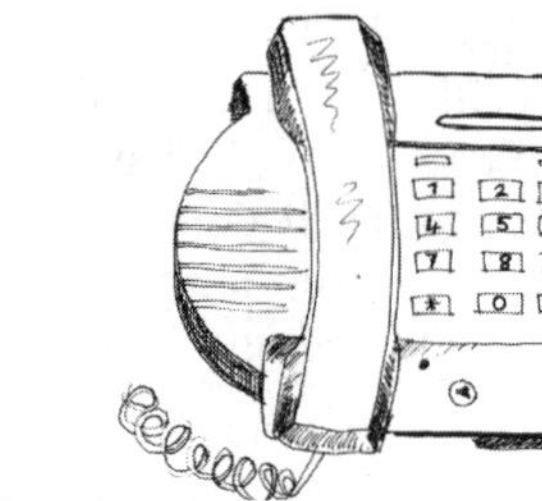

Telephone numbers are another function.
If you ring 196, you get the department for telegrams.
If you ring 1190, you get directory enquiries.
If you ring 1191, you get the speaking clock.
Here are the couples of this function:
(196, Telegrams), (1190, Directory Enquiries),
(1191, Speaking Clock), ...

Even the bar codes on goods in a supermarket perform a function, which determines price. When the check-out person swipes through one bar code, a certain price comes through. When (s)he swipes through another, a different price comes through.

A more tenuous and subtle function might be the amount of study you do in Maths and the mark you get in the Leaving. Do you agree with the following function?:

(Regular hard work, A1) , (Moderate work, B2), (No work at all, E), ...

Can you think of any ***functions*** which you meet in your life?

THE DEFINITION OF A FUNCTION

Take the set of couples: {(1, 4), (2, 6), (3, 8), (4, 10)}. This set of couples ***is*** a function. When you put in 1, out comes 4; when you put in 2, out comes 6, etc.

But take the set of couples: {(1, 3), (2, 5), (3, 11), (2, 13)}.

When the machine gets up-and-running, what happens when you put in the number 2? Will the machine send out 5 or will it send out 13? We cannot tell. We say that this set of couples is ***not*** a function, because two of the first components are the same.

This brings us to a formal definition of a function:

> A ***function*** is a set of couples, no two of which have the same first component.

For example, {(2, 5), (7, 7), (5, 5), (11, 7)} ***is a function***, since all first components (2, 7, 5, and 11) are different. It doesn't matter that some of the second components are the same.
But the set of couples: {(5, 2), (7, 7), (5, 5), (3, 11)} is ***not*** a function since two of the first components are the same.

DOMAIN AND RANGE

> The set of first components of a function is called the ***domain***.
> The set of second components of a function is called the ***range***.

For example, take the function
$f = \{(10, 27), (3, 13), (-6, -5)\}$.
The domain of $f = \{10, 3, -6\}$.
The range of $f = \{27, 13, -5\}$.

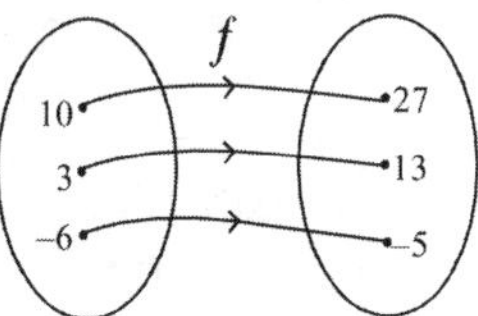

THREE WAYS OF DEPICTING FUNCTIONS

A function which squares a number and then adds 2, can be depicted in three different ways: $f(x) = x^2 + 2$ or $f : x \to x^2 + 2$ or $y = x^2 + 2$. These all mean the same thing: that if you put in a number, you will get out the–number–squared–plus–two. If the domain is {–1, 0, 1}, what is the range?

The couples of this function are
(–1, 3), (0, 2) and (1, 3).
The range is {2, 3}

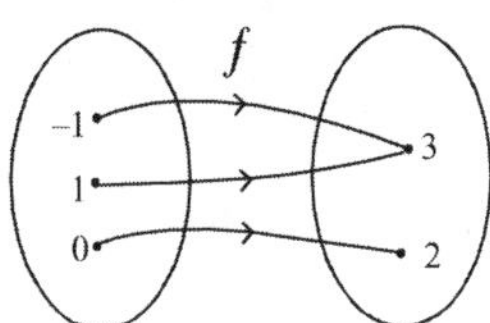

Example 1: f is a function defined by $f : x \to 3x^2 - 2$. The domain of f is {2, 1, 0, –1, –2}. Find the range.

Solution: $f(2) = 3(2)^2 - 2 = 10$. This couple is (2, 10).

$f(1) = 3(1)^2 - 2 = 1$. This couple is (1, 1).

$f(0) = 3(0)^2 - 2 = -2$. This couple is (0, –2).

$f(-1) = 3(-1)^2 - 2 = 1$. This couple is (–1, 1).

$f(-2) = 3(-2)^2 - 2 = 10$. This couple is (–2, 10).

The range = the set of second components = {10, 1, –2}

[NOTE: You never repeat an element in a set, even if it turns up twice as an output.]

Example 2: $f : x \to 5x - k$ is a function.

(i) If $f(-3) = -21$, find k.

(ii) Find the value of x for which $f(x + 5) = -16$.

Solution: (i)

$$\begin{aligned} f(-3) &= -21 \\ \therefore\quad -15 - k &= -21 \\ \therefore\quad -k &= -21 + 15 \\ \therefore\quad -k &= -6 \\ \therefore\quad k &= 6 \end{aligned}$$

[And therefore $f(x) = 5x - 6$]

(ii)

$$\begin{aligned} f(x + 5) &= -16 \\ \therefore\quad 5(x + 5) - 6 &= -16 \\ \therefore\quad 5x + 19 &= -16 \\ \therefore\quad 5x &= -35 \\ \therefore\quad x &= -7 \end{aligned}$$

Example 3: The diagram shows part of the graph of the function $y = ax + b$.
Find the values of a and of b.

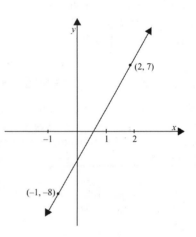

Solution: The couple (–1, –8) is on the graph.

$$\begin{aligned} \text{Therefore,}\quad f(-1) &= -8 \\ \therefore\quad a(-1) + b &= -8 \\ \therefore\quad -a + b &= -8 \\ \therefore\quad a - b &= 8 \text{ ... equation I} \end{aligned}$$

The couple (2, 7) is on the graph.

$$\begin{aligned} \text{Therefore,}\quad f(2) &= 7 \\ \therefore\quad a(2) + b &= 7 \\ \therefore\quad 2a + b &= 7 \text{... equation II} \end{aligned}$$

We solve the simultaneous equations I and II in the usual way:

$$\begin{aligned} \text{I:}\quad a - b &= 8 \\ \text{II:}\quad 2a + b &= 7 \\ \hline \text{Add!}\quad 3a &= 15 \\ \therefore\quad a &= 5 \\ \text{II:}\quad 2a + b &= 7 \\ \therefore\quad 2(5) + b &= 7 \\ \therefore\quad 10 + b &= 7 \\ \therefore\quad b &= -3 \end{aligned}$$

Answer: $a = 5, b = -3$

Exercise 6.A

1. State, giving a reason, if these are functions or not.
- (i) $\{(1, 4), (3, 6), (5, 7)\}$
- (ii) $\{(1, 2), (3, 7), (1, 5)\}$
- (iii) $\{(4, 4), (3, 4), (10, 9)\}$
- (iv) $\{(1, 9), (2, 11), (-1, 7), (2, -6)\}$
- (v) $\{(0, 9), (9, 0), (11, 11), (1, -7)\}$
- (vi) $\{(1, 0), (0, 1)\}$
- (vii) $\{(1, 2), (1, 3), (1, 4)\}$
- (viii) $\{(-1, 1), (0, 0), (1, 1)\}$
- (ix) $\{(1, -3), (-3, 1), (2, 0), (3, -3)\}$
- (x) $\{(0, 0), (1, 0), (2, 0), (3, 0), (4, 0)\}$

2. $f : x \to 2x + 6$ is a function. Find the values of the following:
- (i) $f(5)$,
- (ii) $f(1)$.

3. $f : x \to 5x - 2$ is a function. Find the values of the following:
- (i) $f(4)$,
- (ii) $f(-1)$,
- (iii) $f(0)$.

4. $f : x \to 12 - x$ is a function. Find the values of the following:
- (i) $f(7)$,
- (ii) $f(5)$,
- (iii) $f(-2)$.

5. $f : x \to x^2$ is a function. Find the values of the following:
- (i) $f(10)$,
- (ii) $f(-10)$,
- (iii) $f(0)$.

6. $f : x \to x^2 + 1$ is a function. Find the values of the following:
- (i) $f(1)$,
- (ii) $f(2)$,
- (iii) $f(3)$.

Investigate if $f(1) + f(2) = f(3)$.

7. $f : x \to 4x - 1$ is a function. Find
- (i) the value of $f(1)$,
- (ii) the value of $f(^1/_2)$,
- (iii) the value of k if $f(k) = 9$.

8. $f : x \to 3x - 12$ is a function. Find
- (i) the value of $f(3\frac{1}{2})$,
- (ii) the value of n if $f(n) = 0$,
- (iii) the value of x if $f(x) = x$.

9. $f : x \to x^2 + 2x - 24$ is a function. Find
- (i) the value of $f(4)$,
- (ii) the value of $f(-6)$,
- (iii) the value of k if $f(6) = kf(0)$.

10. $f : x \to 2x + k$ is a function. Find the value of k if $f(1) = 10$.

11. $f : x \to ax - 9$ is a function. Find the value of a if $f(7) = 5$.

12. $f : x \to 2x^2 + k$ is a function. Find the value of k if $f(3) = 11$.

13. $f : x \to 2x + \dfrac{20}{x}$ is a function.

Find
- (i) the value of $f(1)$,
- (ii) the value of $f(5)$,
- (iii) the value of $f(^1/_2)$.

Investigate if $2f(^1/_2) = f(1)$.

14. $f : x \to x^2 + x - k$ is a function. Find the value of k if $f(3) = 0$.

15. $f : x \to x^2 - x - 12$ is a function. Find the two values of x for which $f(x) = 0$.

16. $f : x \to x^2 - 12x + k$ is a function.
- (i) Find the value of k if $f(4) = 0$.
- (ii) Find a value of x (other than 4) for which $f(x) = 0$.

17. $f : x \to 3x + 5$ is a function.
- (i) Find the value of $f(11)$.
- (ii) Find $f(x + 2)$.
- (iii) If $f(x + 2) = 26$, find x.

18. $g : x \to 4x - 7$ is a function.
- (i) Find the value of $g(-1)$.
- (ii) Find $g(x + 3)$.
- (iii) If $g(x + 3) = 37$, find x.

19. f is a function such that $f(x) = 3x - 4$.
(i) Evaluate $f(1) - f(-1)$
(ii) Find the value of k if $f(k) - f(-k) = 66$

20. $f : x \rightarrow 2x + 11$ and $g: x \rightarrow x^2 - 4$ are two functions.
(i) Evaluate $f(4)$.
(ii) Evaluate $g(4)$.
(iii) Verify that $f(-3) = g(-3)$.
(iv) Find a value of k, other than -3 for which $f(k) = g(k)$.

21. f is a function defined by

$$f(x) = \frac{x^2 - 6}{x}, \text{ for } x \neq 0.$$

(i) Evaluate $f(6)$.
(ii) Find two values of x for which $f(x) = 1$.
(iii) Show that there is no value of x for which $f(x) = x$.

22. The diagram shows part of the graph of the function $y = ax + b$.

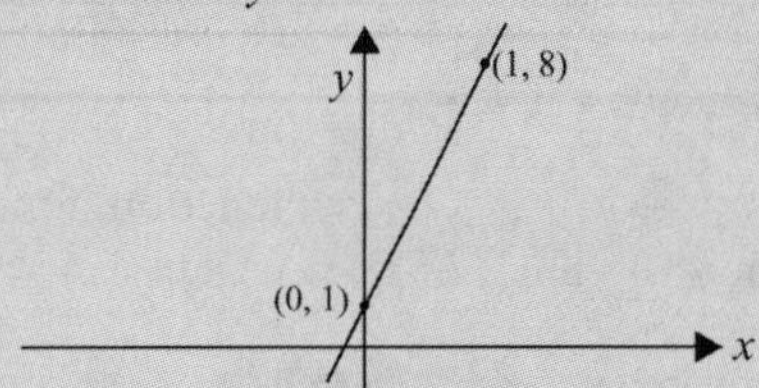

Find the values of a and b.

23. The diagram shows part of the graph of the function $y = x^2 + ax + b$

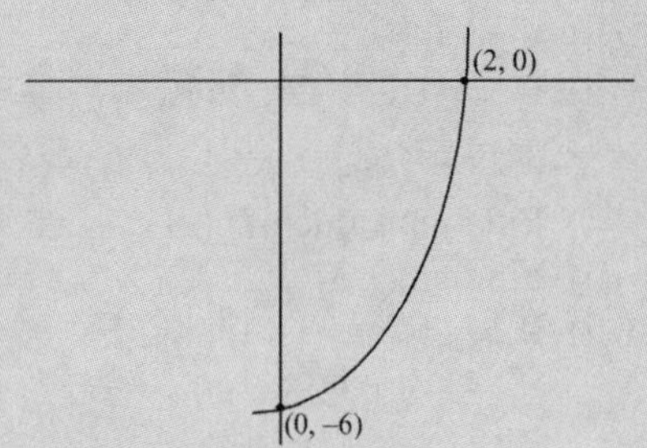

Find the values of a and b.

24. The diagram shows part of the graph of the function $y = ax + b$.

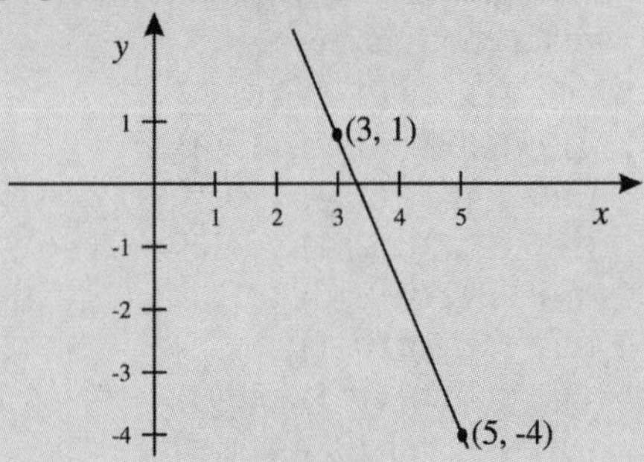

Find the values of a and b.

25. The diagram shows part of the graph of the function $y = x^2 + ax + b$.

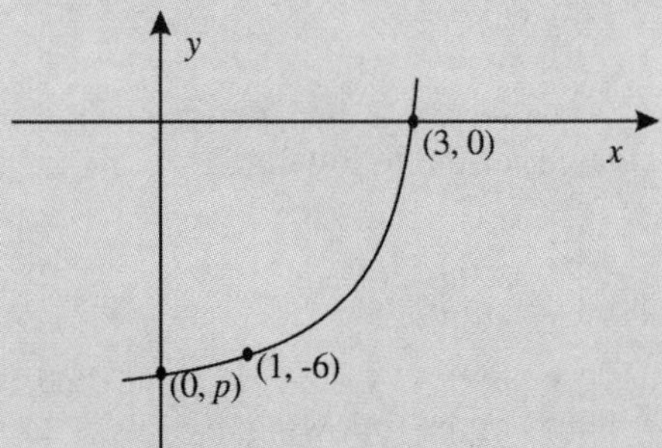

(i) Find the values of a and b,
(ii) If $(0, p)$ is a point on the graph, find the value of p.

26. The diagram shows part of the graph of the function $y = f(x) = ax^2 + bx$.

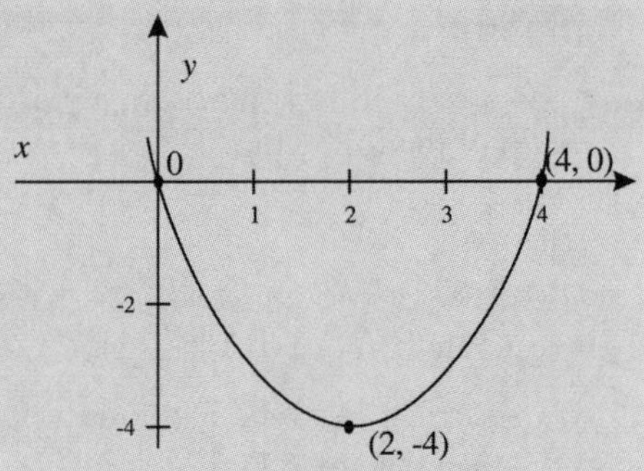

(i) Find the values of a and b.
(ii) Show that $f(2 + x) = f(2 - x)$.

27. The diagram shows part of the graph of the function $y = ax^2 + bx - 12$.

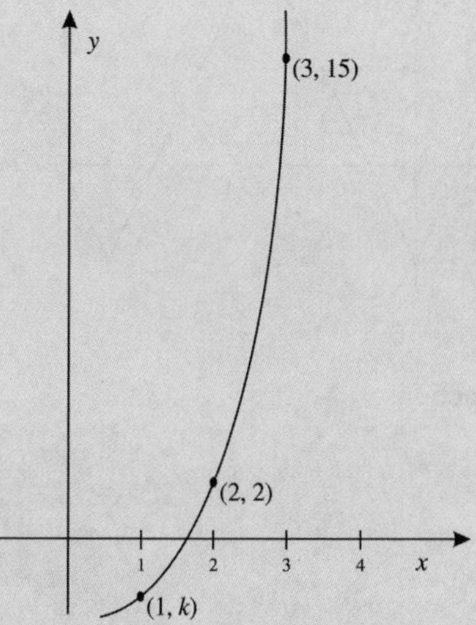

(i) Find the values of a and b.
(ii) Find the value of k.

28. The diagram shows part of the graph of the function $y = p + qx - x^2$.

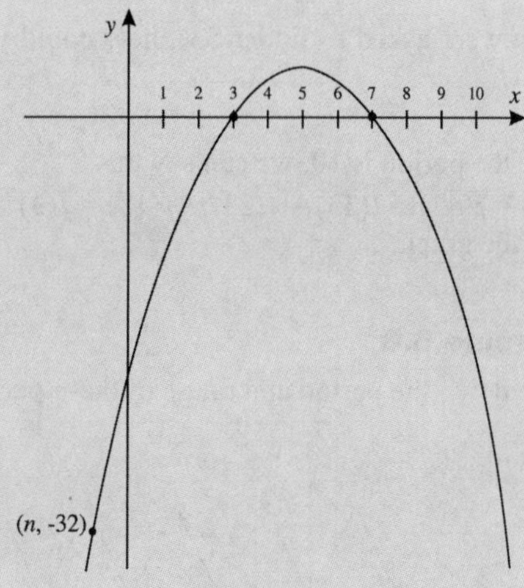

(i) Find the values of p and q.
(ii) Find the value of n, where $n < 0$.
(iii) Show that $f(5 + x) = f(5 - x)$.

PERIODIC FUNCTIONS

The graphs of some functions, like the one shown here, go in cycles. We call such functions ***periodic functions***. The length of each cycle is called the ***period*** of the function.

In this case the period is 4, since each cycle is 4 units in length.

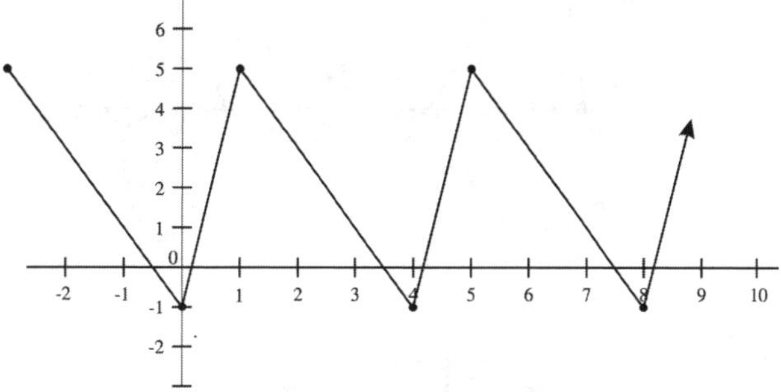

What is the range of this function? We can see from the graph that the highest output (or y-value) is 5 and the lowest is –1. Therefore, the range of this function is the set of real numbers between –1 and 5, inclusive. This is written $\{ x \mid -1 \leq x \leq 5, x \in R\}$ or [–1, 5]. The second shorter notation is usually used, since it is so handy and neat.

The period of this periodic function is 7 and the range is [0, 4].

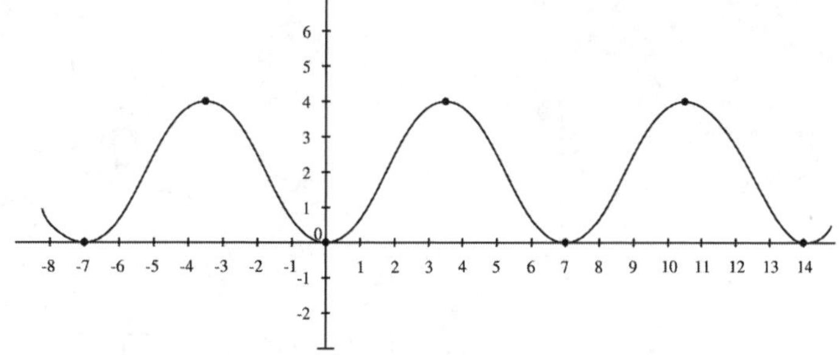

The period of this periodic function is 10 and the range is $[-3, 7]$.

If you were asked to find $f(53)$, how could you find it?

Since the period is 10, we can say that $f(53) = f(43) = f(33) = f(23) = f(13) = f(3) = 3$, from the graph.

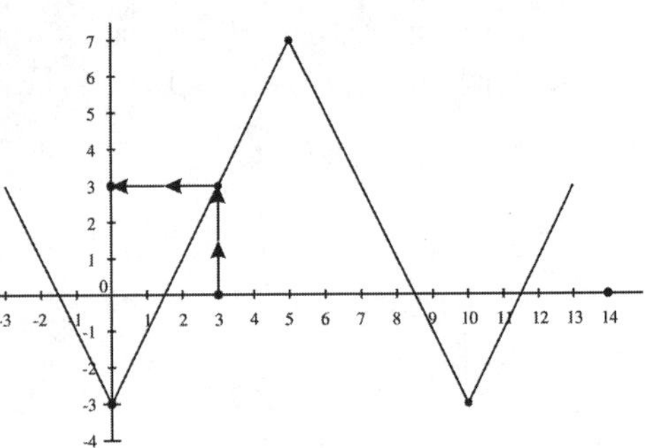

Exercise 6.B

Write down the period and range of these periodic functions:

1.

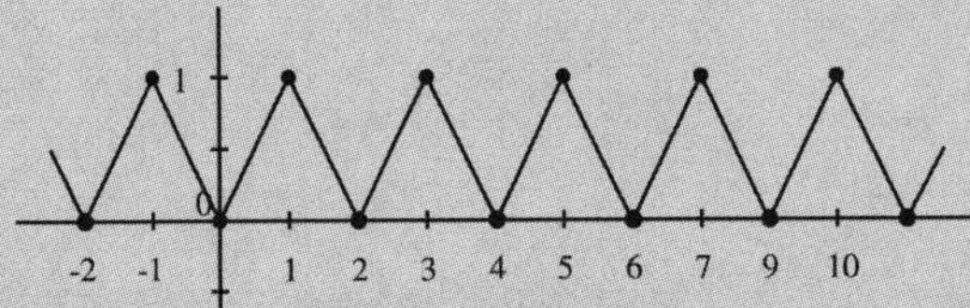

2.

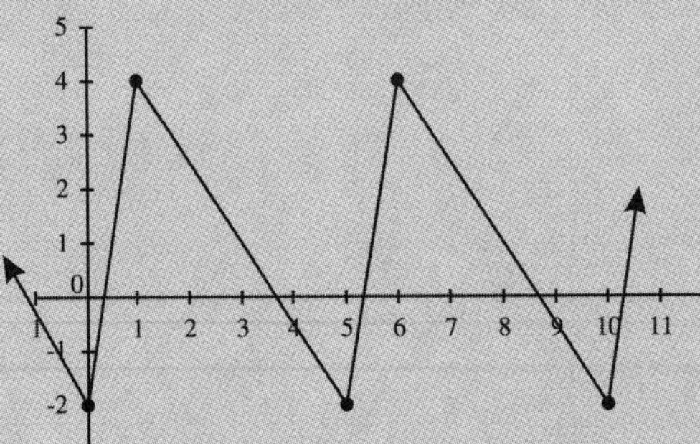

3.

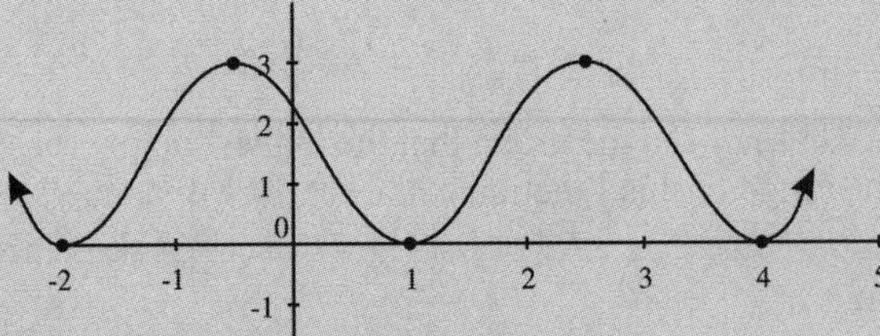

4.

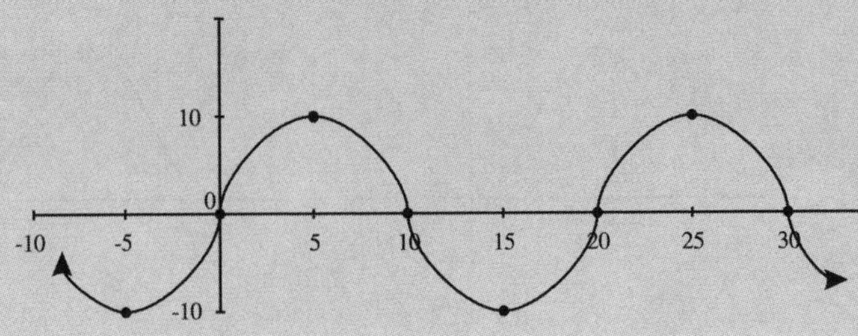

5.

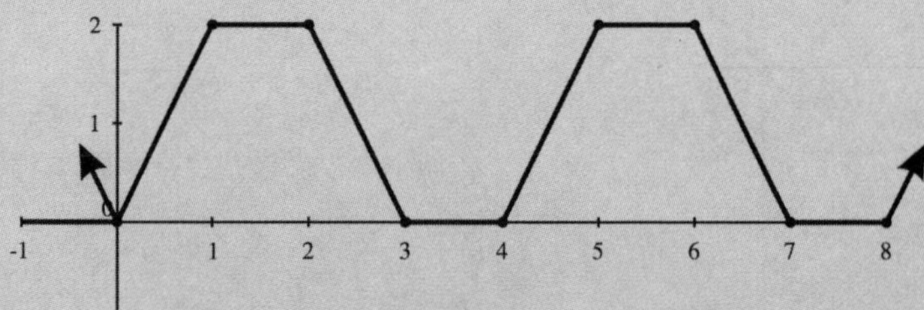

6.

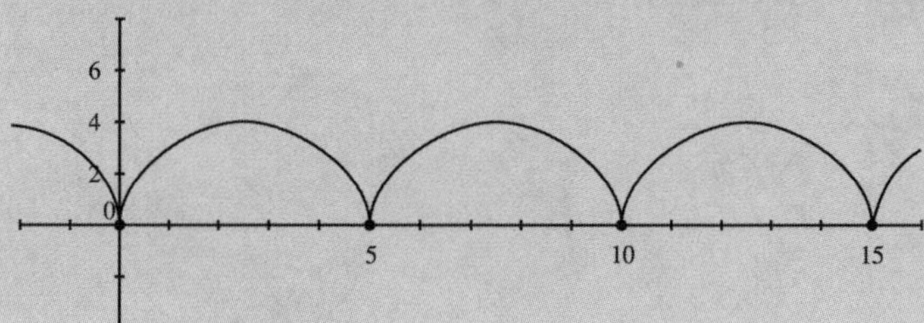

7.

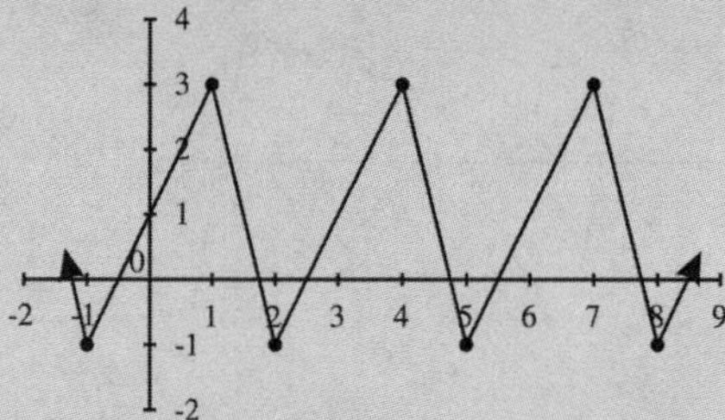

8.

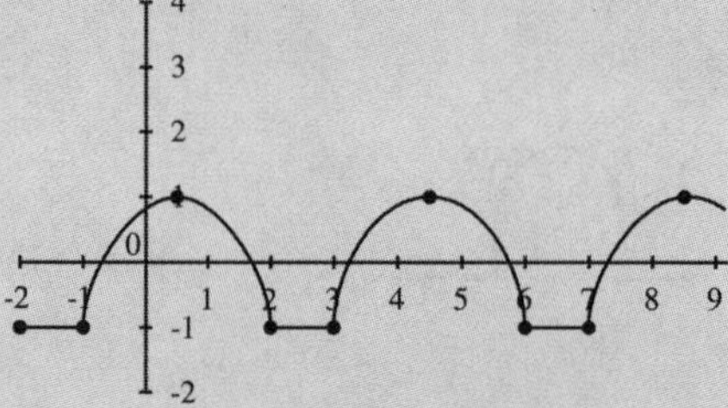

9.

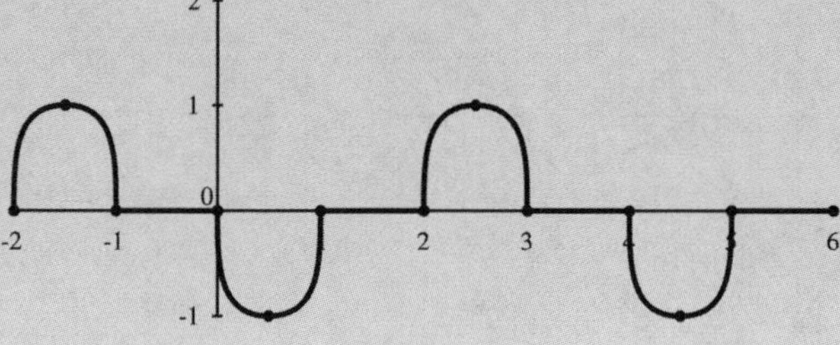

10.

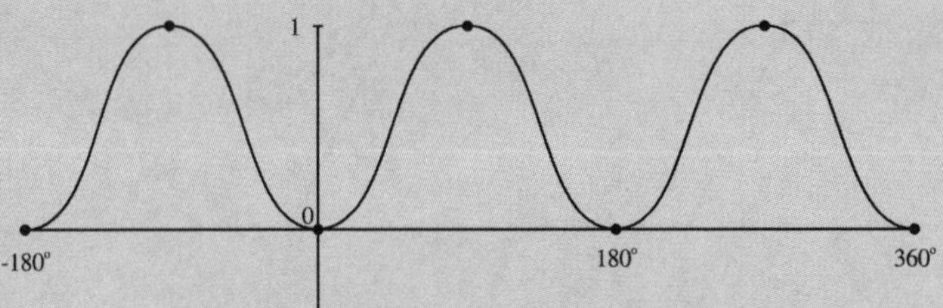
1
0
-180°
180°
360°

11.

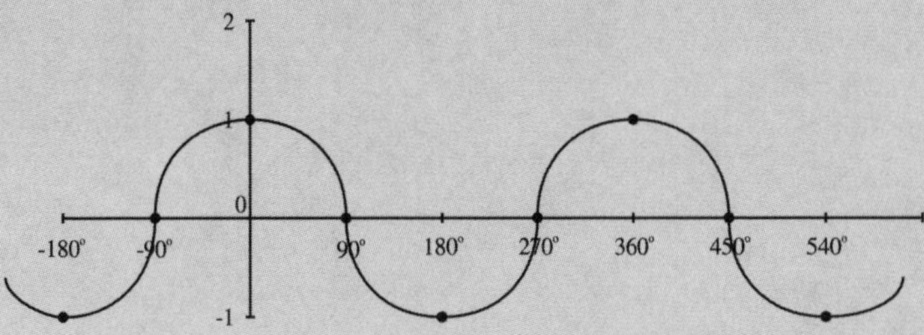
2
1
0
-1
-180°
-90°
90°
180°
270°
360°
450°
540°

12.

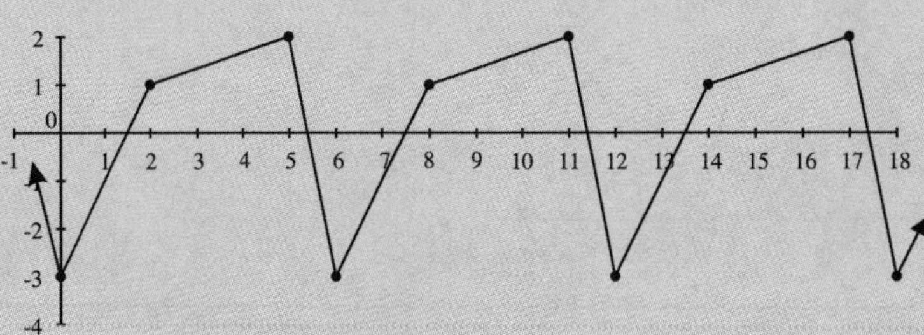
2
1
0
-2
-3
-4
-1
1
2
3
4
5
6
7
8
9
10
11
12
13
14
15
16
17
18

13.

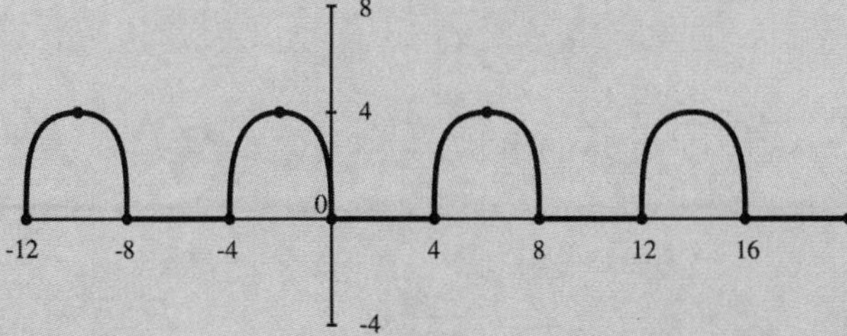
8
4
0
-4
-12
-8
-4
4
8
12
16

14.

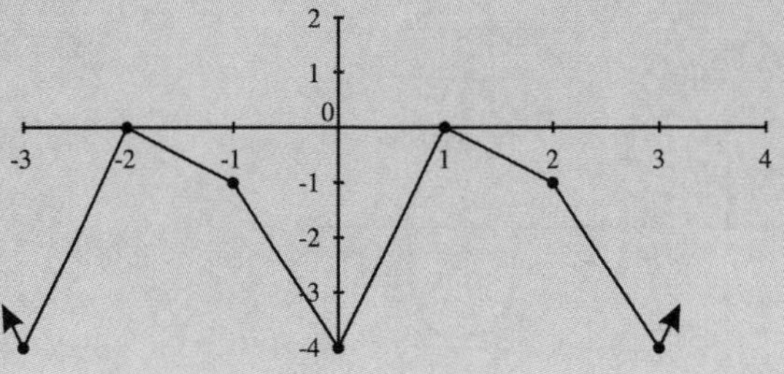
2
1
0
-1
-2
-3
-4
-3
-2
-1
1
2
3
4

15.

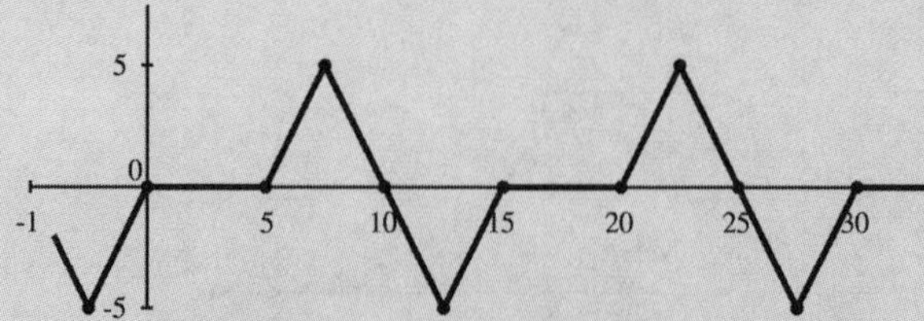

16.

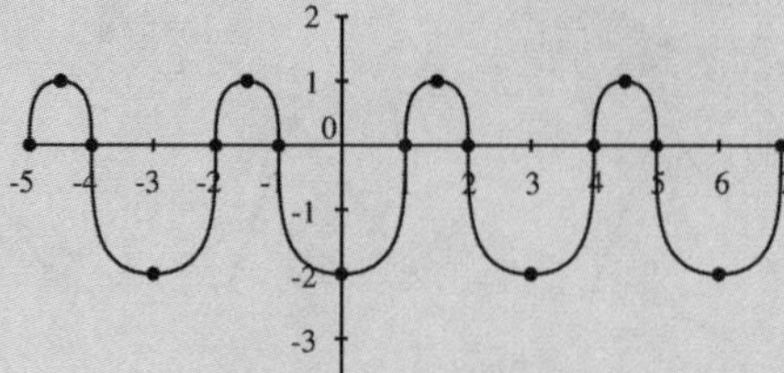

17. Here is part of the graph of a periodic function f.

(i) What is the range?
(ii) What is the period?
(iii) Find $f(4)$.
(iv) Find $f(15)$.

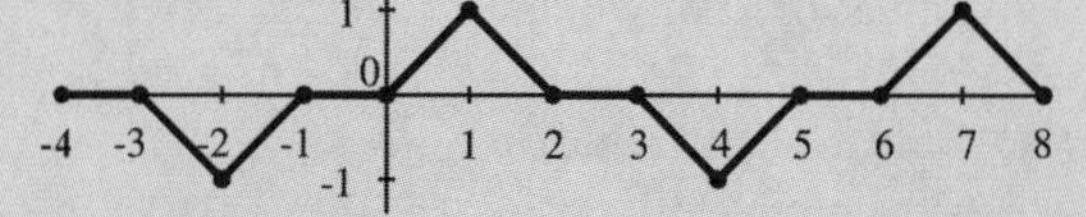

18. Here is a section of the graph of a periodic function f.

(i) What is the range?
(ii) What is the period?
(iii) Find $f(^1/_2)$.
(iv) Find $f(21)$.

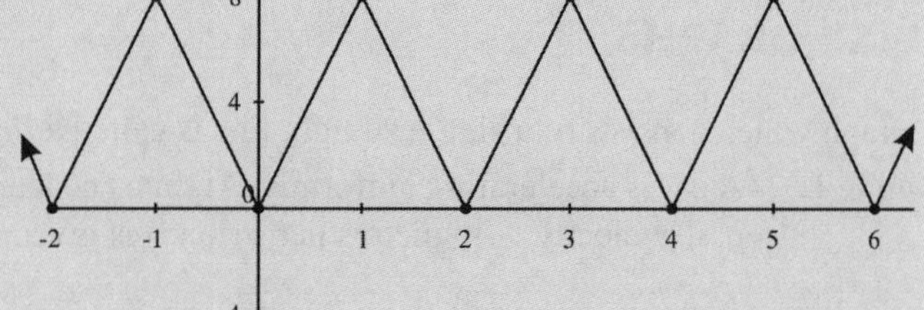

19. Here is part of the graph of a periodic function f.

(i) What is the range?
(ii) What is the period?
(iii) Find $f(44)$ and $f(-44)$
(iv) Is $f(x) = f(-x)$ for all $x \varepsilon R$? Give a reason for your answer.

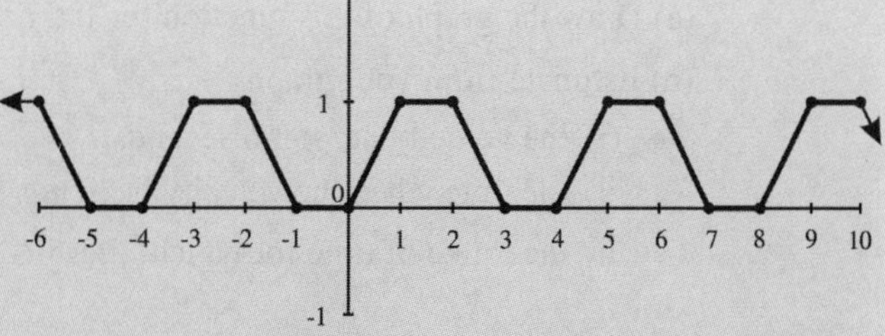

20. Here is a section of the graph of a periodic function f.

(i) What is the range?
(ii) What is the period?
(iii) Find $f(95)$.
(iv) Find $f(85)$.

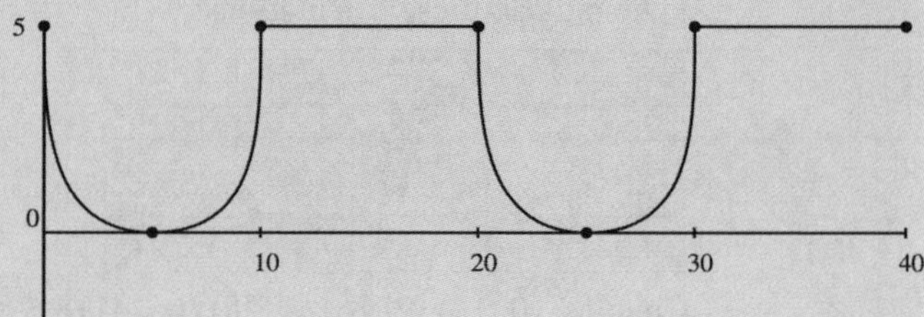

21. Here is a section of the graph of a periodic function f.
(i) What is the period?
(ii) What is the range?
(iii) Find $f(20.5)$.
(iv) Find three values of x, where $40 < x < 50$ such that $f(x) = 0$.

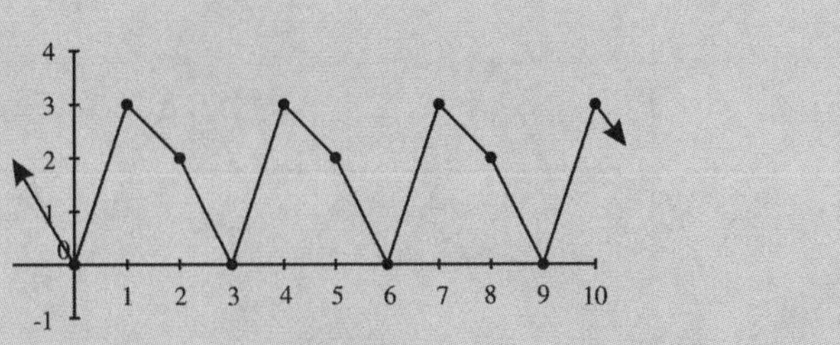

22. Here is a section of the graph of a periodic function f.
(i) Write down the period and the range.
(ii) What is the value of $f(1)$?
(iii) Write down two values of x for which $f(x) = 4$.
(iv) Find the least value of x, where $x > 50$, for which $f(x) = 2.5$

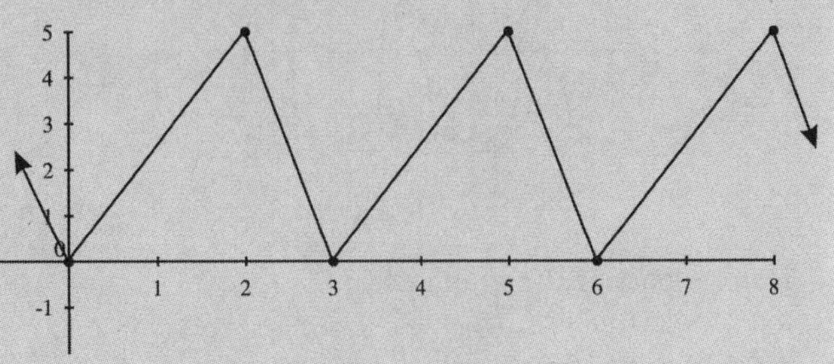

LINEAR GRAPHS

Any graph which consists of a single straight line is called a ***linear graph***.

Example 1: A car is accelerating uniformly. At time t seconds after it passes through a point p, its velocity v (in metres per second) is given by the formula

$$v = 2t + 12$$

(a) Draw the graph of this function for $0 \le t \le 10$.
(b) Estimate from your graph
(i) the velocity at $t = 3.6$ seconds,
(ii) the time when the velocity is 29 m/s,
(iii) the range of time for which $20 \le v \le 25$.

Solution: (a) To find the velocity, we double the time and add 12. Hence, here is a table to help us do these calculations:

t	0	2	4	6	8	10
$2t$	0	4	8	12	16	20
12	12	12	12	12	12	12
v	12	16	20	24	28	32

Couples: (0, 12) (2, 16) (4, 20) (6, 24) (8, 28) (10, 32)

Here, then, is the linear graph, joining these points:

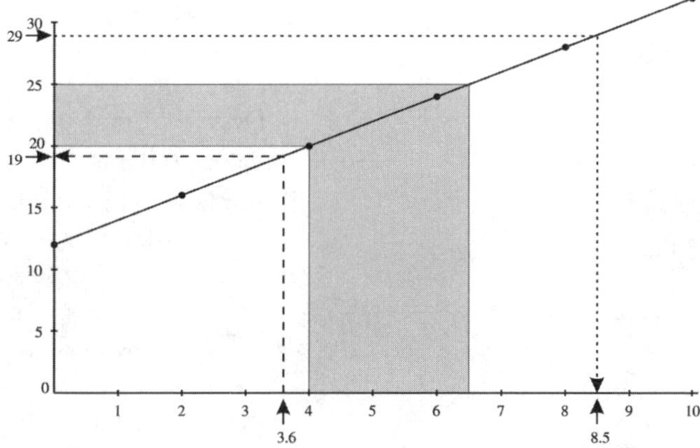

(b) (i) Draw a line from $t = 3.6$ to the graph, then draw a horizontal line to the v–axis. The reading is approximately 19 m/s.

(ii) Draw a line from $v = 29$ to the graph and then down to the t–axis. The reading is approximately 8.5 seconds.

(iii) Draw parallel lines from $v = 20$ and $v = 25$ to the graph and then to the t–axis. Shade in between them. The corresponding values of t are: $4 \leq t \leq 6.5$

Exercise 6.C

1. Draw a graph of the linear function $f : x \rightarrow 3x - 1$ in the domain $-3 \leq x \leq 4$, $x \in R$.

Use your graph to estimate

(i) $f(1.3)$,

(ii) the value of x for which $f(x) = -6$.

2. Draw a graph of the linear function $f : x \rightarrow 2x - 3$ in the domain $-2 \leq x \leq 3$, $x \in R$.

Use your graph to estimate

(i) the value of $f(x)$ when $x = -0.8$,

(ii) the value of x for which $f(x) = 0$,

(iii) the range of values of x for which $f(x) > 0$.

3. Use the same scales and axes to draw the two graphs $y = 2x - 1$ and $y = 8 - 4x$ in the domain $-1 \leq x \leq 4$. What is the point of intersection of the two graphs?

4. A car passes a point p. Its speed v (in m/s) after that is given by the function: $v = 15 - 3t$ where t is the time in seconds.

Draw a graph of v for $0 \leq t \leq 5$.

Use your graph to estimate

(i) the speed at $t = 2.3$,

(ii) the time when the speed is 10 m/s,

(iii) the speed as the car passes p,

(iv) the time when the car stops.

5. The time t (in minutes) for which a whole trout should be cooked in the oven is given by $t = 20(2m + 1)$ where m is the mass (in kg) of the trout.

(i) Copy and complete the following table and hence draw the graph:

Mass (m)	0	1	2	3	4	5	6
Time (t)	20	60					

(ii) Estimate the time taken to cook a 2.4 kg trout.

(iii) A trout is cooked for $3^1/_4$ hours. Estimate its mass.

(iv) For what values of m is $t < 100$?

6. The conversion formula for changing Celsius (C) readings to Fahrenheit (F) is $F = 1.8C + 32$

(i) Copy and complete the following table and hence draw the graph:

Celsius	−10	0	10	20	30	40
Fahrenheit		32				

(ii) Estimate the temperature in degrees Fahrenheit when it is 18° Celsius.

(iii) The temperature in Athens is 100° Fahrenheit. Estimate this in degrees Celsius.

(iv) The weather forecast is for temperatures in the range $11 \le C \le 15$.
What is the range of expected temperatures in Fahrenheit?

7. The number of minutes (t) which a turkey of mass m kilograms should be cooked for is given by the formula: $t = 25(2m + 3)$

(i) Draw the graph of t for the values $0 \le m \le 10$.

(ii) For how long should a turkey of mass 7.2 kg be cooked?

(iii) A turkey was cooked for $5\frac{3}{4}$ hours. What was its mass?

(iv) What are the masses of turkeys whose cooking times are between 3 and 4 hours?

8. $C = {}^5/_9(F - 32)$ is the formula for converting degrees Fahrenheit (F) to degrees Celsius (C).

(i) Copy and complete the following table, giving the values to the nearest integer.

Fahrenheit	0	20	40	60	80	100
Celsius	−18					

(ii) Draw a graph to illustrate this data.

(iii) Estimate the temperature in degrees Celsius when it is 77° Fahrenheit.

(iv) Estimate the temperature in degrees Fahrenheit when it is 15° Celsius.

(v) If $0 \le C \le 15$, estimate the range of values of F.

QUADRATIC GRAPHS

Any graph of the form $y = ax^2 + bx + c$ is called a ***quadratic graph***. All such graphs have the shape of a parabola, which is shaped like a wineglass. If a is a negative number then the wineglass is upside-down.

$y = ax^2 + bx + c$ (if a is positive) $y = ax^2 + bx + c$ (if a is negative)

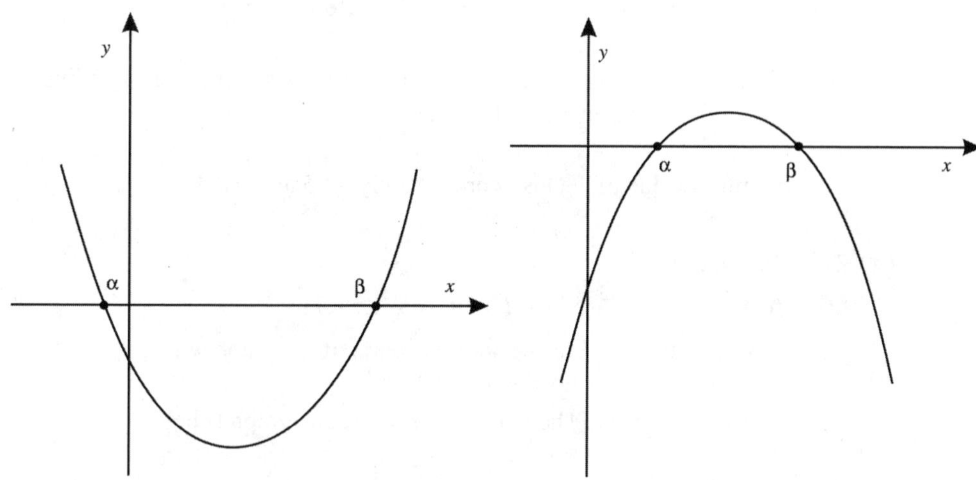

The points (α and β) at which these graphs cut the x–axis mark the ***roots*** of the quadratic equation $ax^2 + bx + c = 0$.

Example 1 Draw the graph of the function $f : x \rightarrow 3x^2 - 2x - 7$ in the domain $-2 \leq x \leq 3$, $x \in R$. Find, from your graph,

(i) the value of $f(2.5)$,
(ii) the values of x for which $f(x) = 3$,
(iii) the minimum value of $f(x)$ and the value of x at which it occurs,
(iv) the values of x for which $3x^2 - 2x - 7 \leq 0$.

Solution:

x	−2	−1	0	1	2	3
$3x^2$	12	3	0	3	12	27
$-2x$	4	2	0	−2	−4	−6
-7	−7	−7	−7	−7	−7	−7
y	9	−2	−7	−6	1	14

Points: (−2, 9), (−1, −2), (0, −7), (1, −6), (2, 1), (3, 14)

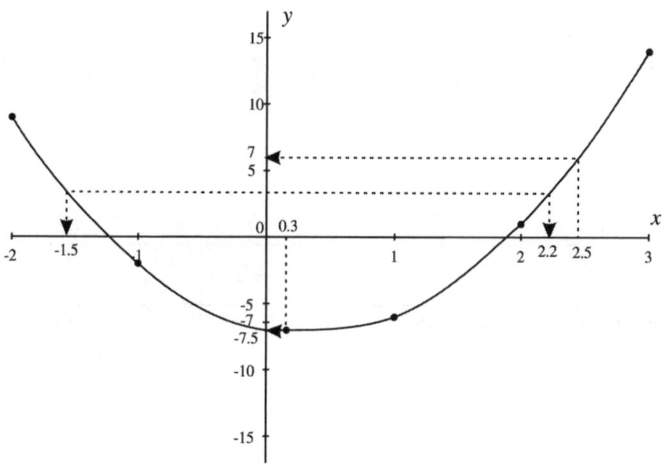

(i) Draw a line from $x = 2.5$ on the x–axis, up to the graph and across to the y–axis. The reading is approximately 7. Therefore $f(2.5) = 7$.

(ii) Draw lines east and west from $y = 3$ on the y–axis. The corresponding readings on the x–axis are $x = -1.5,\ 2.2$

(iii) The minimum value of $f(x)$ is approximately -7.5 at $x = 0.3$

(iv) $3x^2 - 2x - 7 \leq 0$

$\therefore\quad f(x) \leq 0$ [Since $f(x) = 3x^2 - 2x - 7$]

$\therefore\quad y \leq 0$ [So, we look for parts of the graph where the y-value is negative]

$\therefore\quad -1.2 \leq x \leq 1.9$ [The values of x where the graph is below the x-axis]

Example 2: Using the same scales and axes, draw the graphs of the functions $f : x \rightarrow 4 - 2x - x^2$ and $g : x \rightarrow 1 - 2x$ in the domain $-4 \leq x \leq 3,\ x\ \varepsilon\ R$. Use your graph to estimate

(i) the range of values of x for which $4 - 2x - x^2 < 0$,

(ii) the solutions of the equation $2x^2 + 4x - 5 = 0$,

(iii) the value of $\sqrt{3}$.

Solution:

	x	-4	-3	-2	-1	0	1	2	3
	4	4	4	4	4	4	4	4	4
	$-2x$	8	6	4	2	0	-2	-4	-6
$f(x)$	$-x^2$	-16	-9	-4	-1	0	-1	-4	-9
	$f(x)$	-4	1	4	5	4	1	-4	-11
	Points	$(-4,-4)$	$(-3,1)$	$(-2, 4)$	$(-1, 5)$	$(0, 4)$	$(1, 1)$	$(2, -4)$	$(3, -11)$

	x	-4	-3	-2	-1	0	1	2	3
	1	1	1	1	1	1	1	1	1
$g(x)$	$-2x$	8	6	4	2	0	-2	-4	-6
	$g(x)$	9	7	5	3	1	-1	-3	-5
	Points	$(-4, 9)$	$(-3, 7)$	$(-2, 5)$	$(-1, 3)$	$(0, 1)$	$(1, -1)$	$(2, -3)$	$(3, -5)$

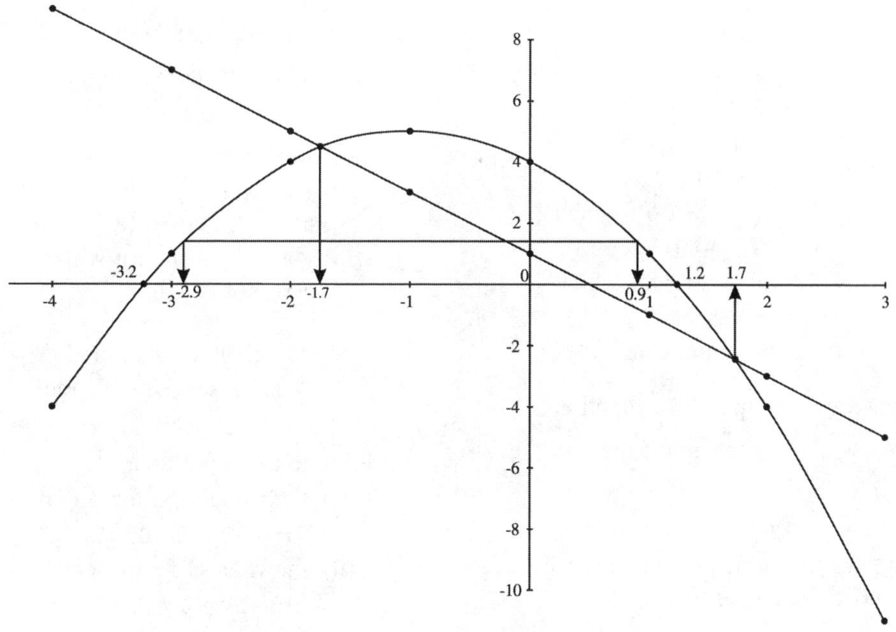

(i) $4 - 2x - x^2 < 0$

$\therefore \quad f(x) < 0$

$\therefore \quad x < -3.2$ or $x > 1.2$ [The values of x for which the graph is below the x–axis]

(ii) Change both sides of the equation until you end up with $f(x)$ [i.e. $4 - 2x - x^2$] on one side:

$2x^2 + 4x - 5 = 0$

$\therefore \quad x^2 + 2x - 2.5 = 0$ [Dividing both sides by 2]

$\therefore \quad 2.5 - 2x - x^2 = 0$ [Multiplying both sides by -1]

$\therefore \quad 4 - 2x - x^2 = 1.5$ [Adding 1.5 to both sides to give us $f(x)$ on the left]

$\therefore \quad f(x) = 1.5$

$\therefore \quad x = -2.9$ or 0.9

(iii) $x = \sqrt{3}$. [Again, we will try to get $4 - 2x - x^2$ on one side]

$\therefore \quad x^2 = 3$

$\therefore \quad 0 = 3 - x^2$ [Subtracting x^2 from both sides]

$\therefore \quad 1 - 2x = 4 - 2x - x^2$ [Adding $1 - 2x$ to both sides to give $f(x)$ on the right]

$\therefore \quad g(x) = f(x)$

$\therefore$ We want the x–value of the points of intersection of the two graphs.

These are $x = -1.7$ and $x = 1.7$

Since $\sqrt{3}$ is a positive number, we can say that $\sqrt{3} = 1.7$

Exercise 6.D

1. Draw the graph of the function $f : x \to x^2 - 2x - 5$ in the domain $-2 \le x \le 4, x \in R$.
   Find, from your graph,
   (i) the value of $f(2.2)$,
   (ii) the values of x for which $x^2 - 2x - 5 = 0$,
   (iii) the values of x for which $x^2 - 2x - 5 < 0$,
   (iv) the minimum value of $f(x)$.

2. Draw the graph of the function $y = x^2 - 4x + 5$ in the domain $0 \le x \le 4$.
   Use your graph to find
   (i) the value of y when $x = 3.5$,
   (ii) the values of x if $y = 2$.

3. Draw the graph of the function $y = x^2 - 6x + 7$ in the domain $0 \le x \le 6$.
   Use your graph to find
   (i) the value of y when $x = 0.5$,
   (ii) the values of x if $y = 0$.

4. Draw the graph of the function $f : x \to x^2 - 3x - 4$ in the domain $-2 \le x \le 5, x \in R$.
   Find, from your graph,
   (i) the values of $f(4,5)$,
   (ii) the solutions to $x^2 - 3x - 4 = 0$,
   (iii) the approximate solutions to $x^2 - 3x - 4 = -2$.

5. Draw the graph of the function $y = x^2 + x - 6$ in the domain $-4 \le x \le 3, x \in R$.
   Use your graph to find
   (i) the value of y when $x = 1.5$,
   (ii) the values of x if $y = 0$,
   (iii) the approximate values of x for which $y = 2$.

6. Draw the graph of the function $y = x^2 - x - 5$ in the domain $-3 \le x \le 4, x \in R$.
   Use your graph to find
   (i) the value of y when $x = 1.8$,
   (ii) the values of x if $y = 0$,
   (iii) the values of x for which $y = 4$.

7. Draw the graph of the function $f : x \to 2x^2 - 3x - 7$ in the domain $-2 \le x \le 3, x \in R$.
   Find, from your graph,
   (i) the values of x for which $2x^2 - 3x - 7 = 0$,
   (ii) the values of x for which $2x^2 - 3x - 2 = 0$,
   (iii) the range of values of x for which $2x^2 - 3x - 7 \le 0$,
   (iv) the minimum value of $f(x)$ and the value of x at which it occurs.

8. Draw the graph of the function $f : x \to 4 + x - x^2$ in the domain $-2 \le x \le 3, x \in R$.
   Find, from your graph,
   (i) the values of x for which $4 + x - x^2 = 0$,
   (ii) the values of x for which $f(x) > 0$,
   (iii) the solution set of $1 + x - x^2 = 0$,
   (iv) the maximum value of $f(x)$.

9. Draw the graph of the function $f : x \to 6 - x - 2x^2$ in the domain $-3 \le x \le 3, x \in R$.
   Estimate, from your graph, the values of x for which
   (i) $6 = x + 2x^2$,
   (ii) $2(6 - x^2) = x$,
   (iii) $6 \le x(2x + 1)$.

10. Draw the graph of the function $f : x \to 3x^2 - 3x - 4$ in the domain $-2 \le x \le 3, x \in R$.
Use your graph to estimate
(i) the values of x for which $3x^2 = 3x + 4$,
(ii) the values of x for which $x^2 - x - 5 = 0$,
(iii) the solution set of $x^2 - x < 0$,
(iv) the minimum value of $f(x)$ and the value of x at which it occurs.

11. Draw the graph of the function $f : x \to 4x^2 + 6x - 7$ in the domain $-3 \le x \le 1, x \in R$.
Find, from your graph,
(i) the value of $f(-2.8)$,
(ii) the values of x for which $2x^2 + 3x - 3 = 0$,
(iii) the range of values of x for which $2x(2x + 3) < 7$,
(iv) a negative value of x for which $f(x) = f(1)$.

12. Copy and complete the following table for the function $f : x \to 4 - x - 2x^2$

x	−3	−2	−1	0	1	2	2.5
$f(x)$	−11			4			−11

Draw the graph of $y = f(x)$ in the domain $-3 \le x \le 2.5$, $x \in R$.
Use your graph to find
(i) the values of x for which $2x^2 + x = 4$,
(ii) the range of values of x for which $2x^2 + x < 4$,
(iii) the maximum value of $f(x)$,
(iv) the values of x which satisfy $4x^2 + 2x - 5 = 0$,
(v) the least value of $n \in N$ for which $f(x) = n$ has ***no*** solution.

13. Use the same scales and axes to draw the graphs of the two functions $f : x \to 4x^2 + 7x - 3$ and $g : x \to 2x + 5$ in the domain $-3 \le x \le 1, x \in R$.
Use your graph to estimate
(i) the value of x for which $g(x) = 0$,
(ii) the values of x for which $f(x) = 0$,
(iii) the values of x for which $f(x) = g(x)$,
(iv) the range of values of x for which $g(x) > f(x)$.

14. Draw the graph of the function $f : x \to 5 - 3x - x^2$ in the domain $-5 \le x \le 2, x \in R$.
Using your graph,
(i) estimate the maximum value of $f(x)$,
(ii) draw the axis of symmetry of the graph and write down its equation in the form $x = k$,
(iii) find the values of $f(k + 2)$ and $f(k - 2)$,
(iv) draw the graph of the line $y = x$ and hence solve the equation $f(x) = x$.

15. (a) Solve the equation $x^2 - 6x - 1 = 0$ correct to one decimal place, using the quadratic formula

$$\frac{-b \pm \sqrt{b^2 - 4ac}}{2a}.$$

(b) Draw the graph of the function $y = x^2 - 6x - 1$ in the domain $-1 \le x \le 7, x \in R$.
(i) Use the graph to estimate the solutions to $x^2 - 6x - 1 = 0$.
(ii) Estimate the values of x for which $x^2 - 6x - 1 > 0$.

16. (a) Solve the equation $5x^2 - 2x - 4 = 0$ correct to one decimal place, using the quadratic formula

$$\frac{-b \pm \sqrt{b^2 - 4ac}}{2a}.$$

(b) Draw the graph of the function $y = 5x^2 - 2x - 4$ in the domain $-2 \le x \le 2, x \in R$.

(i) Use the graph to estimate the solutions to $5x^2 - 2x - 4 = 0$.

(ii) Estimate the values of x for which $5x^2 - 2x - 4 < 0$.

17. Using the same scales and axes, graph the two functions:
$f : x \to 15 - x - 2x^2$ in the domain $-3 \le x \le 2.5, x \in R$ and $g : x \to 6x - x^2$ in the domain $0 \le x \le 3, x \in R$.
$f(x)$ represents the height (in km) of a foreign rocket which is launched at 4.30 p.m. ($x = -3$).
$g(x)$ represents the height (in km) of a guided missile which is launched at 5.00 p.m. ($x = 0$) to intercept the foreign rocket.
Use the graphs to estimate

(i) the maximum height of the foreign rocket,

(ii) the time at which the guided missile intercepts the foreign rocket,

(iii) the height at which the collision occurs.

CUBIC GRAPHS

The graph of any function of the form $f : x \to ax^3 + bx^2 + cx + d$ is called a ***cubic graph***.

Its shape usually looks like a one-humped camel – something like this:

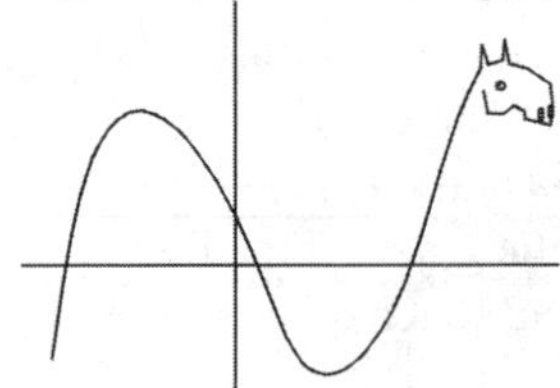

But if a (the coefficient of x^3) is a negative number, the camel looks west, like this:

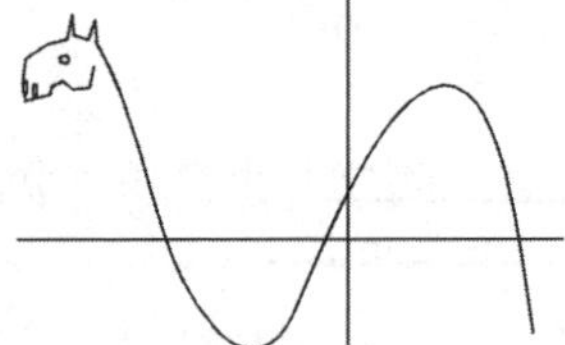

Example 1: Draw the graph of the cubic function $f : x \to x^3 - 2x^2 - 4x + 1$ in the domain $-2 \le x \le 4, x \in R$.

Estimate from your graph,

(i) the values of x for which $f(x) = 0$,

(ii) the value of $f(2.5)$,

(iii) the minimum value of $f(x)$ where $x > 0$,

(iv) the values of x for which $f(x)$ is decreasing,

(v) the solutions of $x^3 = 2(x^2 + 2x - 3)$.

Solution:

x	-2	-1	0	1	2	3	4
x^3	-8	-1	0	1	8	27	64
$-2x^2$	-8	-2	0	-2	-8	-18	-32
$-4x$	8	4	0	-4	-8	-12	-16
$+1$	1	1	1	1	1	1	1
y	-7	2	1	-4	-7	-2	17
Points	$(-2, -7)$	$(-1, 2)$	$(0, 1)$	$(1, -4)$	$(2, -7)$	$(3, -2)$	$(4, 17)$

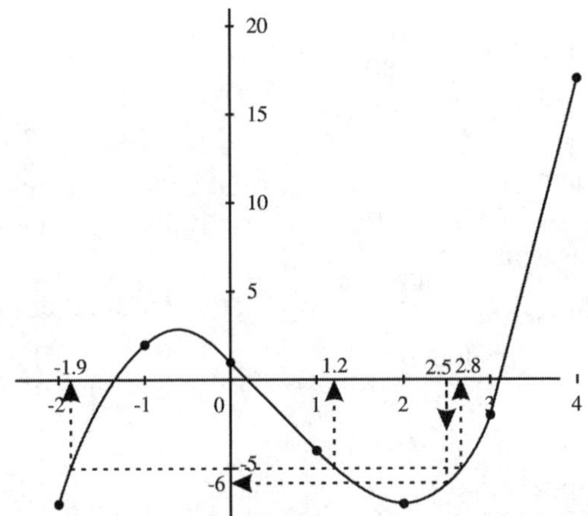

(i) We want the values of x where the graph cuts the x–axis.
They are $x = -1.3$, 0.2 and 3.1

(ii) Draw a line from $x = 2.5$ to the graph and then to the y–axis. The reading is approximately -6.

(iii) The minimum value of $f(x)$, when $x > 0$ is -7 (when $x = 2$).

(iv) We 'read' a graph, as we read English or Irish, from left to right. If the graph is 'going up', we say that the function is ***increasing***. When the graph is 'going down', we say that the function is ***decreasing***.

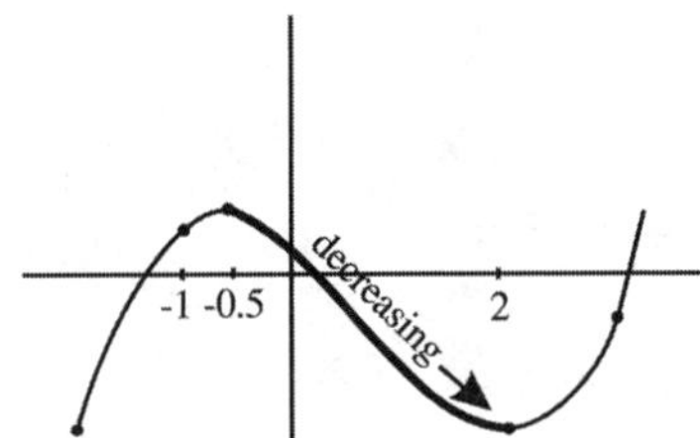

In this case the graph is decreasing between -0.5 and 2.
That is to say, the values of x for which $f(x)$ is decreasing are: $-0.5 < x < 2$

(v)
$$x^3 = 2(x^2 + 2x - 3)$$
$$\therefore \quad x^3 = 2x^2 + 4x - 6$$
$$\therefore \quad x^3 - 2x^2 - 4x + 6 = 0$$
$$\therefore \quad x^3 - 2x^2 - 4x + 1 = -5$$
$$\therefore \quad f(x) = -5$$
$$\therefore \quad y = -5$$

Draw the straight line at $y = -5$.

It cuts the graph at $x = -1.9$, 1.2, 2.8 : ***Answer***

Exercise 6.E

1. Draw the graph of the function $f : x \rightarrow 2x^3 + x^2 - 8x - 4$ in the domain $-3 \leq x \leq 3, x \varepsilon R$.

Estimate from your graph

(i) the values of x for which $f(x) = 0$,
(ii) the values of x for which $f(x) = 2$.

2. Draw the graph of the function $f : x \rightarrow x^3 + 4x^2 + x - 6$ in the domain $-4 \leq x \leq 2, x \varepsilon R$.

Estimate from your graph

(i) the values of x for which $f(x) = 0$,
(ii) the values of x for which $f(x) < 0$,
(iii) the values of $x < 0$ for which $f(x) > 0$.

3. Draw the graph of the function $f : x \rightarrow x^3 - 2x^2 - 4x + 1$ in the domain $-2 \leq x \leq 4, x \varepsilon R$.

Estimate from your graph the solutions to these three equations:

(i) $x^3 - 2x^2 - 4x + 1 = 0$,
(ii) $x^3 - 2x^2 - 4x - 1 = 0$,
(iii) $x^3 = 2(x^2 + 2x - 4)$.

4. Draw the graph of the function $f : x \rightarrow x^3 + 3x^2 - x - 3$ in the domain $-4 \leq x \leq 2, x \varepsilon R$.

Estimate from your graph the values of x for which

(i) $f(x) = 0$,
(ii) $f(x)$ is both negative and increasing,
(iii) $x^3 + 3x^2 - x = 0$.

Estimate, also, the value of $f(1.5)$.

5. Draw the graph of the function $f : x \rightarrow x^3 - 12x + 6$ in the domain $-4 \leq x \leq 4, x \varepsilon R$.

Estimate from your graph the values of x for which

(i) $f(x) = 0$,
(ii) $f(x)$ is both positive and increasing,
(iii) $x^3 > 12x$.

6. Draw the graph of the function $f : x \rightarrow -3 + x + 3x^2 - x^3$ in the domain $-2 \leq x \leq 4, x \varepsilon R$.

Estimate from your graph

(i) the maximum value of $f(x)$ when $x > 0$,
(ii) the solutions of the equation $-3 + x + 3x^2 - x^3 = 0$,
(iii) the value of $f(0.7)$.

7. The diagram shows part of the graph of the function $f(x) = x^3 - 3x^2 - 4x + 12$.

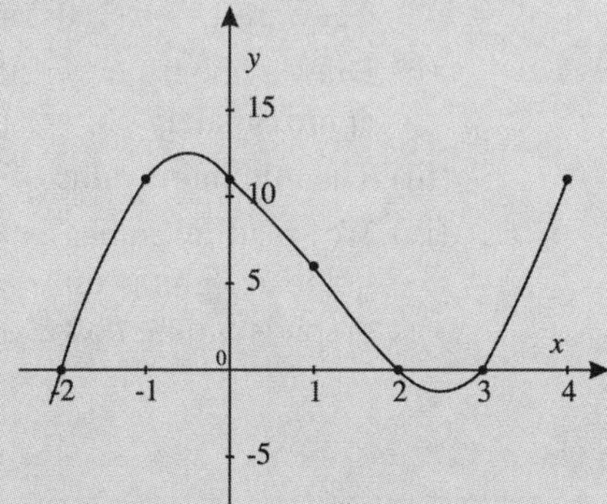

Use the graph to estimate,

(i) the value of $f(3.3)$
(ii) the values of x for which $x^3 - 3x^2 - 4x = 0$
(iii) the values of x for which $x(x^2 + 2) = 3[(x + 1)^2 - 5]$.

8. (a) Show that 3 is a root of the equation
$$10x^3 - 19x^2 - 39x + 18 = 0$$
(b) Use the factor theorem to find the other two roots.
(c) Draw the graph of $x \rightarrow 10x^3 - 19x^2 - 39x + 18$ in the domain $-2 \leq x \leq 4, x \varepsilon R$.
Use your graph to verify the roots of $10x^3 - 19x^2 - 39x + 18 = 0$ which you found in parts (a) and (b).

9. Draw the graph of $y = x^3$ in the domain $-3 \leq x \leq 3, x \in R$.
Use your graph to estimate the value of
(i) $\sqrt[3]{14}$,
(ii) $\sqrt[3]{-20}$.

10. The diagram shows the graphs of the two functions $y = x^3 - x^2 - 3$ and $y = 4x - 7$.

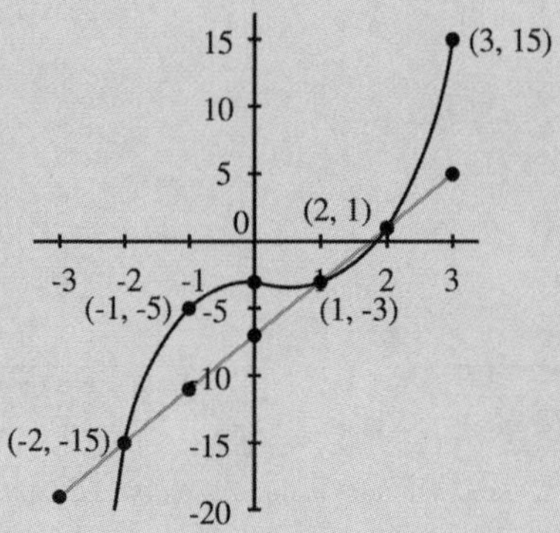

Use the graphs to solve these equations:
(i) $x^3 - x^2 - 3 = 0$
(ii) $x^3 - x^2 - 4x + 4 = 0$

11. Draw the graph of the function $f : x \rightarrow x^3 - 7x + 1$ in the domain $-3 \leq x \leq 3, x \in R$.
Estimate from your graph the values of x for which $f(x) = 1$ and hence estimate the value of $\sqrt{7}$.

12. $A = \{ x \mid -2 \leq x \leq 3, x \in R\}$.
$f : x \rightarrow x^3 - 3x^2 + 5$ is defined on A.
Copy and complete this table

x	−2	−1	0	1	1.5	2	3
f(x)	− 15		5		1.625		

Draw a graph of $y = f(x)$ and hence write down the ***number*** of solutions in A to each of these equations:
(i) $f(x) = 3$
(ii) $f(x) = -3$
(iii) $f(x) = 5$
(iv) $f(x) = -10$
Write down the range of values of k for which $f(x) = k$ has exactly ***one*** solution in A.

13. Draw the graph of the function $f : x \rightarrow x^3 - 5x + 2$ in the domain $-3 \leq x \leq 3, x \in R$.
Using your graph
(i) find the values of $x > 0$ for which $f(x) < 0$,
(ii) solve $f(x) = 2$ and hence estimate $\sqrt{5}$,
(iii) by drawing a suitable line, solve the equation $x^3 - 6x - 1 = 0$.

14. A function f is defined as $f : x \rightarrow x^3 - 2x^2 - 6x + 4$ in the domain $-2 \leq x \leq 4, x \in R$.
Copy and complete the table:

x	−2	−1	0	1	2	3	4
f(x)	0				− 8		

Using your graph
(i) find the values of $x > 0$ for which $f(x) < 0$,
(ii) by drawing a suitable line, solve the equation $x^3 - 2x^2 - 8x + 9 = 0$.

RECIPROCAL GRAPHS AND ASYMPTOTES

Any graph of the form $y = \frac{1}{x + a}$ is called a ***reciprocal graph***. There is a special problem associated with these graphs. The problem is that there is no such number as $\frac{1}{0}$.
So the denominator of a fraction must never be zero.

In the graph of $y = \frac{1}{x+a}$, when $x = -a$, there is no real value of y. We draw a vertical barrier (called an asymptote) at $x = -a$, as shown on the diagram.

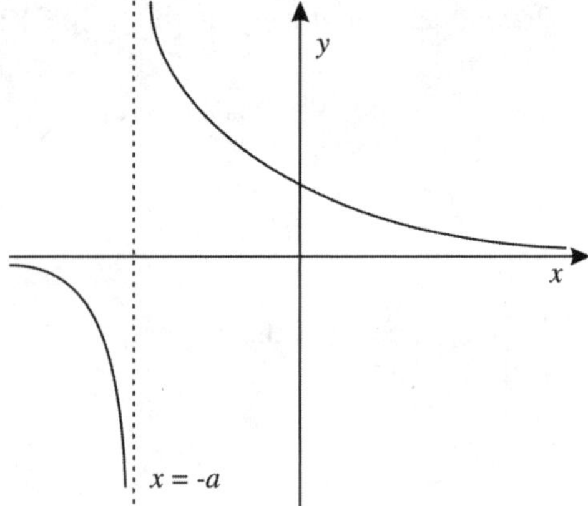

The word asymptote comes from three Greek words:
α – συμ – πιπτων = not–meeting–together.
The graph gets closer and closer to the asymptote but the two never meet together.

Example 1: Draw the graph of $y = \frac{1}{x+2}$

in the domain $-6 \leq x \leq 3$, x ε R.

Find the values of x for which $y > 1$.

Solution:

x	-6	-5	-4	-3	-2	-1	0	1	2	3
y	$-^1/_4$	$-^1/_3$	$-^1/_2$	-1	*	1	$^1/_2$	$^1/_3$	$^1/_4$	$^1/_5$

* There is an ***asymptote*** at $x = -2$, since y is undefined when $x = -2$.

Here is the graph: We always try to show how the graph gets very close to the asymptote.

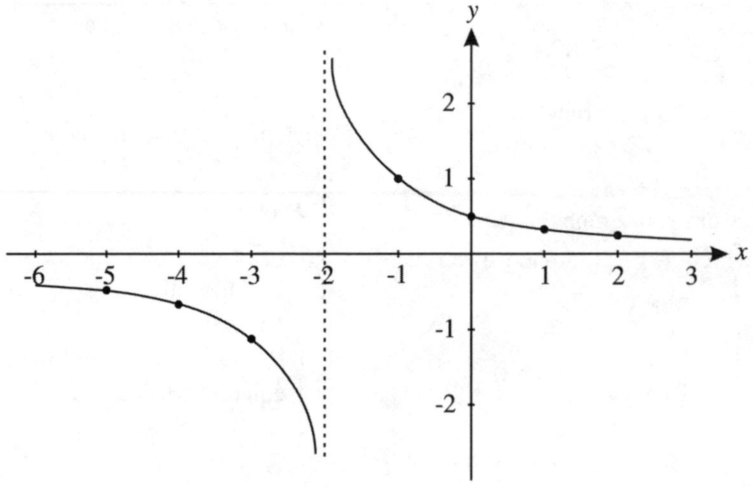

From the graph, we see that $y > 1$ when $-2 < x < -1$.

Exercise 6.F

1. A function is defined by $y = \frac{1}{x+1}$

Copy and complete this table:

x	-3	-2	-1.5	-1	0	1	2	3
y	-0.5		-2	*	1			0.25

Draw the graph in the domain $-3 \leq x \leq 3$, $x \in R$, showing the asymptote at $x = -1$.

2. A function is defined by $y = \frac{1}{x-1}$

Copy and complete this table:

x	-2	-1	0	0.5	1	1.5	2	3	4
y		-0.5			*		1		

Draw the graph in the domain $-2 \leq x \leq 4$, $x \in R$, showing the asymptote at $x = 1$.
For what values of x is $y > \frac{1}{2}$?

3. A function is defined by $f(x) = \frac{1}{x-2}$

Copy and complete this table:

x	0	1	1.5	2	2.5	3	4
$f(x)$			-2	*			

Draw the graph of $y = f(x)$ in the domain $0 \leq x \leq 4$, $x \in R$, showing the asymptote at $x = 2$.
Find from your graph
(i) the value of x for which $f(x) = 1.5$
(ii) the range of values of x for which $f(x) < -1$.

4. A function is defined by $f(x) = \frac{1}{x}$
Draw the graph of $y = f(x)$
in the domain $\frac{1}{2} \leq x \leq 6$, $x \in R$.
Find from your graph,
(i) the value of x for which $f(x) = 1.6$
(ii) the range of values of x for which $f(x) < \frac{1}{4}$.

5. A function is defined by $f(x) = \frac{1}{x-3}$.
(i) Evaluate $f(3\frac{1}{4})$.
(ii) Evaluate $f(3\frac{1}{2}) + f(2\frac{1}{2})$.
(iii) Prove that $f(3 + x) + f(3 - x) = 0$.
(iv) Draw the graph of $y = f(x)$ in the domain $0 \leq x \leq 7$, $x \in R$, showing the asymptote at $x = 3$.
(v) By drawing the line $y = \frac{1}{2}(x - 4)$ or otherwise, solve the equation
$$\frac{1}{x-3} = \tfrac{1}{2}(x-4).$$

6. A function is defined by $f(x) = \frac{1}{x+4}$
(i) Evaluate $f(-3\frac{1}{4})$.
(ii) Prove that
$$f(x-4) + f(2x-4) = \frac{3}{2x}.$$
(iii) If $f(k) + f(1) = 0$, find k.
(iv) For what value of x is $f(x)$ undefined?
(v) Sketch the graph of $y = f(x)$ in the domain $-8 \leq x \leq 1$.

7. Draw the graphs of the two functions
$f(x) = \frac{1}{x-4}$ and $g(x) = x - 4$
in the domain $0 \leq x \leq 8$.
Deduce, from your graph, the values of x in the domain for which
(i) $f(x) = g(x)$,
(ii) $f(x) < g(x)$.

REVISION EXERCISE 6.G

1. (a) $f(x) = 5x - 2$ is a function.

(i) Evaluate $f(0)$.

(ii) If $f(x) = 0$, find the value of x.

(b) Let $g(x) = (x - 1)(7 - 2x)$

(i) Verify that $g(1) = 0$ and find another value of x for which $g(x) = 0$.

(ii) Given that $g(x + 1) = ax^2 + bx$, find the values of a and b, where $a, b \in R$.

(c) Draw the graph of $y = 2x^2 - x - 1$ in the domain $-2 \le x \le 2$. Use your graph to solve the inequality

$$2x^2 - x - 1 < 0$$

2. (a) $f(x) = 7x + k$ is a function. If $f(5) = 10$, find the value of k.

(b) The diagram shows part of the graph of $y = g(x) = x^2 + ax + b$

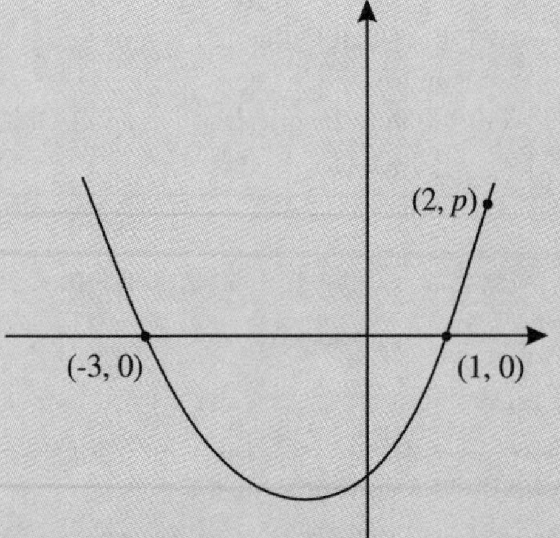

(i) Find the values of the real numbers a and b.

(ii) Find the value of p, where $p \in R$.

(c) Draw the graph of $y = x^3 - 3x^2$ in the domain $-1 \le x \le 4$. Use your graph to find the values of x for which

(i) $x^3 - 3x^2 = 0$,

(ii) $x^3 - 3x^2 > 0$.

3. (a) Write down the range and period of the periodic function, part of whose graph is illustrated below:

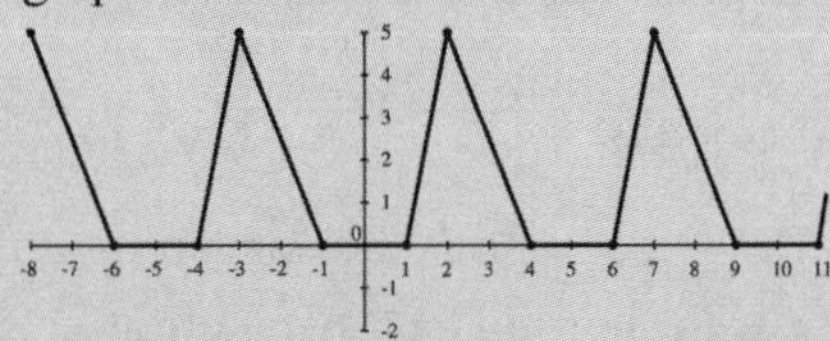

(b) $f(x) = x^2 + bx + c$ is a function such that $f(-1) = -7$ and $f(1) = -1$. Find the values of b and c and hence find a value of k (other than -1) for which

$$f(k) = f(-1)$$

(c) Let $g(x) = \dfrac{1}{x-5}$, for $x \in R, x \neq 5$.

Copy and complete this table:

x	1	2	3	4	$4\frac{1}{4}$	$4\frac{1}{2}$	$4\frac{3}{4}$
$g(x)$	$-\frac{1}{4}$						

Draw the graph of $y = g(x)$ for $1 \le x < 5$. Estimate, from the graph, the values of x for which

(i) $g(x) = -0.7$,

(ii) $g(x) < -1$.

4. (a) $f(x) = \dfrac{x}{x-2}$

(i) Evaluate $f(4)$ and $f(\frac{1}{4})$.

(ii) Find the value of x if $f(x) = \frac{1}{4}$.

(b) The diagram shows part of the graph of a periodic function $y = g(x)$.

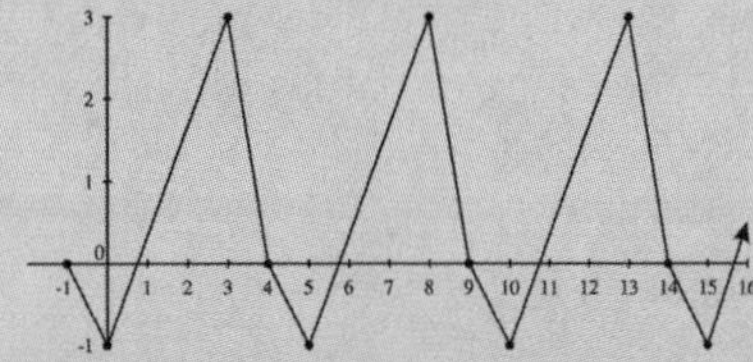

(i) Write down the range.

(ii) Write down the period.

(iii) Estimate the value of $g(22.5)$.

(c) $h(x) = \dfrac{1}{x-2}$ is a function.

(i) For what value of x is $h(x)$ undefined?

(ii) Show that $h\left(\dfrac{1}{x}\right) = -\dfrac{x}{2x-1}$

(iii) Show that $h(x) - h\left(\dfrac{1}{x}\right) = \dfrac{(x-1)(x+1)}{(x-2)(2x-1)}$

5. (a) Draw a graph of $y = x^3$ for $0 \le x \le 3, x \varepsilon R$.

Use your graph to estimate $\sqrt[3]{20}$.

(b) Using the same scales and axes draw the graphs of the two functions:
$f: x \to 8 + 2x - x^2$ and
$g: x \to 2x + 1$ in the domain
$-3 \le x \le 5, x \varepsilon R$.
Use your graph to estimate

(i) the range of values of x for which $8 + 2x - x^2 > 0$,

(ii) the value of $\sqrt{7}$.

6. If $f(x) = x^3 - 3x + 1$, complete the following table:

x	-3	-2	-1	0	1	2
$f(x)$	-17					

(i) Draw the graph of $f: x \to x^3 - 3x + 1$ in the domain $-3 \le x \le 2, x \varepsilon R$.

(ii) Use your graph to estimate the range of values of x for which the graph is decreasing.

(iii) Using the same axes and the same scales, draw the graph of the function: $g: x \to 1 - x$ for $x \varepsilon R$.

(iv) Write down the values of x at which the two graphs intersect.

(v) Solve algebraically $x^3 - 3x + 1 = 1 - x$.

7. (a) $f(x) = {}^1/x$ is a function defined for $x > 0$.

(i) Evaluate $f(2^1/_2)$

(ii) If $f(6) + f(3) = f(k)$, find the value of k.

(iii) Write as a single fraction $f(x) - f(x + 1)$ and hence solve $f(x) - f(x + 1) = {}^1/_{20}$.

(b) The depth of water (d) (measured in metres) in a harbour is given by the formula $d = 2t^2 + 5t + 7$, where t is the time (in hours) after 12.00 noon. Draw the graph of d in the domain $-4 \le x \le 2$. Use your graph to estimate

(i) the minimum depth in the harbour and the time at which it occurs,

(ii) the times at which the depth is 10 metres,

(iii) the depth at 1.45 p.m.,

(iv) the length of time for which the depth is less than 12 metres.

8. (a) The domain of the function $f: x \to 2x^2 - 1$ is $\{-2, -1, 0, 1, 2\}$. Find the range.

(b) The diagram shows part of the graph of $y = x^3 + ax + b$

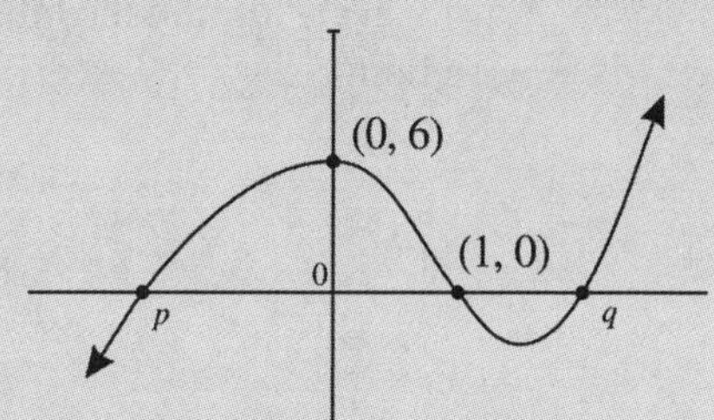

(i) Find the value of a and b

(ii) Find the coordinates of p and q.

(c) Draw the graph of $g(x) = \frac{1}{x+3}$ in the domain $0 \le x \le 5$, $x \varepsilon R$. Using the same scales and axes, draw the graph of $h(x) = x - 3$. Show how your graph may be used to estimate the value of $\sqrt{10}$.

9. (a) The diagram shows part of the graph of the periodic function p. Write down the range and period of the function. Find the value of $p(207)$.

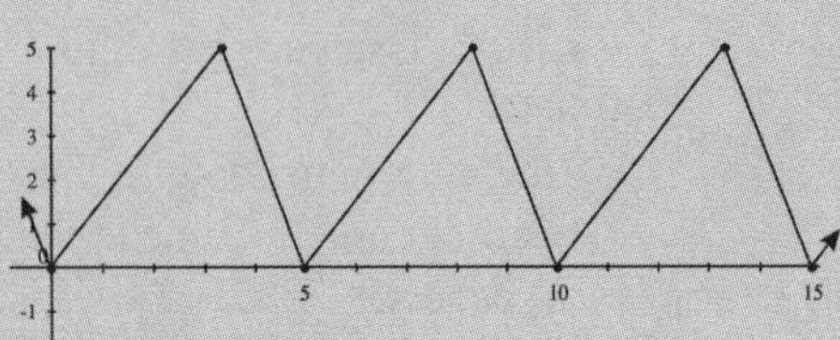

(b) Using the same scales and axes, draw the graphs of $y = {}^1/x$ and $y = 2x^2$ for $0 < x \leq 2$. Show how your graphs may be used to estimate the value of $\sqrt[3]{\frac{1}{2}}$.

(c) Let $f(x) = (4 - x)(3 + x)$, $x \in R$. Let $g(x) = 5x - k$, where k is a constant.

(i) Write down the roots of $f(x) = 0$.

(ii) If $x = 2$ is a solution to $f(x) + g(x) = 0$, find the other solution.

10. (a) $f(x) = 6(x - 4)^2$

(i) Evaluate $f(-1)$.

(ii) Find k, where $k > 0$, if $f(k) = f(-1)$.

(b) $g(x) = \dfrac{1}{x-5}$ is defined for $x \in R \setminus \{5\}$.

(i) Evaluate $g(2.5)$.

(ii) Prove that $g(x) + g(10 - x) = 0$.

(iii) Draw a graph of $y = g(x)$ in the domain $0 \leq x \leq 10, x \in R$. showing the asymptote at $x = 5$.

(c) The diagram shows the graph of $h(x) = x^3 - 6x + 2$.

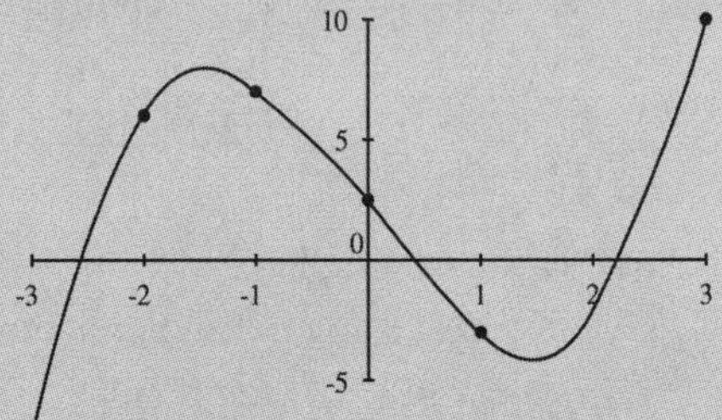

(i) Estimate the values of x for which $h(x) = 2$ and hence estimate $\sqrt{6}$, explaining your answer.

(ii) Show that $h(\sqrt{6}) + h(-\sqrt{6}) = 2\,h(0)$.

1. A ***function*** is a set of couples, no two of which have the same first component.
2. If the input of a function f is x and the output is y, we write $f(x) = y$ or (x, y) or we plot the point (x, y) on a graph.
3. The ***domain*** is the set of inputs. The ***range*** is the set of outputs.
4. A function which goes in repeated cycles is called a ***periodic*** function. The length of the cycle is called the ***period***.
5. The graph of $y = \dfrac{1}{x+a}$ has an ***asymptote*** at $x = -a$.

Chapter 7

Co-ordinate Geometry of the Line

THE DISTANCE BETWEEN TWO POINTS

Let (x_1, y_1) and (x_2, y_2) be two points.
Let d = the distance between them.
By Pythagoras' theorem, the square on the hypotenuse is equal to the sum of the squares on the other two sides.

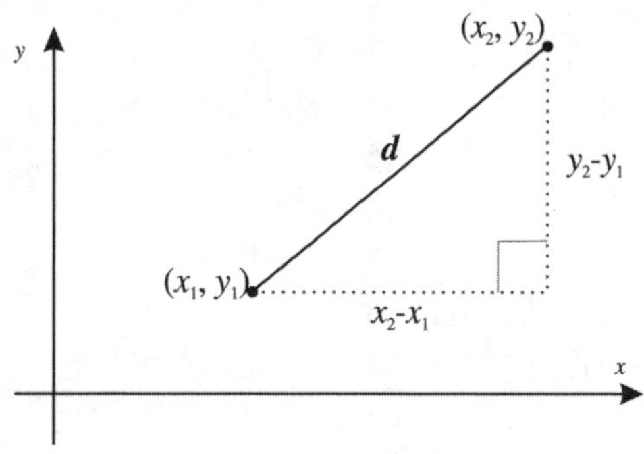

$$d^2 = (x_2 - x_1)^2 + (y_2 - y_1)^2$$

$$d = \sqrt{(x_2 - x_1)^2 + (y_2 - y_1)^2}$$

We use this formula to find the distance between any two points on the x-y co-ordinate plane.

Example 1: The vertices of a triangle are $a(-1, 4)$, $b(4, -6)$ and $c(10, 2)$. Prove that Δabc is isosceles but not equilateral.

Solution: An ***isosceles*** triangle has ***two*** sides of equal length.
An ***equilateral*** triangle has ***three*** sides of equal length.
A diagram always helps to get an idea of what is going on:

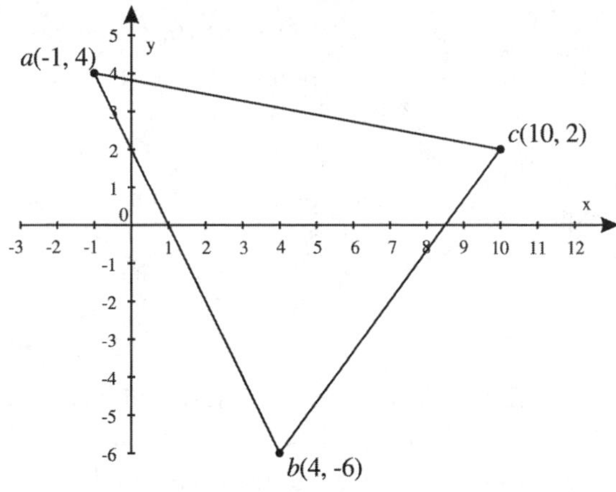

$$|ab| = \sqrt{(4 - -1)^2 + (-6-4)^2} = \sqrt{5^2 + (-10)^2} = \sqrt{25 + 100} = \sqrt{125}$$

$$|bc| = \sqrt{(10 - 4)^2 + (2 - -6)^2} = \sqrt{6^2 + 8^2} = \sqrt{36 + 64} = \sqrt{100} = 10$$

$$|ac| = \sqrt{(10 - -1)^2 + (2 - 4)^2} = \sqrt{11^2 + (-2)^2} = \sqrt{121 + 4} = \sqrt{125}$$

Since $|ab| = |ac|$, the triangle is an isosceles triangle.

Since $|ab| \neq |bc|$, the triangle is not an equilateral triangle.

Exercise 7.A

Find the distance between these pairs of points. Use surd form where necessary.

1. (1, 3), (3, 6)
2. (2, 1), (6, 4)
3. (1, 2), (9, 8)
4. (−1, 3), (2, −2)
5. (0, 0), (10, 2)
6. (−3, 5), (3, 0)
7. (−6, 2), (−1, 7)
8. (−1, −1), (1, 1)
9. (−11, 7), (1, 12)
10. (3, 4), (4, 3)
11. (−1, 1), (2, −3)
12. (5, 2), (5, −1)
13. (−1, 6), (4, 6)
14. (6, 1), (4, −1)
15. (−1, 3), (3, −1)
16. (6, 0), (0, 6)
17. (4, 10), (−2, 2)
18. (0, 0), (8, 15)
19. (−1, 2), (2, 0)
20. (−½, ½), (½, −½)
21. Find the distance from (0, 0) to (7, −4) and from (0, 0) to (6, −5). Which of the points (7, −4) or (6, −5) is farthest from the origin?
22. Which of these two points is nearest to the point (−3, 5):
    (6, 1) or (4, −2)?
23. $a = (-1, 8)$, $b = (4, 3)$ and $c = (-3, 2)$.
    Verify that $|ab| = |bc|$.
24. $a = (-1, 8)$, $b = (7, 7)$ and $c = (-5, 1)$.
    Verify that $|ab| = |ac|$.
25. $p(-2, 5)$, $q(-12, 5)$ and $r(-6, -3)$ are the vertices of a triangle. Verify that it is an isosceles triangle, but not an equilateral triangle.
26. $p(2, 0)$, $q(-2, 3)$ and $r(1, -1)$ are the vertices of a triangle. Verify that it is an isosceles triangle, but not an equilateral triangle.
27. $p(-1, 5)$, $q(7, 3)$ and $r(6, -1)$ are the vertices of a triangle.
    (i) Verify that $|pq|^2 + |qr|^2 = |pr|^2$
    (ii) Deduce that $|\angle pqr| = 90°$
28. $a = (-1, 3)$, $b = (3, 1)$ and $c = (1, 0)$ are three points. Verify that $|ab| = 2|bc|$.
29. $a = (-3, 2)$, $b = (3, -1)$ and $c = (2, 1)$ are three points. Verify that $|ab| = 3\,|bc|$.
30. $p(3, 8)$ and $q(-1, 1)$ are two points. $r(4, y)$ is a third point.
    (i) Find $|pq|$.
    (ii) If $|pq| = |pr|$, find two possible values of y.
31. $a = (-9, 2)$, $b = (2, 4)$ and $c = (x, -1)$ are three points. If $|ab| = |bc|$, find two possible values of x.
32. $a = (-4, 1)$, $b = (2, -7)$ and $c = (4, k)$ are three points. If $|ab| = |ac|$, find two possible values of k.
33. $a = (-1, 0)$, $b = (0, 1)$ and $c = (-3, k)$ are three points. If $2|ab| = |ac|$, find two possible values of k.
34. $a = (9, 2)$, $b = (-4, 2)$ and $c = (x, -10)$ are three points. If $|ab| = |bc|$, find two possible values of x.

MIDPOINT

If you start school when you are 4 and finish when you are 18, how old were you when you were half-way through your schooling? The answer is $\frac{4 + 18}{2} = 11$.
Indeed, to find half-way between any two numbers, we add them up and then divide by two. We use this to get the midpoint formula.

Let $a(x_1, y_1)$ and $b(x_2, y_2)$ be two points.
The midpoint, m, of $[ab]$ is given by

the formula: $m = \left(\frac{x_1 + x_2}{2}, \frac{y_1 + y_2}{2}\right)$

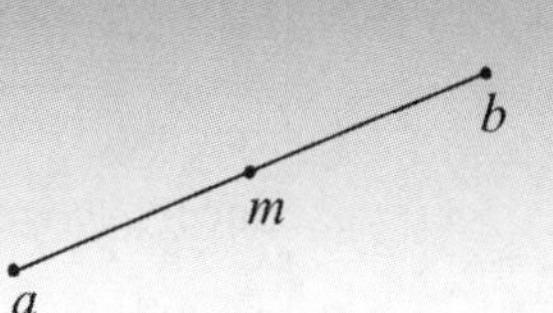

Example 1: $p(-12, 5)$ and $q(-6, -3)$ are two points. Find the midpoint, m, of $[pq]$.

Solution: $m = \left(\frac{x_1 + x_2}{2}, \frac{y_1 + y_2}{2}\right) = \left(\frac{-12 + (-6)}{2}, \frac{5 + (-3)}{2}\right) = \left(\frac{-18}{2}, \frac{2}{2}\right) = (-9, 1).$

Exercise 7.B

Find the midpoint of the line-segments joining these pairs of points:

1. (2, 6) and (4, 10)
2. (12, 0) and (2, 6)
3. (10, 1) and (–4, 7)
4. (–2, 11) and (4, –5)
5. (–7, 6) and (1, 0)
6. (–9, 1) and (–7, –7)
7. (2, 5) and (–4, –5)
8. (–3, 6) and (0, 1)
9. (2, 1) and (–7, –2)
10. (6, 1) and (– 4, 4)
11. (0, –1), and (5, 5)
12. (15, 8) and (–5, 2)
13. (–1, 3) and (11, –7)
14. (6, –1) and (–10, 1)

15. $a(5, 3)$, $b(0, 4)$, $c(-3, -5)$ and $d(2, -6)$ are four points.
    (i) Show that the midpoint of $[ac]$ is also the midpoint of $[bd]$.
    (ii) What does this result reveal about the quadrilateral $abcd$?

16. $p(3, -7)$ and $q(5, 7)$ are two points. Show that the midpoint of $[pq]$ lies on the x-axis.

17. $p(-3, 4)$ and $q(3, 6)$ are two points. Show that the y-axis bisects $[pq]$.

18. $p(-17, -4)$ and $q(7, 6)$ are two points.
    (i) Find the co-ordinates of m, the midpoint of $[pq]$.
    (ii) Verify, using the distance formula, that $|pm| = |mq|$.

19. $a(-5, 3)$, $b(1, 11)$, $c(10, -5)$ and $d(2, -11)$ are four points.
    (i) Find the co-ordinates of m and n, the midpoints of $[ab]$ and $[cd]$, respectively
    (ii) Find $|mn|$.

20. $p(0, 1)$ and $q(6, -7)$ are two points. $[pq]$ is the diameter of a circle.

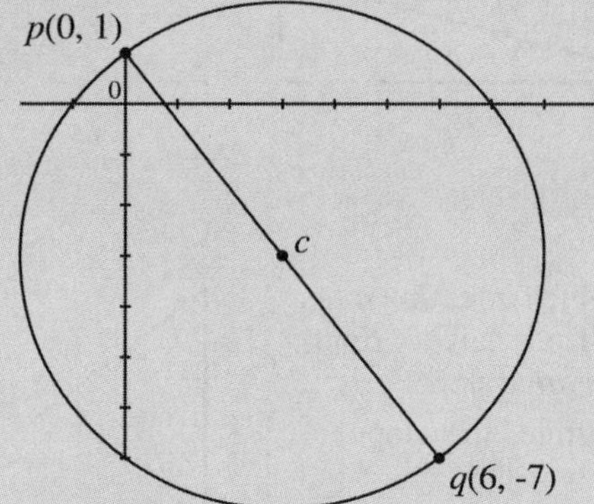

    (i) Find the co-ordinates of c, the centre of the circle.
    (ii) Find the radius of the circle.

21. $a(2, 8)$ and $b(x, y)$ are two points. If $(5, 10)$ is the midpoint of $[ab]$, find the values of x and y.

22. $a(4, y)$ and $b(x, 7)$ are two points. If $(3, 5)$ is the midpoint of $[ab]$, find the values of x and y.

23. $a(-2, y)$ and $b(x, 11)$ are two points. If $(-1, 3)$ is the midpoint of $[ab]$, find the values of x and y.

SLOPE

Slope is the way that we measure the steepness of a straight line. It is measured by dividing the ***rise*** by the ***run***.

$$\text{Slope} = \frac{\text{rise}}{\text{run}}$$

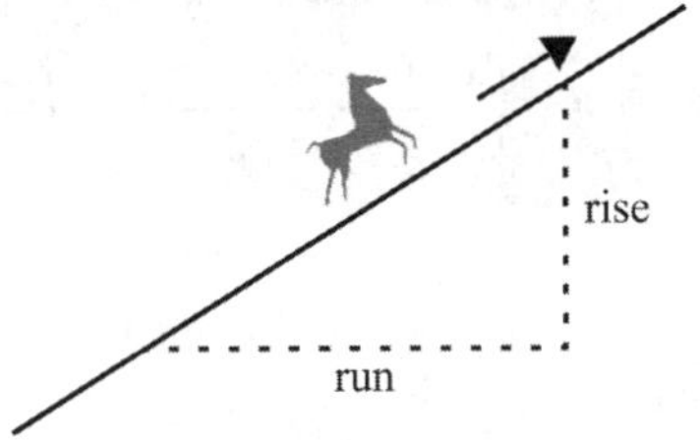

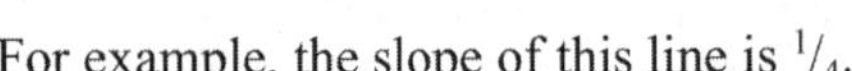

For example, the slope of this line is $^1/_4$.

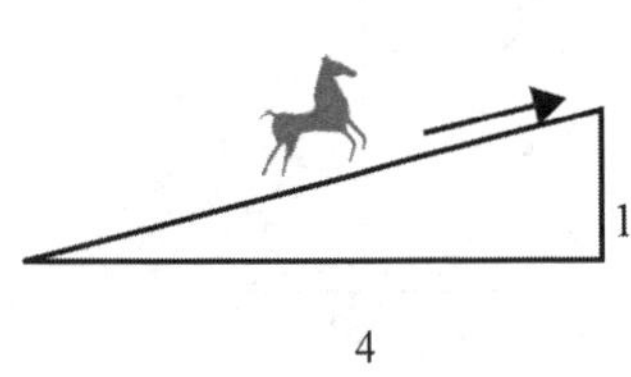

The slope of this line is $^3/_5$.

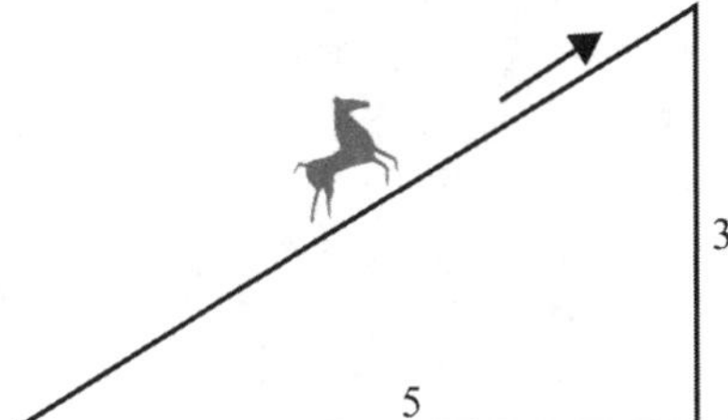

A line which goes ***down*** (as you go from left to right) has a ***negative*** slope.
For example, the slope of this line is $-\frac{3}{4}$

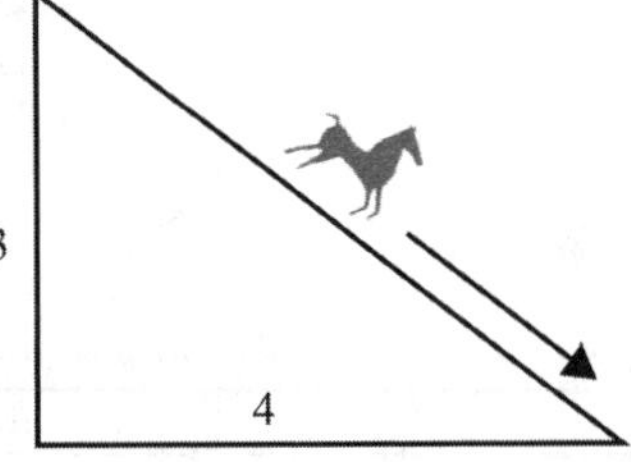

The slope of this line = –3

THE FORMULA FOR SLOPE

There is a formula for finding the slope (m) of a line which passes through the two points (x_1, y_1) and (x_2, y_2).

$$\text{Slope} = m = \frac{y_2 - y_1}{x_2 - x_1}$$

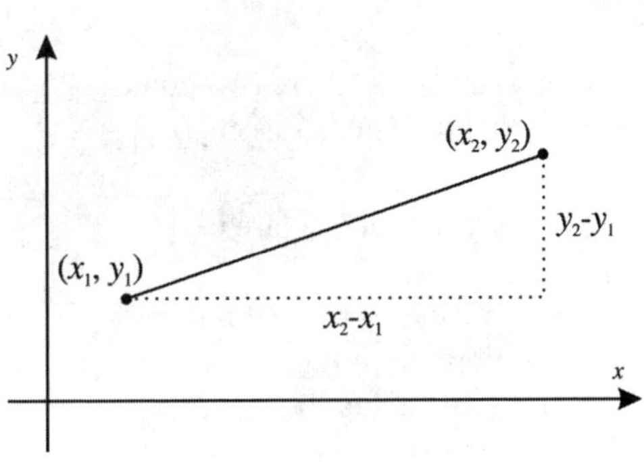

We can use this formula to find the slope of any line, once we know the co-ordinates of any two points on the line.

For example, the slope of the line through the points (1, 2) and (5, 7) is

$$m = \frac{y_2 - y_1}{x_2 - x_1} = \frac{7-2}{5-1} = \frac{5}{4}$$

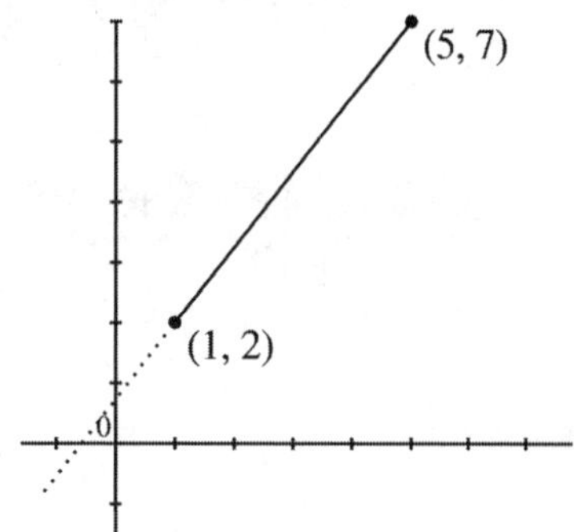

The slope of the line through the points (–1, 6) and (7, 0) is

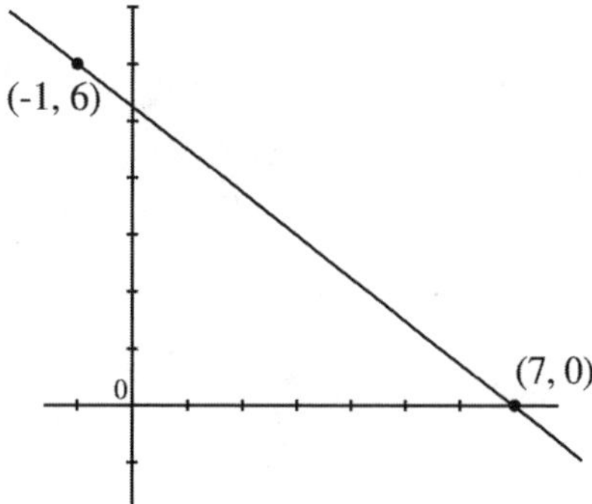

$$m = \frac{y_2 - y_1}{x_2 - x_1} = \frac{0-6}{7-(-1)} = \frac{-6}{8} = -\frac{3}{4}$$

This slope is ***negative***, since the line goes ***down***, as you move from left to right.

The slope of the line through the points (10, 6) and (–6, –2) is

$$m = \frac{y_2 - y_1}{x_2 - x_1} = \frac{-2\ -6}{-6\ -10} = \frac{-8}{-16} = \frac{1}{2}$$

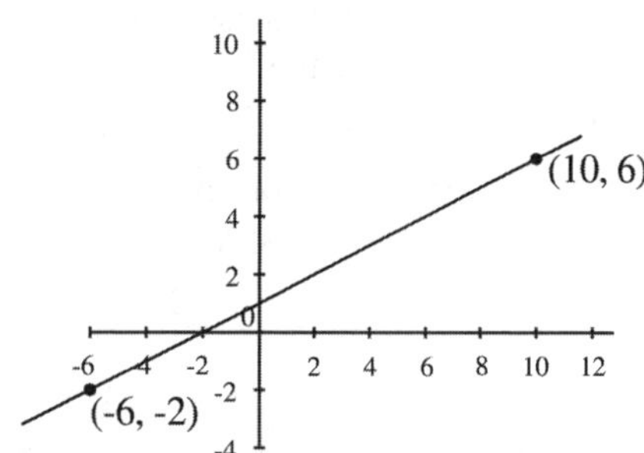

This slope is ***positive***, since the line goes ***up***, as you move from left to right.

PARALLEL AND PERPENDICULAR SLOPES

The slopes of L is m_1.
The slope of K is m_2.

L is parallel to K if and only if
$m_1 = m_2$

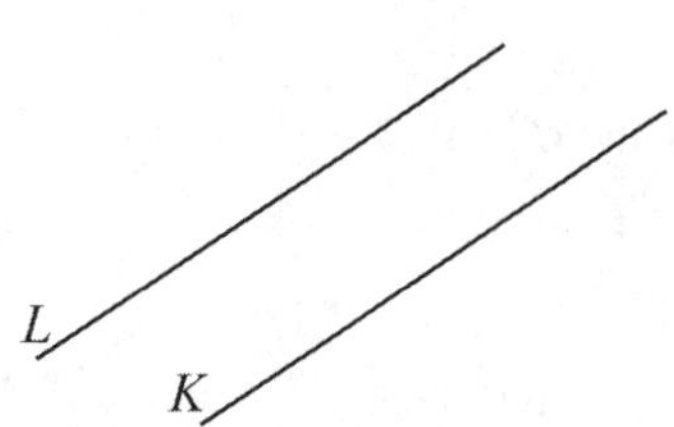

L is perpendicular to K if and only if $m_1 \, . \, m_2 = -1$

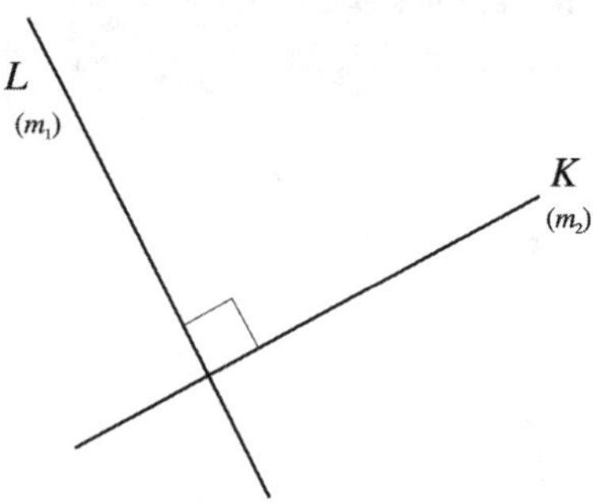

Example 1: $a(1, 6)$, $b(5, 4)$, $c(4, 2)$ and $d(6,1)$ are four points.

(i) Prove that $ab \parallel cd$

(ii) Prove that $ab \perp bc$.

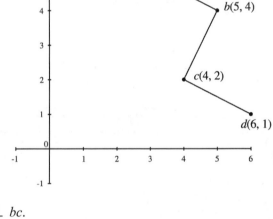

Solution:

(i) Slope of ab =

$$\frac{4-6}{5-1} = \frac{-2}{4} = -\frac{1}{2}$$

Slope of cd =

$$\frac{1-2}{6-4} = \frac{-1}{2} = -\frac{1}{2}$$

Since these slopes are equal, $ab \parallel cd$.

(ii) Slope of $ab = m_1 = -\frac{1}{2}$

Slope of $bc = m_2 =$

$$\frac{2-4}{4-5} = \frac{-2}{-1} = 2$$

$m_1 \, . \, m_2 = (-\frac{1}{2})(2) = -1$

Since $m_1 \, . \, m_2 = -1$, $ab \perp bc$.

Exercise 7.C

Find the slopes of the line segments which pass through these pairs of points:

1. (1, 3) and (4, 5)

2. (1, 1) and (6, 7)

3. (4, 2) and (5, 7)

4. (1, 0) and (6, 5)

5. (–1, 2) and (5, 5)

6. (–3, –6) and (1, –2)

7. (0, –7) and (1, 1)

8. (–5, 2) and (1, 0)

9. (11, 3) and (3, –1)

10. (–1, –3) and (–4, –6)

11. (10, –3) and (–14, 5)

12. (1, 3) and (4, –18)

13. (2, –8) and (3, –5)

14. (4, –1) and (5, –3)

15. $a(-2, 4)$, $b(3, -1)$, $c(-11, 4)$ and $d(-5, -2)$ are four points. Prove that $ab \parallel cd$.

16. $a(5, 4)$, $b(4, -1)$, and $c(-11, 2)$ are three points. Prove that $ab \perp bc$.

17. $p(4, -1)$, $q(2, 3)$, $r(2, -2)$ are three points. Prove that $pq \perp pr$.

18. $a(-1, 3)$, $b(5, 0)$, $c(3, -3)$ and $d(-3, 0)$ are four points.
(i) Prove that $ab \parallel cd$.
(ii) Prove that $bc \parallel ad$

19. $a(0, 6)$, $b(10, 1)$ and $c(6, -7)$ are three points. Prove that $ab \perp bc$.

20. $p(-3, 1)$, $q(-1, 5)$, $r(7, 1)$ and $s(5, -3)$ are four points.
(i) Prove that $pq \parallel rs$.
(ii) Prove that $pq \perp qr$.

21. $a(5, 6)$, $b(1, 4)$, $c(-1, 3)$ are three points. Prove that a, b and c are **collinear**, (i.e. that the three of them are all **on the same line**).

22. Show that $(-1, 3)$, $(2, 15)$ and $(3, 19)$ are collinear.

23. Investigate if $(-14, 6)$, $(-7, 5)$, $(22, 1)$ are collinear.

24. Investigate if $(-100, 96)$, $(25, -4)$, $(0, 16)$ are collinear.

25. $p(-1, 11)$ and $q(7, 5)$ are two points. Find
(i) the slope of pq
(ii) the midpoint of $[pq]$

26. $p(-2, 2)$, $q(1, 0)$ and $r(5, 6)$ are three points.
(i) Prove that $pq \perp qr$.
(ii) Verify that $|pr|^2 = |pq|^2 + |qr|^2$

27. $p(-4, 4k)$, $q(k, -11)$ are two points. If the slope of pq is -3, find the value of k.

28. $p(-2, 1)$, $q(0, 5)$ and $r(t, t-9)$ are three points. If $|\angle qpr| = 90°$, find the value of t.

29. If $(-9, 4)$, $(3, 1)$ and $(1, k)$ are collinear, find the value of k.

30. $a(0, k)$, $b(2, 5)$ and $c(k, 1)$ are three points such that $|\angle abc| = 90°$. Find the value of k.

31. $a(-1, 1)$, $b(k+5, k-5)$ and $c(9, 1)$ are three points such that $|\angle abc| = 90°$. Find two possible values of k.

EQUATION OF A LINE

When we say that $x + y = 6$ is the equation of a line we really mean the following:
'If you plot all points (x, y) which satisfy the equation $x + y = 6$, those points will form a line.'

Such points might include:
$(7, -1)$ $(6, 0)$, $(5, 1)$, $(4, 2)$, $(3, 3)$, $(2, 4)$, $(1, 5)$, $(0, 6)$, etc.

The illustration shows this line.

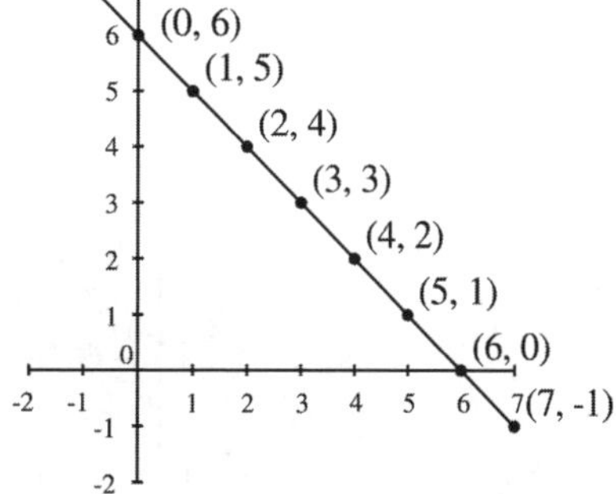

Note:

Slope
If you have the equation of a line and you want to know the slope, write the line in the form
$$y = mx + c$$
and the slope of the line is m.
For example, the above line could be written in the form $y = -\mathbf{1}x + 6$. Therefore its slope $= -1$.

Point of intersection
The point of intersection of two lines is found by solving their ***simultaneous equations***.

Example 1: The equation of a line K is $x - 2y = 4$.
The equation of a line L is $2x + y - 7 = 0$

(i) Sketch the two lines.
(ii) Find the slope of K.
(iii) Investigate if $L \perp K$.
(iv) Find the point of intersection of L and K.
(v) Investigate if the point $(14, -22)$ is on the line L.

Solution: (i) To sketch a line, you must find two points on it. The easiest ones to find are the points where $x = 0$ and where $y = 0$.

K: $x - 2y = 4$.
If $x = 0$, then $0 - 2y = 4$ $\quad \therefore y = -2 \quad \therefore (0, -2)\ \varepsilon\ K$.
If $y = 0$, then $x - 0 = 4$ $\quad \therefore x = 4 \quad \therefore (4, 0)\ \varepsilon\ K$.

L: $2x + y = 7$ [Bringing the 7 to the R.H.S.]
If $x = 0$, then $0 + y = 7$ $\quad \therefore y = 7 \quad \therefore (0, 7)\ \varepsilon\ L$.
If $y = 0$, then $2x - 0 = 7$ $\quad \therefore x = 3\frac{1}{2} \quad \therefore (3\frac{1}{2}, 0)\ \varepsilon\ L$.
We can now plot the two lines, using the points which we've found.

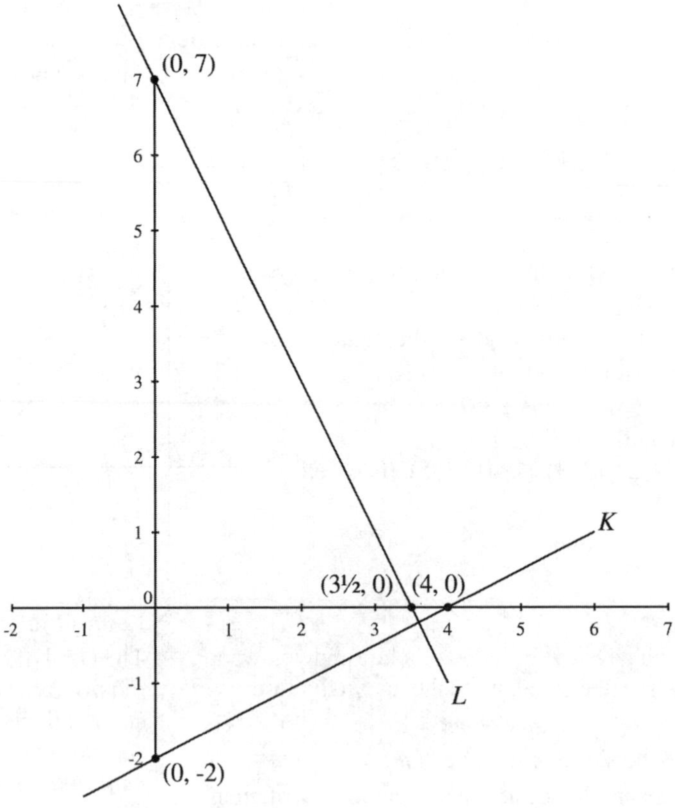

(ii) K's equation is $x - 2y = 4$

$\therefore \quad -2y = -x + 4$

$\therefore \quad 2y = x - 4$

$\therefore \quad y = \frac{1}{2}x - 2$

The slope of K is ½ .

(iii) L's equation is $2x + y - 7 = 0$

$\therefore \quad y = -2x + 7$

$\therefore$ The slope of L is -2.

$\therefore$ The product of their slopes $m_1 \cdot m_2 = \frac{1}{2}(-2) = -1$

$\therefore \quad K \perp L$

(iv) To find the point of intersection, we solve the simultaneous equations:

$K: \quad x - 2y = 4$

$L: \quad 2x + y = 7$

We will get $-2y$ in the first equation and $+ 2y$ in the second.

$K: \quad x - 2y = 4$

$2 \times L: \quad \underline{4x + 2y = 14}$

Add! $\quad 5x = 18$

$\therefore \quad x = 3.6$

L reads: $2(3.6) + y = 7$

$\therefore \quad 7.2 + y = 7$

$\therefore \quad y = -0.2$

$\therefore$ The point of intersection is $(3.6, -0.2)$

(v) Test $(14, -22)$ in the equation $2x + y - 7 = 0$ to see if it fits.

$2(14) + (-22) - 7 = 0$

$\therefore \quad 28 - 22 - 7 = 0$

$\therefore \quad -1 = 0$ [Which is false]

$\therefore \quad (14, -22) \notin L$

Exercise 7.D

Find the slopes of these lines:

1. $3x + y = 9$
2. $5x + y = 8$
3. $2x - y = 11$
4. $4x - y - 9 = 0$
5. $5x - 2y + 4 = 0$
6. $6x + 3y - 11 = 0$
7. $3x + 2y = 9$
8. $7x + 5y - 10 = 0$
9. $x - y - 1 = 0$
10. $x + y = 0$
11. $x - 6y = 12$
12. $3x - 12y = 7$
13. $9x - 11y - 13 = 0$
14. $7x + 8y - 8 = 0$
15. $y = x + 16$
16. $x = 5y - 5$
17. $2x = 7y$
18. $x = \frac{1}{2}y$
19. $3x = 2y - 7$
20. $x = y$

Sketch these lines and write down their slopes:

21. $2x + y = 6$

22. $3x + 4y = 12$

23. $x + y = 4$

24. $x - 2y = 8$

25. $2x - 3y - 9 = 0$

26. $x - y - 2 = 0$

27. $2x + 5y - 8 = 0$

28. $2x - y = 5$

29. $x - 3y = 0$

30. $2x + y = 0$

31. Investigate if $(11, -14)$ is on the line $2x + y - 8 = 0$.

32. Investigate if $(-10, 11)$ is on the line $x + y - 1 = 0$.

33. Investigate if $(-31, 17)$ is on the line $x + 2y - 2 = 0$.

34. If $(5, k)$ is a point on the line $4x - 3y + 1 = 0$, find the value of k.

35. If $(-2, k)$ is a point on the line $7x - 2y - 6 = 0$, find the value of k.

36. If $(t, 11)$ is a point on the line $2x - 3y + 1 = 0$, find the value of t.

37. Investigate if $3x - y + 7 = 0$ and $x + 3y - 9 = 0$ are perpendicular.

38. Investigate if $2x + y = 9$ and $4x + 2y - 11 = 0$ are parallel.

39. Investigate if $x + 4y - 9 = 0$ and $2x - y = 0$ are perpendicular.

40. Investigate if the two lines $y = x$ and $x - y - 9 = 0$ are parallel.

41. If $2x + y - 13 = 0$ and $6x + ky - 1 = 0$ are parallel lines, find the value of k.

42. If $2x - y - 9 = 0$ and $3x + ky = 0$ are perpendicular lines, find the value of k.

43. If $2x - 4y - 11 = 0$ and $x + ky - 10 = 0$ are parallel lines, find the value of k.

44. If $12x + 3y + 8 = 0$ and $x + ky = 5$ are perpendicular lines, find the value of k.

45. Find the point of intersection of the two lines:
$2x - 7y = 3$
$x + y = 6$

46. Find the point of intersection of the two lines:
$3x - y = 10$
$x + 4y = -1$

47. Find the point of intersection of the two lines:
$5x + 2y + 7 = 0$
$x + 3y + 17 = 0$

48. If $(2, -1)$ is the point of intersection of the lines $2x + 11y + k = 0$ and $x - ty + 12 = 0$, find the values of k and t.

49. Find the point where the line $4x - 5y - 19 = 0$ intersects the y-axis.

50. The equation of a line K is $x - 2y = 6$.
The equation of a line L is $4x + 2y = 19$.
(i) Sketch the two lines.
(ii) Find the slope of K.
(iii) Investigate if $L \perp K$.
(iv) Find the point of intersection of L and K.
(v) Investigate if $(17, -24) \in L$.

PARALLEL AND PERPENDICULAR LINES

As we have seen, parallel lines have equal slopes, and the product of perpendicular slopes is -1. If the slope of a line is $^a/_b$, then a parallel line also has slope $^a/_b$, and a perpendicular line has slope $-\,^b/_a$ [since $-\,^b/_a \,.\, ^a/_b = -1$] . In other words, to get a perpendicular slope, ***turn the fraction upside–down and change its sign***.
Here are some examples:

Slope	Parallel slope	Perpendicular slope
$^2/_3$	$^2/_3$	$-\,^3/_2$
$-\,^{11}/_7$	$-\,^{11}/_7$	$^7/_{11}$
4	4	$-\,^1/_4$
$-\,^1/_2$	$-\,^1/_2$	2

FINDING THE EQUATION OF A LINE

If you want to ***find*** the equation of a line, then you must first find out two pieces of information:

1. Its slope m.
2. A point (x_1, y_1) which is on the line. Any point will do.

Then the equation is given by the formula

$$y - y_1 = m\,(x - x_1)$$

Example 1: Find the equation of the line which has slope -2 and which passes through the point (3, 8).

Solution: $m = -2;\ x_1 = 3;\ y_1 = 8$
The equation is $y - y_1 = m\,(x - x_1)$
$y - 8 = -2(x - 3)$
$y - 8 = -2x + 6$
$2x + y - 14 = 0$

Example 2: Find the equation of the line which passes through the points $(-3, 1)$ and $(1, 3)$.

Solution: $m = \dfrac{y_2 - y_1}{x_2 - x_1} = \dfrac{3-1}{1+3} = \dfrac{2}{4} = \dfrac{1}{2}$

$m = {}^1/_2;\ x_1 = -3;\ y_1 = 1$ [Using the first point]
The equation is $y - y_1 = m\,(x - x_1)$

$y - 1 = {}^1/_2(x - -3)$
$y - 1 = {}^1/_2(x + 3)$
$2y - 2 = 1(x + 3)$ [Doubling both sides]
$2y - 2 = x + 3$
$0 = x - 2y + 5$

Example 3: Find the equation of the line which passes through (1, 0) and which is perpendicular to the line L, whose equation is $5x - 2y - 9 = 0$.

Solution: L has equation

$$5x - 2y - 9 = 0$$
$$\therefore \quad -2y = -5x + 9$$
$$\therefore \quad 2y = 5x - 9$$
$$\therefore \quad y = {}^5/_2 x - {}^9/_2$$

The slope of L is ${}^5/_2$

$\therefore$ A perpendicular line has slope $-{}^2/_5$ [Since ${}^5/_2 \times -{}^2/_5 = -1$]

$$m = -{}^2/_5 \; ; x_1 = 1 \; ; y_1 = 0$$

The equation is $y - y_1 = m(x - x_1)$

$$y - 0 = -{}^2/_5(x - 1)$$
$$5y = -2(x - 1) \quad \text{[Multiplying both sides by 5]}$$
$$5y = -2x + 2$$
$$2x + 5y - 2 = 0$$

Exercise 7.E

Copy and complete this table:

	Slope	$\parallel$ slope	$\perp$ slope
e.g.	¾	¾	$-{}^4/_3$
1.	½		
2.	${}^4/_5$		
3.	${}^7/_9$		
4.	$-{}^5/_6$		
5.	$-{}^1/_5$		
6.	2		
7.	–4		
8.	$-{}^{10}/_9$		
9.	1		
10.	–7		

Find the equation of the lines with these slopes and containing the given point:

11. $m = 3$ containing the point (1, 2).

12. $m = 1$ containing the point (4, –1).

13. $m = 2$ containing the point (4, 0).

14. $m = -1$ containing the point (–1, 5).

15. $m = 1$ containing the point (–9, 6).

16. $m = -3$ containing the point (1, 2).

17. $m = 4$ containing the point (0, –1).

18. $m = -2$ containing the point (0, 0).

19. $m = 5$ containing the point (1, 4).

20. $m = -4$ containing the point (–2, 9).

21. $m = ½$ containing the point (1, 5).

22. $m = -½$ containing the point (0, 0).

23. $m = -¾$ containing the point (0, 0).

24. $m = {}^3/_7$ containing the point (–3, 3).

25. $m = -{}^7/_{11}$ containing the point (–2, –2).

26. A line passes through the points (2, 3) and (3, 5). Find
   (i) its slope,
   (ii) its equation.

27. A line passes through the points (–1, 0) and (7, 4). Find
   (i) its slope,
   (ii) its equation.

28. Find the equation of the line which passes through the two points (4, 1) and (–2, –4).

29. Find the equation of the line which passes through the two points (–1, 8) and (11, 4).

30. Find the equation of the line which passes through the two points (½, ½) and (–2½, –4½).

31. L is a line with equation $x - 3y - 9 = 0$. Find

(i) the slope of L,

(ii) the equation of a line parallel to L, passing through the origin.

32. L is a line with equation $x + y - 11 = 0$. Find

(i) the slope of L,

(ii) the equation of a line which is perpendicular to L and which passes through the point $(0, -3)$.

33. L is a line with equation $3x - 2y - 2 = 0$. Find

(i) the slope of L,

(ii) the equation of a line parallel to L, passing through $(1,-1)$.

34. $a(2, -3)$ and $b(6, 4)$ are two points. Find

(i) the slope of ab,

(ii) the equation of ab,

(iii) the equation of a line through b which is perpendicular to ab.

35. L is the line $x - 2y - 9 = 0$. M is the line which is perpendicular to L and which contains the point $(4, 0)$. Find

(i) the equation of M,

(ii) the point of intersection of L and M.

36. $a(1, 2)$, $b(-1, 5)$ and $c(0, -3)$ are three points. Find

(i) the slope and equation of ab,

(ii) the equation of the line L which is perpendicular to ab and which contains the point c,

(iii) the point of intersection of ab and L.

37. L is the line $7x - 2y + 9 = 0$. M is the line perpendicular to L and passes through the point $q(-8, 3)$. Find

(i) the equation of M,

(ii) the co-ordinates of p where $L \cap M = \{p\}$.

38. From the diagram below, find

(i) the equation of L,

(ii) the equation of M,

(iii) the co-ordinates of p.

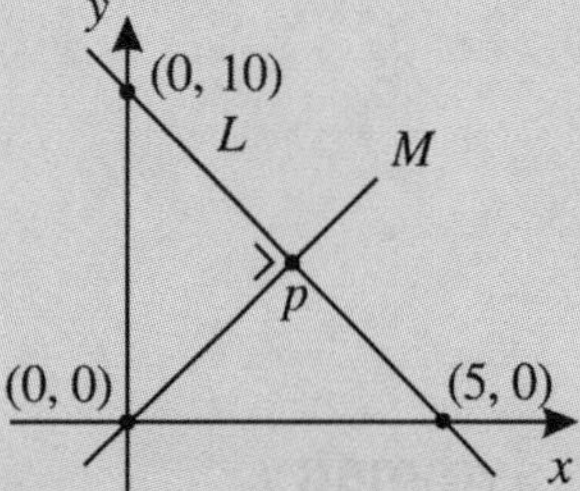

39. $a(3, 4)$ and $b(-1, 6)$ are two points. Find the equation of the line which passes through the midpoint of $[ab]$ and which is perpendicular to ab.

40. $p(0, 8)$, $q(4, 5)$ and $r(-2, -5)$ are three points. m is the midpoint of $[qr]$. Find the equation of the line through m which is parallel to pq.

41. (i) $2x - y + 1 = 0$ is the equation of the line L. Verify that $p(1, 3)$ is on L.

(ii) If a line $K \perp L$ contains the point p, find the equation of K.

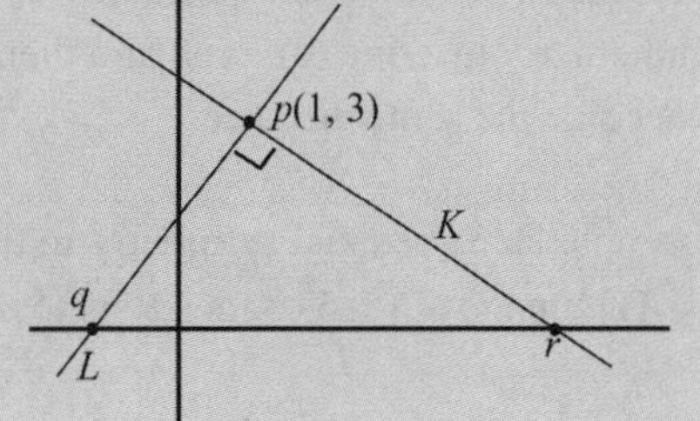

THREE TRANSFORMATIONS

1. Translation:

Under a translation, all points move the same distance and the same direction.

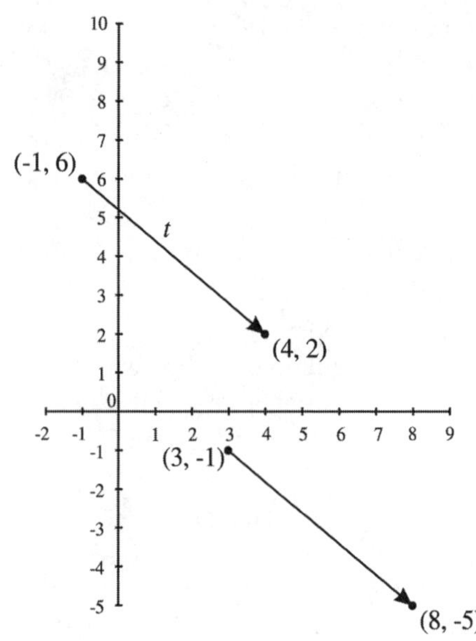

For example, suppose that t is a translation which maps $(-1, 6)$ onto $(4, 2)$. What is the image of $(3, -1)$ under t?

$(-1, 6) \rightarrow (4, 2)$: (Up 5, Down 4)
$\therefore (3, -1) \rightarrow (3 + 5, -1 - 4) = (8, -5)$

2. Central symmetry.

Under central symmetry in a point c, [which is written S_c] every point goes to c and then out the other side the same distance.
It is like a double-translation.

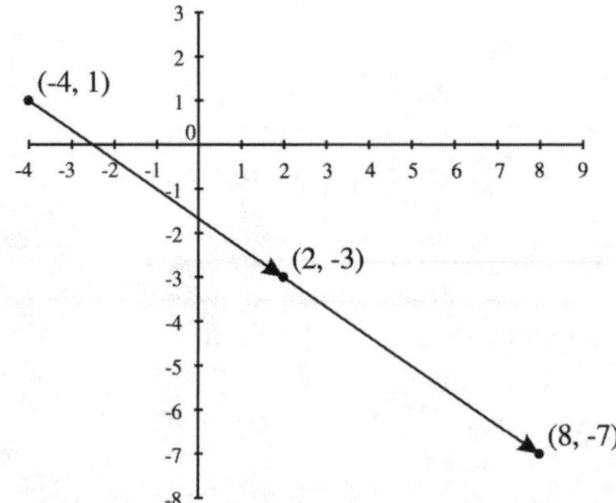

For example, let $c = (2, -3)$. What is the image of $(-4, 1)$ under S_c (central symmetry in c)?

$(-4, 1) \rightarrow (2, -3) \rightarrow (2 + 6, -3 - 4) = (8, -7)$
(Up 6, Down 4) (Up 6, Down 4)

3. Axial symmetry.

Under axial symmetry, every point moves perpendicularly to a line (or axis) and then out the other side the same distance.

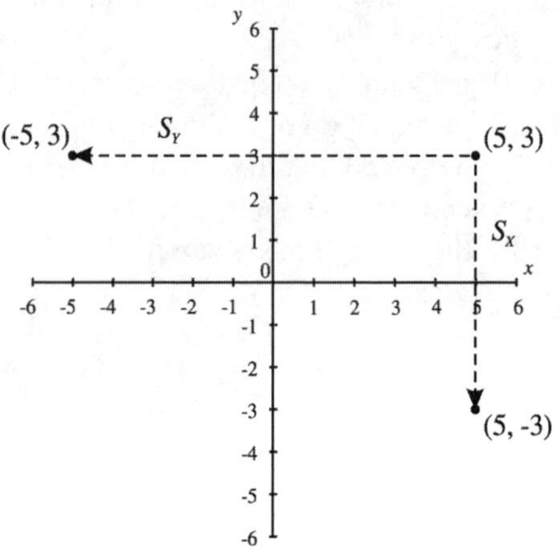

For example let S_X be axial symmetry in the x-axis. The image of $(5, 3)$ under S_X is $(5, -3)$.

Let S_Y be axial symmetry in the y-axis. The image of $(5, 3)$ under S_Y is $(-5, 3)$.

FINDING THE IMAGE OF A LINE

To find the image of a line under any of our three transformations, follow these three steps:

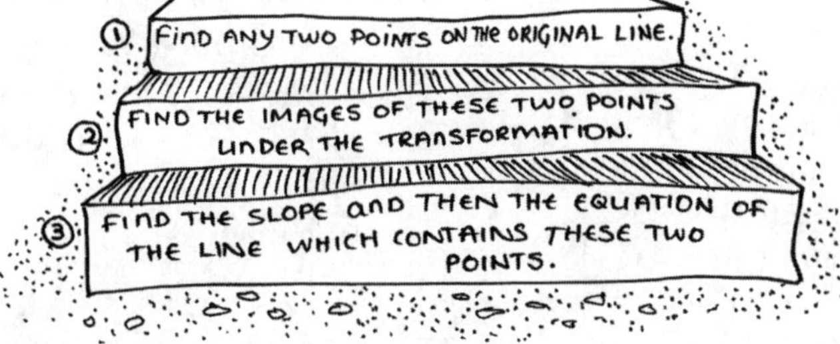

① FIND ANY TWO POINTS ON THE ORIGINAL LINE.
② FIND THE IMAGES OF THESE TWO POINTS UNDER THE TRANSFORMATION.
③ FIND THE SLOPE AND THEN THE EQUATION OF THE LINE WHICH CONTAINS THESE TWO POINTS.

Example 1: Find the equation of the image of the line $2x - y = 8$ under central symmetry in the point $(1, -1)$.

Solution:

1. Find any two points on $2x - y = 8$: $(4, 0)$ and $(0, -8)$
2. Find their images under central symmetry in $(1, -1)$:
   $(4, 0) \rightarrow (1, -1) \rightarrow (-2, -2)$
   $(0, -8) \rightarrow (1, -1) \rightarrow (2, 6)$
3. The new line passes through the points $(-2, -2)$ and $(2, 6)$.

$\therefore$ Its slope $= \dfrac{6+2}{2+2} = \dfrac{8}{4} = 2$

$\therefore m = 2, x_1 = -2$ and $y_1 = -2$

$\therefore$ The equation is $y + 2 = 2(x + 2)$

$\therefore \quad y + 2 = 2x + 4$

$\therefore \quad 0 = 2x - y + 2$

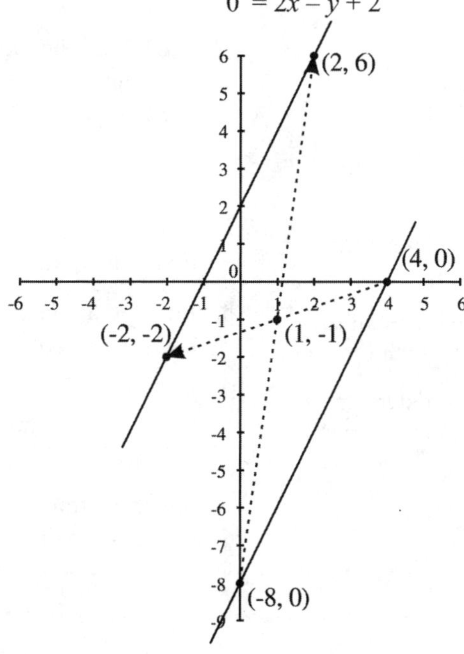

Exercise 7.F

1. Find the image of these points under the given translation:
   (i) (4, 1) under t:(0, 0) → (2, 4)
   (ii) (1, 2) under t:(0, 0) → (3, 1)
   (iii) (1, 1) under t:(0, 0) → (5, 6)
   (iv) (–1, 2) under t:(0, 0) → (5, 2)
   (v) (–3, 4) under t:(0, 0) → (1, –1)
   (vi) (2, 1) under t:(1, 3) → (2, 4)
   (vii) (3, 7) under t:(2, 4) → (1, 6)
   (viii) (7, –4) under t:(4, 0) → (0, 3)
   (ix) (10, –10) under t:(3, 2) → (0, 0)
   (x) (–2, 1) under t:(–2, 4) → (3, –1)

2. $t:(0, 0) \rightarrow (5, -1)$ is a translation. Find the image of the point (4, 4) under the translation t.

3. t is a translation which maps (2, –3) onto the origin (0, 0). Find the images of these points under t:
   (i) (5, 5) (ii) (–2, 3) (iii) (0, 0).

4. Find the images of these points under central symmetry in the origin (0, 0)
   (i) (4, 1) (iv) (4, 0)
   (ii) (3, 2) (v) (–5, –2)
   (iii) (–1, 3)

5. Find the image of (1, 2) under central symmetry in the point (3, 3).

6. Find the image of (3, 1) under central symmetry in the point (5, 4).

7. Find the image of (2, 4) under central symmetry in the point (1, 5).

8. c(5, 1) is a point. Find the image of (0, 0) under S_c (central symmetry in the point c).

9. Find the image of (–1, –3) under central symmetry in the point (–1, 1).

10. Find the images of these points under S_X, axial symmetry in the x-axis:
    (i) (4, 2) (vi) (–3, 1)
    (ii) (3, 1) (vii) (3, –3)
    (iii) (1, 3) (viii) (–5, 1)
    (iv) (0, 5) (ix) (2, 0)
    (v) (–2, –3) (x) (–4, 0)

11. Find the images of these points under S_Y, axial symmetry in the y-axis:
    (i) (5, 1) (vi) (–6, 5)
    (ii) (2, 3) (vii) (–2, –1)
    (iii) (3, 2) (viii) (–4, 1)
    (iv) (4, 0) (ix) (0, 5)
    (v) (–2, 2) (x) (0, –2)

12. p(3, 2) is a point. Find the image of p under
    (i) S_X axial symmetry in the x-axis,
    (ii) S_Y axial symmetry in the y-axis.

13. Find the image of (–6, –5) under axial symmetry in the y-axis.

14. Find the image of (4, 0) under axial symmetry in the x-axis.

15. Find the image of the point (–3, 1) under,
    (i) axial symmetry in the y-axis,
    (ii) central symmetry in the origin,
    (iii) the translation t: (0, 0) → (3, –1).

16. A translation t: (2, 5) → (0, 9).
    (i) Find the image of (4, 6) under t.
    (ii) Find the image of the origin under t.
    (iii) A point p is mapped onto the origin under t. Find the co-ordinates of p.

17. Find the image of the line $x + y = 4$ under the translation (0, 0) → (2, 1).

18. Find the image of the line $3x + y = 6$ under axial symmetry in the y-axis.

19. Find the image of the line $4x - y = 4$ under axial symmetry in the x-axis.

20. Find the image of the line $x - 2y - 8 = 0$ under the translation which maps (4, –2) onto the point (3, –3).

21. Find the image of the line whose equation is $3x + 4y - 12 = 0$ under central symmetry in the origin.

22. f is axial symmetry in the x-axis. L is the line $y = 3x$. Find the equation of $f(L)$.

THE AREA OF A TRIANGLE

If the co-ordinates of the vertices of a triangle are (0, 0), (x_1, y_1) and (x_2, y_2) then the area of the triangle is given by the formula:

$$\text{Area} = {}^1/_2 \,|\, x_1 y_2 - x_2 y_1 \,|$$

1. One of the vertices must be (0, 0) if this formula is to be used.
2. The straight brackets in this formula mean that the answer must be a positive number. If you get a negative answer, change it to make it positive. After all, the area of any triangle cannot be less than zero.

Example 1: Find the area of the triangle with vertices (0, 0), (8, 1) and (2, 6).

Solution: $x_1 = 8, y_1 = 1, x_2 = 2$ and $y_2 = 6$.
The area = ½ | (8)(6) – (2)(1) | = ½ | 48 – 2 | = ½ | 46 | = 23 square units.

Example 2: Find the area of the triangle with vertices (–1, 7), (6, 3) and (2, 0).

Solution: When none of the vertices is at (0, 0), we ***translate*** the triangle so that one of the vertices will be at (0, 0).

(–1, 7) → (0, 0) [Up 1, down 7]

(6, 3) → (7, –4) [Up 1, down 7]

(2, 0) → (3, –7) [Up 1, down 7]

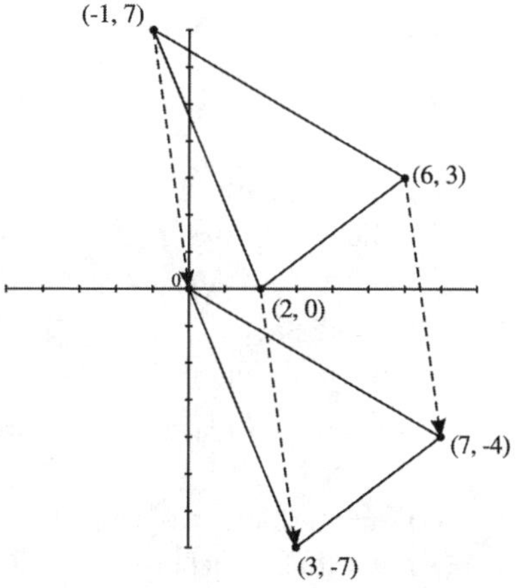

We find the area of the translated triangle
(0, 0), (7, –4) , (3, –7)
$x_1 = 7, y_1 = -4, x_2 = 3$ and $y_2 = -7$.

∴ The area = ½ | (7)(–7) – (3)(–4) | = ½ | – 49 + 12 | = ½ | –37 | = ½ (37)
= 18½ square units.

Exercise 7.G

Find the areas of the triangles with these vertices:

1. (0, 0), (5, 2), (3, 10)

2. (0, 0), (6, 1), (2, 3)

3. (0, 0), (2, 2), (3, 7)

4. (0, 0), (–5, 1), (3, –3)

5. (0, 0), (–1, 4), (–1, 11)

6. (4, 1), (7, 2), (3, 6)

7. (3, 8), (2, –1), (0, 3)

8. (–1, 3), (1, 2), (2, –7)

9. (–5, 6), (–1, 1), (5, 0)

10. (4, –5), (1, –8), (–3, –2)

11. $a(3, -2)$, $b(1, 6)$ and $c(7, 0)$ are the vertices of Δabc. Let m be the midpoint of $[bc]$.
Find the co-ordinates of m.
Verify that area Δabm = area Δacm.

12. $p(-3, 1)$, $q(1, 3)$, $r(3, 0)$ and $s(-1, -2)$ are the vertices of a parallelogram.
Illustrate $pqrs$ on a diagram.
Find the area of $pqrs$, by dividing it into two triangles.

13. $a(0, -4)$, $b(-1, -1)$, $c(5, 4)$, and $d(8, 0)$ are the vertices of a quadrilateral. Find its area, by dividing it into two triangles.

14. $(0, 0)$, $(6t, t)$, $(2t, 3t)$ are the vertices of a triangle of area 72 square units. Find two possible values of t.

15. The area of the triangle whose vertices are $(0, 0)$, $(7k, k)$, $(k, 3k)$ is 40 square units. Find two possible values of k.

16. The vertices of a triangle are $a(0, 0)$, $b(x, 6)$ and $c(1, 3)$.
If $x = -3$, verify that area $\Delta abc = 7\frac{1}{2}$.
Find a positive value of x for which area $\Delta abc = 7\frac{1}{2}$.

17. The vertices of a triangle are $a(-1, -1)$, $b(5, 1)$ and $c(1, k)$.
If $k = -2$, verify that area $\Delta abc = 5$.
Find a positive value of k for which area $\Delta abc = 13$.

18. $a(3, 4)$, $b(5, 0)$, $c(2, -3)$, $d(0, k)$ are four points. If area Δabc = area Δabd, find two possible values of k.

REVISION EXERCISE 7.H

1. $p(5, 1)$, $q(1, -2)$ and $r(-1, 5)$ are three points. Find
(i) the slope of pq,
(ii) the equation of pq,
(iii) the area of Δpqr,
(iv) the distance $|qr|$,
(v) the midpoint of $[pr]$.

2. $o(0, 0)$, $p(4, 3)$ and $q(-3, 4)$ are three points. Verify that
(i) the midpoint of $[pq] = (\frac{1}{2}, 3\frac{1}{2})$
(ii) the line op is perpendicular to the line oq,
(iii) Δopq is an isosceles triangle.

3. (a) Find the equation of the line which passes through the point (0, 0) and which is perpendicular to the line $4x - y = 9$.
(b) $a(-1, 3)$, $b(4, 1)$, $c(0, -1)$ and $g(1, 1)$ are four points.
(i) Find the co-ordinates of m, the midpoint of $[bc]$.
(ii) Verify that a, g, m are collinear.
(iii) Verify that $|ag| : |gm| = 2 : 1$.
(iv) Verify that area $\Delta abg : \Delta gbm = 2 : 1$.
(v) Find the slope and equation of the line ac.

4. L is the line with equation $4x - 3y - 11 = 0$.
   (i) Verify that $p(5, 3)$ is on L.
   (ii) Find the slope of L.
   (iii) Find the equation of the line M, which is perpendicular to L and which contains the point $q(-2, 2)$.
   (iv) Find the co-ordinates of r, such that $L \cap M = \{r\}$.
   (v) Verify that $|pr| = |qr|$.

5. (a) If $x - 6y - 3 = 0$ and $12x + ky = 1$ are perpendicular, find the value of k.
   (b) $4x - 7y = 11$, $x + 8y = 32$ and $5x + y = 4$ are the equations of three lines. Show that the triangle which they form is an isosceles triangle and find its area.

6. (a) Find the equation of the line K which is parallel to $2x - 5y - 10 = 0$ and which passes through the point $(11, -2)$.
   Investigate if $(56, 16) \in K$.
   (b) The line L contains the point $p(0, 3)$ and $q(4, -1)$.
   (i) Find the slope of L.
   (ii) Find the equation of L.
   (iii) L intersects the x-axis at the point r.
   Find the co-ordinates of r.
   (iv) Calculate the ratio
   Area of Δorp : Area Δorq.

7. (a) Find the distance between the two points $(-11, 9)$ and $(9, -12)$.
   (b) L is the line $x - 2y + 1 = 0$.
   M is the line $3x + y - 11 = 0$.
   (i) Find the co-ordinates of p, the point of intersection of L and M.
   (ii) L and M cut the x-axis at q and r respectively. Find the area of triangle pqr.
   (iii) Investigate if $L \perp M$.
   (c) The distance from $(5, 6)$ to $(k, 2)$ is $2\sqrt{5}$. Find two possible values of k.

8. K is the line which contains the points $a(0, 4)$ and $b(5, 0)$.
   (i) Find the equation of K.
   (ii) Find the equation of the line N, which is perpendicular to K and which contains the origin.
   (iii) Find the point of intersection p of K and N, giving the co-ordinates in the form $^a/_b$ (where $a, b \in Z$).
   (iv) Investigate if a is the image of b under S_p, the axial symmetry in the point p.
   (v) Calculate the ratio
   $$\frac{\text{Area } \Delta aop}{\text{Area } \Delta bop}$$

9. (a) Find the image of $3x - y - 6 = 0$ under the translation
   $$t : (0, 0) \rightarrow (2, -4)$$
   (b) $a(2, 5)$, $b(-2, -1)$ and $c(5, 3)$ are the vertices of a triangle abc.
   (i) Verify that $ab \perp ac$.
   (ii) Verify that $|bc|^2 = |ab|^2 + |ac|^2$.
   (iii) If a circle were drawn with $[bc]$ as diameter, prove mathematically that $a(2, 5)$ would be on the circle.

10. L is the line which passes through the points $p(3, -1)$ and $q(1, 0)$.
   M is the line $x + 2y - 11 = 0$.
   (i) Calculate the slope of L.
   (ii) Verify that $L \parallel M$.
   (iii) Find the equation of the line K which is perpendicular to L and which contains p.
   (iv) Calculate the co-ordinates of the point of intersection of K and M.
   (v) H is the line through q parallel to K. Calculate the area of the rectangle formed by the lines H, K, L and M.

1. The distance between two points
   (x_1, y_1) and (x_2, y_2) is $\sqrt{(x_2-x_1)^2+(y_2-y_1)^2}$

2. The midpoint of the line segment from (x_1, y_1) to (x_2, y_2) is
   $$\left(\frac{x_1+x_2}{2}, \frac{y_1+y_2}{2}\right)$$

3. The slope of the line through (x_1, y_1) and (x_2, y_2) is $\dfrac{y_2-y_1}{x_2-x_1}$

4. If a line is written in the form $y = \boldsymbol{m}x + c$, then the slope is $\boldsymbol{m}$.

5. The equation of the line with slope m which contains the point (x_1, y_1) is $y - y_1 = m(x - x_1)$.

6. If L has slope m_1 and K has slope m_2 then
   $m_1 = m_2 \Leftrightarrow L \parallel K$ $\qquad$ $m_1 . m_2 = -1 \Leftrightarrow L \perp K$

7. To get a perpendicular slope, turn the fraction upside down and change its sign.

8. The point of intersection of two lines is found by solving their simultaneous equations.

9. Area of triangle with vertices $(0, 0)$, (x_1, y_1) and (x_2, y_2) is given by
   $$\text{Area} = {}^1\!/_2\,|\,x_1 y_2 - x_2 y_1\,|$$

Chapter 8

The Circle

THE EQUATION OF A CIRCLE

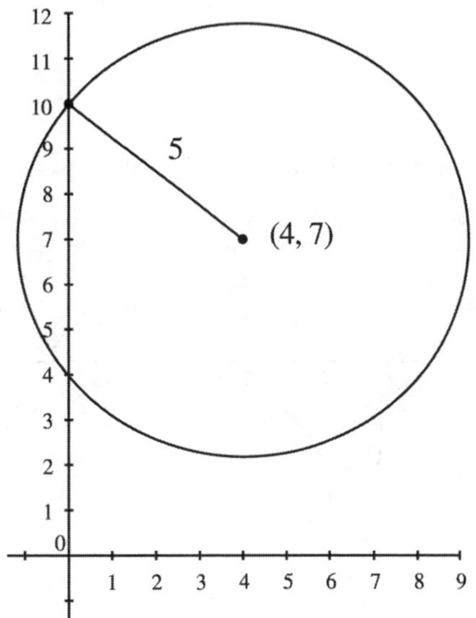

Here is a circle, whose centre is at (4, 7) and whose radius is 5 units in length. If (x, y) is any point on the circle, then the distance between (x, y) and (4, 7) is equal to 5.

$$\therefore \sqrt{(x-4)^2 + (y-7)^2} = 5$$

$$\therefore (x-4)^2 + (y-7)^2 = 25$$

$(x-4)^2 + (y-7)^2 = 25$ is called the ***equation of the circle*** whose centre is at (4, 7) and whose radius-length is 5.

Similarly, the equation of any circle, with centre (h, k) and whose radius-length is r is

$$(x-h)^2 + (y-k)^2 = r^2$$

Example 1: Find the equation of the circles with the following centres and radius-lengths:

	Centre	Radius-length
(i)	(3, –6)	10
(ii)	(–8, 0)	2
(iii)	(0, 0)	7
(iv)	(0, –4)	$\sqrt{5}$
(v)	(0, 0)	$2\sqrt{7}$

Solution:

(i) $(x-3)^2 + (y--6)^2 = 10^2 \Rightarrow (x-3)^2 + (y+6)^2 = 100$

(ii) $(x--8)^2 + (y-0)^2 = 2^2 \Rightarrow (x+8)^2 + y^2 = 4$

(iii) $(x-0)^2 + (y-0)^2 = 7^2 \Rightarrow x^2 + y^2 = 49$

(iv) $(x-0)^2 + (y--4)^2 = (\sqrt{5})^2 \Rightarrow x^2 + (y+4)^2 = 5$

(v) $(x-0)^2 + (y-0)^2 = (2\sqrt{7})^2 \Rightarrow x^2 + y^2 = 28$

Example 2: Find the centres and radius-lengths of the circles with the following equations and hence draw a sketch of each circle:

(i) $(x-9)^2 + (y+8)^2 = 36$

(ii) $x^2 + y^2 = 16$

(iii) $x^2 + (y+3)^2 = 11$

(iv) $4x^2 + 4y^2 = 25$

Solution:

(i) Centre = (9, –8)

Radius = $\sqrt{36} = 6$

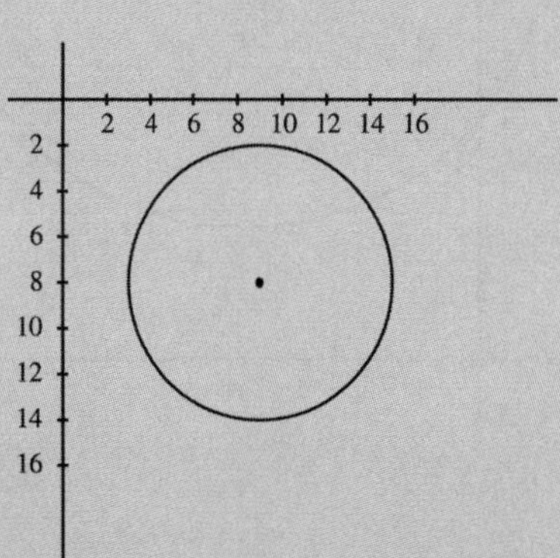

(iii) Centre = (0, –3)

Radius = $\sqrt{11} \approx 3.3$

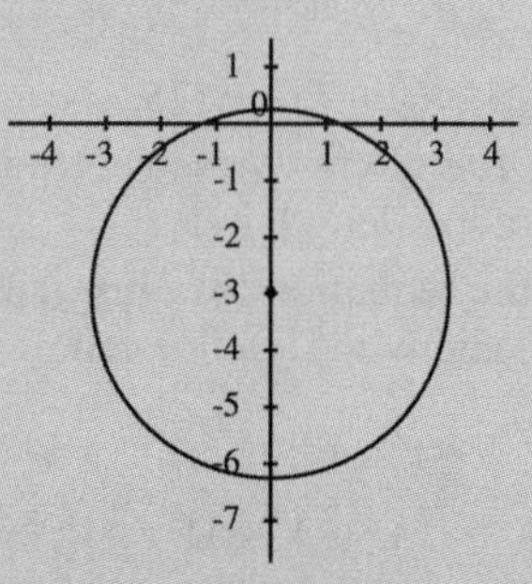

(ii) Centre = (0, 0)

Radius = $\sqrt{16} = 4$

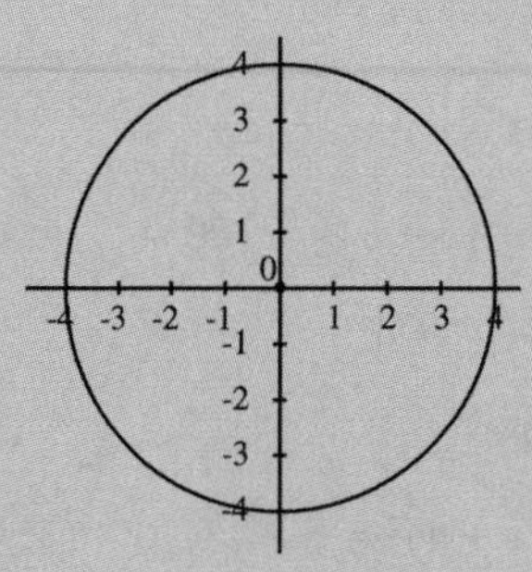

(iv) $4x^2 + 4y^2 = 25$

$\therefore\ x^2 + y^2 = \dfrac{25}{4}$

$\therefore$ Centre = (0, 0) and

Radius = $\sqrt{\dfrac{25}{4}} = \dfrac{5}{2}$

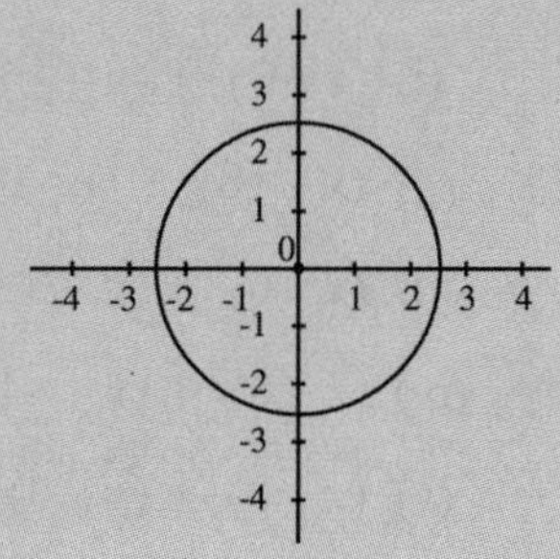

Exercise 8.A

Write down the equation of the circles with the following centres and radius-lengths:

1. Centre = (0, 0); Radius = 3
2. Centre = (0, 0); Radius = 4
3. Centre = (0, 0); Radius = 11
4. Centre = (0, 0); Radius = $\sqrt{10}$
5. Centre = (0, 0); Radius = $\sqrt{2}$
6. Centre = (0, 0); Radius = $\sqrt{19}$
7. Centre = (5, 1); Radius = 4
8. Centre = (3, 7); Radius = 3
9. Centre = (4, 8); Radius = 2
10. Centre = (5, –8); Radius = 10
11. Centre = (–1, 0); Radius = 5
12. Centre = (–6, –2); Radius = $\sqrt{3}$
13. Centre = (7, 1); Radius = $\sqrt{13}$
14. Centre = (0, –5); Radius = $\sqrt{7}$
15. Centre = (–4, 2); Radius = $2\sqrt{3}$
16. Centre = (0, 1); Radius = $3\sqrt{2}$
17. Centre = (–1, –2); Radius = $3\sqrt{3}$
18. Centre = (0, 4); Radius = $3\sqrt{10}$
19. Centre = (0, 0); Radius = $10\sqrt{3}$
20. Centre = (–2, –2); Radius = $2\sqrt{2}$

Write down the centres and radius-lengths of the following circles:

21. $(x-6)^2+(y-4)^2 = 9$
22. $(x-1)^2+(y+2)^2 = 16$
23. $(x-7)^2+(y+10)^2 = 64$
24. $(x+1)^2+(y-1)^2 = 36$
25. $x^2+y^2 = 100$
26. $x^2+y^2 = 144$
27. $x^2+y^2 = 25$
28. $(x+7)^2+y^2 = 121$
29. $x^2+(y-3)^2 = 400$
30. $4x^2+4y^2 = 49$
31. $4x^2+4y^2 = 1$
32. $4x^2+4y^2 = 81$
33. $x^2+(y+5)^2 = 12.25$
34. $25x^2+25y^2 = 121$

Draw the following circles by finding their centres and radii:

35. $(x-2)^2+(y-2)^2 = 4$
36. $x^2+y^2 = 9$
37. $(x-3)^2+(y+2)^2 = 16$
38. $x^2+(y+4)^2 = 25$
39. $x^2+y^2 = 6.25$
40. $(x+2)^2+(y-3)^2 = 4$
41. $x^2+y^2 = 1$
42. $(x+8)^2+(y-7)^2 = 49$
43. $x^2+(y-1)^2 = 12$
44. $9x^2+9y^2 = 100$

OUTSIDE, INSIDE OR ON?

Let $(x-h)^2+(y-k)^2 = r^2$ be the equation of a circle. If you want to check if a certain point (p, q) is ***outside, inside or on*** this circle, simply do the 'Goldilocks Test'. Here is how it works:

Goldilocks Test

Step 1: Substitute $x = p$ and $y = q$ into the equation.

Step 2:
(i) If $(x-h)^2+(y-k)^2 > r^2$, then the point is too far from the centre, and lies ***outside*** the circle.

(ii) If $(x-h)^2+(y-k)^2 < r^2$, then the point is too near to the centre, and lies ***inside*** the circle.

(iii) If $(x-h)^2+(y-k)^2 = r^2$, then the point is just the right distance from the centre, and lies ***on*** the circle.

Example 1: Let $x^2+y^2 = 65$ be the equation of a circle C.

(i) Investigate if $(7, -4)$ is outside, inside or on C.
(ii) Investigate if $(0, 8)$ is outside, inside or on C.
(iii) Investigate if $(-6, 6)$ is outside, inside or on C.
(iv) If $(k, 1)$ is on C, find two possible values of k.
(v) If $(3, n)$ is inside C, find the greatest possible value of n, where $n \in N$.

Solution:

(i) Let $x = 7$ and $y = -4$ in the equation $x^2+y^2 = 65$. We get the result: $7^2+(-4)^2 = 49+16 = 65$. Just right! Therefore $(7, -4)$ is ***on*** the circle.

(ii) Let $x = 0$ and $y = 8$ in the equation $x^2+y^2 = 65$. We get the result: $0^2+8^2 = 0+64 < 65$. Too small! Therefore $(0, 8)$ is ***inside*** the circle.

(iii) Let $x = -6$ and $y = 6$ in the equation $x^2+y^2 = 65$. We get the result: $(-6)^2+6^2 = 36+36 = 72 > 65$. Too big! Therefore $(-6, 6)$ is ***outside*** C.

(iv) Let $x = k$ and $y = 1$ in the equation $x^2+y^2 = 65$. We get the result: $k^2+1^2 = 65 \Rightarrow k^2+1 = 65 \Rightarrow k^2 = 64 \Rightarrow k = \pm 8$

(v) Let $x = 3$ and $y = n$ in the inequality $x^2+y^2 < 65$, since $(3, n)$ is ***inside*** C. We get the result:

$3^2+n^2 < 65 \Rightarrow 9+n^2 < 65 \Rightarrow n^2 < 56 \Rightarrow n < \sqrt{56} \Rightarrow n < 7.48$

The greatest natural number which is less than 7.48 is $n = 7$.

Exercise 8.B

1. Verify that (4, 3) lies on the circle $x^2 + y^2 = 25$.

2. Verify that (4, –2) lies on the circle $x^2 + y^2 = 20$.

3. Verify that (–1, 2) lies on the circle $x^2 + y^2 = 5$.

4. Is (11, 3) inside, outside or on the circle $x^2 + y^2 = 130$?

5. Is (2, 3) inside, outside or on the circle $x^2 + y^2 = 12$?

6. Is (7, 3) inside, outside or on the circle $x^2 + y^2 = 60$?

7. Is (6, 4) inside, outside or on the circle $x^2 + y^2 = 50$?

8. Is (7, –1) inside, outside or on the circle $x^2 + y^2 = 50$?

9. Is (–1, –1) inside, outside or on the circle $x^2 + y^2 = 3$?

10. Is (7, –5) inside, outside or on the circle $(x - 4)^2 + (y + 1)^2 = 25$?

11. C is the circle with equation $x^2 + y^2 = 125$.
(i) Verify that $(10, -5) \in C$.
(ii) Investigate if (9, –3) is inside, outside or on C.
(iii) If $(k, 2) \in C$, find two possible values of k.

12. C is the circle with equation $x^2 + y^2 = 50$
(i) Verify that $(5, -5) \in C$.
(ii) Investigate if (4, 6) is inside, outside or on C.
(iii) If $(1, k) \in C$, find two possible values of k.

13. C is the circle with centre (0, 0) and radius-length 10.
(i) Write down the equation of C.
(ii) If $(-6, t) \in C$, find two possible values of t.
(iii) If (p, p) is inside the circle C, where $p \in N$, find the greatest possible value of p.

14. C is the circle with centre (4, –2) and radius 13.
(i) Write down the equation of C.
(ii) If $(-8, t) \in C$, find two possible values of t.
(iii) If $(14, p)$ is outside the circle C, where $p \in N$, find the least possible value of p.

15. C is the circle with centre (0, 0) and radius $\frac{5}{2}$.
(i) Write down the equation of C.
(ii) If $(-\frac{3}{2}, t) \in C$, find two possible values of t.

16. C is the circle with centre (0, 3) and radius 5. K is the circle with equation $(x - 9)^2 + (y - 15)^2 = 100$.
(i) Write down the equation of the circle C.
(ii) Verify that $p(3, 7)$ is on both C and K.
(iii) Show that p lies on the straight line which joins the centres of these two circles.

17. Let $x^2 + y^2 = 841$ be the equation of a circle K.

(i) Write down the centre and the radius-length of K.

(ii) At what points does K intersect the x-axis?

(iii) If $(x, 21)$ is on K, find two possible values of x.

18. C is the circle whose equation is

$x^2 + y^2 = 3.25$

If $(1, q) \in C$, find the values of q.

19. C is the circle whose equation is

$9x^2 + 9y^2 = 169$

(i) If $(p, 4) \in C$, find the values of p.

(ii) Find the coordinates of the two points where C intersects the y-axis.

(iii) If $(3, n)$ is outside the circle, find the least value of n, where $n \in N$.

20. $p(5, -2)$ lies on the circle C whose equation is $(x-2)^2 + (y-2)^2 = r^2$.

(i) Find the value of $r > 0$.

(ii) Verify that $q(-1, 6) \in C$.

(iii) Show that the centre of C is the midpoint of $[pq]$.

FINDING THE EQUATION OF A CIRCLE

We have seen that if you want to find the equation of a circle, there are two essential pieces of information which you must find out first:

1. **The centre**
2. **The radius**

In the following examples, these two pieces of information will not be given explicitly. However, enough information will be given to **find** the centre and radius, with a bit of detective work. The greatest aid in the hunt for these two elusive unknowns is a good diagram!

Example 1: $p(-2, 6)$ and $q(4, 0)$ are two points. $[pq]$ is the diameter of a circle. Find its equation.

Solution: Here is a good diagram of the circle which we are looking for.

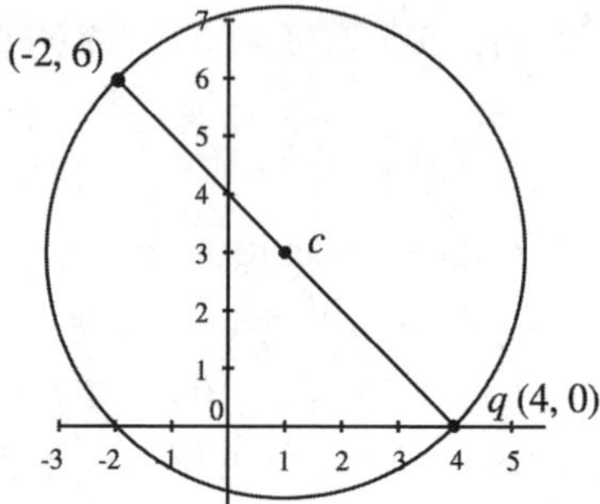

The centre of the circle is the midpoint of $[pq]$.

$$\therefore \text{ Centre} = \left(\frac{-2+4}{2}, \frac{6+0}{2}\right) = (1, 3)$$

The radius-length is the distance from the centre to, say, p.

$$\text{Radius} = \sqrt{(1 - -2)^2 + (3-6)^2}$$
$$= \sqrt{9+9} = \sqrt{18}$$

Therefore, the equation of the circle is $(x-1)^2 + (y-3)^2 = 18$

Example 2: Find the equation of the circle whose centre is (4, 2) and which ***touches*** the x-axis.

Solution: Here is a sketch of the circle. Note how it just ***touches*** the x-axis, as the question stated.

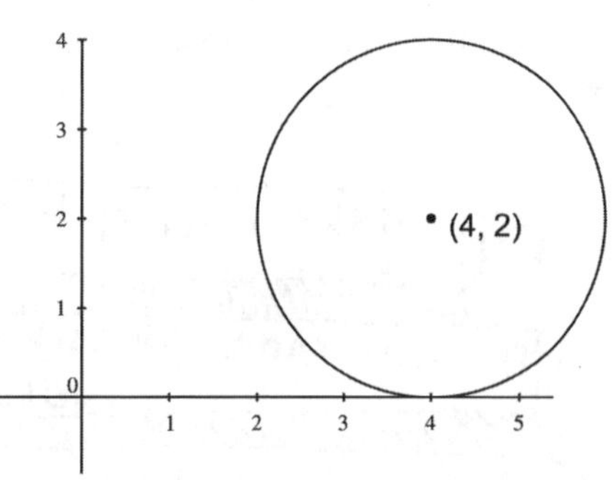

The centre = (4, 2).
The radius = 2 units
[from (4, 0) to (4, 2)]
Therefore, the equation is
$(x-4)^2+(y-2)^2 = 4$

Exercise 8.C

1. Find the equation of the circle which has centre (0, 0) and which contains the point (4, 3).
2. Find the equation of the circle with centre (0, 0) which passes through the point (5, –2).
3. Find the equation of the circle with centre (2, 1) which passes through the point (4, 4).
4. $p(-6, 3)$ and $q(2, -3)$ are two points. Find the equation of the circle which has $[pq]$ as a diameter.
5. $a(4, 1)$ and $b(-10, 5)$ are two points. Find the equation of the circle which has $[ab]$ as a diameter.
6. Find the equation of the circle, centre (3, 3) which passes through the origin (0, 0).
7. Find the equation of the circle with diameter $[ab]$ where $a = (4, 3)$ and $b = (-2, -1)$
8. Find the equation of the circle with centre (5, 2) which passes through the point (5, 0).
9. Find the equation of the circle with centre (–3, 6) which contains the point (0, 2).
10. $o(0, 0)$, $a(4, 0)$, $b(4, 4)$ and $c(0, 4)$ are the vertices of a square.
    (i) Find the equation of the circle C which passes through each vertex of the square.
    (ii) Find the equation of the circle K which ***touches*** each side of the square.
    (iii) Use the formula $A = \pi r^2$ to find the ratio
    Area of C : Area of K
11. K is the circle with equation $(x-7)^2+(y+4)^2 = 52$
    (i) Write down the coordinates of c, the centre of K.
    (ii) Verify that $p(1, 0)$ is on K.
    (iii) Find the equation of the circle with $[cp]$ as diameter.
12. K_1 is the circle with equation $(x-5)^2+(y+12)^2 = 64$
    K_2 is the circle $x^2+y^2 = r^2$
    (i) Write down the centres of K_1 and K_2.
    (ii) Find the distance between their two centres.
    (iii) Given that the two circles ***touch*** each other externally, draw a sketch of the two circles.
    (iv) Find the value of r, the radius of K_2.

TRANSFORMING CIRCLES

When we transform a circle (under a ***translation***, or a ***central symmetry*** or an ***axial symmetry***) we will want to find the centre and radius-length of the new circle. Here are the three steps to follow:

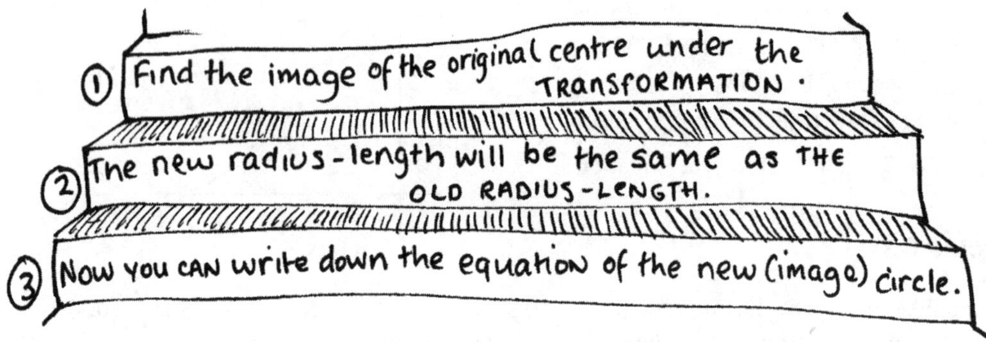

① Find the image of the original centre under the TRANSFORMATION.
② The new radius-length will be the same as THE OLD RADIUS-LENGTH.
③ Now you can write down the equation of the new (image) circle.

Example 1: Find the image of the circle $(x-3)^2+(y+5)^2 = 16$ under the translation which maps (0, 0) onto (5, –1).

Solution: $(x-3)^2+(y+5)^2 = 16$ has centre (3, –5) and radius-length 4.

1. Under the translation, $(0, 0) \rightarrow (5, -1)$. Therefore, $(3, -5) \rightarrow (8, -6)$.
2. The new radius-length will be the same as the original : 4.
3. Therefore, the image circle has centre (8, –6) and radius 4.
   Its equation is $(x-8)^2+(y+6)^2 = 16$.

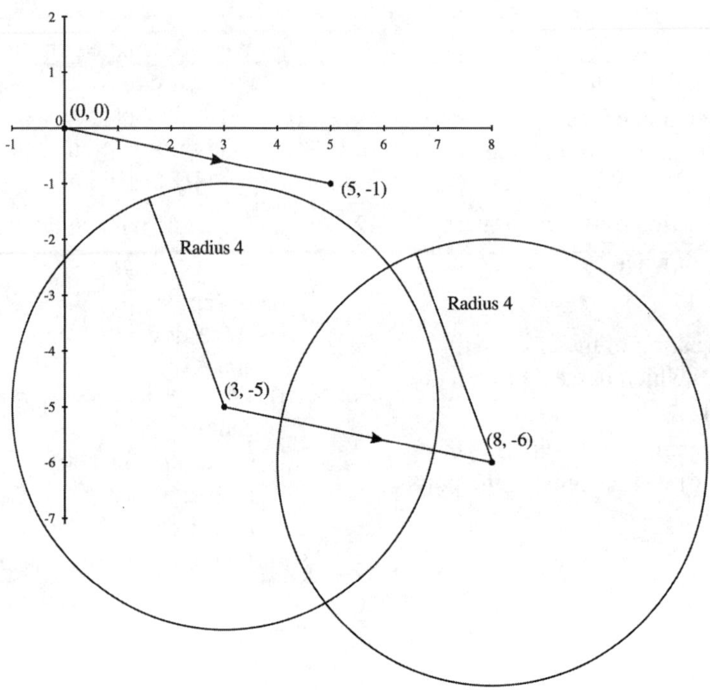

Exercise 8.D

1. C is the circle $x^2 + y^2 = 9$
   (i) Write down the centre and radius-length of C.
   (ii) Find the equation of the image of C under the translation which maps (0, 0) onto (6, 4).

2. $(x-3)^2 + y^2 = 1$ is the equation of a circle K.
   (i) Write down the centre and radius of K.
   (ii) Find the equation of the image of K under axial symmetry in the y-axis.

3. $(x-3)^2 + (y-5)^2 = 4$ is the equation of a circle K_1.
   (i) Write down the centre and radius of K_1.
   (ii) Draw a sketch of K_1.
   (iii) Find the equation of the image of K_1 under central symmetry in the origin.

4. (a) K_1 is the circle with centre (0, 0) which passes through the point (3, 1). Write down the equation of K_1.
   (b) K_2 is the image of K_1 under the translation
   t: $(0, 0) \rightarrow (6, -1)$
   Find the equation of K_2.

5. C is the circle $(x-1)^2 + (y+1)^2 = 81$
   (i) Write down the centre and radius-length of C.
   (ii) Find the equation of the image of C under the translation which maps (1, –2) onto (3, 4).

6. Find the image of
   $(x+6)^2 + (y-4)^2 = 20$
   under axial symmetry in the x-axis.

7. C is the circle $x^2 + y^2 = 10$
   (i) Write down the centre and radius-length of C.
   (ii) Find the equation of the image of C under central symmetry in the point (2, –4).

8. K is the circle with centre (4, –1) and radius $3\sqrt{2}$ in length.
   (i) Write down the equation of K.
   (ii) Find the equation of the image of K under the translation
   t: $(11, -7) \rightarrow (5, -1)$
   (iii) Verify that the point (1, 2) is on both K and its image.

9. (a) K_1 is the circle with $[ao]$ as diameter, where $a = (3, 4)$ and o is the origin. Find the equation of K_1.
   (b) K_2 is the image of K_1 under central symmetry in the origin. Find the equation of K_2.
   (c) Find the equation of a circle, whose centre = (0, 0) and which ***touches*** both K_1 and K_2.

10. K_1 is the circle $(x-6)^2 + y^2 = 4$.
   K_2 is the image of K_1 under axial symmetry in the y-axis.
   (i) Find the equation of K_2.
   (ii) $x^2 + y^2 = r^2$ is the equation of a circle which touches both K_1 and K_2. Find two values of r.

INTERSECTION OF A LINE AND A CIRCLE

A line and a circle usually intersect at two points.

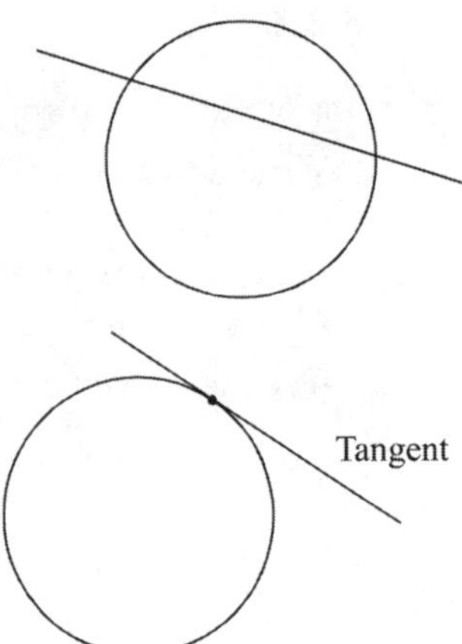

If a line touches a circle at only ***one*** point, the line is called a ***tangent*** to the circle. The word ***tangent*** is a Latin word, which means 'touching'.

The way to find the points (or point) of intersection of a line and a circle is '**substitution**', which we studied in Chapter 4. If you find that there is only one point of intersection, you may say that the line is a tangent to the circle.

Example 1: Find the points of intersection of the line $x + 2y = 7$ and the circle $x^2 + y^2 = 10$.

Solution: **Step 1:**

Start with the line. Write it in the form $x = ...$ or $y = ...$, whichever is the easier. In this case $x + 2y = 7 \Rightarrow x = 7 - 2y \Rightarrow x = (7 - 2y)$.

Step 2:

Now take the equation of the circle. Change x to $(7 - 2y)$.

$$\begin{aligned} x^2 + y^2 &= 10 \\ \Rightarrow (7 - 2y)^2 + y^2 &= 10 \\ \Rightarrow 49 - 28y + 4y^2 + y^2 &= 10 \\ \Rightarrow 5y^2 - 28y + 39 &= 0 \\ \Rightarrow (y - 3)(5y - 13) &= 0 \\ \Rightarrow y &= 3 \text{ or } y = \frac{13}{5} = 2.6 \end{aligned}$$

Step 3:

Now find the corresponding values of x, using the 'substitution equation': $x = 7 - 2y$.

If $y = 3$, then $x = 7 - 2(3) = 1$ $\therefore$ $(1, 3)$ is one of the points of intersection.

If $y = 2.6$, then $x = 7 - 2(2.6) = 1.8$ $\therefore$ $(1.8, 2.6)$ is the other point.

Example 2: Prove that $2x - y = 5$ is a tangent to the circle $x^2 + y^2 = 5$.

Solution: **Step 1:**

The line: $2x - y = 5 \Rightarrow -y = -2x + 5 \Rightarrow y = 2x - 5 \Rightarrow y = (2x - 5)$

Step 2:

Now, let's take the equation of the circle.

$$x^2 + y^2 = 5$$
$$\therefore \quad x^2 + (2x - 5)^2 = 5$$
$$\therefore \quad x^2 + 4x^2 - 20x + 25 = 5$$
$$\therefore \quad 5x^2 - 20x + 20 = 0$$
$$\therefore \quad x^2 - 4x + 4 = 0 \quad \text{[Dividing both sides by 5]}$$
$$\therefore \quad (x-2)(x-2) = 0$$
$$\therefore \quad x = 2$$

Step 3:

Find the corresponding value of y, using $y = (2x - 5)$.
If $x = 2$, $y = 2(2) - 5 = -1$.

Therefore, there is only one point of intersection $(2, -1)$ and hence we can conclude that the line is a tangent to the circle.

Exercise 8.E

1. Find the points of intersection of the line $x + y = 4$ and the circle $x^2 + y^2 = 10$.
2. Find the points of intersection of the line $x - y = 1$ and the circle $x^2 + y^2 = 13$.
3. Find the points of intersection of the line $x - y + 2 = 0$ and the circle $x^2 + y^2 = 10$.
4. Find the points of intersection of the line $2x + y - 3 = 0$ and the circle $x^2 + y^2 = 26$.
5. Find the points of intersection of the line $x - 2y + 3 = 0$ and the circle $x^2 + y^2 = 9$.
6. Find the points of intersection of the line $x + 7y - 4 = 0$ and the circle $x^2 + y^2 = 10$.
7. Prove that $x - 2y + 10 = 0$ is a tangent to the circle $x^2 + y^2 = 20$ and find the point of contact.
8. Prove that $x - y - 2 = 0$ is a tangent to the circle $x^2 + y^2 = 2$ and find the point of contact.
9. K is a circle with centre $(0, 0)$ and which contains the point $(2, \sqrt{21})$.
   (i) Find the equation of K.
   (ii) If the line $x - 2y + 5 = 0$ cuts K at p and q. Calculate $|pq|$.
10. C is a circle, whose centre is $(0, 0)$ and whose radius is $\sqrt{5}$.
    (i) Write down the equation of C.
    (ii) Prove that the line L: $y = 2x + 5$ is a tangent to C and find the coordinates of $L \cap C$.
11. Prove that $x + y - 3 = 0$ is a tangent to the circle $2x^2 + 2y^2 = 9$ and find the point of contact.
12. K is the circle $x^2 + y^2 = 17$
    (i) Write down the centre and radius of K.
    (ii) Prove that T: $x + 4y = 17$ is a tangent to K.
    (iii) Draw a sketch of K and T.
    (iv) Find the equation of a second tangent to K which is parallel to T.

FINDING TANGENTS

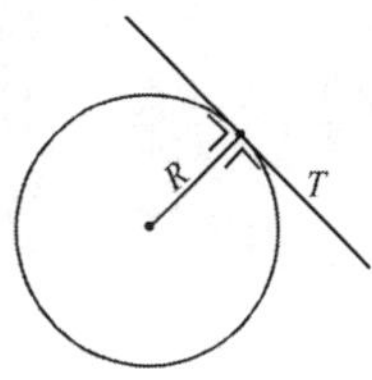

A tangent is perpendicular to the radius from the centre to the point of contact. In the diagram, $T \perp R$. We use this fact to find the equation of a tangent to a circle.

Example 1: K is the circle with equation $x^2 + y^2 = 29$.
Verify that the point $p(5, -2)$ is on K.
Find the equation of the tangent to K at p.

Solution: (i) Let $x = 5$ and $y = -2$ in the equation $x^2 + y^2 = 29$.

$\therefore \quad 5^2 + (-2)^2 = 25 + 4 = 29$

$\therefore \quad (5, -2)$ is on K. Q.E.D.

(ii) The slope of R is $\frac{-2-0}{5-0} = -\frac{2}{5}$.

Therefore the slope of $T = +\frac{5}{2}$.

Therefore the equation of T is

$y - -2 = \frac{5}{2}(x - 5)$

$\therefore y + 2 = \frac{5}{2}(x - 5)$

$\therefore 2(y + 2) = 5(x - 5)$

$\therefore 2y + 4 = 5x - 25$

$\therefore 5x - 2y - 29 = 0$

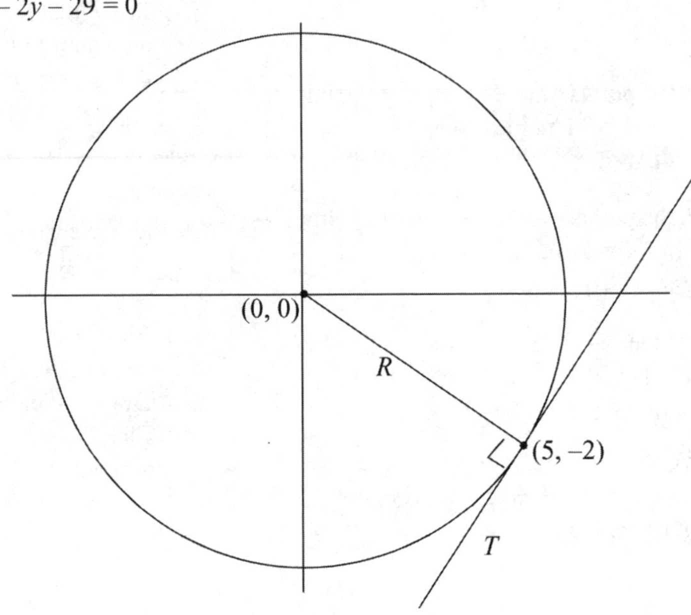

Exercise 8.F

1. K is the circle with equation
   $$x^2 + y^2 = 10$$
   (i) Verify that the point $p(3, 1)$ is on K.
   (ii) Find the equation of the tangent to K at p.

2. K is the circle with equation
   $$x^2 + y^2 = 13$$
   (i) Verify that the point $p(3, -2)$ is on K.
   (ii) Find the equation of the tangent to K at p.

3. K is the circle with equation
   $$x^2 + y^2 = 20$$
   (i) Verify that the point $p(-4, 2)$ is on K.
   (ii) Find the equation of the tangent to K at p.

4. Find the equation of the tangent to the circle $x^2 + y^2 = 45$ at the point $(-6, -3)$ in the form $ax + by + c = 0$.

5. A circle C has equation $x^2 + y^2 = 25$
   (i) Verify that $p(4, 3) \varepsilon C$.
   (ii) If $[pq]$ is a diameter of C, find the coordinates of q.
   (iii) Find the equation of the tangent T to C at the point p.
   (iv) Find the equation of another tangent to C which is parallel to T.

6. K is the circle with equation
   $$(x + 3)^2 + (y + 4)^2 = 25$$
   (i) Verify that the point $o(0, 0)$ is on K.
   (ii) Find the equation of the tangent to K at p.

7. K is the circle with equation
   $$x^2 + y^2 = 9$$
   (i) Draw a sketch of the circle K.
   (ii) Find the equations of two tangents to K which are parallel to the x-axis.

8. K is the circle with equation
   $$(x - 4)^2 + (y + 2)^2 = 36$$
   (i) Draw a sketch of the circle K.
   (ii) Find the equations of two tangents to K which are parallel to the y-axis.
   (iii) What is the distance between these two tangents?

9. K is the circle with centre $(0, 0)$ and radius $\sqrt{17}$.
   (i) Draw a sketch of the circle K.
   (ii) Write down the equation of K.
   (iii) Verify that $(-1, 4)$ is on K and find the equation of the tangent T to K at $(-1, 4)$.
   (iv) Find the equation of the line L which passes through the centre of K and which is parallel to T.
   (v) Find the coordinates of $L \cap K$.

10. Sketch the two circles:
    $$C_1: \ (x - 6)^2 + (y + 3)^2 = 20$$
    $$C_2: \ x^2 + y^2 = 5.$$
    Find the equation of the tangent T to C_1 at the point $p(2, -1)$.
    Verify that T is also a tangent to C_2.

REVISION EXERCISE 8.G

1. A circle C has equation
$x^2 + y^2 = 25$
(i) Write down the centre and radius of C.
(ii) Verify that $p(3, 4) \varepsilon C$.
(iii) If $[pq]$ is a diameter of C, find the coordinates of q.
(iv) Find the equation of the tangent T to C at the point p.
(v) Find the equation of the image of C under the translation which maps $(0, 0)$ onto $(7, -2)$.

2. (a) Write down the centre and radius of the circle whose equation is
$(x - 5)^2 + y^2 = 64.$
At what points does this circle cut the x-axis?
(b) Find the points of intersection of the line $x + y = 1$ and the circle $x^2 + y^2 = 25$.
(c) Write down the coordinates of the point on
$(x + 1)^2 + (y - 4)^2 = 49$
which is furthest from the x-axis.

3. (i) Write down the centre and radius-length of the circle S_1 whose equation is
$x^2 + y^2 = 20.$
(ii) $T : x - 2y + 10 = 0$ is a tangent to S_1. Find the coordinates of p, the point of contact.
(iii) S_2 is the image of S_1 under central symmetry in p. Find the equation of S_2.
(iv) Find the coordinates of the points where S_2 cuts the y-axis.

4. $(-5, 12)$ and $(5, -12)$ are the end-points of a diameter of a circle S.
(i) Find the coordinates of the centre.
(ii) Find the length of the radius.
(iii) Find the equation of S.
(iv) Find the equation of the tangent to S at $(-5, 12)$.
(v) $(x - 8)^2 + (y + 4)^2 = 169$ is the image of S under the translation $(0, 0) \rightarrow (a, b)$. Find the coordinates of a and b.

5. K_1 is the circle $x^2 + y^2 = 9$.
(i) Write down the centre and radius of K_1.
(ii) Calculate the coordinates of the points common to K_1 and the line $2x - y + 3 = 0$.
(iii) Write down the equation of K_2, the image of K_1 under the translation $(1, 0) \rightarrow (10, 0)$.
(iv) Draw a sketch of both K_1 and K_2 and hence write down the equations of K_3 and K_4, two of the circles which ***touch*** each of K_1 and K_2 and which have their centres on the x-axis.

6. A circle C has centre $o(0,0)$ and passes through the point $p(-5, 1)$.
(i) Find the length of the radius of C.
(ii) Write down the equation of C.
(iii) Find the equation of T, the tangent to C at the point p.
(iv) Find the equation of T_2, the tangent to C which is parallel to T.
(v) Find the equation of the circle which has $[op]$ as diameter.

7. Write down the equation of the circle

(i) K_1, of centre (0, 0) and radius length 10.

(ii) K_2, of centre (3, 4) and which contains (0, 0) as in the diagram below.

(iii) K_3, of centre (–3, –4) which contains (0, 0).

(iv) Find the equation of the tangent *T*, through (0, 0) common to K_2 and K_3.

(v) Find the coordinates of $T \cap K_1$.

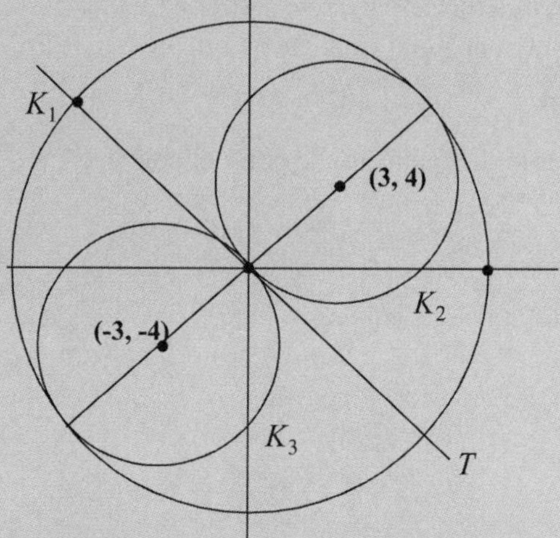

8. (a) The point $(4, 3\sqrt{2})$ is on a circle *K*, which has its centre at the origin (0, 0). Find the equation of *K*. The line $y = x - 2$ cuts *K* at the points *p* and *q*. Calculate $|pq|$.

(b) The image of the circle $x^2 + y^2 = 16$ under central symmetry in (r, s) is the circle $(x - 12)^2 + (y + 6)^2 = 16$. Find the values of *r* and *s*.

(c) Find the equation of a circle which has centre (7, 4) and which touches the *x*-axis at one point only.

9. (a) Find where the line $x - 3y = 10$ cuts the circle $x^2 + y^2 = 10$. Investigate if the line is a tangent.

(b) The vertices of a rectangle are $a(1, 2)$, $b(-3, -6)$, $c(9, -12)$ and $d(13, -4)$. Find the equation of the circle *K*, drawn through all four vertices of the rectangle. What is the equation of the image of this circle under axial symmetry in the *y*-axis? If $(n, 3)$ is on *K*, find two possible values for *n*.

10. The point $(1, -7)$ is on a circle *K*, which has its centre at the origin $o(0, 0)$.

(i) Find the equation of *K*.

(ii) If $(p, p) \in K$, find two possible values of *p*.

(iii) If the point $(3, n)$ is ***inside*** the circle, find the greatest possible value of $n \in N$.

(iv) *T* is the tangent to *K* at the point $(1, -7)$. *T* cuts the axes at points *a* and *b*. Find the coordinates of *a* and *b*.

(v) Which is greater in area: the circle *K* or the triangle *oab*? [The area of a circle = πr^2]

1. $x^2 + y^2 = r^2$ is the equation of a circle with centre $(0, 0)$ and radius-length r.

2. $(x - h)^2 + (y - k)^2 = r^2$ is the equation of a circle with centre (h, k) and radius-length r.

3. If a line touches a circle at one point only, it is called a ***tangent*** to the circle.

4. The points of intersection of a line and a circle are found by **substitution**. If there is only one point of intersection, the line is a tangent.

5. A tangent is perpendicular to the radius to the point of contact.

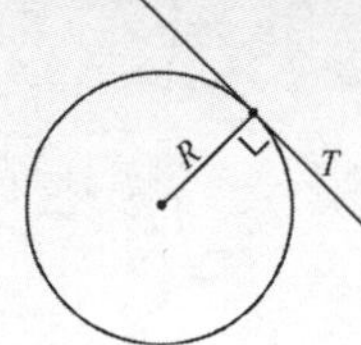

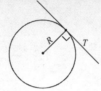

Chapter 9

Complex Numbers

At the time of the Renaissance, mathematicians felt that they had discovered all the numbers in the universe. Those were, they believed, all represented by points on the real number line. But they were wrong.

The man who showed up the short-comings of the real number line was an Italian mathematician called Rafaelo Bombelli. He asked the simple question: 'What is the square root of -1? That is to say, what is $\sqrt{-1}$?'

The answer cannot be $+1$ or -1, since when you square $+1$, you get $+1$ and when you square -1, you also get $+1$. So, what is the answer to Rafaelo Bombelli's question?

Bombelli solved the problem himself, by inventing a new number i. He said that $\sqrt{-1} = i$. This new number i is not a real number, and does not appear on the real number line. It is an ***imaginary number***. And that is why Bombelli chose the letter i to represent his new number; i for imaginary.

The next question we might ask is 'What is $\sqrt{-4}$?' The answer is this: $\sqrt{-4} = \sqrt{4}\sqrt{-1} = 2i$. Similarly, $\sqrt{-16} = \sqrt{16}\sqrt{-1} = 4i$. Again, $\sqrt{-81} = \sqrt{81}\sqrt{-1} = 9i$. $\sqrt{-3} = \sqrt{3}\sqrt{-1} = \sqrt{3}i$.

We could even add real numbers to imaginary numbers: $5 + 4i$, $8 - 3i$, $2 + i$, $11 - 2i$, $-3 + i$, etc. The set of all such numbers (numbers which can be written as $a + bi$) is called the set of ***complex numbers***, and is denoted by the letter ***C***.

Here is the definition:

$C = \{a + bi \mid a \varepsilon R \text{ and } b \varepsilon R, \text{ where } i = \sqrt{-1}\}$ = The set of Complex Numbers.

When Bombelli invented this revolutionary new set of complex numbers, I'm sure he did not foresee its usefulness. Today, engineers, applied mathematicians and physicists all use this set to study such things as the flow of water around a barrier, or the movement of air over the wing of an aeroplane, or the design of 'spoilers' on the backs of cars, or even the oscillations of quantum mechanical wave functions. An Irish mathematician, William Rowan Hamilton, extended Bombelli's invention, when he discovered the Quanternion group. This discovery was made as he crossed Broome Bridge in Dublin one Sunday morning.

Since these numbers do not appear on the number line – how can we represent them? A Swiss mathematician, Argand, invented a diagram to represent all complex numbers. It is called the ***Argand diagram*** in his honour. In the Argand diagram, there is a horizontal axis, called the ***real axis***. There is a vertical axis, called the ***imaginary axis***.

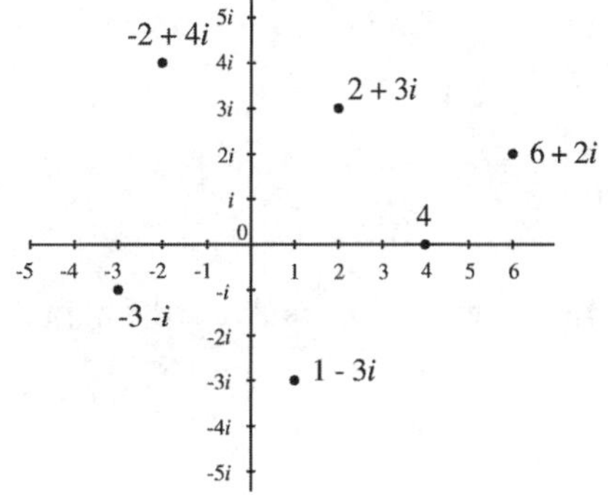

The Argand diagram on the right shows a few Complex numbers. Notice how the real number 4, which is the same as $4 + 0i$, is represented by a point on the real axis. This is because 4 is a real number.

This illustrates that the set of real numbers, R, is a subset of the set of complex numbers, C.

Exercise 9.A

Write these as ki:

1. $\sqrt{-9}$
2. $\sqrt{-16}$
3. $\sqrt{-100}$
4. $\sqrt{-144}$
5. $\sqrt{-25}$
6. $\sqrt{-81}$
7. $\sqrt{-121}$
8. $\sqrt{-49}$
9. $\sqrt{-64}$
10. $\sqrt{-400}$
11. $\sqrt{-169}$
12. $\sqrt{-441}$
13. $\sqrt{-1.44}$
14. $\sqrt{-900}$
15. $\sqrt{-0.81}$
16. $\sqrt{-0.01}$
17. $\sqrt{-\frac{1}{4}}$
18. $\sqrt{-\frac{9}{16}}$
19. $\sqrt{-\frac{25}{49}}$
20. $\sqrt{-\frac{100}{121}}$

Write these as $a \pm bi$:

21. $3 + \sqrt{-4}$
22. $5 + \sqrt{-49}$
23. $-4 + \sqrt{-9}$
24. $8 - \sqrt{-25}$
25. $10 - \sqrt{-36}$
26. $1 - \sqrt{-144}$
27. $-4 - \sqrt{-1}$
28. $7 - \sqrt{-81}$
29. $\frac{1}{2} + \sqrt{-\frac{1}{16}}$
30. $\frac{3}{2} + \sqrt{-\frac{1}{25}}$
31. Show these in an Argand diagram:
    (i) $3 + 4i$ (ii) $5 - 2i$
    (iii) $-3 + 6i$ (iv) $-4 - i$
32. Show these in an Argand diagram:
    (i) $4i$ (ii) $7 - i$
    (iii) $-5 + 0i$ (iv) $-2 - 4i$
33. Show these in an Argand diagram:
    (i) $3 + \frac{1}{2}i$ (ii) $5\frac{1}{2} - 2i$
    (iii) $-4 + 1\frac{1}{2}i$ (iv) $-2\frac{1}{2} - 2\frac{1}{2}i$
34. Show $4 + \sqrt{-9}$ on an Argand diagram.
35. Show $3 - \sqrt{-4}$ on an Argand diagram.
36. Show $2 + \sqrt{-\frac{36}{25}}$ on an Argand diagram.
37. Show $5 - \sqrt{-\frac{49}{16}}$ on an Argand diagram.
38. Show $3 + \sqrt{-3}$ on an Argand diagram.
39. Show $-1 + \sqrt{-6}$ on an Argand diagram.
40. Show $-5 + \sqrt{-18}$ on an Argand diagram.

QUADRATIC EQUATIONS WITH COMPLEX ROOTS

Example 1: Solve the equations

(i) $x^2 - 6x + 13 = 0$ (ii) $2(x^2 + 2x) = 5(2x - 1)$

Solution: (i) $x^2 - 6x + 13 = 0$

$\therefore\ a = 1, b = -6, c = 13$

$$\therefore\ x = \frac{-b \pm \sqrt{b^2 - 4ac}}{2a} = \frac{6 \pm \sqrt{36 - (4)(1)(13)}}{2} = \frac{6 \pm \sqrt{-16}}{2}$$

$$= \frac{6 \pm 4i}{2} = 3 \pm 2i = 3 + 2i \text{ and } 3 - 2i$$

(ii) $2(x^2 + 2x) = 5(2x - 1)$

$\therefore\ 2x^2 + 4x = 10x - 5$

$\therefore\ 2x^2 - 6x + 5 = 0$

$\therefore\ a = 2, b = -6, c = 5$

$$\therefore\ x = \frac{-b \pm \sqrt{b^2 - 4ac}}{2a} = \frac{6 \pm \sqrt{36 - (4)(2)(5)}}{4} = \frac{6 \pm \sqrt{-4}}{4}$$

$$\frac{6 \pm 2i}{4} = \frac{3}{2} \pm \frac{1}{2}i = \frac{3}{2} + \frac{1}{2}i \text{ or } \frac{3}{2} - \frac{1}{2}i$$

Exercise 9. B

Solve the following quadratic equations:

1. $x^2 + 4x + 13 = 0$

2. $x^2 - 2x + 5 = 0$

3. $x^2 - 2x + 10 = 0$

4. $x^2 - 8x + 17 = 0$

5. $x^2 + 6x + 25 = 0$

6. $x^2 + 14x + 50 = 0$

7. $x^2 = 12x - 40$

8. $x^2 = -2(5x + 17)$

9. $x^2 = 2(x - 1)$

10. $x^2 + 4 = 0$

Solve these equations and show the solutions on an Argand diagram:

11. $x^2 - 4x + 5 = 0$

12. $x^2 - 8x + 25 = 0$

13. $x^2 + 2x + 17 = 0$

14. $x^2 + 4x + 40 = 0$

15. $x^2 + 16 = 0$

16. $(x - 3)(x + 3) + 34 = 0$

17. $4x^2 - 12x + 25 = 0$

18. $9x^2 - 6x + 5 = 0$

19. Show that $x = 3$ is a root of
$x^3 - x^2 - 4x - 6 = 0$
and hence find the other two roots.

20. Show that $x = -1$ is a root of
$x^3 - 5x^2 + 4x + 10 = 0$
and hence find the other two roots.

CONJUGATES

The conjugate of $z = a + bi$ is $a - bi$ and is denoted by the symbol $\bar{z}$.
For example, if $z = 3 + 4i$, then $\bar{z} = 3 - 4i$. If $z_2 = -4 - 2i$, then $\bar{z}_2 = -4 + 2i$.

ADDING AND SUBTRACTING COMPLEX NUMBERS

To add (or subtract) complex numbers, we add the real parts to the real parts and the imaginary parts to the imaginary parts.

Example 1: Let $z_1 = 3 + 2i$ and let $z_2 = 5 - 4i$. Write these in the form $a + bi$:

(i) $z_1 + z_2$ (ii) $z_1 - z_2$ (iii) $2z_1 + z_2$ (iv) $3z_1 - 5z_2$ (v) $\bar{z}_1 + \bar{z}_2$

Solution:

(i) $z_1 + z_2 = (3 + 2i) + (5 - 4i) = 8 - 2i$

(ii) $z_1 - z_2 = (3 + 2i) - (5 - 4i) = 3 + 2i - 5 + 4i = -2 + 6i$

(iii) $2z_1 + z_2 = 2(3 + 2i) + (5 - 4i) = 6 + 4i + 5 - 4i = 11 + 0i = 11$

(iv) $3z_1 - 5z_2 = 3(3 + 2i) - 5(5 - 4i) = 9 + 6i - 25 + 20i = -16 + 26i$

(v) $\bar{z}_1 + \bar{z}_2 = (3 - 2i) + (5 + 4i) = 8 + 2i$

[Don't forget! If $z = (a + bi)$, then the conjugate of z, $\bar{z} = (a - bi)$].

Example 2: If $z_1 = 3 - 7i$ and $z_2 = -1 + 2i$, write the following in the form $a + bi$:

(i) $\bar{z}_1$ (ii) $\bar{z}_2$ (iii) $\bar{z}_1 + \bar{z}_2$

Investigate if $\overline{z_1 + z_2} = \bar{z}_1 + \bar{z}_2$

Solution:

(i) $\bar{z}_1 = 3 + 7i$ (ii) $\bar{z}_2 = -1 - 2i$ (iii) $\bar{z}_1 + \bar{z}_2 = (3 + 7i) + (-1 - 2i) = 2 + 5i$

Investigation: $z_1 + z_2 = (3 - 7i) + (-1 + 2i) = 2 - 5i$

$\therefore\ \overline{z_1 + z_2} = 2 + 5i$

But $\bar{z}_1 + \bar{z}_2 = 2 + 5i$ (see above)

$\therefore\ \overline{z_1 + z_2} = \bar{z}_1 + \bar{z}_2$

Exercise 9.C

1. Let $z_1 = 7 + 5i$ and let $z_2 = 2 + i$.
Write these as $(a + bi)$:
(i) $z_1 + z_2$
(ii) $z_1 - z_2$
(iii) $3z_1 + 2z_2$
(iv) $2z_1 - 3z_2$
(v) $\bar{z}_1 + \bar{z}_2$

2. Let $z_1 = 5 + 2i$ and let $z_2 = 3 - 4i$.
Write these as $(a + bi)$:
(i) $z_1 + z_2$
(ii) $z_1 - z_2$
(iii) $z_1 + 3z_2$
(iv) $2z_1 - 5z_2$
(v) $\bar{z}_1 + \bar{z}_2$

3. Let $z_1 = -1 + 2i$ and let $z_2 = 2 + 3i$.
Write these as $(a + bi)$:
(i) $2z_1 + z_2$
(ii) $2z_1 - z_2$
(iii) $2z_2 - 3z_1$
(iv) $z_2 - z_1$
(v) $\bar{z}_1 + \bar{z}_2$

4. Let $z = 4 + 5i$. Show the following on an Argand diagram:
(i) z
(ii) $\bar{z}$
(iii) $z - 3$
(iv) $z - 3i$
(v) $1 + \bar{z}$

5. Let $z = 2 - 3i$. Show the following on an Argand diagram:
(i) z
(ii) $\bar{z}$
(iii) $\frac{1}{2}(z + i)$
(iv) $2z + 6i$
(v) $1 - \bar{z}$

6. Let $z_1 = -8 + 2i$ and let $z_2 = -2 + i$. Write these as $(a + bi)$:
(i) $z_1 - z_2$
(ii) $z_1 - 4z_2$
(iii) $\frac{1}{4}(3z_1 + 2z_2)$
(iv) $2z_1 - 3z_2$
(v) $1 - (\bar{z}_1 + \bar{z}_2)$

7. Let $z_1 = 1 + 3i$ and let $z_2 = 2 - i$.
Write these as $(a + bi)$:
(i) $z_1 + z_2$
(ii) $\bar{z}_1 + \bar{z}_2$
(iii) $\overline{z_1 + z_2}$

Investigate if $\bar{z}_1 + \bar{z}_2 = \overline{z_1 + z_2}$

8. Let $z_1 = 4 + 2i$ and let $z_2 = 5 + i$.
Write these as $(a + bi)$:
(i) $z_1 - z_2$
(ii) $\bar{z}_1 - \bar{z}_2$
(iii) $\overline{z_1 - z_2}$

Investigate if $\bar{z}_1 - \bar{z}_2 = \overline{z_1 - z_2}$

9. Let $z = 1 + 7i$.
Write these as $(a + bi)$:
(i) $2 + z$
(ii) $2 + \bar{z}$
(iii) $\overline{2 + z}$

Investigate if $2 + \bar{z} = \overline{2 + z}$

10. Let $z = 2(1 - 3i)$.
Write these as $(a + bi)$:
(i) $z - 1$
(ii) $\bar{z} - 1$
(iii) $\overline{z - 1}$

Investigate if $\bar{z} - 1 = \overline{z - 1}$

MULTIPLYING COMPLEX NUMBERS

The key to the multiplication of complex numbers is the fact that $i^2 = -1$. When you see i^2, change it to (–1). Hence, for example, $3i^2 = 3(-1) = -3$.

Example 1: Let $z_1 = -1 + 2i$ and let $z_2 = 2 + 3i$. Write in the form $a + bi$:

(i) $z_1 z_2$ (ii) $z_1 \bar{z}_1$ (iii) $z_2 \bar{z}_2$

Solution: (i)

$$\begin{aligned} z_1 z_2 &= (-1 + 2i)(2 + 3i) = -2 - 3i + 4i + 6i^2 \\ &= -2 - 3i + 4i + 6(-1) \\ &= -2 - 3i + 4i - 6 \\ &= -8 + i \end{aligned}$$

(ii)

$$\begin{aligned} z_1 \bar{z}_1 &= (-1 + 2i)(-1 - 2i) \\ &= 1 + 2i - 2i - 4i^2 \\ &= 1 + 2i - 2i - 4(-1) \\ &= 1 + 2i - 2i + 4 \\ &= 5 \end{aligned}$$

It is worth noting here that the product of a complex number and its conjugate will always be a *real number*. Furthermore, $(a+bi)(a-bi) = a^2 + b^2$. We will use this shortcut to solve part (iii).

(iii) $z_2 \bar{z}_2 = 2^2 + 3^2 = 4 + 9 = 13$ [Be warned! This shortcut is to be used only when you are multiplying a complex number by its conjugate]

Exercise 9.D

Write these products as $a + bi$:

1. $(2 + 7i)(3 - 5i)$
2. $(1 + 4i)(2 + 5i)$
3. $(6 + i)(-2 + 3i)$
4. $i(2 - 7i)$
5. $(2 + 7i)(2 - 7i)$
6. $(3 + 2i)(3 - 2i)$
7. $(2 - i)(3 - i)$
8. $(2 - i)(2 + i)$
9. $(10 - 2i)(10 + 2i)$
10. $3i(2 + 4i)$
11. $(\tfrac{1}{2} + \tfrac{1}{2} i)(\tfrac{1}{2} - \tfrac{1}{2} i)$
12. $(1 - i)(1 + i)$
13. $(-2 - 2i)(-2 + 2i)$
14. $(\sqrt{3} + 2i)(\sqrt{3} - 2i)$
15. $(3\sqrt{7} + 5i)(3\sqrt{7} - 5i)$
16. $3(1 + 5i) + i(2 - 3i)$

Write these as $a + bi$:

17. $3i(1 + i) - 5(1 + 7i)$

18. $(2 + 3i)^2$

19. $(6 + i)^2$

20. $(-1 + 2i)^2$

21. If $w = 3 - 2i$, write these as $a + bi$:
(i) $6w$
(ii) w^2
(iii) $w^2 - 6w + 13$

22. If $z = 1 + i$, write these as $a + bi$:
(i) iz
(ii) z^2
(iii) $z^2 - 2z$

23. Let $z = (2 - i)(1 + 3i)$. Plot, on one Argand diagram: z, $z - 3$ and $\bar{z}$

24. Write as $p + qi$:
(i) $3 + 2i(4 - i)$
(ii) $(3 + 2i)(4 - i)$

25. If $z = -2 - i$, write these as $p + qi$:
(i) $z\bar{z}$ (ii) z^2 (iii) $z^2 + 4z + 5$

26. If $z = -3 + i$, show these on an Argand diagram:
(i) $z\bar{z}$ (ii) $\frac{1}{2} z^2$ (iii) $z^2 + 6z$

27. If $z = 1 + i$, write these as $p + qi$:
(i) z^2 (ii) z^3 (iii) z^4

28. If $z = 3i$, verify that
$z^3 - 2z^2 + 9z - 18 = 0$

29. If $\omega = -1 + \sqrt{3}i$, show that $\omega^3 = 8$.

30. Find the value of $k \in R$, if
$(1 + \sqrt{3}i)^3 = k$.

DIVISION OF COMPLEX NUMBERS

When we are dividing one complex number by another, we multiply above and below by the ***conjugate of the divisor***. In this way, we end up dividing by a ***real number***, which poses no difficulty.

Example 1: Write these as $a + bi$: (i) $\dfrac{7 + i}{1 - 2i}$ (ii) $\dfrac{4 + i}{1 + 3i}$

Solution:

(i) $$\frac{7 + i}{1 - 2i} = \frac{7 + i}{1 - 2i} \cdot \frac{1 + 2i}{1 + 2i} = \frac{7 + 14i + i - 2}{5} = \frac{5 + 15i}{5} = 1 + 3i$$

(ii) $$\frac{4 + i}{1 + 3i} = \frac{4 + i}{1 + 3i} \cdot \frac{1 - 3i}{1 - 3i} = \frac{4 - 12i + i + 3}{10} = \frac{7 - 11i}{10} = \frac{7}{10} - \frac{11}{10}i$$

Exercise 9.E

Write these as $p + qi$:

1. $\dfrac{5+5i}{1+2i}$
2. $\dfrac{1-5i}{1-i}$
3. $\dfrac{10}{1-3i}$
4. $\dfrac{5}{1+2i}$
5. $\dfrac{1+3i}{1+i}$
6. $\dfrac{5-5i}{2+i}$
7. $\dfrac{6}{1-i}$
8. $\dfrac{1+5i}{i}$
9. $\dfrac{6+8i}{2i}$
10. $\dfrac{-7+24i}{3+4i}$

Write these as $a + bi$, where $a, b \in Q$:

11. $\dfrac{1}{1+i}$
12. $\dfrac{1+2i}{1+3i}$
13. $\dfrac{1+5i}{2-i}$
14. $\dfrac{11+10i}{2(2+3i)}$
15. $\dfrac{1-9i}{2i}$
16. If $z = 1 + 2i$, write $\dfrac{z^2}{z-i}$ in the form $a + bi$.
17. If $z = 1 - 3i$, write $\dfrac{\bar{z}}{z}$ in the form $a + bi$.
18. Let $z = -1 + i$. Write $\dfrac{z^2+2}{z}$ in the form $a + bi$.
19. Let $z_1 = -1 + 5i$ and let $z_2 = 2 + 3i$. Investigate if $\overline{\left(\dfrac{z_1}{z_2}\right)} = \dfrac{\bar{z}_1}{\bar{z}_2}$
20. Let $z_1 = -15 + 16i$ and let $z_2 = 6 + i$. Investigate if $\overline{\left(\dfrac{z_1}{z_2}\right)} = \dfrac{\bar{z}_1}{\bar{z}_2}$

MODULUS

The ***modulus*** of $a + bi$ (which is written $|a + bi|$) is its distance from the origin $0 + 0i$. In accordance with Pythagoras' theorem, this distance is given by the formula:

$$|a+bi| = \sqrt{a^2+b^2}$$

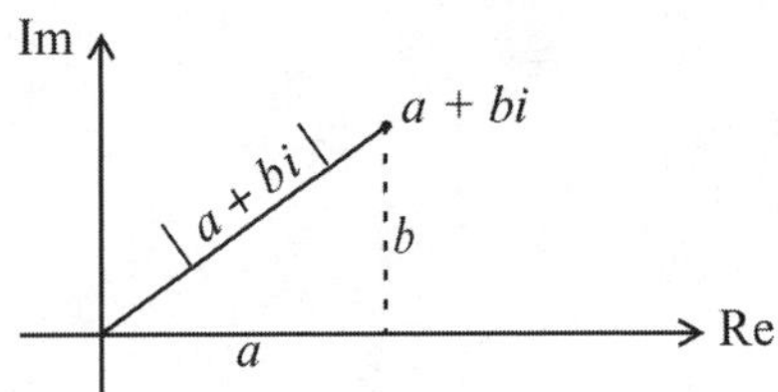

Example 1: Let $z_1 = 3 + 4i$, let $z_2 = 8 - i$, and let $z_3 = 7 + ki$.

(i) Evaluate $|z_1|$

(ii) Evaluate $|z_2|$

(iii) If $|z_3| = |z_2|$, find two possible values of $k \varepsilon R$.

Solution: (i) $|z_1| = \sqrt{3^2 + 4^2} = \sqrt{9 + 16} = \sqrt{25} = 5$

(ii) $|z_2| = \sqrt{8^2 + (-1)^2} = \sqrt{64 + 1} = \sqrt{65}$

(iii)

$$|z_3| = |z_2|$$

$$\therefore \sqrt{7^2 + k^2} = \sqrt{65}$$

$$\therefore \sqrt{49 + k^2} = \sqrt{65}$$

$$\therefore 49 + k^2 = 65 \qquad \text{[Squaring both sides]}$$

$$\therefore k^2 = 65 - 49$$

$$\therefore k^2 = 16$$

$$\therefore k = \pm 4$$

Exercise 9.F

Evaluate the following:

1. $|8 + 6i|$
2. $|4 + 3i|$
3. $|1 + 2i|$
4. $|2 + 2i|$
5. $|8 - 6i|$
6. $|3 - i|$
7. $|5 - 2i|$
8. $|12 - 5i|$
9. $|1 - i|$
10. $|3 - 10i|$
11. $|3 + \sqrt{7}i|$
12. $|1 + \sqrt{8}i|$
13. $|3 + 2\sqrt{10}i|$
14. $|½ + ½i|$
15. $|¾ - i|$
16. If $|11 + 2i| = |10 + ki|$, find two possible values of k.
17. If $|8 + ki| = 10$, find two possible values of k.
18. If $z = 3 - i$, verify that $|z| = |\bar{z}|$.
19. If $|4 + ki| = ½\,|6 - 8i|$, find two possible values of k.
20. If $w = 2 + 7i$, verify that $|w|^2 = w\bar{w}$.
21. If $|p + pi| = |7 - i|$, find two possible values of p.
22. Evaluate $\left|\frac{6 - 4i}{5 + i}\right|$.
23. Let $z_1 = 3 + 4i$, and let $z_2 = 5 + 2i$ verify that $|z_1| + |z_2| > |z_1 + z_2|$.

24. Let $z_1 = 1 + i$, and let $z_2 = 3 + i$ verify that $|z_1| \cdot |z_2| = |z_1 \cdot z_2|$

25. Let $z_1 = 7 - i$, let $z_2 = 1 + 2i$ verify that $\frac{|z_1|}{|z_2|} = \left|\frac{z_1}{z_2}\right|$

26. Write down the modulus of $12 - 5i$ and hence write down three other complex numbers with the same modulus.

27. If $|p + 2i| = |3 - \sqrt{20}\,i|$, find two possible values of p.

28. If $|x + yi| = 5$, find an equation satisfied by x and y. Is this the equation of a line or a circle?

29. If $z = 3 + 3i$, find the value of $|z + i| - |z + 1|$

30. $|15 + ki| - |8 - 6i| = |6 + \sqrt{13}\,i|$, find two possible values of k.

COMPLEX EQUATIONS

Let $z = a + bi$. We call $\boldsymbol{a}$ the real part of z. We call $\boldsymbol{b}$ the imaginary part of z. You should note carefully that the imaginary part of z is $\boldsymbol{b}$ and not $\boldsymbol{bi}$. When you are asked to solve an equation which contains complex numbers, you get two-equations-for-the-price-of-one!

1. The real part of the left hand side = the real part of the right hand side.
2. The imaginary part of the left hand side = the imaginary part of the right.

Example 1: Solve for x and y: $3(2 + i) - 2(x - yi) = 7 - 9i$

Solution:

$$3(2 + i) - 2(x - yi) = 7 - 9i$$

$$\therefore\ 6 + 3i - 2x + 2yi = 7 - 9i$$

$$\therefore\ (6 - 2x) + (3 + 2y)i = 7 - 9i$$

$\therefore$ 1. Real = Real: $6 - 2x = 7 \Rightarrow -2x = 1 \Rightarrow x = -\tfrac{1}{2}$

2. Imaginary = Imaginary: $3 + 2y = -9 \Rightarrow 2y = -12 \Rightarrow y = -6$

Example 2: Let $z = 2 - i$ be one root of the equation $z^2 + pz + q = 0$, where $p, q \in R$. Find the value of p and of q.

Solution: $2 - i$ is a root of $z^2 + pz + q = 0$

$$\therefore\ (2 - i)^2 + p(2 - i) + q = 0$$

$$\therefore\ 4 - 2i - 2i + i^2 + 2p - pi + q = 0$$

$$\therefore\ 4 - 2i - 2i - 1 + 2p - pi + q = 0$$

$\therefore$ Real = Real: $4 - 1 + 2p + q = 0 \Rightarrow 2p + q = -3$

Imaginary = imaginary: $-2 - 2 - p = 0 \Rightarrow p = -4$

$$\therefore\ 2p + q = -3 \Rightarrow -8 + q = -3 \Rightarrow q = 5$$

Exercise 9.G

Solve for the real numbers x and y:

1. $(2 + 3i) + (x + yi) = 8 + 7i$
2. $(2 + 4i) + (x + yi) = 7 + 5i$
3. $(x + yi) + (5 - 2i) = 1 + i$
4. $2(x + yi) + 1 + i = 11 + 7i$
5. $7 + 4i - 3(x - yi) = 1 + i$
6. $1 + i - x - 3yi + 11i = 0$
7. $3x - 5yi - 4 + 15i - x = -14$
8. $4y - xi + 21 + i(3 - 2i) = 7$
9. $2i(5 - 7i) - 3(x + yi) + 1 = i$
10. $2(x - yi) - (7 + 11i) = 0$

Solve for real numbers a and b, using simultaneous equations:

11. $2(a + bi) + 3(b + ai) = 12 + 13i$
12. $2(a + bi) + (b + ai) = 5 + 4i$
13. $3(a - bi) + 2(b + ai) = 1 + 5i$
14. $(a + 3bi) + 5(-1 - i) = b - 2ai$
15. $(a + bi) - 2(b - ai) = 5i(3 - i)$
16. Let $z = 5 - 2i$. Solve for real numbers s and t: $2z + s + 5i - 3ti = 7 - 5i$
17. Solve for real numbers s and t: $s(2 - i) + ti(4 + 2i) = 1 + s + ti$
18. Let $w = 3 - 4i$. Solve for real numbers s and t: $s + w = 3ti$
19. Let $z = x + yi$, where $x, y \in R$. Find the values of x and y if $2z + \bar{z} = 24 - 6i$, where $\bar{z}$ is the conjugate of z.
20. If $z = (1 + 2i)$ is root of the equation $z^2 + az + b = 0$, where a and b are real numbers, find the values of a and b.
21. If $z = (3 - i)$ is root of the equation $z^2 + az + b = 0$, where a and b are real numbers, find the values of a and b.
22. If $z = -1 - 5i$ is root of the equation $z^2 + az + b = 0$, where a and b are real numbers, find the values of a and b.
23. If $z = \frac{1}{2} + \frac{1}{2}i$ is root of the equation $az^2 + bz + 1 = 0$, where a and b are real numbers, find the values of a and b.
24. If $z = 1 + \frac{3}{4}i$ is root of the equation $16z^2 + az + b = 0$, where a and b are real numbers, find the values of a and b.
25. Let $w = p + qi$, where p and q are real numbers. Find the values of p and q if
$$3w + 4i(1 + i) = \overline{w}$$
26. Solve for real numbers x and y: $(x + yi)(1 + 5i) = 11 + 3i$
27. Solve for real numbers x and y: $(x + 2yi)(1 - i) = 11 + i$
28. If $z_1 = 4 - 2i$ and $z_2 = 3 + i$, find a real number t such that $z_1 + tz_2$ is a real number. [HINT: Any real number can be written as $k + 0i$].
29. If $z_1 = 2 - 3i$ and $z_2 = -1 - i$, find the values of real numbers α and β, if $z_1 + \alpha z_2 = \beta$.
30. Find a complex number $z = x + yi$ such that $2z + i\bar{z} = 5 + i$.

REVISION EXERCISE 9.H

1. (a) Write as $a + bi$: $(3 - 5i)(4 + 11i)$

(b) If $\frac{11 - 10i}{4 + i} = u + vi$, find the value of the real numbers u and v.

(c) Show that $z = (2 + 2i)$ is a root of the equation: $z^2 - 4z + 8 = 0$.

2. (a) If $z_1 = -3 - i$ and $z_2 = 1 - i$, write the following in the form $a + bi$:

(i) $3z_1 - z_2$

(ii) $\overline{z_2}$

(iii) $\frac{z_1}{z_2}$

(b) Show on an Argand diagram the roots of the equation

$z^2 - 8z + 25 = 0$

3. Let $z_1 = 4 + 3i$ and $z_2 = 2 - i$. Show z_1 and z_2 on an Argand diagram, and prove that z_2 is nearer to the origin than z_1.

Show that $\frac{|z_1|}{|z_2|} = \left|\frac{z_1}{z_2}\right|$.

Verify that $z_1 - 2z_2$ is on the imaginary axis and find a real number k such that $z_1 - kz_2$ is on the real axis.

4. Let $z = 2 - 3i$, where $i = \sqrt{-1}$.

(i) Show that z is a root of the equation $z^2 - 4z + 13 = 0$.

(ii) Plot i, z and iz on an Argand diagram.

(iii) Verify that $|iz - z| > |iz| - |z|$

(iv) If $z + i + 3(p + 2qi) = iz - 5$, find the values of the real numbers p and q.

5. (a) Simplify $4(1 - 5i) + i(3 - 7i)$ and write your answer in the form $a + bi$.

(b) If $|a + 12i| = 13$, find two possible values of $a \in R$.

(c) Let $z = 1 - i$ and let $\bar{z}$ be the complex conjugate of z.

Express $\left(\frac{z}{\bar{z}}\right)$ in the form $x + yi$, where $x, y \in R$.

Hence solve for real k and t:

$$2k\left(\frac{z}{\bar{z}}\right) + tz = 1 - 7i$$

6. (a) Let $z = 4 - 2i$. Plot on an Argand diagram: z, $z - 2$ and iz.

(b) If $\frac{9 - 7i}{3 + i} = u + vi$, find the value of the real numbers u and v. If $|1 + ki| = \sqrt{2}\,|u + vi|$, find two possible values of $k \in R$.

(c) If $z = (7 + i)$ is a root of the equation: $z^2 - az + b = 0$, find the values of the real numbers a and b.

7. (a) Let $z_1 = -1 + 5i$ and $z_2 = -3 + 2i$, and $z_3 = z_2 - iz_1$ and $z_4 = \frac{z_1}{z_2}$.

Plot z_3 and z_4 on an Argand diagram and show that $|z_3| = |z_2|$ and that $|z_4| = \frac{|z_1|}{|z_2|}$.

(b) Show on an Argand diagram the roots of the equation $z^2 - 10z + 26 = 0$.

8. (a) On an Argand diagram plot the complex number $p = 2 + 3i$. Write down the complex number which represents the image of p under
(i) axial symmetry in the imaginary axis,
(ii) central symmetry in the origin.

(b) Find the values of the real numbers x and y which satisfy the equation:
$(x + yi) + i(x + yi) = 1 - 7i$
Using these values for x and y, write $\dfrac{1-7i}{x+yi}$ in the form $a + bi$.

Hence evaluate $\left|\dfrac{1-7i}{x+yi}\right|$.

9. (a) Let $z_1 = 2 + 3i$ and $z_2 = 6 + i$. Plot (i) z_1 (ii) z_2 (iii) $z_2 - z_1$ on an Argand diagram.

(b) Express $\dfrac{13}{1-5i}$ in the form $a + bi$.

(c) If $z = \frac{1}{2} - \frac{1}{2}i$ is a root of the equation $az^2 - bz + 1 = 0$, find the values of the real numbers a and b.

10. (a) Plot on an Argand diagram the set of all $x + yi$ such that $|x + yi| = 4$

(b) Let $z_1 = 3 - i$, $z_2 = 1 - 7i$, $z_3 = z_1 + z_2$ and $z_4 = \dfrac{z_2}{z_1}$.

Verify that
(i) $\overline{z_3} = \overline{z_1} + \overline{z_2}$
(ii) $|z_3| < |z_1| + |z_2|$
(iii) $|z_4| = \dfrac{|z_2|}{|z_1|}$

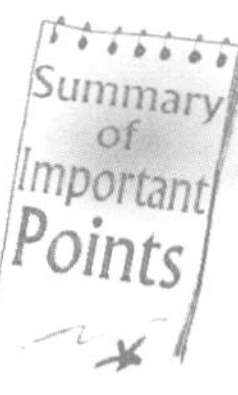

1. $i = \sqrt{-1}$. $\therefore i^2 = -1$.

2. If $z = a + bi$ then $\bar{z} = a - bi$ is the conjugate of z.

3. $(a + bi)(a - bi) = a^2 + b^2$.

4. If $z = a + bi$, then the modulus of $z = |a + bi| = \sqrt{a^2 + b^2}$.

5. To divide by a complex number, multiply above and below by the conjugate of the divisor.

6. If $a + bi = c + di$, then
   (i) the real parts are equal: $a = c$,
   (ii) the imaginary parts are equal: $b = d$.

Chapter 10

Percentages, Tax and Interest

The word 'percent' means 'per hundred'.
So, 50% means '50 out of every hundred', i.e. one half (or 0.5).

Similarly, $20\% = \frac{20}{100} = \frac{1}{5} = 0.2$

Again, $85\% = \frac{85}{100} = \frac{17}{20} = 0.85$

Don't forget that the word '***of***' means '×' in Mathematics. So, to get 35% ***of*** €250, we get 0.35 × €250 = €87.50

Similarly, to get 84% of 2 kilograms = 0.84 × 2000 grams = 1680 grams.

[Page 5 of the Mathematical tables contains all the information you will need about the units of measurement of length, area, volume and mass. For example it contains the fact that '1000 grams (g) = 1 kilogram (kg)'.]

Decimals and fractions can be converted to percentages, by multiplying them by 100.

For example, 0.3 = 0.3 × 100 % = 30%

Also, $\frac{3}{20} = \frac{3}{20} \times \frac{100}{1}\% = 15\%$

If you are asked to 'write 35 cm as a percentage of 1¾ metres', you must convert both values to the same quantity. We will convert both to centimetres. The question then reads:

'Write 35 cm as a percentage of 175 cm.' The answer is: $\frac{35}{175} \times \frac{100}{1}\% = 20\%$.

Exercise 10. A

1. Copy and complete this table:

%	Fraction	Decimal
50%		
25%		
40%		
75%		
45%		
36%		
120%		
88%		
108%		
90%		
12½%		

2. Copy and complete this table:

%	Fraction	Decimal
80%		
	$^7/_{10}$	
		0.16
2½%		
	$^5/_8$	
		1.1
18¾%		
	$^2/_3$	
		0.375
$3^1/_3$%		
		0.03

3. Find 55% of €360.

4. Find 2% of €1140

5. Find 4% of $8.50

6. Find 7½% of €240

7. 43 500 students sit the Ordinary Level Maths exam. 14% of these get an A grade. How many students get an A grade?

8. In a class of 30 students, nine are aged 16, eighteen are aged 17 and the rest are aged 18. What percentage of the class are
(i) aged 16,
(ii) aged 17,
(iii) aged 18?

9. Write 48 minutes as a percentage of one hour.

10. Write 75 grams as a percentage of a half-kilogram.

11. All Irish secondary students must attend 180 schooldays per year. What percentage of days are schooldays (to the nearest percent)?

12. A party gets 18% of the vote in a general election. How many of the 166 Dáil seats (to the nearest whole number) does this party deserve to win?

13. In a normal 24-hour day, a student spends 35% of her time asleep. In one day, for how many hours and minutes is she
(i) asleep,
(ii) awake?

14. A bottle of shampoo used to contain 385 ml of shampoo. New bottles have "30% extra free", according to the label. How many millilitres should the new bottles contain?

15. What is 75% of 75% of €200?

16. The price of a tennis racquet is reduced in a sale from €80 to €68. What percentage reduction is this? [Remember that percentage reduction is calculated as a percent of the ***original*** price]

17. €1 = 256 Hungarian forint. An Irish tourist wants to convert €250 into forint. The bureau de change charges 2½% commission. How many forint will the tourist get?

18. A woman leaves her home in Donegal at 08.50 and travels 180 km to Athlone. She arrives at 13.20.
(i) What was her average speed in km/h?
(ii) She stopped for 35 minutes along the way. What percentage of the total time was spent on the road (to the nearest whole number)?

19. The population of a town increased by 5% to 4914. What was the original population?

20. (i) A sports shop buys footballs from the manufacturer for €8 and sells them for €11. What percentage profit is this?
(ii) The shop buys hockey-sticks for €9 and sells them making 22% profit. What is the selling price?
(iii) The shop sells tennis raquets for €84 at a profit of 12%. What is the cost price?

INCOME TAX, VAT AND RATES

Example 1: The standard rate of tax is 20% and the higher rate is 42%. A woman has a standard rate cut-off point of €28 000 and tax credits of €3000.

(i) If she earns €60 000, how much annual tax will she pay?

(ii) If she pays €13 940 in tax, what did she earn?

Solution: (i) Gross tax = 20% of €28 000 + 42% of the rest

= 20% of €28 000 + 42% of €32 000

= $0.2 \times 28\,000 + 0.42 \times 32\,000$

= €5600 + €13440

= €19040

But her tax credits are €3000

Tax payable = € (19040 – 3000) = €16040

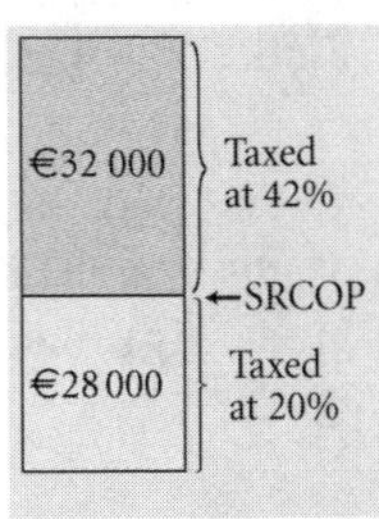

(ii) Gross tax = €13 940 + €3000 = €16940

Let x = amount taxed at higher rate.

∴ Gross tax = 0.2 × €2800 + 0.42 × €x

= € $(5600 + 0.42x)$

Equation: $5600 + 0.42x = 16940$

$\therefore 0.42x = 11340$

$\therefore x = \dfrac{11340}{0.42} = 27\,000$

∴ She earns €(28 000 + 27 000) = €55 000

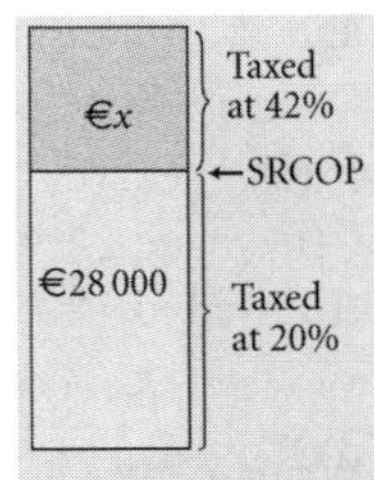

Example 2: When VAT (Value Added Tax) of 21% is added to a car maintenance bill, it amounts to €72.60. How much of this is tax?

Solution:

I 121% of the original cost = €72.60

II ∴ 1% of the original cost = € 72.60 ÷ 121 = €0.60

III ∴ 21% of the original cost = €0.60 × 21 = €12.60

Answer: The VAT is €12.60

Example 3: A woman owns a shop in a town with a rateable valuation of €70.

(i) How much will she have to pay in rates if the town council strike a rate of €31 in the euro?

(ii) The next year, the rates bill is €2240. What rate did the town council strike that year?

Solution: (i) She will pay €70 × 31 = €2170

(ii) The rate struck = € $\dfrac{2240}{70}$ = €32 in the euro.

Exercise 10.B

1. A man earns €50 000. His standard rate cut-off point is €28 000 and his tax credits are €2400. If the standard rate is 20% and the higher rate is 42%, calculate
   (i) his tax payable
   (ii) his take-home pay.

2. An electricity bill for €50.60 includes VAT at 15%. How much of this bill is VAT?

3. The county council strikes a rate of €28 in the euro.
   (i) The rateable valuation of a shoe-shop is €35. What will the rates bill be?
   (ii) A DIY store pays a rates bill of €1820. What is the rateable valuation of this store?

4. A couple earn €57 000. They have a standard rate cut-off point of €37000 and tax credits of €4000. Assuming that the standard rate is 20% and the higher rate is 42%, calculate their annual take-home pay.

5. The standard rate of tax is 20% and the higher rate is 42%. A woman has a standard rate cut-off point of €28 000 and tax credits of €4400. Find their taxable pay if
   (i) she earns €40 000
   (ii) she earns €25 000
   (iii) she earns €14 000.

6. A man earns €770 per week. His standard rate cut-off point is €550 and his weekly tax credits amount to €153. Assuming that the standard rate is 20% and the higher rate is 40%, calculate
   (i) his weekly tax payable
   (ii) his weekly take-home pay.

7. The standard rate of tax is 20% and the higher rate is 42%. A man has a standard rate cut-off point of €28 000 and tax credits of €5000. He earns €30 000.
   (i) Find his take-home pay.
   (ii) If he gets a pay rise of 10%, find the percentage rise in his take-home pay correct to one decimal place.

8. The standard rate of tax is 20% and the higher rate is 40%. A man has a standard rate cut-off point of €21 000 and tax credits of €3600. He earns €20 000.
   (i) Find his take-home pay.
   (ii) If he gets a pay rise of 15%, find the percentage rise in his take-home pay correct to one decimal place.

9. An auctioneer sells a house for a client. The price of the house is €80 000. The auctioneer's fee is $1\frac{1}{2}$% of the cost of the house.
   (i) What is the fee?
   (ii) When VAT is added to the fee, it goes up to €1452. What is the percentage rate of VAT?

10. A tanker delivered heating oil to a school. Before the delivery there were 13 810 litres of oil in the tanker. After delivery, there were 8530 litres. Oil costs $22\frac{1}{2}$ cent per litre.

(i) Calculate the cost of the oil.

(ii) When VAT is added the bill goes up to €1366.20. Calculate the % rate of VAT added.

11. The standard rate of tax is 20% and the higher rate is 42%. A man has a standard rate cut-off point of €28 000 and tax credits of €6020.

(i) If he pays €2940 in tax, what does he earn?

(ii) What is the maximum amount he can earn and still pay no tax?

12. The standard rate of tax is 20% and the higher rate is 42%. A man has a standard rate cut-off point of €28 000 and tax credits of €7700.

(i) If he pays €5040 in tax, what does he earn?

(ii) What is the maximum amount he can earn and still pay no tax?

COMPOUND INTEREST

If the rate of interest is 6% compound interest, your money will be multiplied by 1.06 each year.
If the rate is 8%, the multiplier will be 1.08
If the rate is 12%, the multiplier will be 1.12
If the rate is $13\frac{1}{2}$%, the multiplier will be 1.135
If the rate is $4\frac{3}{4}$%, the multiplier will be 1.0475

Let P = the principal (i.e. the money put in at the beginning) and
let A = the amount (i.e. the money in the account at the end) and
let n = the number of years for which the money is left in the account, and
let R = the multiplier. Then the formula for calculating the amount is:

$$A = PR^n$$

Example 1: Find the compound interest on an investment of €600 for five years at 7% compound interest per annum.

Solution: Since the rate is 7%, the multiplier is 1.07

$P = 600$, $n = 5$, $R = 1.07$ and $A = ?$

$$\therefore\ A = PR^n = 600(1.07)^5 = 600(1.40255) = 841.53$$

Therefore, the interest = €841.53 – €600 = €241.53

Example 2: How much (to the nearest euro) should I invest now at 10½% compound interest per annum, in order to have €10 000 in my account in 10 years' time?

Solution: In this case, $R = 1.105$, $A = 10\ 000$, $n = 10$ and $P = ?$

$$A = PR^n$$

$$\therefore 10000 = P(1.105)^{10}$$

$$\therefore 10000 = P(2.714)$$

$$\therefore P = \frac{10000}{2.714} = \text{IR£}3684 \quad [\text{to the nearest €1}]$$

Example 3: €2500 amounts to €2704 in two years. What is the rate of compound interest paid annually?

Solution: In this case, $P = 2500$, $A = 2704$, $n = 2$ and $R = ?$

$$A = PR^n$$

$$\therefore 2704 = 2500R^2$$

$$\therefore \frac{2704}{2500} = R^2$$

$$\therefore R^2 = 1.0816$$

$$\therefore R = \sqrt{1.0816}$$

$$\therefore R = 1.04$$

$\therefore$ The rate of interest = 4%

DEPRECIATION

If depreciation is at a rate of 12%, the value of the object will be multiplied by a factor of 0.88 for each year. If the depreciation rate is 15%, the multiplier is 0.85. If the rate of deprecation is 7%, the multiplier will be 0.93, etc.

Example 4: A car depreciates at 14% per annum. It was bought for €15 000. How much is it worth three years later?

Solution: In this case, $P = 15\ 000$, $n = 3$, $R = 0.86$ and $A = ?$

$$A = PR^n = 15000(0.86)^3 = €9540.84$$

Exercise 10.C

1. Find the compound interest on €400 at 5% for two years.

2. What will €20 000 amount to after three years at 6% compound interest per annum?

3. Find the compound interest on €1550 at 12% for four years, giving your answer to the nearest €1.

4. What will €300 amount to after seven years at 8% compound interest per annum? [Give your answer to the nearest cent]

5. Find the compound interest (to the nearest cent) on €5400 at 5½% for three years.

6. What will €10 000 amount to after ten years at 10% compound interest per annum (to the nearest euro)?

7. €40 is put in a bank. The bank pays compound interest at 2½% per annum. What will the investment amount to at the end of six years (to the nearest cent)?

8. Which will earn more interest: €1000 for 3 years at 2% compound interest per annum or €1000 for 2 years at 3% compound interest per annum?

9. A car depreciates at a rate of 15% per annum. It was bought for €12 000. What will it be worth
(i) after 2 years,
(ii) after 3 years?

10. A television depreciates at a rate of 20% per year. It was bought for €350. What will it be worth in four years' time?

11. How much should I invest (to the nearest cent) at 6% compound interest per annum, in order to have €2000 in my account in three years' time?

12. How much should I invest (to the nearest euro) at 4¼% compound interest per annum, in order to have €500 in my account in eight years' time?

13. A woman invests a certain sum of money at a constant rate of compound interest. After a year it amounts to €650. After another year it €676.
(i) What is the annual rate of compound interest?
(ii) What was the original sum?

14. A man has €1000 to invest for a five-year term in either of two banks: X or Y. Bank X gives 7% compound interest per annum. Bank Y guarantees 40% interest at the end of five years. Which bank will give the greater return on the investment?

15. What is the annual rate of compound interest if an investment of €2500 amounts to €2601 after two years?

16. A woman invests €A at r% compound interest per annum. After a year it amounts to €1680. After ***two more*** years it amounts to €1852.20.
Find the values of r and A.

17. A married couple borrow €500 from a bank which charges 14.8% compound interest per annum. They repay the entire debt after two years. How much do they have to pay back (to the nearest euro)?

18. An investment of €10 000 amounts to €13 862 in three years. Calculate the annual rate of compound interest to the nearest ½%.

19. A woman borrows €2000 from a bank at a constant rate of compound interest. After four years, she clears her debt, paying back €3147. What was the annual rate of interest, to the nearest unit?

20. A sum of money doubles in 7 years at r% compound interest per annum. Find r correct to one decimal place.

CHOPPING AND CHANGING

The formula $A = PR^n$ may be used only when the investment is put into the account and left there without alteration for a certain time at a constant rate of compound interest. If the money in the account, or the rate of interest, is changed in any way, then the formula no longer works. Instead, we solve such problems "one year at a time".

Example 1: A woman borrows €500 for two years at 12% compound interest per annum. She agrees to repay €300 at the end of the first year and to clear the debt at the end of the second year. How much will she have to pay back at the end of the second year?

Solution:

YEAR 1:

Beginning:	500
	×1.12
End:	560
Repays:	−300
Debt:	260

YEAR 2:

Beginning	260
	×1.12
End:	291.2

Answer: €291.20

Example 2: The population of a town increased by 7% one year. The next year it increased by 8% and the following year by 4%. What is the overall percentage increase over the three-year period (to the nearest percent)?

Solution: Let P = the population at the start.

At the end of the first year the population is $1.07P$.

At the end of the second year the population is $1.08(1.07P) = 1.1556P$.

At the end of the third year the population is $1.04(1.1556P) = 1.201824P$.

Therefore, the population has increased by 20%, to the nearest percent.

Example 3: A couple borrow €800 at 11% compound interest per annum. They agree to repay it in two equal annual instalments. Find the value of each instalment to the nearest euro.

Solution: Since the rate is 11%, the multiplier is 1.11

Let x = the value of each instalment.

YEAR 1:

Beginning:	800
	$\times 1.11$
End:	888
Repays €x:	$-x$
Still owes:	$888 - x$

YEAR 2:

Beginning:	$888 - x$
	$\times 1.11$
End:	$985.68 - 1.11x$
Repays €x:	$-x$
Still owes:	$985.68 - 2.11x$

But the debt is now cleared, and so the amount still owed must be zero.

$$\therefore \quad 985.68 - 2.11x = 0$$

$$\therefore \quad 985.68 = 2.11x$$

$$\therefore \quad x = \frac{985.68}{2.11} = 467.15 = €467 \text{ [to nearest euro]}$$

Exercise 10.D

1. A woman put €1000 in a bank which gives 10% compound interest per annum. She withdrew €400 at the end of the first year. How much did she have in her account at the end of the second year?

2. A man borrows €300 from a bank at a rate of 12% compound interest per annum. He agrees to pay back €200 at the end of the first year and to clear the debt at the end of the second year. How much will he have to pay back at the end of the second year?

3. Ms Perkins puts €100 into her account ***each*** year for three successive years. The bank pays 6% compound interest per annum. How much will she have in her account at the end of the third year?

4. A boy put his birthday money, €60, into a building society account, which yields 5% compound interest per annum. After one year, he takes out €43 to buy a pair of jeans. How much will he have in his account at the end of the second year?

5. A farmer borrows €6000 at 11% compound interest per annum. He agrees to repay €2500 at the end of the first year and another €2500 at the end of the second year. How much would he have to repay at the end of the third year in order to clear the debt?

6. A woman borrows €2000 from a bank at 14% compound interest per annum. If she pays back €700 at the end of the first year and €800 at the end of the second year, how much of the debt is still outstanding at the end of the third year?

7. A girl invests €75 in a bank for three years. During the first year the interest rate was 6%. During the second year it was 7%. During the third year it was 6½%. Find the amount in her account at the end of the third year.

8. A woman borrowed €8000 from a bank for two years. During the first year, the interest rate on borrowings was 12.5%. During the second year it was 12.8%. How much did she owe the bank after two years?

9. A man borrows €300 at 10% compound interest per annum. He repays the entire debt by paying back €x at the end of the first year and another €x at the end of the second year. Find the value of x to the nearest integer.

10. A woman borrowed €100 at 12% annual compound interest. She repays the entire debt in two equal annual instalments at the end of the first and second years. Find the amount of each instalment to the nearest euro.

11. A woman borrows €1000 from a credit union at 10% compound interest per annum. She repays €350 at the end of the first year, €x at the end of the second year and €550 at the end of the third year, which clears the debt. Find x.

12. During three successive years, the interest rates for investors at a post-office were 11%, 12% and 10%.
    (i) Mr Black put €300 in the post-office at the beginning of this three-year term, and left it there. How much will he have in his account at the end of the three-year term?
    (ii) Ms White put €100 into a post-office account at the beginning of ***each*** of the three years. How much will she have in her account at the end of the three-year term?

13. A person invested €P in a building society at compound interest. The rate for the first year was 8%. After one year, the person put in a further €P into the building society. The rate for the second year was 10%. The person had €4004 in the account at the end of the second year. Find the value of P.

If the money is left in the account and amounts to €4504.50 at the end of the third year, find the interest rate during the third year.

14. A student borrowed €K at the beginning of her first year at university. The bank charges 10% compound interest on student loans. One year later, at the start of her second year, she borrowed a further €K from the bank. Again, at the start of her third year she borrowed yet another €K.
When she graduated at the end of her third year, the bank informed her that she now owed them €7282. Find the value of K.

15. A bank gives 12½% compound interest per annum on investments. A man invests €800 in this bank. After a year, he withdraws a certain amount. After a second year he withdraws €50 less than the first year. He now has no money left in his account.

How much did he withdraw each year?

16. A woman borrowed €800 at 10% compound interest per annum. She repays it in three equal annual instalments over the following three years. Find the amount of each instalment to the nearest cent.

17. The value of a car depreciates at a rate of 20% in the first year, 15% in the second year and 12½% in the third year. A woman buys a car for €12 000.

(i) Find its value after three years.

(ii) If its value after 4 years is €6426, find the rate of depreciation in the fourth year.

18. The population of a town went down by 20% during the 1970s and up by 20% during the 1980s. By what percent did the population decrease over this twenty-year period?

19. During three successive years the rate of compound interest paid by a bank to investors was 11%, 10% and 9%. However tax of 40% is paid on all the ***interest*** annually.

(i) Patrick put €100 in this bank at the beginning of the three-year term. How much will he have in his account at the end of the three year term?

(ii) His cousin Patricia put €100 in another bank for the same time. This bank paid out a constant rate of r% per annum compound interest, tax free. She ended up with the same amount as her cousin. Find r to the nearest integer.

20. (i) If the rate of inflation is 10% for two successive years, what is the overall percentage rise in prices over this two-year period?

(ii) In a certain country, the rate of inflation for four successive years is 3%, 5%, 7% and 9%. Find, to the nearest percent, the overall increase in prices over this four-year period.

RELATIVE ERROR & PERCENTAGE ERROR

At a sale-of-work there are two competitions. In one, you have to guess the number of sweets in a jar; in the other, you have to guess the mass of a cake.

The 'Count the sweets' competition was won by Pól Ó Murchú. He guessed that there were 547 sweets. The correct answer was 570.

The 'Guess the mass' competition was won by Delilah Smythe. She guessed that the mass was 8.9 kilograms. The true mass was 8.5 kilograms.

But which of these two winners is the better guesser? We can compare their efforts by finding the ***relative error*** or the ***percentage error*** in each case.

Definition: ***Relative error*** $= \dfrac{\text{Error}}{\text{Correct value}}$

Percentage error $= \dfrac{\text{Error}}{\text{Correct value}} \times \dfrac{100}{1}$

In the case of Pól Ó Murchú, the error = 570 – 547 = 23

Therefore, the ***relative error*** $= \dfrac{23}{570} = 0.04035$ and

the ***percentage error*** $= \dfrac{23}{570} \times \dfrac{100}{1} = 4.035\%$

In the case of Delilah Smythe, the error = 8.9 – 8.5 = 0.4

Therefore, the ***relative error*** $= \dfrac{0.4}{8.5} = 0.04706$ and

the ***percentage error*** $= \dfrac{0.4}{8.5} \times \dfrac{100}{1} = 4.706\%$

Since Pól's percentage error is less than Delilah Smythe, we can conclude that he is the better of the two guessers.

1. Always take the error to be a positive number.
2. If the correct value is not available, use an **estimated value** instead, as happens in Example 2, below.

Example 1: Find the percentage error, correct to two decimal places, when 7.5 is rounded off to 8.

Solution: The error = 8 – 7.5 = 0.5

$\therefore$ The percentage error = $\frac{0.5}{7.5} \times \frac{100}{1} = 6.67\%$

Example 2: The width of a house and the adjoining garage are measured to the nearest metre. The house is found to be 7 m wide. The garage is found to be 4 m wide. Find the maximum possible percentage error in saying that the combined width is 11 metres.

Solution: When we measure something to the nearest metre, the maximum possible error is 0.5 metres. For example, if the actual width of the house is 6.5 m, we would say that the width is 7 m, correct to the nearest metre.

So, the width of the house = 7 m ± 0.5 m

The width of the garage = 4 m ± 0.5 m

$\therefore$ The combined width = 11 m ± 1 m

$\therefore$ The maximum % error = $\frac{1}{11} \times \frac{100}{1} = 9.09\%$

[Note that we did not know what the actual widths were, so we used the estimated values instead]

Exercise 10.E

1. A child guesses that the number of peas in a packet is 190. The correct number was 200. Find the percentage error.
2. A debate is held in a school. The headmistress guesses that 60 people will turn up. In fact, 50 people turn up. Find the percentage error in the headmistress' guess.
3. A jockey predicts that he will win 70 races in a season. In fact he wins 80. Find the percentage error in his prediction.
4. Jemima guesses that her granny is 54 years old. In fact, her granny is 60. Find
   (i) the relative error,
   (ii) the percentage error,
   in Jemima's guess.
5. An auctioneer predicts that a painting will sell for €18 000. In fact it sold for €25 000. Find
   (i) the relative error,
   (ii) the percentage error,
   in the auctioneer's prediction.
6. Find the percentage error if the number 1.6 is rounded off to 2.
7. A builder estimates that he will take 37 days to complete a job. In fact, it takes him 40 days. Find the percentage error in his prediction.
8. Find, to the nearest integer, the percentage error when €147 is rounded off to €150.
9. When 2.5 is rounded up to 3, find
   (i) the relative error,
   (ii) the percentage error.

10. Which of these has the greater percentage error?
(i) 43 being rounded off to 40.
(ii) 108 being rounded down to 100.

11. Which of these has the greatest percentage error?
(i) 5 being taken as an approximation for 4.8.
(ii) 50 being taken as an approximation for 53.
(iii) 200 being taken as an approximation for 213.

12. Which of these involves the least percentage error?
(i) 0.4 being taken as an approximation for 0.35.
(ii) 6 being taken as an approximation for 5.5.
(iii) 90 being taken as an approximation for 85.

13. Let $x = 52.47$ and let $y = 58.1$
Find (to one decimal place) the percentage error in each of the following approximate values:
(i) $x = 50$,
(ii) $y = 60$,
(iii) $x + y = 110$.

14. Let $x = 6.7$ and let $y = 12.45$
Find (to two decimal places) the percentage error in each of the following approximate values:
(i) $x = 7$,
(ii) $y = 12$,
(iii) $x + y = 19$,
(iv) $y - x = 5$.

15. Two adjoining houses are measured to the nearest metre. One is found to measure 9 m (to the nearest metre), the other 11 m. Find the maximum possible percentage error in taking their combined widths to be 20 m.

16. If $a = 434$ and $b = 121$, find the percentage error (correct to one decimal place) in the approximation:
$a + b = 400 + 100$.

17. Two adjoining gardens are measured to the nearest metre. One is found to measure 25 m (to the nearest metre), the other 20 m. Find the maximum possible percentage error in taking
(i) the first width to be 25 m,
(ii) the next width to be 20 m,
(iii) their combined width to be 45 metres.

18. Ken and Leah are brother and sister. They measure their heights to the nearest centimetre. Ken finds that his height is 125 cm (to the nearest cm). Leah finds that her height is 135 cm. Find the maximum possible percentage error (correct to one decimal place) in the following statements:
(i) Ken's height is 125 cm,
(ii) Leah's height is 135 cm,
(iii) Leah is 10 cm taller than Ken.

19. $\pi = 3.141592654$ [The mnemonic for the first 10 digits of π is to count the letters in the phrase: "Can I have a large container of coffee right away?"]
Find the percentage error (correct to two significant figures) in these approximations for π:
(i) 3 (ii) 3.14 (iii) $\frac{22}{7}$

20. A Junior Certificate student writes down that $\frac{1}{3} = 0.3$
(i) Find the relative error in this mistake.
(ii) Find the percentage error in this mistake.

REVISION EXERCISE 10.F

1. (a) Find the percentage error when 6.4 is rounded off to 6.

(b) Calculate the compound interest on €10 000 for five years at 6% per annum.

(c) A person deposited €10 000 in a bank account on June 1st, ***each year***, for four consecutive years. The bank pays 6% compound interest per annum. When the fourth deposit had remained earning interest for one full year, how much is in the account?

2. (a) Write 22½ grams as a percentage of ¼ kilogram.

(b) A person invests €750 at 4% compound interest per annum. At the end of the first year, the person withdraws €380. How much will be in the account at the end of the second year?

(c) A woman has a weekly standard rate cut-off point of €520 and weekly tax credits of €75. The standard rate of tax is 20%. The higher rate is 42%. How much will she pay if her weekly wage is (i) €700 (ii) €504.

3. (a) A car depreciates at 15% per annum. It is worth €16 000 in the year 1998. What will it be worth in the year 2001?

(b) The population of a town is 4200. It increases by 10% in a certain year. It decreases by 10% the next year. Find the population at the end of the second year. By what percentage has the population decreased over the two-year period?

(c) A person invests €2000 at r% compound interest per annum. After two years, it amounts to €2205. Find

(i) the value of r,
(ii) the amount after a third year.

4. (a) Write 27 minutes as a percentage of one hour.

(b) A student estimates that the time needed to do her Maths homework is 45 minutes. It acually takes 48 minutes. Find the percentage error in the original estimate.

(c) A man earns €X. He has a standard rate cut-off point of €25 000 and tax credits of €2000. The standard rate of tax is 20% and the higher rate is 42%. If he pays €5520 in tax, find X.

5. (a) A man sleeps from 00.55 until 07.40. What percentage of the 24-hour day did he spend asleep?

(b) Given that $x = 58.8$ and $y = 10.5$, find the percentage error (to the nearest unit) in the following approximations: (i) $x = 60$ (ii) $x + y = 70$

(c) A man invests €y at r% compound interest per annum. After three years it amounts to €1 591 812 and after another year, it amounts to €1 623 648.24.
Find the values of r and y.

6. (a) The acceleration due to gravity, $g = 9.81$. A student takes $g = 10$, for convenience. Find the percentage error, correct to two decimal places.

(b) A person purchased an Investment Bond for €5000. The bond earned interest at a rate of 20% per annum for the first year. At the end of the second year the bond was worth €7500. Find the rate of interest for the second year. During the third year, the rate of compound interest was the average of the rates for the first two years. At the end of the third year, the person cashed the bond, and in doing so, paid 1% commission of the final value of the bond. How much commission was paid, and how much money was left for the person?

7. (a) How much (to the nearest euro) do I have to invest at $4\frac{1}{2}\%$ compound interest per annum in order to have €2000 in my account in four years' time?

(b) Two adjoining houses are measured to the nearest metre. The first is found to have a width of 17 m, the second to have a width of 8 m. Find the maximum possible percentage error in taking their combined width to be 25 m.

(c) A person put €*W* into a Savings Bank, at compound interest. The rate for the first year was 10%. At the end of the first year, the person added another €*W* to the account. The rate for the second year was 8% and for the third year was 5%. If the total investment was worth €5953.50 at the end of three years, find *W*.

8. (a) Which of these involves the greater percentage error?

(i) Rounding 444 off to 450.

(ii) Rounding 7.88 off to 8.

(b) Find the rate of compound interest if \$75 000 amounts to \$84 270 in two years.

(c) A student borrowed €100 at 15% compound interest per annum. He repays the debt in two equal annual instalments – the first at the end of the first year, the second at the end of the following year. Find, to the nearest cent, the value of each instalment.

9. (a) Express 28 as a percentage of 365 (correct to two significant figures).

(b) x, y and z are three real numbers. When they are corrected to one decimal place, the results are

$x = 4.1$; $y = 19.6$; $z = 312.8$

Find the maximum percentage error (correct to two significant figures) in the following statements:

(i) $x + y = 23.7$,

(ii) $x + y + z = 336.5$

(c) The value of a car depreciates at a rate of 15% per annum.

(i) A woman bought a car for €9500. What will it be worth three years later?

(ii) Her husband bought a car five years ago. It is now worth €3549.64. What did he buy it for?

10. (a) In a co-educational school, 40% of the students are girls and 60% are boys. The following year, the number of girls goes up by 10% and the number of boys goes down by 20%. What percentage (to the nearest whole number) of the pupils are now girls?

(b) A couple have annual earnings of €50 000. Their standard rate cut-off point is €37 000 and their tax credits are €2860. The standard rate of tax is 20% and the higher rate is 42%. Calculate

(i) their annual take-home pay

(ii) the percentage increase in their take-home pay if their earnings increase by 8%.

(c) A woman borrows €1000 for three years at 12% compound interest per annum. She repays it in three equal annual instalments at the end of each year. Find the value of each instalment to the nearest euro.

1. To change fractions or decimals to percentages, multiply by 100.

2. If the rate of compound interest is 6%, multiply by 1.06 each year.
   If the rate is 13%, the multiplier is 1.13 etc.
   If the rate of depreciation is 6%, the multiplier is 0.94
   If the rate of depreciation is 13%, the multiplier is 0.87 etc.

3. The compound interest formula: $A = PR^n$,
   where A = the amount, P = the principal, R = the multiplier and n = the number of years.

4. ***Relative error*** $= \dfrac{\text{Error}}{\text{Correct value}}$

5. ***Percentage error*** $= \dfrac{\text{Error}}{\text{Correct value}} \times \dfrac{100}{1}$

Chapter 11

Arrangements, Choices and Probability

THE FUNDAMENTAL PRINCIPLE OF COUNTING

In a restaurant, there are five choices of main course: Burger, Chicken, Fish, Lasagne or Salad. There are two choices for dessert: Apple tart or Ice-cream. How many different meals can be eaten there?

The answer is $5 \times 2 = 10$.
Here they are:

1. (Burger **and** Apple tart)
2. (Chicken **and** Apple Tart)
3. (Fish **and** Apple Tart)
4. (Lasagne **and** Apple Tart)
5. (Salad **and** Apple Tart)
6. (Burger **and** Ice-cream)
7. (Chicken **and** Ice-cream)
8. (Fish **and** Ice-cream)
9. (Lasagne **and** Ice-cream)
10. (Salad **and** Ice-cream)

This is an example of the 'Fundamental Principle of Counting', which is given here:

The Fundamental Principle of Counting:

If one task can be accomplished in x different ways and, following this, a second task can be accomplished in y different ways, then the first task followed by the second task can be accomplished in xy different ways.

Here are the three steps for solving any problems which involve ***arranging***, or one task followed by another:

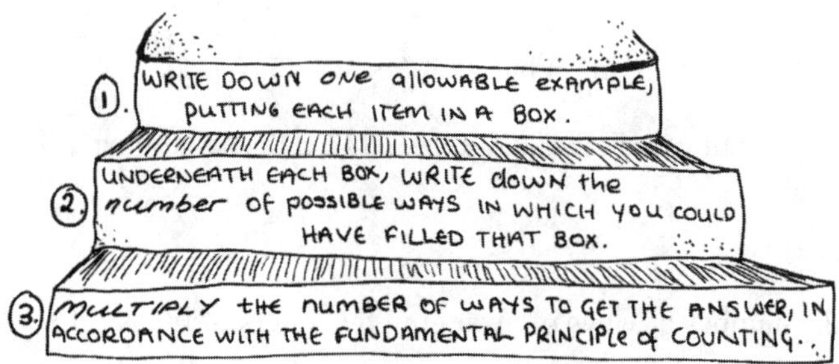

1. WRITE DOWN ONE ALLOWABLE EXAMPLE, PUTTING EACH ITEM IN A BOX.
2. UNDERNEATH EACH BOX, WRITE DOWN THE NUMBER OF POSSIBLE WAYS IN WHICH YOU COULD HAVE FILLED THAT BOX.
3. MULTIPLY THE NUMBER OF WAYS TO GET THE ANSWER, IN ACCORDANCE WITH THE FUNDAMENTAL PRINCIPLE OF COUNTING.

In this way, the above example would be done like this:

	1st Course		2nd Course	
One example:	Lasagne		Ice Cream	
Number of ways:	5	•	2	= 10 : ***Answer***

Example 1: Raffle tickets are each labelled with a letter followed by one digit. (F5, Y9, J0, etc.). How many different such tickets could there be?

Solution: There are 26 letters in the English alphabet. There are 10 digits in the decimal system (0, 1, 2, 3, 4, 5, 6, 7, 8, 9).

One example:	M	8	
Number of ways:	26	10	= 260 : ***Answer***

Example 2: How many ways are there of arranging the letters of these words?
(i) **SUM** (ii) **MATHS**

Solution:

(i)

One example:	U	S	M	
Number of ways:	3	2	1	= 6 : ***Answer***

[The 6 arrangements are SUM, SMU, USM, UMS, MUS, MSU]

(ii)

One example:	A	S	M	T	H	
Number of ways:	5	4	3	2	1	= 120 : ***Answer***

FACTORIALS!

There is a special mathematical way of writing (and calculating) $5 \times 4 \times 3 \times 2 \times 1$. It is 5!

Your calculator has a button marked [*n!*] or [*x!*] .

Take your calculator, and press [5] [*n!*]. The number 120 should come

Example 3: Find the number of ways of arranging the letters of the word **LEAVING**

(i) if there are no restrictions,
(ii) if they must begin with V,
(iii) if they must ***not*** begin with V,
(iv) if they must begin and end with a vowel.

Solution: (i) Since there are no restrictions, we can write ***any*** letter in each slot:

One example:	E	L	A	G	N	V	I	
Number of ways:	7 .	6 .	5 .	4 .	3 .	2 .	1	= 7! = 5040

(ii) When we write this, there is 1 choice for the first letter (it has to be V). After that, any letter will do.

One example:	V	A	E	G	N	I	L	
Number of ways:	1 .	6 .	5 .	4 .	3 .	2 .	1	= 1 x 6! = 720

(iii) Here is one such arrangement: ENVGLIA.

But this time we will use the ***subtraction method*** to count the number of arrangements.

There are 5040 arrangements altogether [from (i)].

Of these, 720 ***do*** begin with V [from (ii)].

Hence, the number of arrangements which ***do not*** begin with V = 5040 – 720 = 4320.

(iv) The ***first*** letter has to be a vowel: 3 choices.

The ***last*** letter must be another vowel: 2 choices.

Then fill the ***remaining 5 slots*** with any of the five remaining letters (5-4-3-2-1 choices).

It is very important to fill the slots (and their corresponding numbers) in this order: first, last, the rest. Here is a rule, called the Three-F-rule, to help you remember this:
Fix up the **F**ussy places **F**irst!

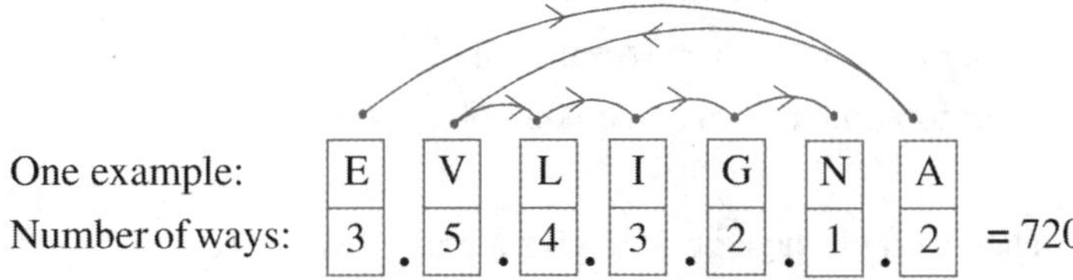

Example 4: (i) How many 3-digit numbers can be made using some of the digits: 5, 6, 7, 8, 9 without repeating any digit?
[e.g. 586, 796, 578 – but ***not*** 556 or 888]

(ii) How many of these are greater than 800?

(iii) How many are even?

(iv) How many are odd?

(v) How many are multiples of 5?

Solution (i)

One example:	6	9	5	
Number of choices:	5 .	4 .	3	= 60

[Note: If repetitions ***were*** allowed, the answer would be $5 \times 5 \times 5 = 125$, since ***any*** of the five digits would have been allowable in each case.]

(ii) The ***first digit*** must be either 8 or 9 : 2 choices.

Then the rest are chosen from the remaining 4 digits.

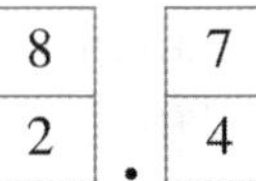

One example:	8	7	5	
Number of choices:	2 .	4 .	3	= 24

(iii) The ***last*** digit must be 6 or 8 (2 choices) in order to give an even number. Use the Three-F-rule: **F**ix up the **F**ussy places **F**irst! So we fill the ***last*** slot first, then the rest.

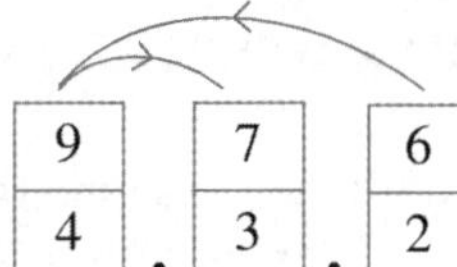

One example:	9	7	6	
Number of choices:	4 .	3 .	2	= 24

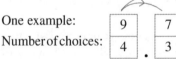

(iv) Use the ***subtraction method***.

There are 60 arrangements, altogether [from (i)].

Of these, 24 were even [from (iii)].

Therefore, the rest must be odd: $60 - 24 = 36$

(v) The ***last*** digit must be 5, to give a multiple of 5. [e.g. 675, 985, 785]

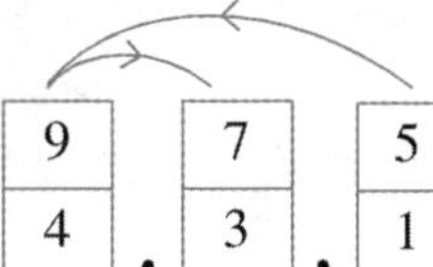

One example:	9	7	5	
Number of choices:	4 .	3 .	1	= 12

Exercise 11.A

1. In a restaurant there are 6 choices of main course (Fish, Beef, Mussels, Pasta, Lasagne, Nut loaf) and 3 choices of dessert (Black Forest Gateau, Rhubarb Crumble, Ice-cream). How many different two-course meals are possible?

2. A boy is preparing to dress for a disco. He has five different tee-shirts and three pairs of jeans. Ignoring the rest of his attire, how many different ways can he dress?

3. The menu in a diner has 5 choices of starter, 10 main courses and 4 choices of dessert. How many different three-course meals are possible?

4. There are three harbours on the north side of the river and six harbours on the south side. You have to sail from a harbour on the north side to a harbour on the south side. How many possible routes could you choose?

5. Every member of a computer society is given an access code, which consists of two ***different*** letters (RP, LH, ZK, KZ, but not KK or ZZ). How many members could the society have, if each member has a different code?

6. How many ways are there of arranging the letters of **NAME**?

7. In how many ways can the letters of the word **MEDIAN** be arranged?

8. In how many ways can the letters of the word **TRIANGLES** be arranged
   (i) if there are no restrictions,
   (ii) if they must begin with N,
   (iii) if they must not begin with N?

9. In how many ways can the letters of the word **LINEAR** be arranged
   (i) if there are no restrictions,
   (ii) if they must begin with R,
   (iii) if they must begin with a vowel,
   (iv) if the first two letters must both be vowels?

10. How many ways of arranging the letters of the name **NICHOLAS** are there
   (i) if there are no restrictions,
   (ii) if they must begin with S and end with C,
   (iii) if the first and last letters must be vowels,
   (iv) if the first and last letters must be consonants,
   (v) if the first three letters must be vowels?

11. How many ways are there of arranging the letters of the word **FACETIOUS**
   (i) if there are no restrictions,
   (ii) if they must begin with F and end with C,
   (iii) if the first and last letters must be vowels,
   (iv) if the first and last letters must be consonants,
   (v) if the first four letters must be consonants?

12. Six dogs enter a race. A betting slip has to be filled out. You must guess which dog will come first, which second and which third. In how many ways can a betting slip be filled out?

13. How many four digit numbers can be made by arranging the digits 1, 4, 6, 8 without repetitions
(i) if there are no restrictions,
(ii) if they must be even,
(iii) if they must be odd,
(iv) if they must be greater than 7000,
(v) if they must be less than 7000?

14. Five horses (A, B, C, D and E) enter a race.
(i) In how many different orders can they finish the race?
(ii) If A comes first, how many different orders are possible?
(iii) If A comes first and B comes last, how many different orders are possible?

15. How many three-digit numbers can be made using any of the digits 2, 3, 4, 5
(i) if repetitions are not allowed,
(ii) if repetitions are allowed?

16. How many four-digit numbers can be made using only the digits 1, 3, 4, 5
(i) if repetitions are not allowed,
(ii) if repetitions are allowed?

17. How many different numbers between 3000 and 9000 can be made using the digits 1, 3, 5, 7
(i) if no digit may be repeated,
(ii) if digits may be repeated?

18. In how many ways can the letters of the word **PARKING** be arranged
(i) if there are no restrictions,
(ii) if the A must come immediately before the I,
[HINT: Treat AI as **one** letter.]
(iii) if the two vowels must be together (as AI or IA),
(iv) if the two vowels must be apart?
[HINT: Use the subtraction method.]

19. In how many different ways can the letters of the word **WINTER** be arranged
(i) if there are no restrictions,
(ii) if the two vowels must be together,
(iii) if the two vowels must be apart?

20. An athlete has to run from A to B to C to D. There are three ways to travel from A to B, four ways for the journey from B to C and four ways for the last leg, from C to D.
(i) In how many different ways can the athlete go?
(ii) If one of the routes from C to D is blocked, how many different routes can be taken?

21. Every PIN number for an A.T.M. (for getting money-from-the-wall) consists of four digits. The first digit is never zero. How many different PIN numbers are there? [NOTE: Digits may be repeated: e.g. 8819, 5022, 7777, etc.]

22. Ten pop-groups sing in a contest. Each judge has to write down their choice for the first four places (first, second, third and fourth).
(i) In how many different ways can a judge's decision go?
(ii) If a certain judge has made her mind up which group will come first, how many different ways can the remainder of her decisions go?

23. Three girls (Alison, Betty, Carol) and three boys (Darren, Eddy, Ferdia) are to line up for a photograph. How many ways are there of arranging them in a straight line
(i) if they may line up in any order,
(ii) if the arrangement must be girl-boy-girl-boy-girl-boy?

24. Eleven people (six girls and five boys) are to line up in a straight line for a photograph. In how many different ways can they be arranged
- (i) if they can be arranged in any order,
- (ii) if the arrangement must be girl-boy-girl-boy- etc.,
- (iii) if the six girls must be on the left and then the five boys on the right?

25. Evaluate:
- (i) $3! + 4!$
- (ii) $3! \times 2!$
- (iii) $1! + 2! + 3!$

26. Investigate if
- (i) $2! + 3! = 5!$
- (ii) $7! - 3! = 4!$
- (iii) $2! \times 4! = 8!$

27. Evaluate:
- (i) $\dfrac{6!}{4!}$
- (ii) $\dfrac{3! \times 7!}{2! \times 5!}$
- (iii) $\dfrac{10!}{3!\,7!}$

28. If $n(9!) = 10!$, find the value of n.

29. If $n(7!) = 9!$, find the value of n.

30. If $\dfrac{20!}{19!} = k$, find the value of k.

31. Simplify:
- (i) $\dfrac{(n+1)!}{n!}$
- (ii) $\dfrac{n!}{(n-1)!}$

32. If $x!\,(23!) = 24!$, write down the value of x.

33. (a) Prove that $n! = \dfrac{(n+1)!}{n+1}$
- (b) By letting $n = 0$ in the above formula, show that $0! = 1$.
- (c) Show that $0! + 1! = 2!$

34. How many ways are there of arranging the letters of the word **PIRATES**
- (i) if there are no restrictions,
- (ii) if the arrangement must alternate: consonant-vowel-consonant-vowel etc.,
- (iii) if the three vowels must be together in any order?

CHOOSING VERSUS ARRANGING

Take 5 letters: A, B, C, D, E. If we want to ***arrange*** these letters three at a time, there are $5 \times 4 \times 3 = 60$ ways. And here they are:

ABC	ABD	ABE	ACD	ACE	ADE	BCD	BCE	BDE	CDE
ACB	ADB	AEB	ADC	AEC	AED	BDC	BEC	BED	CED
BAC	BAD	BAE	CAD	CAE	DAE	CBD	CBE	DBE	DCE
BCA	BDA	BEA	CDA	CEA	DEA	CDB	CEB	DEB	DEC
CAB	DAB	EAB	DAC	EAC	EAD	DBC	EBC	EBD	ECD
CBA	DBA	EBA	DCA	ECA	EDA	DCB	ECB	EDB	EDC

But if we want to ***choose*** three of these letters, how many choices do we have? When we choose, the ***order*** in which the three are chosen does not matter. The three choices are just thrown into a bag without order. Here are the choices:

But could we have found the answer 10, without listing them out? Is there a formula for working it out? The answer is 'YES!'. Read on to find out.

CHOOSING r ITEMS FROM A SAMPLE OF n

If you have a group of n items and you have to ***choose*** a sample of r of them, then the number of different samples which you could possibly pick is written $\binom{n}{r}$ [spoken 'n – C – r'] and is evaluated in this way:

Note:

$$\binom{n}{r} = \frac{n!}{r!(n-r)!}$$

For example, if you have 7 people on a panel, and you have to ***choose*** a team of three of them, then the number of different teams which you could pick is:

$$\binom{7}{3} = \frac{7!}{3!\ 4!} = \frac{7.6.5.4.3.2.1}{3.2.1.4.3.2.1} = \frac{7.6.5}{3.2.1} = 35$$

If there are 10 students in your class and you have to ***choose*** 4 of them for a debating team, then the number of different teams which you could choose is:

$$\binom{10}{4} = \frac{10!}{4!\ 6!} = \frac{10.9.8.7.6.5.4.3.2.1}{4.3.2.1.6.5.4.3.2.1} = \frac{10.9.8.7}{4.3.2.1} = 210$$

TWO SHORT-CUTS

There are two short ways of evaluating, say, $\binom{10}{4}$.

1. On a calculator, press [1] [0] [nCr] [4] [=].
   The number 210 will come up on the screen.

2. Think of the countdown: 10-9-8-7-6-5-4-3-2-1.

Note:

$$\binom{10}{4} = \frac{\text{The first 4 in the countdown}}{\text{The last 4 in the countdown}} = \frac{10.9.8.7}{4.3.2.1} = 210$$

Take another example: $\binom{10}{2} = \frac{\text{The first 2 in the countdown}}{\text{The last 2 in the countdown}} = \frac{10.9}{2.1} = 45$

Similarly, $\binom{7}{3} = \dfrac{\text{First 3 numbers in 7-6-5-4-3-2-1}}{\text{Last 3 numbers in 7-6-5-4-3-2-1}} = \dfrac{7.6.5}{3.2.1} = 35$

And also, $\binom{7}{4} = \dfrac{\text{First 4 numbers in 7-6-5-4-3-2-1}}{\text{Last 4 numbers in 7-6-5-4-3-2-1}} = \dfrac{7.6.5.4}{4.3.2.1} = 35$

What a surprise! $\binom{7}{4} = \binom{7}{3}$.

This is an example of the 'Twin rule':

Twin rule: $\binom{n}{r} = \binom{n}{n-r}$

i.e. Two 'chooseys' will be equal if the top numbers are the same and the two bottom numbers add up to the top number.

This means, that $\binom{20}{18} = \binom{20}{2}$ [since 18 + 2 = 20.]

Again, $\binom{16}{12} = \binom{16}{4}$ [Since 12 + 4 = 16]

And also, $\binom{11}{10} = \binom{11}{1}$ [since 10 + 1 = 11]

Now, if there are n people on a panel and you have to pick a team of n players, how many different teams can you pick? Obviously, the answer is ***'one'***. From this, we can make two conclusions: $\binom{n}{n} = 1$ and, by the twin rule, $\binom{n}{0} = 1$.

Summary

$\binom{n}{n} = 1, \quad \binom{n}{0} = 1, \quad \binom{n}{r} = \dfrac{\text{First } r \text{ in the countdown}}{\text{Last } r \text{ in the countdown}}$

If r is rather large, use the 'twin rule': $\binom{n}{r} = \binom{n}{n-r}$

Example 1: Show that $\binom{12}{3} + \binom{12}{4} = \binom{13}{4}$.

Solution: Left Hand Side = $\binom{12}{3} + \binom{12}{4} = \dfrac{12.11.10}{3.2.1} + \dfrac{12.11.10.9}{4.3.2.1}$

$= 220 + 495$

$= 715$

Right Hand Side = $\binom{13}{4} = \dfrac{13.12.11.10}{4.3.2.1} = 715$

Both sides = 715. Therefore the proposition is true. ***Q.E.D.***

Example 2: There are 8 people on a panel of soccer players: A, B, C, D, E, F, G and H. The manager has to choose 6 players for a six-a-side match.

(i) How many choices are there?

(ii) If H must be chosen, how many choices are there?

(iii) If H must not be chosen, how many choices are there?

Solution:

(i) $\binom{8}{6} = \binom{8}{2} = \frac{8.7}{2.1} = 28$

(ii) H must be chosen. Therefore the manager has to choose 5 more players from the remaining 7 members of the panel.

The number of ways $= \binom{7}{5} = \binom{7}{2} = \frac{7.6}{2.1} = 21$

(iii) You could use the ***subtraction method*** here.
There are 28 possible teams [from (i) above].
Of these, 21 include H [from (ii)].
Therefore, the number of teams which ***do not*** include H = 28 – 21 = 7.

Example 3: Fifteen people go to a sherry party. They all shake hands with one another. How many handshakes take place?

Solution: A handshake requires 2 people. Every time you choose two different people from the 15, you get another handshake.

Therefore, the number of handshakes $= \binom{15}{2} = \frac{15.14}{2.1} = 105$

TWO LITTLE WORDS

1. In accordance with the ***Fundamental Principle of Counting***, the word ***and*** corresponds to the mathematical symbol : ×
2. The word ***or*** corresponds to the mathematical symbol: +

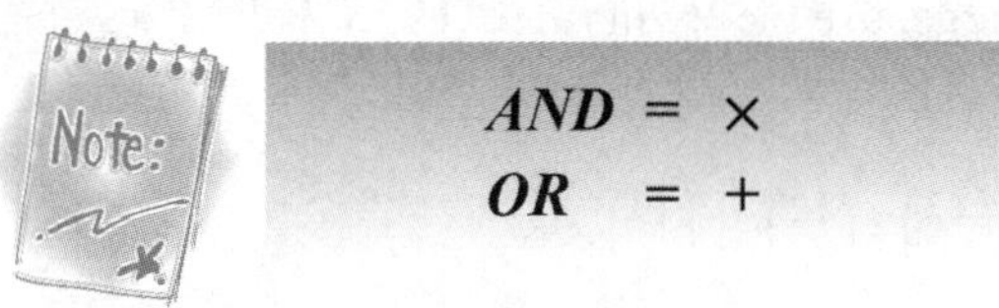

Example 4: There are 7 women and 5 men in a table-tennis club. A team of four has to be chosen. How many different teams can be chosen

(i) if there are no restrictions,

(ii) if there must be two women and two men,

(iii) if there must be more women than men?

Solution: (i) Four of the 12 members have to be chosen: $\binom{12}{4} = 495$

(ii) We must choose 2 women from 7 ***and*** 2 men from 5:

$\binom{7}{2} \times \binom{5}{2} = 21 \times 10 = 210$

(iii) We must choose:

3 women ***and*** 1 man ***or*** 4 women ***and*** 0 men

$$\binom{7}{3} \times \binom{5}{1} + \binom{7}{4} \times \binom{5}{0}$$
$$= 35 \times 5 + 35 \times 1$$
$$= 175 + 35$$
$$= 210$$

Exercise 11.B

Evaluate the following:

1. (i) $\binom{11}{2}$ (ii) $\binom{9}{2}$ (iii) $\binom{14}{2}$

(iv) $\binom{6}{3}$ (v) $\binom{12}{1}$

2. (i) $\binom{16}{2}$ (ii) $\binom{10}{3}$ (iii) $\binom{14}{4}$

(iv) $\binom{7}{5}$ (v) $\binom{19}{18}$

3. (i) $\binom{10}{0}$ (ii) $\binom{7}{6}$ (iii) $\binom{11}{8}$

(iv) $\binom{8}{5}$ (v) $\binom{13}{13}$

4. (i) $\binom{11}{0}+\binom{11}{1}$

(ii) $\binom{9}{6}+\binom{10}{6}$

(iii) $\binom{14}{10}+\binom{14}{11}$

(iv) $\binom{6}{1}+\binom{6}{2}+\binom{6}{3}$

(v) $\binom{4}{0}+\binom{4}{1}+\binom{4}{2}+\binom{4}{3}+\binom{4}{4}$

5. Verify the following:

(i) $\binom{5}{2}+\binom{5}{3}=\binom{6}{3}$

(ii) $\binom{9}{3}-\binom{8}{3}=\binom{8}{2}$

(iii) $\binom{14}{5}+\binom{14}{8}=\binom{15}{6}$

(iv) $\binom{11}{1}+\binom{11}{2}=\binom{12}{2}$

(v) $\binom{12}{1}+\binom{12}{2}+\binom{13}{3}=\binom{14}{3}$

6. If $\binom{12}{x}=\binom{12}{4}$, write down the value of x, where $x \neq 4$.

7. If $\binom{19}{x}=\binom{19}{14}$, write down the value of x, where $x \neq 14$.

8. If $\binom{22}{10}=\binom{22}{x}$, write down the value of x, where $x \neq 10$.

9. How many ways are there of choosing a committee of five people from a panel of twelve?

10. How many ways are there of choosing a team of 11 players from a panel of 13?

11. There are 20 students in a class. Two of them are to be chosen for a debating team. How many possible choices are there?

12. Here is a set: $S = \{a, b, c, d, e, f\}$.
(i) How many subsets, each containing 4 elements can be chosen from the elements of S?
(ii) How many of these contain b?
(iii) How many do not contain b?

13. There are seven members in a club: a, b, c, d, e, f and g. The president has to choose three of them to represent the club at a convention.
(i) How many different choices are there?
(ii) How many choices are there if **g** must be chosen?
(iii) How many choices are there if **g** must ***not*** be chosen?
(iv) How many choices are there if both **a** and **b** must be included?

14. Thirteen people all shake hands with one another. How many handshakes take place?

15. Seventeen people enter a chess competition, in which each player plays everybody else once. How many chess matches take place?

16. Twenty-two teams play a league, in which every team plays every other team ***twice***. How many games take place?

17. A manufacturer makes marbles. Each marble has four colours, chosen from the colours: Red, Green, Yellow, Orange, Brown, Purple, Black, White.
(i) How many different coloured marbles are possible?
(ii) How many different coloured marbles have red as one of their four colours?
(iii) How many different coloured marbles have both white and black as two of their colours?
(iv) How many different coloured marbles have white but not black?

18. A lottery card has 42 numbers on it. You have to choose six of these. How many ways are there of choosing?

19. A fifth-year student has to choose 3 subjects from the following list: Biology, Accounting, Chemistry, German, History, Latin, Physics, Greek and Business Organisation.
(i) How many different choices are possible?
(ii) How many choices include Latin?
(iii) How many choices exclude Latin?
(iv) How many choices contain one and only one science subject?

20. Ten points are marked on a circle.

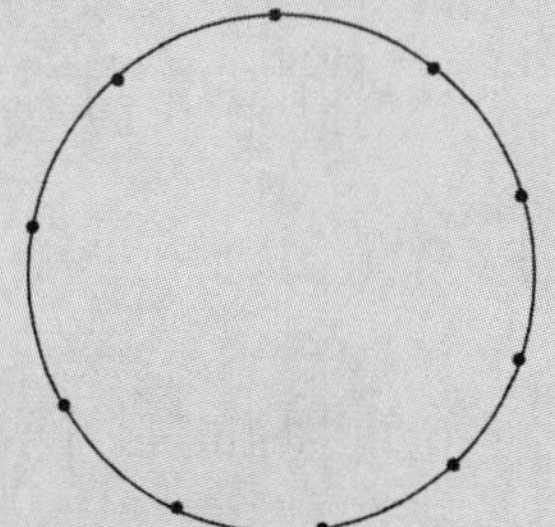

How many ***chords*** can be formed, joining any two of these points?

21. Twelve points are drawn on a circle.

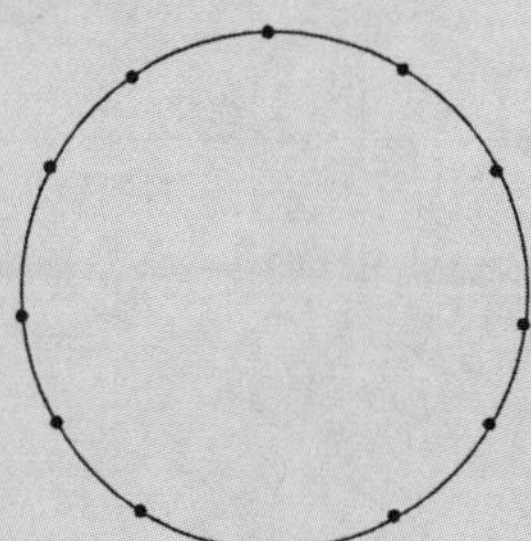

How many triangles can be formed, which have these points as vertices?

22. How many different 'hands' can you be dealt in ordinary poker? [A 'hand' consists of five cards, chosen at random from a pack of fifty-two]. Give your answer to the nearest half-million.

PROBABILITY

Definition:
When an experiment takes place, the probability of an event taking place is defined as the fraction:

$$\frac{\text{Number of ways of the event happening}}{\text{Number of all possible outcomes}}$$

This definition can be written mathematically. If S = the set of all possible outcomes (sometimes called the ***sample space***), and if E is the ***event*** we want to happen, then the probability that E will occur is written P(E) and is given by the definition:

$$P(E) = \frac{\#E}{\#S}$$

Example 1: A fair die is rolled. What is the probability of getting a 'six'?

Solution: There are 6 possible outcomes in the sample space:

$S = \{1, 2, 3, 4, 5, 6\}$. Therefore $\#S = 6$.

The event we want to happen $= E = \{6\}$.

Therefore, $\#E = 1$.

$$P(E) = \frac{\#E}{\#S} = \frac{1}{6}$$

This means that you would expect to get a 'six' one sixth of the time. If you rolled this die 600 times, you would expect to get a 'six' 100 times.

Example 2: A card is drawn at random from a full pack. Find the probability that the card will be

(i) a king,

(ii) a spade,

(iii) a spade or a king.

A card is drawn at random from a full pack and then replaced. This experiment is repeated 100 times. How many times would you expect to get a spade or a king, to the nearest whole number?

Solution:

(i) There are 52 cards in the pack. $\therefore$ $\#S = 52$.

There are 4 kings in the pack. $\therefore$ $\#E = 4$.

$$\text{P}(E) = \frac{\#E}{\#S} = \frac{4}{52} = \frac{1}{13}$$

(ii) There are 52 cards in the pack. $\therefore$ $\#S = 52$.
There are 13 spades in the pack. $\therefore$ $\#E = 13$.

$$P(E) = \frac{\#E}{\#S} = \frac{13}{52} = \frac{1}{4}$$

(iii) You must be careful here not to count the king of spades twice.
There are 52 cards in the pack. $\therefore$ $\#S = 52$.
There are 13 spades and 3 ***other*** kings. $\therefore$ $\#E = 16$.

$$P(E) = \frac{\#E}{\#S} = \frac{16}{52} = \frac{4}{13}$$

This means that you would expect to get a spade or a king $\frac{4}{13}$ of the time. If the experiment is done 100 times, we would expect to get a spade or a king $\frac{4}{13}$ of $100 = 31$ times (to the nearest whole number).

Example 3 You are playing a board game. You roll two dice. What is the probability that you will

(i) get a total of 8 on the dice,

(ii) get a total of 11 or more?

Solution: When two dice are rolled, the sample space is a set of 36 couples:

$S = \{(1,1), (1,2), (1,3), (1,4), (1,5), (1,6),$
$(2,1), (2,2), (2,3), (2,4), (2,5), (2,6),$
$(3,1), (3,2), (3,3), (3,4), (3,5), (3,6),$
$(4,1), (4,2), (4,3), (4,4), (4,5), (4,6),$
$(5,1), (5,2), (5,3), (5,4), (5,5), (5,6),$
$(6,1), (6,2), (6,3), (6,4), (6,5), (6,6)\}$

(i) You want to get a total of 8.
$\therefore E = \{(2, 6), (3, 5), (4, 4), (5, 3), (6, 2)\}$

$$\therefore P(E) = \frac{\#E}{\#S} = \frac{5}{36}$$

(ii) You want to get a total of 11 or more.
$\therefore E = \{(6, 5), (5, 6), (6, 6)\}$

$$\therefore P(E) = \frac{\#E}{\#S} = \frac{3}{36} = \frac{1}{12}$$

Exercise 11.C

1. A fair coin is flipped. Find the probability of getting a 'head'.
2. A fair die is rolled. Find the probability of getting
   (i) a 'five',
   (ii) an even number,
   (iii) a number less than 3,
   (iv) a factor of 6,
   (v) a number which is not a factor of 6.
3. Ten tickets are numbered 1, 2, 3, 4, 5, 6, 7, 8, 9, 10. A ticket is chosen at random. Find the probability of getting
   (i) the number 10,
   (ii) a number greater than 6,
   (iii) a number less than 4,
   (iv) a factor of 10,
   (v) a number which is not a factor of 10.
4. A letter is chosen randomly from the eleven letters

   MISSISSIPPI.

   Find the probability that the letter is
   (i) an 'S',
   (ii) a 'P',
   (iii) an 'M',
   (iv) an 'I',
   (v) not an 'I'.
5. A class consists of 18 boys and 6 girls. A student is chosen at random from the class. Find the probability that the student will be
   (i) a girl,
   (ii) a boy.
6. A fair die is rolled 60 times. How many times would you expect to get
   (i) a 'four',
   (ii) a 'five' or a 'six',
   (iii) an odd number?
7. A number is chosen at random from the numbers

   {11, 12, 13, 14, 15, 16, 17, 18, 19}

   Find the probability that the number is
   (i) a multiple of 3,
   (ii) a prime number.
8. A card is picked at random from a full pack of 52 cards. Find the probability that the card will be
   (i) an ace,
   (ii) a diamond,
   (iii) a red card,
   (iv) a diamond or a black card,
   (v) an ace or a diamond.
9. A bag contains marbles; 6 are black, 4 are white and 10 are red. A marble is drawn at random from the bag. Find the probability that the marble is
   (i) red,
   (ii) black,
   (iii) red or black,
   (iv) not red,
   (v) not black.
10. A person is chosen at random and asked on what day of the week she was born. What is the probability that the day of her birth was
    (i) a Sunday,
    (ii) not a Sunday,
    (iii) a Saturday or Sunday,
    (iv) a week day [Monday-Friday],
    (v) a day beginning with the letter T?
11. Two dice are rolled. List the 36 elements of the sample space.
    Find the probability of getting
    (i) a double 'six',
    (ii) a total of 9 on the two dice,
    (iii) a total of 10 or more,
    (iv) at least one 'six',
    (v) a double [i.e. the same score on each die].
12. A person, chosen at random, is asked to name the month of their birthday. Taking all months as equally likely, find the probability that the month will be
    (i) December,
    (ii) a month beginning with the letter J,
    (iii) a month ending with Y.

13. One hundred students, girls and boys, take an exam and the grades which they get are tabled as follows:

Grade	A	B	C	D	E
#Girls	10	12	16	8	2
#Boys	8	16	10	10	8

A student is picked at random. Find the probability that this student is a

(i) girl who got grade A,
(ii) boy who got grade A or B,
(iii) boy or girl who got grade C,
(iv) boy or girl who got an 'honour' (i.e. an A, B or C),
(v) a student who failed the test (i.e. got less than D).

14. The following is the break-down of left-handers and right-handers in a tennis club, which has 99 members.

	Left-handed	Right-handed
Male	14	44
Female	11	30

A member of the club is chosen at random. Find the probability that the person is a

(i) left-handed female,
(ii) right-handed male,
(iii) left-handed player,
(iv) male.

15. A brown bag contains seven tickets labelled 1, 2, 3, 4, 5, 6, 7. A white bag contains three tickets, labelled 8, 9, 10. A ticket is drawn from each bag, at random.

List the 21 couples of the sample space. Find the probability that the total will be

(i) exactly 10,
(ii) 11 or more,
(iii) an even number,
(iv) an odd number,
(v) fifteen or more.

16. A coin is flipped and then a die is rolled. List the set of all possible outcomes. Hence, find the probability that the outcome will be

(i) a head followed by a 6,
(ii) a tail followed by an even number,
(iii) a head followed by a number greater than 2.

17. Three cards, numbered 4, 5, 6, are shuffled and placed, face up, on a table in a row. List the six possible line-ups. Hence find the probability that

(i) the line up is 6-5-4,
(ii) the middle card is 4,
(iii) the first card is even numbered,
(iv) the first card has a greater number than the second card,
(v) the first two cards are even numbered.

18. A pair of dice is rolled 720 times during a game of Monopoly. How many times would you expect to get

(i) a total of 2,
(ii) a total of 3,
(iii) a 'five' on at least one die,
(iv) a total which is a multiple of 5?

19. A coin is flipped three times. Copy and complete the list of possible outcomes: {HHH, HHT, HTH, ... }
Find the probability of getting

(i) three tails,
(ii) exactly two heads,
(iii) at least one head,
(iv) at most one head,
(v) one head exactly.

20. 100 tickets are numbered 1-100. Numbers 1-30 are pink. Numbers 31-80 are green. The rest are white.

A ticket is selected at random. Find the probability that the ticket will be

(i) pink,
(ii) not pink,
(iii) pink and even numbered,
(iv) pink or even numbered.

21. The five letters A, B, C, D, E are arranged in a row.
(i) In how many different ways can this be done?
(ii) How many of these arrangements begin with a vowel?
(iii) If these five letters are arranged at random, what is the probability that the first letter will be a vowel?

22. The letters of the word **POWERS** are arranged.
(i) In how many different ways can this be done?
(ii) How many of these arrangements begin with a vowel and end with a vowel?
(iii) If these five letters are arranged at random, what is the probability that the first and last letters will be vowels?

23. There are 5 girls and 7 boys in a table-tennis club. Two members have to be ***chosen*** for a committee.
(i) How many different committees can be chosen?
(ii) How many of these committees consist of one girl and one boy?
(iii) If the committee is chosen by lot (i.e. at random), what is the probability that there will be one girl and one boy on the committee?

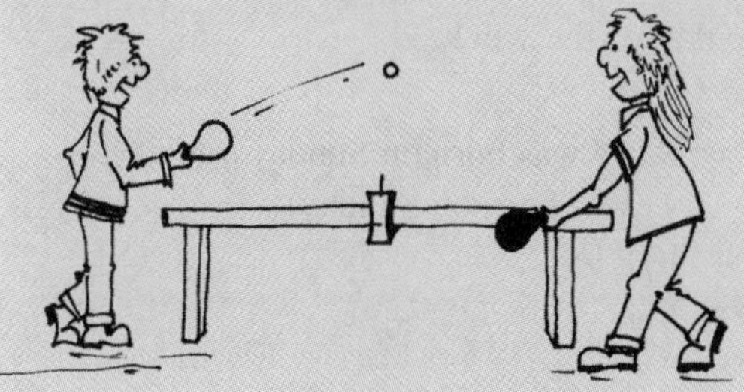

24. There are 10 women and 6 men in a bridge club. Three members have to be ***chosen*** for a committee.
(i) How many different committees can be chosen?
(ii) How many different committees can be chosen, if they must contain 2 women and 1 man?
(iii) If the committee is chosen by lot, what is the probability that there will be two women and one man on the committee?

25. Five letters are chosen at random from the letters of the word **FACETIOUS**. What is the probability of getting 3 vowels and 2 consonants?

26. The letters of the word **DECIMAL** are arranged at random. What is the probability that the arrangement will
(i) begin with a vowel,
(ii) begin with a consonant,
(iii) begin and end with a consonant?

27. A committee (consisting of six people) is chosen at random from a group of five women and five men. Find the probability that the committee will contain three women and three men.

28. The letters of the word **DISCOVERY** are arranged at random. Find the probability that the three vowels will be together.

29. There are 20 tickets in a hat, numbered one to twenty. Two are chosen at random. Find the probability that one is less than 10 and the other is greater than 10 (i.e. the number 10 itself must not appear).

30. Kate, Lucy, Mark, Nora, and Orla are lined up at random for a photo. Find the probability that Mark will be in the middle.

TWO-STEP PROBLEMS

Here are two important laws:

1. If E is an event then $P(E')$, the probability that E does ***not*** happen, is given by the formula:
   $P(E') = 1 - P(E)$.

2. If E and F are independent events, then the probability that E happens and then F happens is given by the formula:
   $$P(E \text{ and then } F) = P(E) \cdot P(F)$$

Example 1: Two cards are drawn at random from a pack. Find the probability that

(i) both of them are spades,

(ii) at least one of them is not a spade.

Solution: (i) When the first card is drawn, there are 52 cards, of which 13 are spades. But when the second card is drawn (if the experiment is to be successful) there are 51 cards, 12 of which are spades.

$\therefore$ P (Both are spades) $= P(1^{st}$ is a spade ***and*** 2nd is a spade)

$= {}^{13}/_{52} \times {}^{12}/_{51}$

$= {}^{1}/_{17}$

P (At least one is not a spade) $=$ 1 – P(Both are spades)

$= 1 - {}^{1}/_{17}$

$= {}^{16}/_{17}$

Example 2: Two people are chosen at random and asked to write down the day of the week on which they were born. Find the probability that

(i) both were born on a Sunday,

(ii) one was born on a Sunday and the other on a Monday,

(iii) the two were born on different days of the week,

(iv) the two were born on the same day of the week.

Solution: (i) P (Both born on Sunday) $=$ P (1st was born on Sunday ***and*** 2nd was born on Sunday)

$= {}^{1}/_{7} \times {}^{1}/_{7}$

$= {}^{1}/_{49}$

(ii) P(one was born on a Sunday and the other on a Monday)
= P(1st born on Sunday ***and*** 2nd on Monday ***or*** 1st on Monday ***and*** 2nd on Sunday)
$= \frac{1}{7} \times \frac{1}{7} + \frac{1}{7} \times \frac{1}{7}$
$= \frac{2}{49}$

(iii) P(They were born on different days)
= P(1st was born on ***any*** day ***and*** the 2nd on any other day)
$= \frac{7}{7} \times \frac{6}{7}$
$= \frac{6}{7}$

(iv) P(they were born on the same day) =
1 – P(Born on different days) $= 1 - \frac{6}{7} = \frac{1}{7}$

Exercise 11.D

1. A fair coin is flipped twice. Find the probability of getting
   (i) two heads,
   (ii) at least one tail.

2. A card is drawn from a pack, but not replaced. Then another card is drawn from the pack. Find the probability that
   (i) both cards are red,
   (ii) at least one card is black.

3. A fair die is rolled three times. Find the probability of getting three sixes.

4. Two people are chosen at random and asked to say in what month their birthday lies. Taking each month as equally likely, find the probability that
   (i) both were born in December,
   (ii) both were born in the same month,
   (iii) they were not born in the same month.

5. Mrs Hubbard has nine children: 4 girls and 5 boys. She chooses a child at random to do the washing up. She then chooses another child (again at random) from the remaining group to do the drying. Find the probability that
   (i) both are boys,
   (ii) both are girls,
   (iii) at least one is a boy.

6. A bag contains 4 black marbles and 6 white ones. A marble is drawn at random from the bag, but not replaced. Another marble is then drawn from the bag. Find the probability that
   (i) both are black,
   (ii) both are white,
   (iii) at least one is black.

7. A bag contains 6 black marbles and 5 white ones. A marble is drawn at random from the bag, but not replaced. Another marble is then drawn from the bag. Find the probability that
   (i) the first is black and the second white,
   (ii) one is black and the other white.

8. Every time she takes a penalty, the probability of our centre forward scoring a goal is $\frac{4}{5}$. During a match, she takes two penalties. Find the probability that
   (i) she scores both goals,
   (ii) she misses both,
   (iii) she scores at least one goal.

9. When Xavier is given a maths problem for homework, the probability that he will get it right is ¾. When Yvonne is given a maths problem, the probability that she will get it right is ½. They are both given a maths problem for homework. Find the probability that

(i) both get it right,
(ii) both get it wrong,
(iii) at least one gets it right.

10. A tennis player gets 50% of his first serves 'in' and 80% of his second serves 'in'. Find the probability of this player getting a 'double fault' (when both first and second serves go 'out').

11. One hundred tickets are put in a hat. Twenty are pink, thirty are blue and fifty are green. A ticket is drawn at random and then put back. Another ticket is then drawn at random. Find the probability that

(i) both are pink,
(ii) both are the same colour,
(iii) they are different colours.

12. This table shows the ages of people in a class:

Age:	16	17	18
Number:	5	11	4

A person is selected at random one day from the class and the age of the person noted. The next day the procedure is repeated. Find the probability that

(i) they are both aged 17,
(ii) the sum of the two ages is 34.

REVISION EXERCISE 11.E

1. (a) How many ways of arranging the letters of the word **WINTER** are there?
How many of these begin with a vowel?

(b) There are ten members of a committee:
A, B, C, D, E, F, G, H, I, J.
A sub-committee of four members must be chosen from these ten people. How many different sub-committees may be chosen

(i) if there are no restrictions,
(ii) if 'B' must be on the sub-committee,
(iii) if 'B' must not be on the sub-committee?

(c) A letter is chosen at random from the letters of the word **MINIMUM**. Find the probability that the letter chosen will be

(i) an M, (ii) an I, (iii) not an I.

2. (a) A bag contains 30 beads, of which 12 are red, 10 are green and 8 are yellow. A bead is drawn at random from the bag. Find the probability that the colour of the bead is

(i) red,
(ii) not red,
(iii) red or yellow.

(b) There are six horses in a race:
A, B, C, D, E and F.

(i) In how many different placing orders can they finish the race?
(ii) If B comes first and F comes last, how many different orders are possible?

(c) How many numbers between 3000 and 10 000 can be made using only the digits 1, 3, 7, 8, 9 – with no repetitions?
How many of these are even?

3. (a) Six people shake hands with one another. How many handshakes take place?

(b) How many ways of arranging the letters of the word **DUBLIN** are there?
(i) How many of these begin with B?
(ii) How many begin with a vowel?
(iii) How many begin and end with a consonant?

(c) A card is drawn at random from a pack. It is replaced and then another card is drawn. Find the probability that
(i) both cards are red,
(ii) both are kings,
(iii) one is a club and the other a spade.

4. (a) A bag contains three cent, four 10-cent pieces, three 20-cent pieces, five 50-cent pieces and nine euro coins. A coin is drawn at random from the bag. Find the probability that the coin is
(i) a euro coin,
(ii) not a euro coin,
(iii) worth 50 cent or more.

(b) A team of six players is to be chosen from ten players.
(i) In how many ways can the six players be chosen if all players may be picked?
(ii) The ten players include just one goal-keeper. In how many ways may the team of six be chosen if every team must include the goal-keeper?

(c) Seven boys: Al, Bob, Con, Des, Ed, Fred and Gus are lined up at random. What is the probability that Ed will be beside Fred?

5. (a) A coin is flipped twice. List the four possible outcomes. Find the probability of getting
(i) two heads,
(ii) the same outcome on both flips?

(b) There are 12 discs in a bag. Six are red, four are yellow and two are green. A disc is drawn at random and then replaced. Another is then drawn at random. Find the probability that
(i) both discs are red,
(ii) both are the same colour,
(iii) the two discs have different colours.

(c) There are 8 girls and 7 boys in a class. Four members of the class must be chosen for a debating team. How many different teams are possible if
(i) there are no restrictions,
(ii) the team must contain 2 girls and 2 boys,
(iii) the team must have at least 2 girls?

6. (a) A class contains 16 boys (5 of whom wear glasses) and 8 girls (1 of whom wears glasses). A student is chosen at random from this class. Find the probability that the student
(i) is a boy,
(ii) wears glasses,
(iii) is a boy who wears glasses.

(b) How many different four-digit numbers can be made from the digits 2, 3, 4, 5 (if no digit may be used more than once)?
How many of these numbers
(i) are less than 3000,
(ii) are even?

(c) Two dice are rolled. Find the probability that the total on the two dice is
(i) equal to five
(ii) five or less.

7. (a) Investigate if (i) $3! + 2! = 5!$ (ii) $\binom{6}{3} + \binom{6}{4} = \binom{7}{3}$

(b) There are 12 boys and 8 girls in a class. A team of three students is to be chosen.

(i) How many different choices may be made?

(ii) How many of these choices contain 2 boys and 1 girl?

(iii) If the choice is done by lot, find the probability that the choice will result in a team of 2 boys and 1 girl.

(c) A couple have four children. Find the probability that

(i) all four are girls,

(ii) at least one is a boy.

8. (a) A coin is tossed and a die is rolled. Write out the 12 elements of the sample space. Hence find the probability of getting

(i) a head and a 'six',

(ii) a tail and an even number,

(iii) a head and a factor of six.

(b) How many ways are there of arranging the letters of the word **MICROBES**? How many of these arrangements

(i) begin with R,

(ii) begin with a vowel,

(iii) have the three vowels as the first three letters,

(iv) have the three vowels together?

(c) Two letters are chosen at random from the alphabet. Find the probability of getting 2 vowels.

9. (a) The results of 40 students in an exam are tabled as follows:

	A	B	C	D	E
Boys	1	4	7	2	1
Girls	2	3	13	5	2

A student is selected at random from the group. Find the probability that the student

(i) is a boy,

(ii) got an A or a B,

(iii) is a girl who got an A or a B.

(b) Nine students (4 girls and 5 boys) are to be lined up for a photo.

(i) How many arrangements are possible?

(ii) How many arrangements are possible if no two boys may stand side-by-side?

(iii) If they are arranged at random, find (correct to one significant figure) the probability that no two boys will stand side-by-side.

(c) A pair of dice is rolled 360 times during a game of Monopoly. How many times would you expect to get a total of 11 or more?

10. (a) How many numbers between 100 and 1000 do not contain the digits 0, 1 or 2?
(b) There are 21 teams in a league. During one season, each team plays each other team twice. How many league matches are there in a season?
(c) A game consists of spinning an arrow on a five-sided board and throwing a die. The board is a regular pentagon, as shown. When the arrow stops spinning it will point to one letter. Each letter is equally likely.
Copy and complete the sample space: {A1, A2, A3, …}.
Find the probability of getting
(i) B5,
(ii) C and an even number,
(iii) a vowel and an odd number.

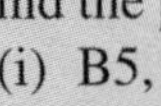

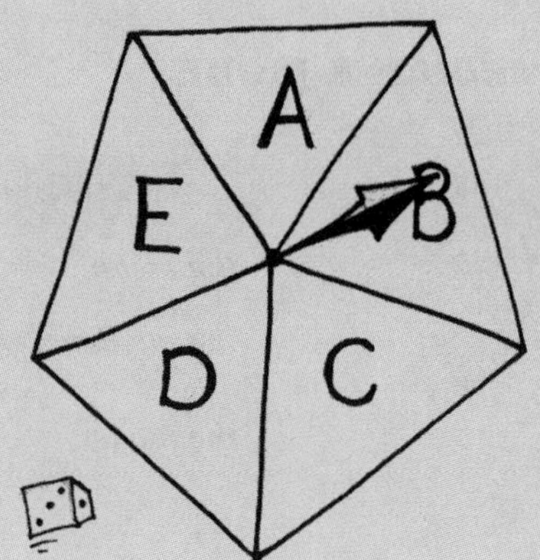

1. $n! = n(n-1)(n-2)\ldots3.2.1$

2. AND = × ; OR = +

3. $\binom{n}{r} = \dfrac{n!}{r!(n-r)!}$; $\binom{n}{n} = 1$; $\binom{n}{0} = 1$;

$$\binom{n}{r} = \frac{\text{First } r \text{ in the countdown}}{\text{Last } r \text{ in the countdown}}$$

4. $P(E) = \dfrac{\#E}{\#S}$

5. If E is an event then $P(E')$, the probability that E does ***not*** happen, is given by the formula: $P(E') = 1 - P(E)$.

6. If E and F are independent events, then the probability that E happens and then F happens is given by the formula:

$$P(E \text{ and then } F) = P(E) \,.\, P(F)$$

Chapter 12

Statistics

MEAN, MEDIAN & MODE

Given a set of numbers,

the mean $= \dfrac{\text{the sum of all the numbers}}{\text{the number of numbers}}$

the median = the middle value when they are written in ascending order

the mode = the most common number in the set

Example 1: Find the mean, median and mode of these sets:

(a) {2, 7, 3, 4, 7}

(b) {0, 2, 5, 2, 3, 4, 2, 5}

Solution: (a) The ***mean*** $= \dfrac{2+7+3+4+7}{5} = \dfrac{23}{5} = 4.6$

To find the ***median***, write the numbers in ***ascending order***, from smallest to biggest: 2, 3, 4, 7, 7 (with 2, 3, 7, 7 crossed out). Cross out the smallest and the biggest and then the second-smallest and the second-biggest etc. The number left in the middle is the median. In this case the median = 4

The ***mode*** = the most common number = 7

(b) The ***mean*** $= \dfrac{0+2+5+2+3+4+2+5}{8} = \dfrac{23}{8} = 2.875$

Here are the numbers in ascending order: 0, 2, 2, 2, 3, 4, 5, 5 (with 0, 2, 2, 4, 5, 5 crossed out)

When there are two middle numbers, we take their mean:

The ***median*** $= \dfrac{2+3}{2} = 2.5$

The ***mode*** = the most common number = 2

Example 2: The mean age of five people is 17. One of them leaves. The mean age of the remaining four people is 16. How old was the person who left?

Solution: The mean age of all five people = 17

∴ The ***total*** age of the five people = 5 × 17 = 85

The mean age of the remaining four people = 16

∴ The ***total*** age of the four people = 4 × 16 = 64

∴ The age of the person who left is 85 – 64 = 21

Exercise 12.A

1. Find the mean, the median and the mode of the set: $\{1, 4, 13, 3, 4\}$.
2. Find the mean, median and mode of the set: $\{1, 0, 5, 2, 2, 2\}$.
3. Find the mean, the median and the mode of this array of numbers:
   1, 3, 3, 4, 4, 5, 5, 5, 5, 5.
4. Find the median of this data:
   4, 7, 8, 1, 2, 5, 6.
5. Find the median of this set:
   8.2, 7.9, 8.1, 7.8, 8.0, 7.8.
6. Find the mean and the mode of this array of numbers:
   9, 9, 9, 9, 9, 9, 11, 11, 11, 11.
7. Find the mean and the mode of this array of numbers:
   3, 3, 3, 3, 3, 3, 3, 3, $7\frac{1}{2}$.
8. The mean of the set $\{4, 1, 3, 6, 2, 5, x\}$ is 4.
   Find the value of x.
9. 2.2 is the mean of this data:
   2.1, 4.4, 2.3, 1.5, 2.5, x.
   Find the value of x.
10. The mean of the set $\{3, 2x-1, 7, x+1, 4, 3, 3x\}$ is 5. Find the value of x.
11. Four boys have mean age 11. The three eldest are aged 14, 12, 10. Find the age of the fourth boy.
12. There are five girls in a family. Two of them are twins. The others are aged 11, 14 and 16. If the mean age of the five girls is 13, find the age of the twins.
13. 10 is the mean of this array:
    $x, x+2, 2x+3, x-1, 10-x$.
    Find the value of x.
14. The mean age of three children is 21. The mean age of their two parents is 46. Find the mean age of the five members of this family.
15. The set $\{2x, x, 4x-1, x+3, 3x+1\}$ has mean 5. Find
    (i) the value of x,
    (ii) the mode of this set,
    (iii) the median of the set.
16. The mean age of six people in a room is 18. One of them leaves. The mean age of the remaining five people is 17. How old was the person who left?
17. Six soldiers are in a room. Their mean height is 145 cm. A seventh soldier enters. Now, the mean height is 144 cm. How tall is the seventh soldier?
18. The mean rainfall over five weekdays was 6 mm per day. The mean rainfall over the following two weekend days was $2\frac{1}{2}$ mm per day. Find the overall mean rainfall for the whole week.
19. Ten people work in a restaurant: three chefs and seven waiters. The mean wage of the chefs is €380 per week. The mean wage of the waiters is €210 per week. Calculate the mean wage of the entire work-force.
20. Three hurling games are played. The attendance at the first two matches was 2107 and 3502. What is the minimum number that must attend the third game so that the mean attendance is ***greater than*** 3000?

FREQUENCY TABLES

When there is a large number of members of a set, we often use a frequency table to illustrate the data. Here are some examples:

Example 1: There are 20 members in a badminton club. Their ages are as follows:

11	14	12	13	14
14	11	14	13	13
14	12	11	13	14
15	11	12	14	15

(i) Fill out a frequency table.
(ii) Name the mode.
(iii) Calculate the mean.
(iv) What percentage of the members have ages greater than the mean?

Solution:

(i)

Age	11	12	13	14	15
Frequency	4	3	4	7	2

(ii) The mode = the most common age = 14
(since 14 has the highest frequency)

(iii) Here is a neat way of calculating the mean. The letter x is used to denote the ages, the letter f the frequency with which that age turns up.
xf is their product.

x	f	xf
11	4	44
12	3	36
13	4	52
14	7	98
15	2	30
	20	260

$$\text{The mean} = \frac{\text{The total of all the ages}}{\text{The total number of people}} = \frac{\Sigma xf}{\Sigma f} = \frac{260}{20} = 13$$

(iv) Those whose ages are greater than the mean are the 14-year-olds and the 15-year-olds.
There are $7 + 2 = 9$ of them.
The percentage of all 20 members is $\frac{9}{20} \times \frac{100}{1}\% = 45\%$.

Example 2: If the mean of this data is 3.4, find the value of y.

x	2	3	4	5	6
$f(x)$	8	4	3	y	3

Solution:

x	f	xf
2	8	16
3	4	12
4	3	12
5	y	$5y$
6	3	18
	$18+y$	$58+5y$

$$\text{The mean} = 3.4$$
$$\therefore \frac{58+5y}{18+y} = 3.4$$
$$\therefore 58+5y = 3.4(18+y)$$
$$\therefore 58+5y = 61.2+3.4y$$
$$\therefore 5y-3.4y = 61.2-58$$
$$\therefore 1.6y = 3.2$$
$$\therefore y = 2$$

GROUPED FREQUENCY TABLES

In a ***grouped frequency table***, the data is grouped into different bands. Here is an example.

Example 1: The wages of ten workers was tabled as follows:

Wages in €	240-260	260-280	280-300	300-400
Frequency	1	4	3	2

(i) Estimate the mean.
(ii) Name the ***modal*** class.

Solution: (i) To estimate the mean, we imagine that the person who earns between 240-260 actually earns exactly 250. The four people who are in the 260-280 class will all be given the value 270. The three who are in the 280-300 class will be given the value 290. Finally, the two people in the 300-400 class will be given the value 350. In each case the class is given the ***mid-interval value*** (i.e. the value at the middle of the interval).

Here then, is the table for calculating the mean – using the mid-interval values:

x	f	xf
250	1	250
270	4	1080
290	3	870
350	2	700
	10	2900

The mean $= \frac{\Sigma xf}{\Sigma f} = \frac{2900}{10} = €290$

(ii) '***Modal***' is the adjective from the noun 'mode'. This question asks for the class which is the mode. It is the 260-280 class, which has the highest frequency.

Exercise 12.B

1. The ages of children in a creche were as follows:

Age	1	2	3	4	5
Frequency	6	7	12	11	4

(i) How many children were in the creche?
(ii) Find the mean age of the children.
(iii) Write down the mode.
(iv) How many of the children have ages greater than the mean?

2. The pupils in a class were given a Maths test. Their marks (out of 10) were tabled as follows:

Mark	4	5	6	7	8	9	10
Frequency	1	4	5	2	2	4	2

(i) Calculate the mean mark.
(ii) Name the mode.
(iii) How many pupils scored less than the mode?

3. The number of goals scored by the Archimedes Academicals in all their matches last season was as follows:

No. of Goals	0	1	2	3	4	5
No. of Matches	6	4	7	8	4	1

(i) In how many matches did they score three goals or more?
(ii) Calculate the mean number of goals per match.
(iii) In how many games did they score less than the mean number of goals?
(iv) Name the mode.

4. Two suspicious parents decide to time the length of all telephone calls made on their phone one day. These are the results (where the times are measured in minutes):

Time	0-2	2-4	4-6	6-8	8-10
Frequency	2	4	6	5	3

(i) Using mid-interval values, estimate the mean time per call.
(ii) What is the modal class?

5. On a certain Sunday, 40 schools' soccer games take place. The number of goals per game is tabled as follows:

No. of Goals	0	1	2	3	4	5	6	7
No. of games	6	8	7	7	4	4	3	1

(i) Calculate the mean number of goals per game.
(ii) Write down the mode.
(iii) How many nil-all draws took place?
(iv) What is the maximum number of games which ***could*** have been draws?

6. Here is a list of the number of occupants per car from a survey of 30 cars passing a certain point:

1	3	2	1	3	4
2	1	1	3	1	1
5	1	2	3	1	4
1	2	2	1	1	3
1	5	1	2	1	1

(i) Copy and complete the following frequency table:

No. of occupants	1	2	3	4	5
No. of cars	15			2	

(ii) Calculate the mean number of occupants per car.
(iii) Write down the mode.
(iv) How many people were travelling in cars with more than two occupants?

7. Twenty competitors enter a trout-fishing competition. At the end of the day, the number of fish caught by each competitor was written down. Here are the results:

1	2	0	3	1
0	1	2	3	5
2	4	3	2	2
1	1	5	2	4

(continued top right)

(i) How many fish were caught?
(ii) Find the mean number of fish per competitor.
(iii) What percentage of the competitors caught less than the mean number of fish?
(iv) Write down the mode.

8. A sample of 50 potato plants is taken. The number of potatoes per plant is counted. The data is then tabled as follows:

No. of potatoes per plant	4	5	6	7	8	9
No. of plants	3	10	13	12	7	5

(i) Name the mode number of potatoes per plant.
(ii) Calculate the mean.
(iii) What percentage of the plants had more than the mean number of potatoes?

9. In a survey, the amount of money which a group of shoppers spent at a minimarket is given below:

Money (€)	0-4	4-10	10-20	20-30	30-50
Frequency	15	10	6	10	9

[Note 0-4 means $0 \leq x < 4$, etc.]

(i) How many shoppers took part in the survey?
(ii) Using mid-interval values, estimate the mean amount of money spent per shopper.

10. A sports-injury expert finds that the ages of those who consult her about tennis elbow are grouped as follows:

Age	0-10	10-30	30-50	50-100
%	10	21	44	25

(i) Using mid-interval values, estimate the mean age of these tennis-elbow sufferers.
(ii) What is the greatest percentage of sufferers who could have been over the mean age?

11. In a survey of all the houses in a street, the number of occupants in each of the houses was written down. Here is the data:

1	2	3	2	4
4	4	1	1	5
2	3	3	4	7
5	4	6	6	5

(i) Make out a frequency table.
(ii) How many houses are on the street?
(iii) What is the mode?
(iv) Calculate the mean number of occupants per house.

12. The length (in minutes) of 20 phone-calls made from a public pay-phone is given in this grouped frequency table:

Length	0-2	2-4	4-6	6-8	8-10
Frequency	3	5	6	4	2

[Note 0-2 means $0 \leq x < 2$ etc.]
(i) Use mid-interval values to estimate the mean length.
(ii) What is the modal class? (i.e. which group is the mode?)
(iii) What is the maximum number of calls which could have been longer than 6.2 minutes?

13. The masses (in kilograms) of all the fifth-year students in a school were tabled as follows:

Mass	20-30	30-40	40-50	50-60	60-80
Frequency	5	7	7	13	10

(where 20-30 means $20 \leq x < 30$ etc.)
(i) How many pupils are there in fifth year?
(ii) Use mid-interval values to estimate the mean mass.
(iii) Eight new students join fifth year. The new mean for the year is 51.6 kg. What is the mean mass of the eight new students?

14. Here are the grades of 10 Ordinary Level Leaving Certificate students in a mock Maths exam:

Grade	A	B	C	D
Marks	85-100	70-84	55-69	40-54
Frequency	2	3	4	1

(i) Using mid-intervals, estimate the mean mark.
(ii) What grade is the mode?

15.

x	1	2	3	4	5
$f(x)$	5	y	13	14	3

(i) The mean of this data is 3; find the value of y.
(ii) Name the mode.

16. Find the value of k if the mean of this data is 2.6:

x	0	1	2	3	4	5
$f(x)$	2	3	5	4	k	3

17.

x	5	6	7	8	9	10
$f(x)$	3	y	8	4	2	1

(i) If 7 is the mean of this data, find the value of y.
(ii) Name the mode.

18. Here is a table of the ages of students in a youth club:

Age	11	12	13	14	15
Frequency	3	3	x	x	$x+3$

(i) If the mean age is 13.5, find the value of x.
(ii) Name the mode.
(iii) How many students are in the club?

19. The marks of 15 students in a test were as follows:

53	67	43	71	21
49	58	48	77	37
82	51	61	98	84

(i) Verify that the mean mark was 60.

(ii) Copy and complete the following grouped frequency table:

Marks	20-40	40-60	60-80	80-100
Frequency	2			3

(iii) Use mid-interval values to estimate the mean.

(iv) Find the percentage error in the estimated mean (as compared with the true mean) to the nearest percent.

20. Twenty people go on a historic bus tour of Galway. Their ages are as follows:

15	14	25	23	33
45	13	51	58	48
19	57	47	56	44
11	38	46	21	16

(i) Verify that 34 is the mean age.

(ii) Copy and fill this grouped frequency table for this data:

Age	0-20	20-40	40-60
Frequency			

(iii) Find, using mid-interval values, an estimate for the mean from the above table.

(iv) Find the percentage error in the estimated mean, to the nearest unit.

THE WEIGHTED MEAN

The percentage price increases during a certain year in meat were as follows:

Type of Meat	Pork	Mutton	Beef	Poultry
% Price rise	2%	8%	3%	5%

The mean percentage rise $= \dfrac{2+8+3+5}{4} = 4.5\%$

But this does not give the full picture, because people spend far more on beef than on mutton. So, the price increase in beef is ***more important*** than the price increase in mutton.

In fact, money is spent on these four types of meat in the ratio 3 : 1 : 4 : 2.

This means that four times as much money is spent on beef as on mutton; three times as much is spent on pork as on mutton, etc.

We assign 'weights' to each type of meat – as a measure of the proportion of money spent on that type:

Type of Meat	Pork	Mutton	Beef	Poultry
% Price rise	2%	8%	3%	5%
Weight	3	1	4	2

To work out the 'weighted mean', which takes into account the relative importance of each type, we use a table much the same as for the mean of a frequency distribution.

% RISE x	WEIGHT w	xw
2	3	6
8	1	8
3	4	12
5	2	10
	10	36

The weighted mean $= \dfrac{\Sigma xw}{\Sigma w} = \dfrac{36}{10} = 3.6\%$

Note that the weighted mean is less than the ordinary mean, because the important price rises are relatively low.

Exercise 12.C

1. The price increases (per 100 cent) for dairy products and their assigned weights were as follows:

	Butter	Cream	Yogurt	Milk	Cheese
Increase	6	2	1	4	3
Weights	4	2	1	10	3

Find the weighted mean.

2. When 100 cent worth of a product costs 109 cent, some time later, we say that the price index of that product is 109. Here are the price index numbers for some petroleum products and their assigned "weights":

	Petrol	Diesel	Car Gas	Car Oil
Index	109	107	105	112
Weight	12	5	2	1

Find the weighted mean index.

3. Find the weighted mean of this data:

x	2	3	4	5	6
w	1	4	1	3	1

4. Find the weighted mean price for this data:

Price	11 cent	12 cent	9 cent	10 cent	14 cent
Weight	6	7	4	2	1

5. Find the weighted mean index, given the following data:

Index	102	104	106	110	101	99
Weight	1	2	5	2	4	6

6. During a sale, a shop reduces the prices of items A, B, C, D, and E as follows:

Item	A	B	C	D	E
Reduction	12 cent	20 cent	2 cent	4 cent	10 cent

(i) Calculate the ordinary mean reduction on these five items.
(ii) If A, B, C, D and E are bought in the ratio $1 : 2 : 2 : 1 : 2$, respectively, find the weighted mean.

7. Students at an American University have to take three subjects: a major, a minor and a general. Here are the marks of two students:

	Major score	Minor score	General score
Alice	56	64	72
Bernard	71	60	58

(i) Which of these two students got the better mean score?
(ii) If weights 5, 3, 2 are assigned to major, minor and general scores, respectively, which student got the higher weighted mean score?

8. Items A, B, C, D, and E are bought in the ratio $3 : 7 : 2 : 3 : 5$.
The price rises of these items in two successive years were as follows:

	A	B	C	D	E
Price rise in Year 1	4 cent	3 cent	12 cent	10 cent	1 cent
Price rise in Year 2	7 cent	6 cent	4 cent	5 cent	4 cent

Which year saw the greater weighted mean increase?

9. Items X, Y and Z are bought in the ratio 5 : 4 : 1. The cost of these items in two shops is shown here:

	X	Y	Z
Cost in shop 1	€13	€10	€15
Cost in shop 2	€x	€12	€22

(i) Find the weighted mean of the cost of these items in shop 1.
(ii) If the weighted mean cost of these items in both shops is the same, calculate the value of x.

10. Students in an Irish University must sit a major and a minor exam. Their weights are k and 2, respectively. Here are the marks of two students:

	Major	Minor
Xavier's marks	58	80
Yvonne's marks	68	55
Assigned weight	k	2

If Xavier's weighted mean was equal to Yvonne's, find the value of k.

HISTOGRAMS

A histogram is like a bar chart which you saw in your studies for the Junior Cert. But there is one significant difference: In a bar chart the frequency is represented by the ***height*** of the bar; in a histogram the frequency is represented by the ***area*** of the bar.

Example 1: Draw a histogram to represent this data, which shows the ages of people in a certain housing estate:

Age	0-10	10-20	20-40	40-60	60-100
Frequency	5	11	24	14	12

Solution: The narrowest bar is the first bar (0-10). We will say that it is ***one*** unit wide. It will have to have height 5, so that its area = $1 \times 5 = 5$ = the frequency.

The next bar (10-20) is also 1 unit wide. Its height must be 11, so that its area will be = $1 \times 11 = 11$ = the frequency.

The next bar (20-40) is 2 units wide. Its height must be 12, so that its area will be = $2 \times 12 = 24$ = the frequency.

The next bar (40-60) is also 2 units wide. Its height must be 7, so that its area will be = $2 \times 7 = 14$ = the frequency.

The last bar (60-100) is 4 units wide. Its height must be 3, so that its area will be = $4 \times 3 = 12$ = the frequency.

Here then, is the histogram:

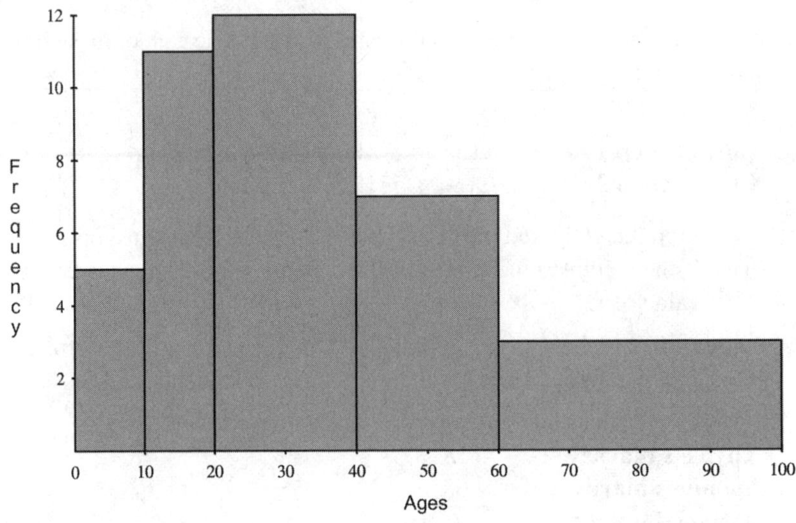

Example 2: This histogram shows the length of 115 telephone calls. Use the histogram to complete the grouped frequency table below.

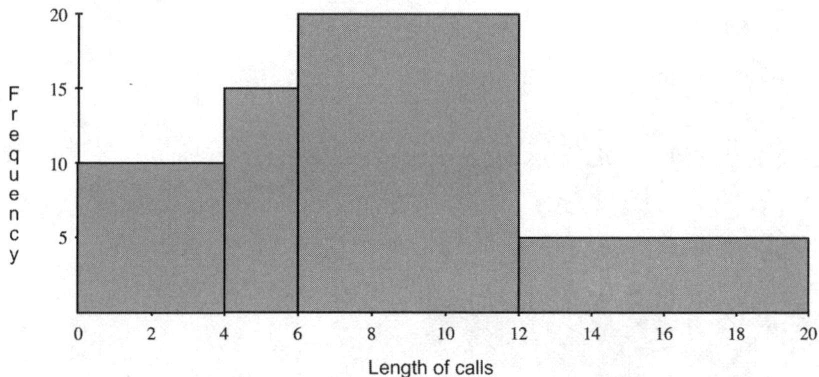

Length of call (minutes)	0-4	4-6	6-12	12-20
Frequency		15		

Solution: The second box (4-6) must have area 15 (since the frequency is 15). Its height is 15, so we say that its width is 1 unit.

The first box (0-4) has width 2 units. Its height is 10.

$\therefore$ The frequency $=$ area $= 2 \times 10 = 20$.

The third box (6-12) has width 3 units. Its height is 20.

$\therefore$ The frequency $=$ area $= 3 \times 20 = 60$.

The fourth box (12-20) has width 4 units. Its height is 5.

$\therefore$ The frequency $=$ area $= 4 \times 5 = 20$.

Here then, is the table:

Length of call (minutes)	0-4	4-6	6-12	12-20
Frequency	20	15	60	20

Exercise 12.D

1. The ages of people at a circus are given in the following table:

Age	0-5	5-10	10-15	15-25	25-40
Frequency	20	25	15	20	15

Illustrate this data on a histogram.

2. The data shows the ages of patients in a children's hospital:

Age	0-2	2-4	4-10	10-18
Frequency	13	15	24	40

Illustrate this data on a histogram.

3. Thirty-nine people donated money to a school fund. The amounts of the contributions are given in this table:

Amount (€)	0-4	4-8	8-20	20-40
Frequency	7	5	12	15

Draw a histogram to illustrate this data.

4. A tour operator finds out the ages of his clients and comes up with the following table:

Age	0-10	10-20	20-60	60-90
Frequency	12	14	44	30

(i) Show this data on a histogram.
(ii) Use mid-interval values to estimate the mean age.

5. Use a histogram to illustrate this data, which shows the heights of 50 students:

Height (cm)	120-140	140-145	145-150	150-160	160-175
Frequency	8	4	6	20	12

6. Illustrate this data by means of a histogram:

x	0-2	2-4	8-14	14-15
$f(x)$	7	11	14	3

7. The hourly wages of 54 student workers are given in the following histogram:

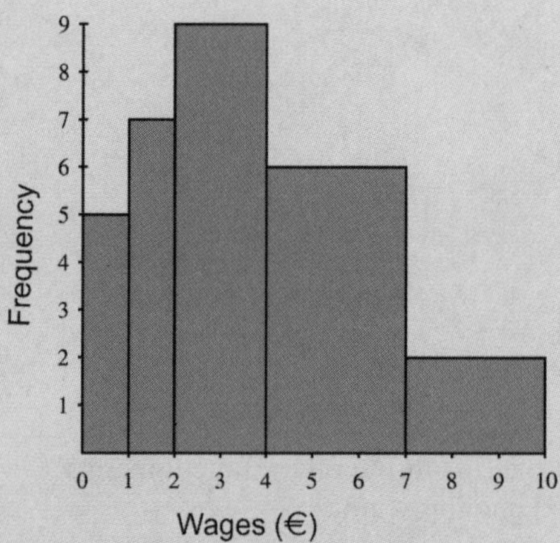

Use this information to complete the following grouped frequency table:

Hourly wage (€)	0-1	1-2	2-4	4-7	7-10
Frequency	5				

8. The length (in minutes) of phone-calls made at a payphone are illustrated in the following histogram:

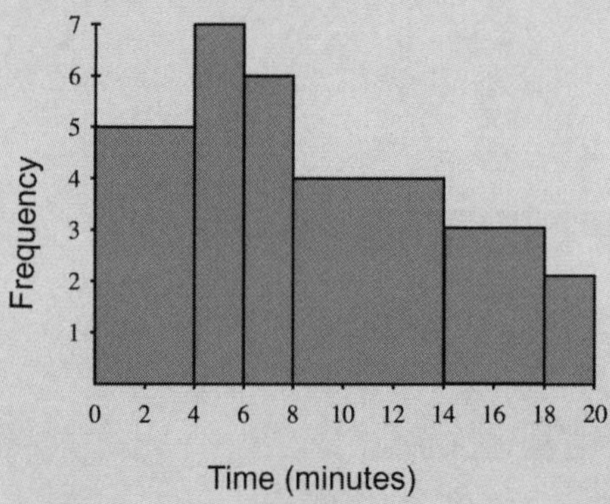

(i) Use the histogram to copy and complete this table:

Time (minutes)	0-4	4-6	6-8	8-14	14-18	18-20
Frequency			6			

(ii) How many phone-calls were made altogether?

9.

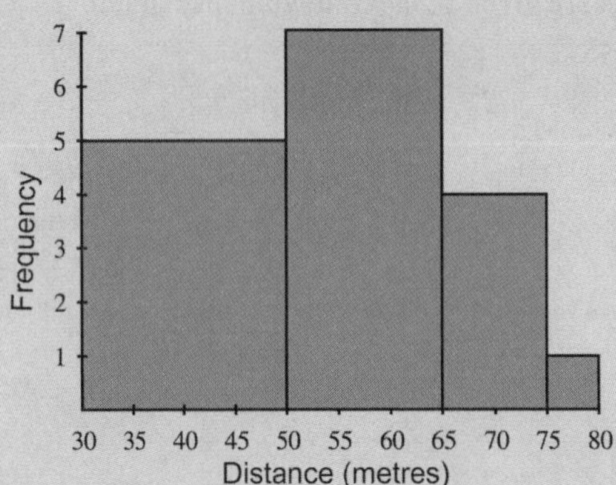

The histogram above shows the distances (in metres) thrown by competitors in a javelin-throwing contest. Each competitor had one throw only.

(i) Copy and complete this table:

Distances (metres)	30-50	50-65	65-75	75-80
Frequency				1

(ii) How many competitors took part?

(iii) Use mid-interval values to estimate the mean distance.

10. The masses of some iceberg lettuces were measured and illustrated as follows in a histogram:

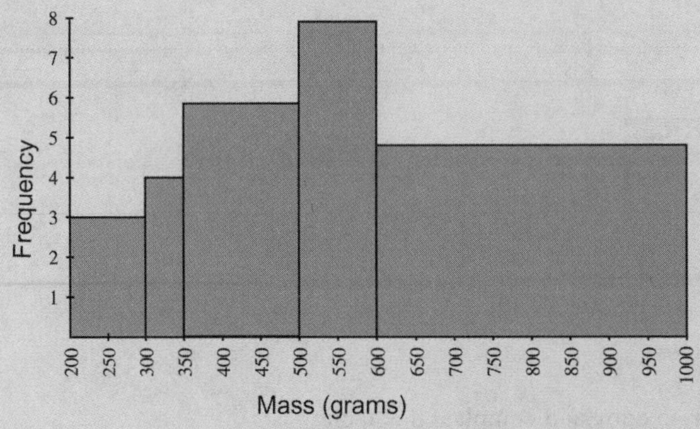

(i) Copy and complete the following grouped frequency table:

Mass (grams)	200-300	300-350	350-500	500-600	600-1000
Number of lettuces		4			

(ii) How many lettuces were there?

(iii) What percentage of the lettuces had a mass of less than ½ kg?

11. The histogram below shows the distribution of the amounts of money (in €s) spent by 100 customers at a local grocery store:

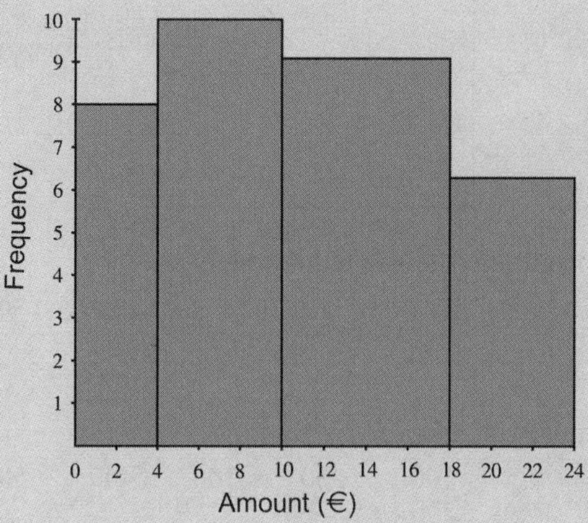

(i) Copy and complete the grouped frequency table:

Money spent (€)	0-4	4-10	10-18	18-24
Frequency	16			

(ii) Use mid-interval values to estimate the total amount of money spent.

(iii) Estimate, also, the mean amount of money spent per customer.

12. The histogram below shows the area (in acres) of the holdings of 350 farmers in a 'small farmers association'.

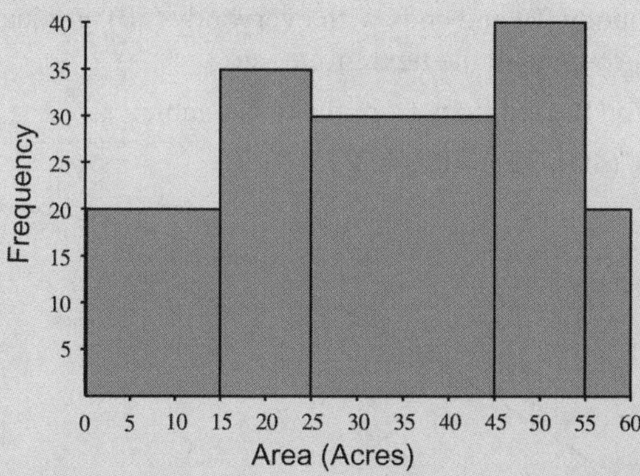

(i) Copy and complete the following grouped frequency table:

Area (acres)	0-15	15-25	25-45	45-55	55-60
Frequency		70			

(ii) Use mid-interval values to estimate the mean area of the holdings.

CUMULATIVE FREQUENCY CURVES

A cumulative frequency curve is used to illustrate data. The shape of all such curves is like the one shown on the right.
This curve can be used to glean all kinds of information, as we shall see.

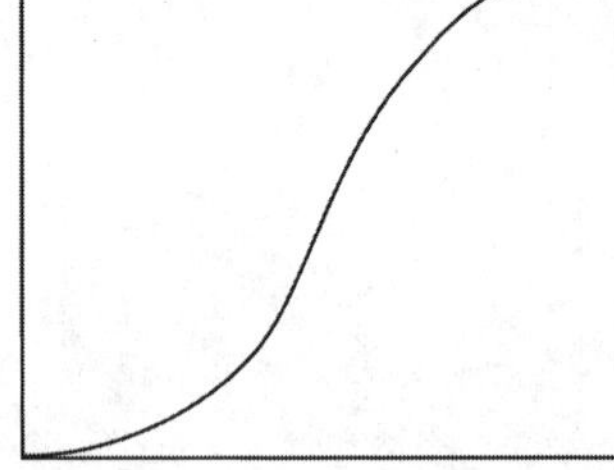

The curve is sometimes called an ***ogive***.

Example 1: The weekly wages of fifty people are shown on this table:

Weekly wage (€)	0-100	100-200	200-300	300-400	400-500
Frequency	6	11	15	13	5

(i) Copy and complete the following ***cumulative frequency table***:

Weekly wage (€)	< 0	< 100	< 200	< 300	< 400	< 500
Frequency						

(ii) Draw a cumulative frequency graph (ogive).
(iii) Estimate the weekly wage of the 10th lowest paid worker.
(iv) Estimate the number of people who earn between €250 and €350 per week.

Solution: (i)

Weekly wage (€)	< 0	< 100	< 200	< 300	< 400	< 500
Frequency	0	6	17	32	45	50

[The graph starts with nobody (0) and ends with everybody (50), gradually ***accumulating*** the next group, then the next group, etc.}

(ii) Here is the curve, based on the readings from the above table:
(0,0), (100, 6), (200, 17), (300, 32), (400, 45), (500, 50)

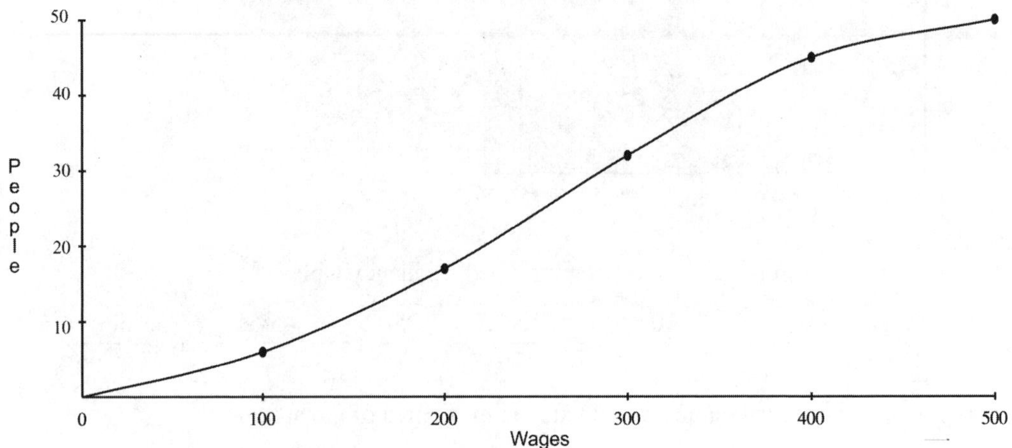

(iii) If you want to estimate the wage of the 10th worst paid worker, start at 10 on the people-axis, draw a line to the graph and then down to the wages-axis. The reading is approximately €140, which is the wage of the 10th worst-paid worker.

(iv) If you want to estimate how many workers earn between €250 and €350, draw two lines from 250 and 350 on the wages-axis, to the graph and across to the people-axis. The readings show that the 25th person earns €250 and the 39th person earns €350. Therefore, the number in the range €250-350 is 39 – 25 = 14

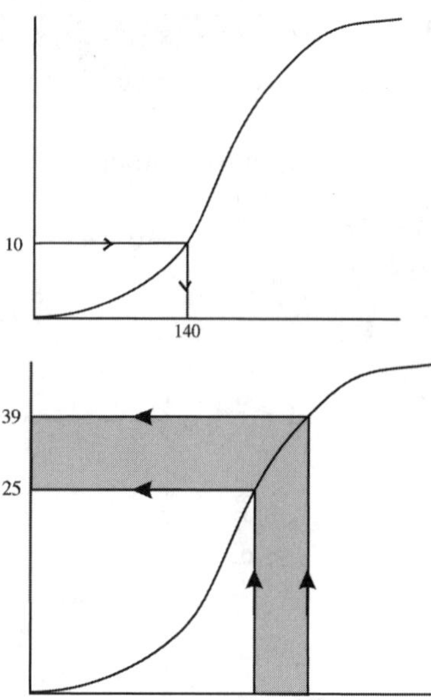

THE FOUR QUARTILES

If you divide the vertical axis of an ogive into four equal parts, as shown, then the readings Q_1, Q_2, Q_3 are defined as:

Q_1 = the ***lower quartile***

Q_2 = the ***median***

Q_3 = the ***upper quartile***

$Q_3 - Q_1$ = the ***interquartile range***

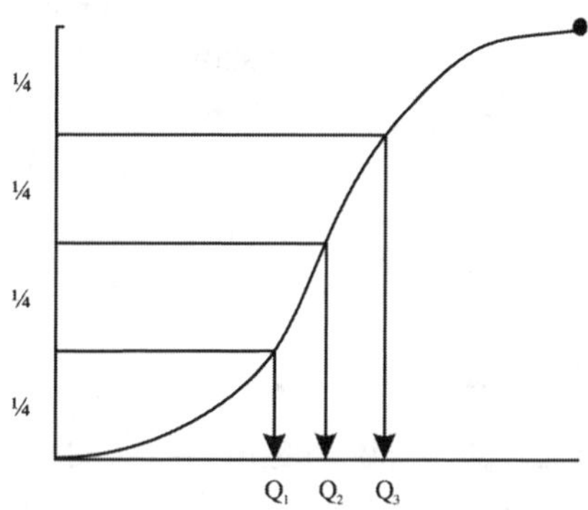

Example 2: The masses of a sample of two hundred students were tabled as follows:

Mass (kg)	20-30	30-40	40-50	50-60	60-70	70-100
Frequency	14	34	48	51	27	26

(i) Use the information to copy and complete this cumulative frequency table:

Mass (kg)	< 20	< 30	< 40	< 50	< 60	< 70	< 100
Frequency							

(ii) Draw a cumulative frequency curve.

(iii) Estimate the lower quartile.

(iv) Estimate the median.

(v) Estimate the upper quartile.

(vi) Estimate the interquartile range.

Solution

(i)

Mass (kg)	< 20	< 30	< 40	< 50	< 60	< 70	< 100
Frequency	0	14	48	96	147	174	200

(ii) Draw a smooth curve. Never use a ruler! The curve passes through the points:
(20, 0), (30, 14), (40, 48), (50, 96), (60, 147), (70, 174), (100, 200)

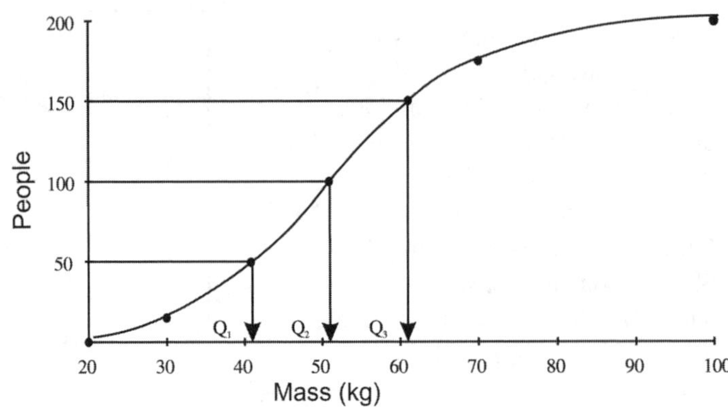

(iii) There are 200 people. Divide these into four groups with 50 people in each, as shown on the graph. The lower quartile = $Q_1 = 41$

(iv) The median = $Q_2 = 51$

(v) The upper quartile = $Q_3 = 61$

(vi) The interquartile range = $Q_3 - Q_1 = 61 - 41 = 20$

Exercise 12.E

1. A sample of 80 students are asked how many kilometres they travel to their local school. Here are the findings (where 0-2 means $0 \leq x < 2$, etc.)

Distance (km)	0-2	2-4	4-6	6-8	8-10
No. of students	7	19	30	18	6

(i) Copy and complete the following cumulative frequency table:

Distance (km)	< 0	< 2	< 4	< 6	< 8	< 10
No. of students	0	7	26			

(ii) Draw a cumulative frequency curve (ogive).

(iii) Use your curve to estimate how many students travel between 3 km and 7 km to school.

2. The marks of 40 pupils are shown in the following table:

Mark	20-40	40-60	60-80	80-100
No. of pupils	7	11	14	8

where 20-40 means $20 \leq x < 40$, etc.

(a) Copy and complete the following cumulative frequency table:

Mark	< 20	< 40	< 60	< 80	< 100
No. of pupils	0	7			

(b) Draw a cumulative frequency curve.

(c) Use your graph to estimate

(i) the lower quartile,

(ii) the median,

(iii) the upper quartile,

(iv) the interquartile range.

3. One hundred students are given a Maths problem to solve. The times taken to solve the problem are tabled as follows:

Time (minutes)	10-14	14-18	18-22	22-26	26-30
No. of students	13	28	26	21	12

(i) Copy and complete the following cumulative frequency table:

Time (minutes)	< 10	< 14	< 18	< 22	< 26	< 30
No. of students						

(ii) Draw a cumulative frequency curve (ogive).

(iii) Use your curve to estimate how many students took between 15 and 21 minutes to solve the problem.

(iv) Estimate the median time.

4. A fifth-year student does a survey of 60 students in her year. She asks them how much pocket-money they get. Here are her findings:

Pocket-money (€)	0-2	2-4	4-6	6-8	8-10
No. of students	6	15	19	13	7

where 0-2 means $0 \leq x < 2$, etc.

(a) Copy and complete the following cumulative frequency table:

Pocket-money	< 0	< 2	< 4	< 6	< 8	< 10
No. of pupils	0					

(b) Draw a cumulative frequency curve.

(c) Use your graph to estimate

(i) the lower quartile,

(ii) the median,

(iii) the upper quartile,

(iv) the interquartile range.

5. The amounts of money spent by 80 shoppers at a supermarket are as follows:

Money (€)	0-5	5-10	10-15	15-20	20-30	30-50
Frequency	9	11	15	16	17	12

Fill in a table based on the amounts <0, <5, <10, <15, < 20, < 30, and < 50.
Draw a cumulative frequency curve. Use the graph to estimate
(i) the median,
(ii) the interquartile range,
(iii) the number of shoppers who spent over €33.

6. A match begins at 3.10 p.m. in a stadium which holds 3000 spectators. All seats have been sold for the match. The times at which the spectators arrive for the match are as follows:

Time	2.00-2.15	2.15-2.30	2.30-2.45	2.45-3.00	3.00-3.15	3.15-4.00
No. of spectators	200	450	650	850	600	250

(a) Copy and complete the following cumulative frequency table:

Time	Before 2.00	Before 2.15	Before 2.30	Before 2.45	Before 3.00	Before 3.15	Before 4.00
No. of spectators							

(b) Draw a cumulative frequency graph.
(c) From your graph, estimate
(i) the time when the stadium was half-full,
(ii) the number of spectators who arrived after 3.10 p.m,
(iii) the length of time it took for the first 1000 spectators to arrive.

7. This cumulative frequency table shows the marks obtained by 28 students in a class test:

Mark	< 20	< 30	< 40	< 50	< 70	<100
No. of students	0	2	8	17	25	28

(a) Draw a cumulative frequency curve, using the above data.
(b) Use your graph to estimate
(i) the median,
(ii) the interquartile range.
(c) Use the above data to copy and complete the following grouped frequency table:

Mark	20-30	30-40	40-50	50-70	70-100
No. of students		6			3

Use mid-interval values to estimate the mean.

8. This cumulative frequency table shows the distances (in km) which 100 students have to travel to school:

Distance	< 2	< 4	< 6	< 8	< 12	< 20
No. of students	8	22	43	60	80	100

(a) Draw a cumulative frequency curve.

(b) Use your curve to estimate

(i) the median,

(ii) the number of students who live between 9 km and 17 km from the school,

(iii) whether or not it is true to say that 10 of these students have to travel over 16 km to school,

(c) Use the above data to copy and complete the following grouped frequency table:

Distance	0-2	2-4	4-6	6-8	8-12	12-20
No. of students		14				

Draw a histogram to represent this data.

STANDARD DEVIATION

Take the two sets: $A = \{8, 8, 9, 11, 14\}$ and $B = \{1, 3, 8, 17, 21\}$

The mean of set $A = \dfrac{8+8+9+11+14}{5} = \dfrac{50}{5} = 10$

The mean of set $B = \dfrac{1+3+8+17+21}{5} = \dfrac{50}{5} = 10$

Therefore, both sets have the same mean. But the members of the set A are more tightly bunched around the mean than the members of set B. The members of B are more scattered or dispersed. To measure ***dispersal*** we use the ***standard deviation from the mean***. The small Greek letter sigma (σ) is used to denote the standard deviation from the mean. Here is how it is calculated:

To find the standard deviation of set A (σ_A) correct to two decimal places:

Step 1: Write down the members of the set: 8, 8, 9, 11, 14

Step 2: Write down the difference (d) between each member and the mean 10: 2, 2, 1, 1, 4

Step 3: Square these numbers: 4, 4, 1, 1, 16

Step 4: Find the mean of these: $\dfrac{4+4+1+1+16}{5} = 5.2$

Step 5: Find the square root of this number: $\sqrt{5.2} = 2.28$

$\therefore \ \sigma_A = 2.28$

To find the standard deviation of set B (σ_B) correct to two decimal places:

Step 1: Write down the members of the set: 1, 3, 8, 17, 21

Step 2: Write down the difference (d) between each member and the mean 10: 9, 7, 2, 7, 11

Step 3: Square these numbers: 81, 49, 4, 49, 121

Step 4: Find the mean of these: $\frac{81+49+4+49+121}{5} = 60.8$

Step 5: Find the square root of this number: $\sqrt{60.8} = 7.80$

$\therefore \; \sigma_B = 7.80$

The set B has the greater standard deviation because the members of B are more widely dispersed then the members of set A, as shown below:

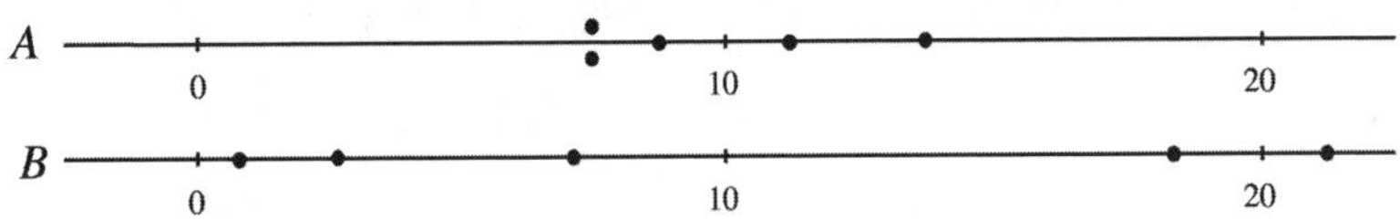

Exercise 12.F

1. Find the mean and the standard deviation from the mean of the set of numbers: {4, 7, 8, 9}

2. $A = \{4, 5, 5, 6, 10\}$ and $B = \{1, 2, 7, 9, 11\}$.
   (i) Verify that both sets have mean 6.
   (ii) Find the standard deviation from the mean in each case, correct to one decimal place.

3. Find the mean and standard deviation from the mean of the set: {1, 0, 2, 5, 7}

4. $S = \{2, 4, 5, 7, 7\}$. Find
   (i) the mode of S
   (ii) the median of S
   (iii) the mean of S
   (iv) the standard deviation from the mean.

5. $A = \{0, 1, 3, 4, 7, 15\}$
   (i) Verify that the mean = 5
   (ii) Verify that the standard deviation from the mean $= \sqrt{30}$

6. Find the mean and standard deviation of the set: 3.1, 3.1, 3.1, 3.2, 3.3

7. $X = \{1, 2, 14, 15\}$ and $Y = \{6, 7, 8, 11\}$ are sets.
   (i) Show that the mean of both sets is the same.
   (ii) Find, correct to one decimal place, the standard deviation of each set.
   (iii) Why is the standard deviation of X greater than that of Y?

8. Find, correct to two significant figures, the mean and standard deviation from the mean of the four numbers: 3.1, 3.22, 3.23, 3.25

9. Three people are aged 12, 17 and 31.
   (i) Find their mean age.
   (ii) Find the standard deviation from the mean correct to the nearest integer.
   (iii) Write down the mean age and the standard deviation from the mean of these three people, five years later.

10. (i) Calculate the mean and standard deviation from the mean of the set: $A = \{1, 4, 7, 8\}$
   (ii) Hence write down the mean and standard deviation of the two sets $B = \{11, 14, 17, 18\}$ $C = \{10, 40, 70, 80\}$

STANDARD DEVIATION OF A FREQUENCY DISTRIBUTION

Example 1: The number of children in twenty families was tabled as follows:

Number of children (x)	0	1	2	3	4	5	6
Frequency (f)	1	2	6	4	3	2	2

(i) Find the mean ($\bar{x}$) and the standard deviation from the mean (σ) of this data, correct to 2 significant figures.

(ii) Calculate the percentage of families which have between $\bar{x} - \sigma$ and $\bar{x} + \sigma$ children in their families.

Solution: (i) When a frequency table is given, we use a 6-columned table; the first three columns are for the mean, the next three for the standard deviation.

How far is x from $\bar{x}$?
↓

x	f	xf	d	d^2	d^2f
0	1	0	3	9	9
1	2	2	2	4	8
2	6	12	1	1	6
3	4	12	0	0	0
4	3	12	1	1	3
5	2	10	2	4	8
6	2	12	3	9	18
	20	60			52

The mean $= \bar{x} = \dfrac{\Sigma xf}{\Sigma f} = \dfrac{60}{20} = 3$

The standard deviation $= \sigma = \sqrt{\dfrac{\Sigma d^2 f}{\Sigma f}} = \sqrt{\dfrac{52}{20}} = \sqrt{2.6} = 1.6$

(ii) $\bar{x} - \sigma = 3 - 1.6 = 1.4$ and $\bar{x} + \sigma = 3 + 1.6 = 4.6$

So, the question asks 'Find the percentage of families which have between 1.4 and 4.6 children?' These include families with 2, 3 or 4 children. There are $6 + 4 + 3 = 13$ such families.

13 as a percentage of 20 $= \dfrac{13}{20} \times \dfrac{100}{1}\% = 65\%$

Answer: 65% of the families have between $\bar{x} - \sigma$ and $\bar{x} + \sigma$ children.

Exercise 12.G

1. The ages of children in a creche were tabled as follows:

Age	1	2	3	4	5
Frequency	1	0	2	2	5

Show that 4 is the mean age and calculate the standard deviation from the mean, correct to two places of decimals.

2.

x	1	2	3	4	5
$f(x)$	6	5	8	5	6

(i) Show that $\bar{x}$, the mean of this data, is equal to 3.
(ii) Find the standard deviation from the mean, σ, correct to one decimal place.
(iii) Calculate the percentage of the given numbers which lie between $\bar{x} - \sigma$ and $\bar{x} + \sigma$.

3. Twelve households were asked the number of pets they kept. Their responses were tabled as follows:

No. of pets	0	1	2	3	4
$f(x)$	4	0	3	2	3

(i) Show that the mean number of pets per household is 2.
(ii) Find the standard deviation from the mean, correct to two decimal places.

4. The number of eggs laid by 20 hens was as follows:

No. of eggs	0	1	2	3	4
$f(x)$	2	4	8	4	2

(i) Find the mean, $\bar{x}$, and the standard deviation from the mean, σ, correct to one decimal place.
(ii) Calculate the number of hens who laid between $\bar{x} - \sigma$ and $\bar{x} + \sigma$ eggs.

5. Assuming that the data can be taken at the mid-interval values, estimate the mean and standard deviation from the mean of the following grouped frequency distribution: [NOTE: 0-4 means $0 \leq x < 4$, etc.]

Class interval	0-4	4-8	8-12	12-16	16-20
Frequency	2	6	12	6	2

6. Twenty students are asked for how many minutes they watched television on a certain day. This table shows their replies:

Time (minutes)	0-40	40-60	60-80	80-100	100-120
Frequency	2	6	5	3	4

(i) Using mid-interval values, estimate the mean viewing time.
(ii) Find the standard deviation to the nearest minute.

7. One hundred cubscouts were taken on a jamboree. Their ages were as follows:

Age	7	8	9
Frequency	33	44	23

(i) Find the mean age.
(ii) Find the standard deviation from the mean, correct to one decimal place.

8. The following table shows the pocket-money of 100 pupils.

Pocket Money (in cent)	0-100	100-200	200-300	300-500
Number of pupils	4	23	31	42

Using mid-interval values, find the mean and the standard deviation from the mean, correct to the nearest cent. Show all your work.

REVISION EXERCISE 12.H

1. The number of goals scored by a school hockey team in their last twenty matches were as follows:

4	1	0	2	1
3	0	1	2	3
3	1	1	0	3
2	0	2	1	1

(i) Copy and fill the following frequency table:

Number of Goals	0	1	2	3	4
Frequency	4				

(ii) Find the mean and the mode of the data.
(iii) What is the greatest number of wins which the team could have had?

2. A school has a total of 850 students on its roll-books. On a certain day, the vice-principal writes down the numbers arriving in certain time-intervals. Not all of the 850 students came to school that day. No student arrived before 8.00 or after 9.30. Here are the findings:

Time	8.00-8.15	8.15-8.30	8.30-8.45	8.45-9.00	9.00-9.15	9.15-9.30
Frequency	40	100	250	350	50	30

(continued over →)

Copy and complete the following cumulative frequency table and draw a cumulative frequency curve:

Time	Before 8.00	Before 8.15	Before 8.30	Before 8.45	Before 9.00	Before 9.15	Before 9.30
Frequency	0	40	140				

(i) How many students were absent that day?

Use your graph to estimate:

(ii) the number of students who arrived after 9.05,

(iii) the median arrival time,

(iv) the number of students who arrived between 8.20 and 8.40.

3. This histogram shows the amounts of money (in €s) which a group of people spent on Christmas presents one year.

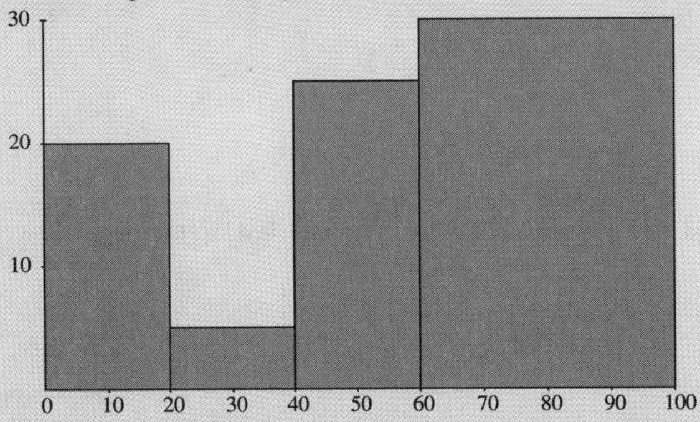

(i) Use the histogram to fill out the following grouped frequency distribution table:

Amount	0-20	20-40	40-60	60-100
Frequency		5		

(ii) Using mid-interval values, find the mean amount spent.

(iii) The following Christmas, 40% of all the people in each interval (except the 60-100 interval) spent €20 more. Fill out a new frequency table for the amounts spent that Christmas, and find the mean.

(iv) By what percentage (to the nearest integer) did the mean amount spent increase over the year?

4. The number of hours sleep taken by 50 people on a certain night was tabled as follows:

Time (hours)	0-3	3-6	6-9	9-12
No. of people	4	11	20	15

(i) What is the greatest possible number of people who had over 8 hours sleep?

(ii) What is the least possible number who had over 8 hours sleep?

(iii) Draw a cumulative frequency curve (based on < 3, < 6, < 9, < 12) and use the curve to estimate the number who had over 8 hours sleep.

(iv) Estimate, also, the interquartile range.

5. (a) The mean of $\{1, 5, 11, 4, 7, x, x + 1\}$ is 7. Find

(i) the value of x,

(ii) the median,

(iii) the mode,

(iv) the standard deviation from the mean, correct to 1 decimal place.

(b) The table shows the ages of toddlers in a creche. The mean age is 2. Find the value of y.

Age	0	1	2	3
Frequency	2	y	2	10

(c) $S = \{1, 1 + x, 1 - x\}$.

Show that the mean of S is 1 and that the standard deviation from the mean is $\sqrt{\frac{2x^2}{3}}$

6. (a) Two supermarkets, S_1 and S_2, made reductions in the prices of the four items A, B, C, and D as shown on the table:

	A	***B***	***C***	***D***
S_1	10 cent	3 cent	5 cent	20 cent
S_2	8 cent	4 cent	3 cent	21 cent

(i) Which supermarket had the best average (mean) reduction per item?

(ii) If sales in A, B, C, and D in each supermarket were in the ratio 2 : 4 : 1 : 3, respectively, which, now, had the best weighted mean reduction?

(b) The following table gives the number of minutes of television watched by a sample of 1000 people on a certain day:

Viewing time (minutes)	0-60	60-120	120-180	180-240
Frequency	130	480	300	90

(i) Taking mid-interval values, estimate the mean viewing time.

(ii) Explain what is the 'median' viewing time.

(iii) Use a cumulative frequency curve (based on < 60, < 120, < 180, < 240) to estimate the median viewing time.

7. (a) Complete this sentence: 'In a histogram, the frequency is proportional to the ...'

(b) (i) Draw a histogram to illustrate the following grouped frquency table:

Class	0-2	2-6	6-12	12-20
Frequency	16	16	24	44

[NOTE: 0-2 means $0 \le x < 2$, etc]

(ii) Assuming that the data can be taken at mid-interval values, calculate the mean and standard deviation from the mean, correct to one decimal place.

8. (a) This histogram shows the marks of a set of students:

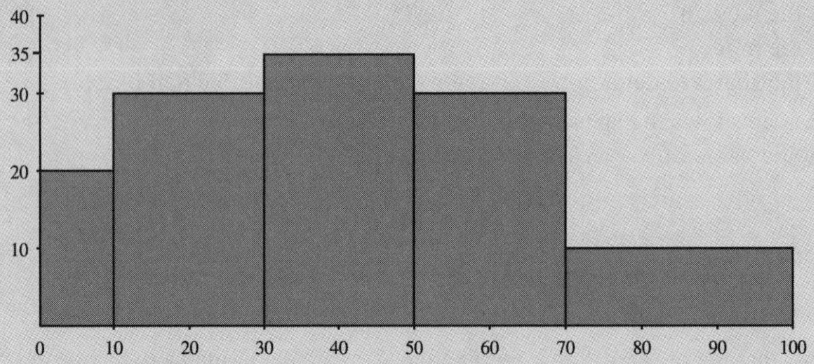

Copy and complete the following grouped frequency table, below, for the histogram above.

Amount	0-10	10-30	30-50	50-70	70-100
Frequency		30			

(b) A garage owner recorded the amount of money spent by customers on petrol over a day. The results were:

Amount (€)	0-5	5-10	10-15	15-20	20-30
No. of customers	50	150	400	300	100

(i) Taking the value of sales at the mid-interval value, estimate the total value of petrol sales that day.

(ii) Complete the cumulative frequency table:

Amount (€)	< 0	< 5	< 10	< 15	< 20	< 30
No. of customers						

(iii) Draw a cumulative frequency curve.

(iv) Use this curve to estimate...

...the median sales value.

...the number of customers who purchased more than €17 worth of petrol.

9. (a) The table shows the distribution of the ages of 100 people:

Age	0-10	10-20	20-30	30-50	50-80
Frequency	10	19	25	30	16

Taking 5, 15, etc. as the mid-interval values, estimate the mean age.

(b) $A = \{3, 7, 5.5, 6, 3.5\}$. Show that 5 is the mean of A. Then, calculate the standard deviation from the mean, correct to one decimal place.

(c) A new shop opened at 0900 hours, one morning. During the first hour of trading, customers were counted as they entered the shop. The following frequency table shows the number of customers who had entered before the given times:

Time	Before 0910	Before 0920	Before 0930	Before 0940	Before 0950	Before 1000
No. of customers	45	69	95	120	144	250

(i) Draw a cumulative frequency curve.
(ii) A photograph was taken of the hundredth customer as he (or she) entered. Use your curve to estimate the time at which the photograph was taken.
(iii) Use your curve to estimate the number of people who entered the shop during the 15 minutes immediately after the photograph was taken.

10. (a) If the mean of this data is 6.9, find the value of n:

x	5	6	7	8
$f(x)$	1	2	n	3

(b) Using mid-interval values, find the mean, $\bar{x}$, and the standard deviation from the mean, σ, (correct to one decimal place) of the data:

x	0-4	4-8	8-12	12-16	16-20
$f(x)$	5	8	10	4	7

Draw a cumulative frequency curve and hence estimate

(i) the number of values between $\bar{x} - \sigma$ and $\bar{x} + \sigma$.
(ii) the interquartile range.

SUMMARY OF IMPORTANT POINTS

1. Mean = Average = $\dfrac{\text{Sum of the numbers}}{\text{Number of numbers}} = \dfrac{\Sigma xf}{\Sigma f}$

2. Mode = The most common value.

3. Median = The middle value when they are written in ascending order.

4. Standard deviation = $\sigma = \sqrt{\dfrac{\Sigma d^2 f}{\Sigma f}}$

5. In a histogram the frequency is proportional to the area of the block.

6. In a cumulative frequency curve, A, B and C are, respectively, ¼, ½ and ¾ way up the left-hand side.

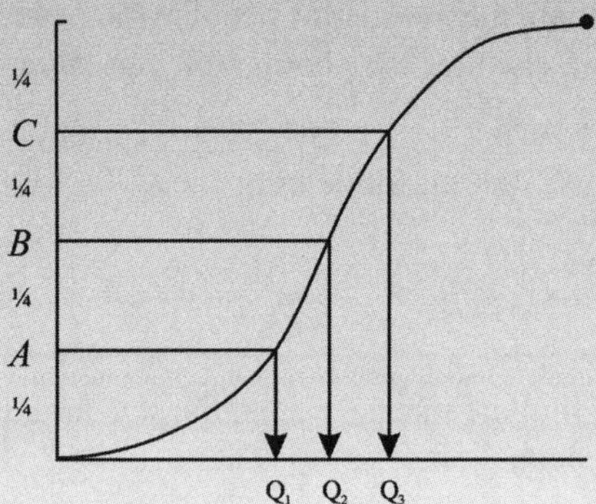

Q_1 = the lower quartile

Q_2 = the median

Q_3 = the upper quartile

$Q_3 - Q_1$ = the inter-quartile range.

Chapter 13

Length, Area and Volume

RECTANGLES

Let l be the length of a rectangle and let b be the breadth (i.e. the width).

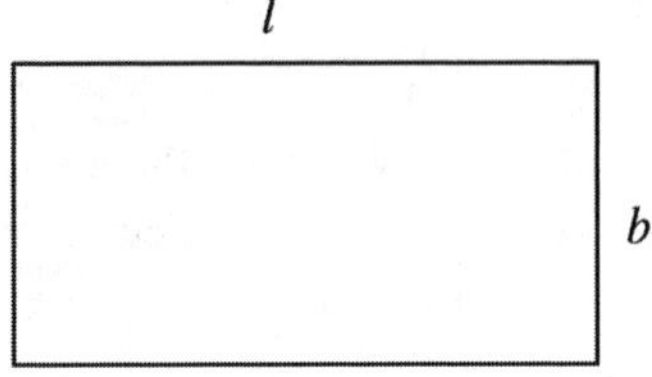

The perimeter of this rectangle is $2l + 2b$

The area of this rectangle = lb.

Example 1: The perimeter of a rectangle is 280 m.
The length of the rectangle is 80 m.
Find
(i) the breadth,
(ii) the area of the rectangle,
(iii) the length of a diagonal.

Solution:

(i) Let x = the breadth

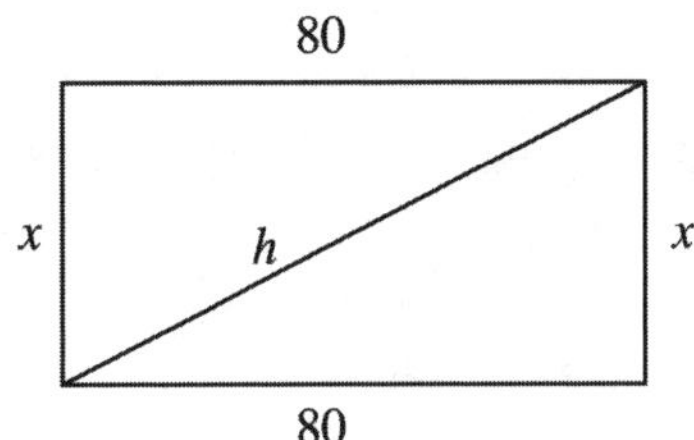

The perimeter = 280

$$\therefore\ x + x + 80 + 80 = 280$$
$$\therefore\ 2x + 160 = 280$$
$$\therefore\ 2x = 120$$
$$\therefore\ x = 60$$

(ii) The area = (80)(60) = 4800 square metres.

(iii) Let h = the length of the diagonal. By Pythagoras' theorem,

$$h^2 = 60^2 + 80^2$$
$$\therefore\ h^2 = 3600 + 6400$$
$$\therefore\ h^2 = 10\,000$$
$$\therefore\ h = 100$$

TRIANGLES

Take the triangle in the diagram.

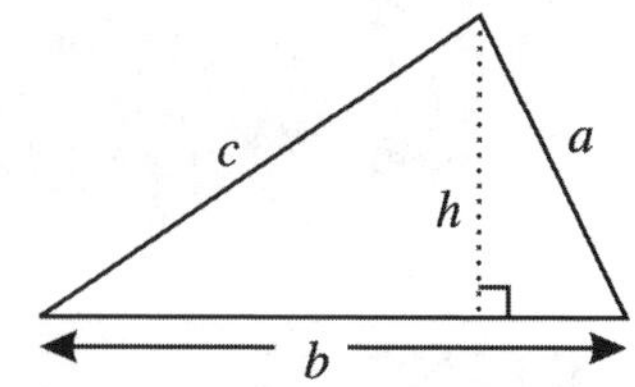

The perimeter of the triangle
$= a + b + c$
The area of the triangle = ½ bh

Example 2: Find the area of the shaded region in this rectangle.

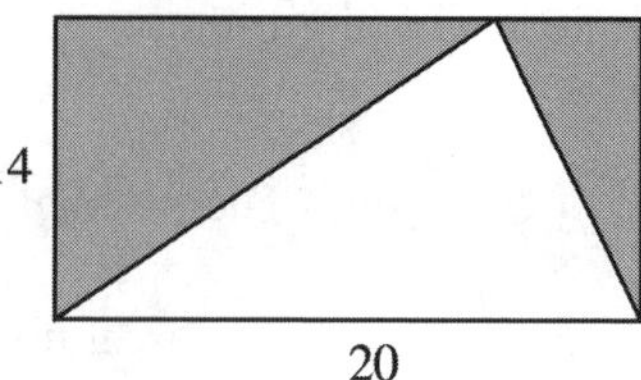

Solution: The area of the rectangle = (20)(14) = 280.

The area of the un-shaded triangle = ½(20)(14) = 140.

Therefore, the area of the remainder = 280 – 140 = 140.

Exercise 13.A

1. An A4 sheet of paper is 30 cm long and 21 cm wide. Find
   (i) its perimeter,
   (ii) its area.
2. A singles tennis court is 25 m long and 8 m wide. Find
   (i) its perimeter,
   (ii) its area.
3. The area of a rectangle is 84 square metres. Its width is 7 metres.
   (i) Find its length.
   (ii) Find its perimeter.
4. The area of a rectangular room is 12 square metres. Its length is 4 m. Find
   (i) its width,
   (ii) the length of a diagonal.
5. The perimeter of a rectangular garden is 34 metres. Its length is 12 m. Calculate
   (i) its width,
   (ii) the length of a diagonal.
6. The perimeter of a rectangular field is 200 m. Its length is 80 metres. Find the area.
7. The length of a rectangular page is 10 cm greater than its width. The perimeter is 1 m. Find the area of the page in square centimetres.
8. The diagram shows the plan of a kitchen floor.

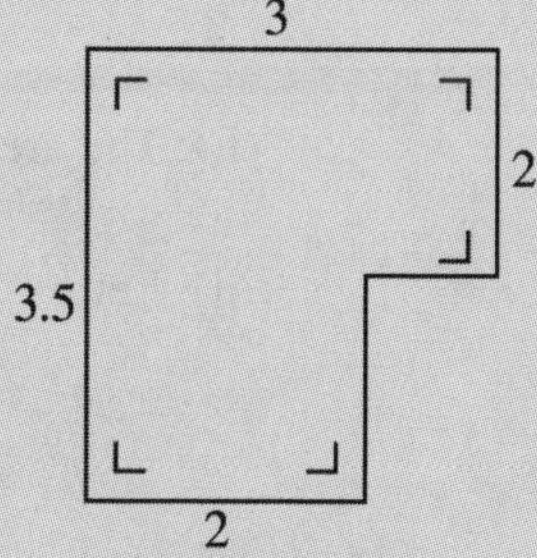

Find the cost of covering the floor with cork tiles, if the cost of each square metre is €23.

9. The width of a rectangle is x cm. The length is 2 cm greater than the width.
(i) Write an expression for the area in terms of x.
(ii) If the area is 48 square centimetres, find the value of x.

10. The length of a rectangle is one centimetre greater than the width. The area is 40 square centimetres. Find, correct to one decimal place, the dimensions of the rectangle.

11. Find the area of this triangle:

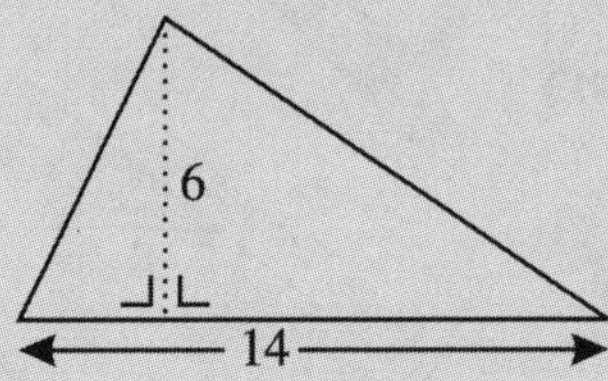

12. Which of these triangles has the greatest area?

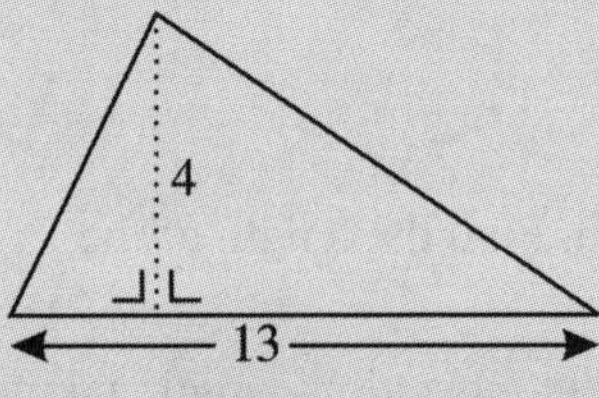

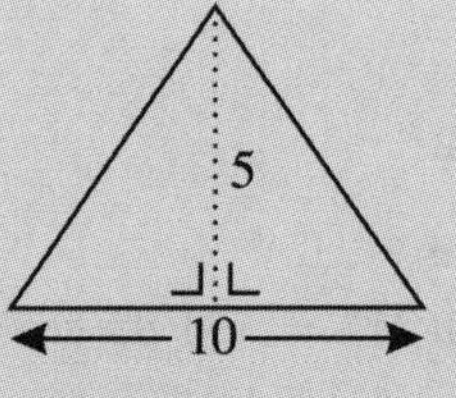

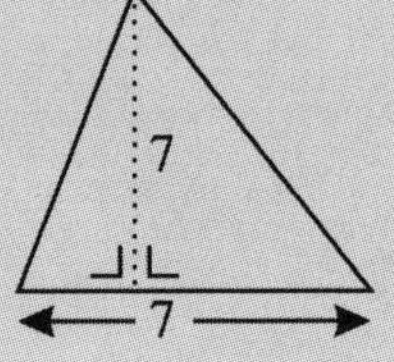

13. Find the area of the shaded region:

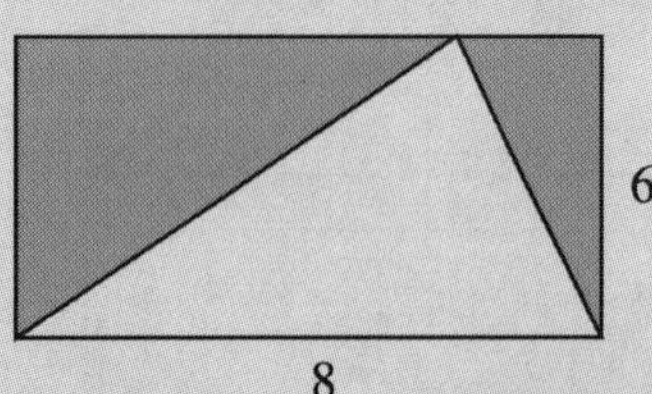

14. The width of a rectangle is x.
Its length is y. The perimeter is 34 metres. The area is 30 square metres.
(i) Write down two equations in x and y.
(ii) Find the dimensions of the rectangle.

15. A square field has area 100cm^2. Find
(i) the length of each side,
(ii) the length of a diagonal correct to two decimal places.

16. Find the perpendicular height (h) and the area of this triangle:

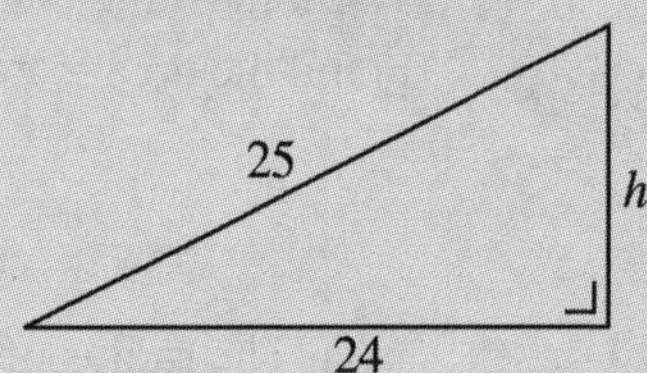

17. (a) How many square centimetres are there in a square metre?
(b) How many square metres are there in a square kilometre?

18.

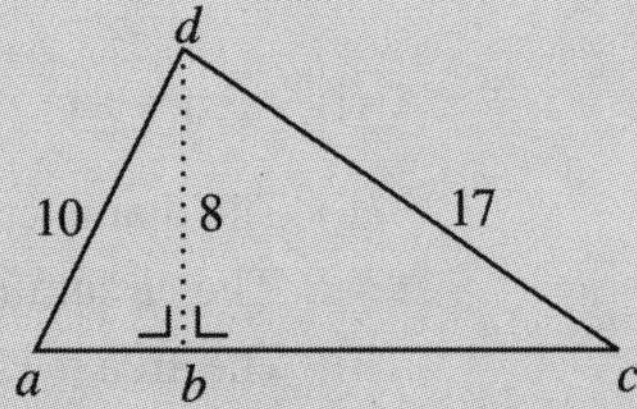

Find
(i) $|ab|$,
(ii) $|bc|$,
(iii) The area of the triangle *acd*.

19.

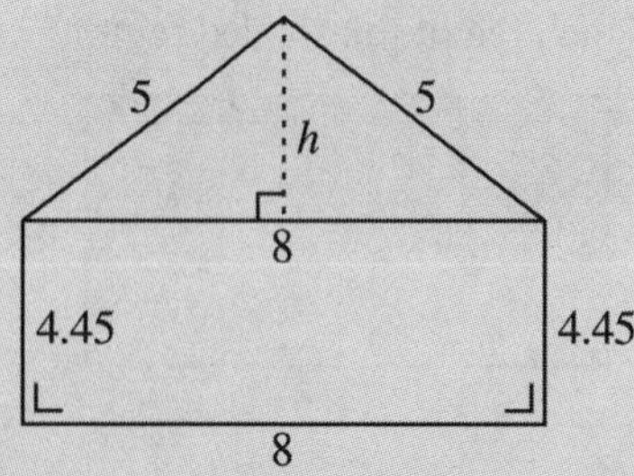

Find
(i) the value of h,
(ii) the area of this gable wall,
(iii) the cost of painting the wall if each square metre costs €0.70 to be painted.

20. The length of the base of this right-angled triangle is x metres. The perpendicular height is $(x + 1)$ metres. The area is 36 square metres.

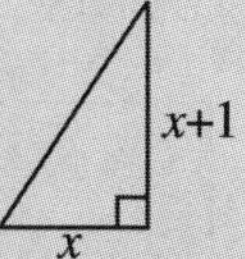

Find
(i) the value of x,
(ii) the length of the perimeter correct to the nearest metre.

CIRCLES, DISCS AND SECTORS

The following diagram explains some important terminology:

If a circle has radius r, then the length of the circumference $= 2\pi r$ and the area $= \pi r^2$

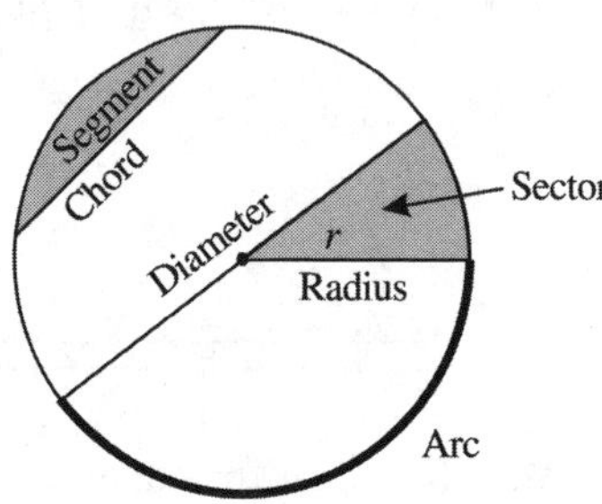

Example 1:

(i) The radius of a disc is 14 cm. Find its area using $\pi = \frac{22}{7}$.

(ii) The diameter of a circle is 42 cm. Find the length of the circumference, taking $\pi = 3.14$

(iii) The area of a disc is 1256cm^2. Find its radius-length, taking $\pi = 3.14$

Solution:

(i) Area $= \pi r^2 = \frac{22}{7} \times \frac{14}{1} \times \frac{14}{1} = 616 \text{ cm}^2$.

(ii) The diameter = 42. Therefore the radius = 21.
The circumference $= 2\pi r = 2(3.14)(21) = 131.88$ cm

(iii) The area = 1256

$$\therefore \quad \pi r^2 = 1256$$

$$\therefore \quad 3.14r^2 = 1256$$

$$\therefore \quad r^2 = \frac{1256}{3.14} = 400$$

$$\therefore \quad r = \sqrt{400} = 20 \text{ cm}$$

Example 2: A circular swimming pool has radius 10 m. It is surrounded by a path 1 m wide. Find the area of the path

(i) in terms of π,

(ii) to the nearest square metre (using $\pi = \frac{22}{7}$).

Solution:

(i) Area of path =

$$\pi R^2 - \pi r^2 = \pi(11)^2 - \pi(10)^2$$
$$= 121\pi - 100\pi$$
$$= 21\pi \text{ m}^2$$

(ii) $21\pi = \frac{21}{1} \times \frac{22}{7} = 66 \text{ m}^2$

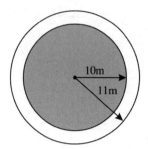

Example 3: Find the area of this sector, where the measurements are in centimetres:

(Use $\pi = 3.14$)

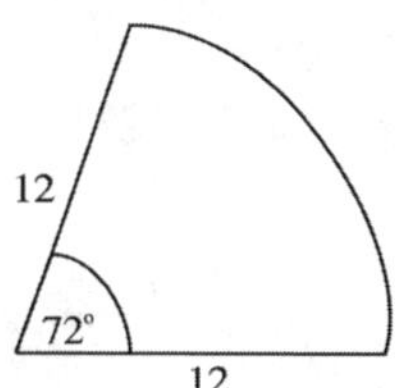

Solution: If C is the circle from which this sector is cut, then $r = 12$ cm.

The area of $C = \pi r^2 = (3.14)(144) = 452.16$

$\frac{72}{360} = \frac{1}{5}$. $\therefore 72° = {}^1/_5$ of $360°$.

Therefore, the area of the sector = ${}^1/_5$ of $452.16 = 90.432 \text{ cm}^2$.

Exercise 13.B

1. Use $\pi = {}^{22}/_7$ to find the areas of these figures:

(i)

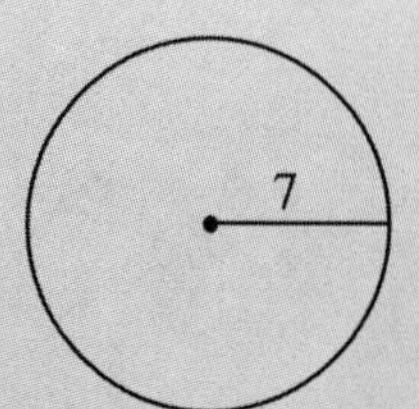

(ii)

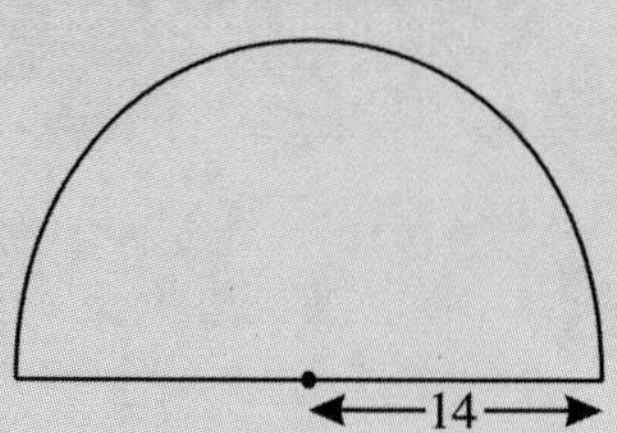

(iii)

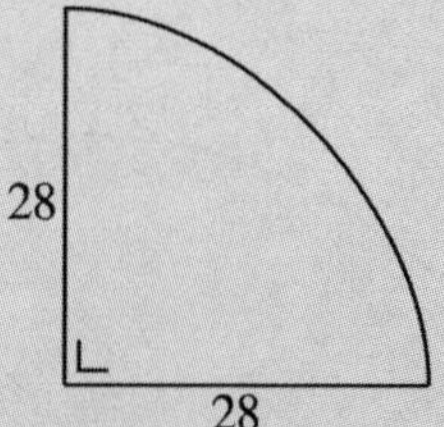

(iv)

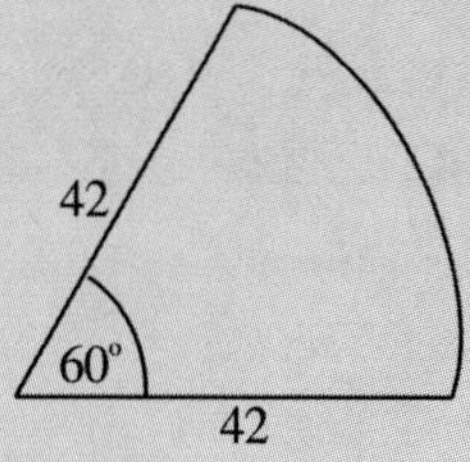

2. Use $\pi = 3.14$ to find the **areas** and **perimeters** of these sectors:

3. Find the area of the shaded region in each case, using $\pi = {}^{22}/_{7}$ where necessary:

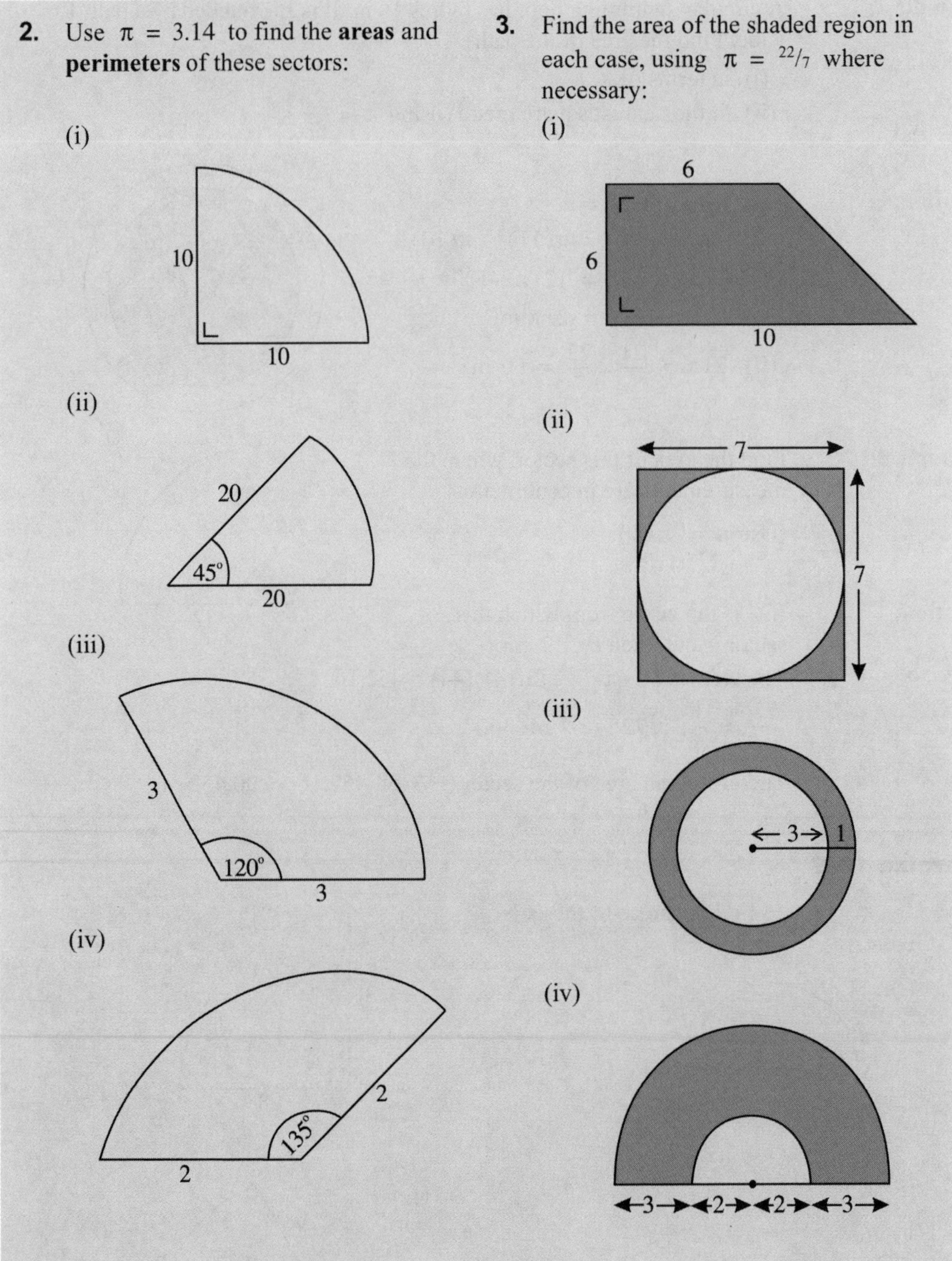

4. (a) The diagram shows 6 circles with the same centre, each a distance x apart. Which has the greater area: the inner shaded region or the outer shaded region?

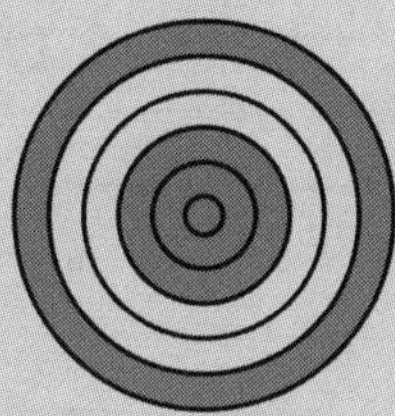

(b) The perimeter of the shaded region consists of three semi-circles. Find, in terms of π

(i) the perimeter of the region,
(ii) the area of the region.

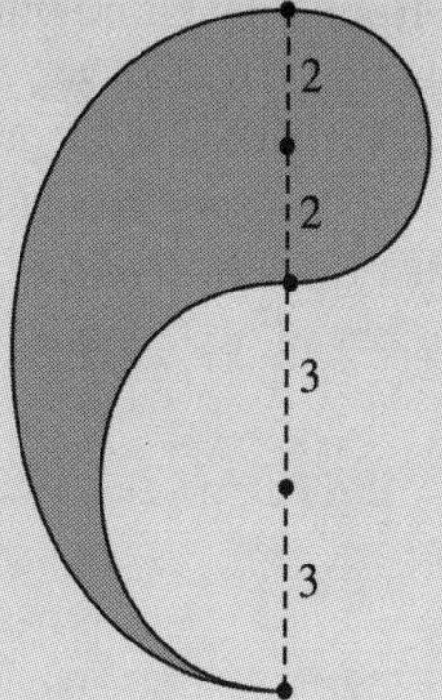

5. K is a disc of radius 10 cm. The sector aob is removed from K.

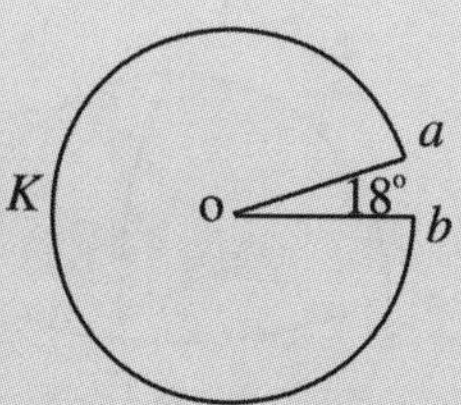

If $|\angle aob| = 18°$, find

(i) what fraction of the disc has been removed,
(ii) the area of the remainder, using $\pi = 3.14$

6. A disc is inscribed in a square, as shown.

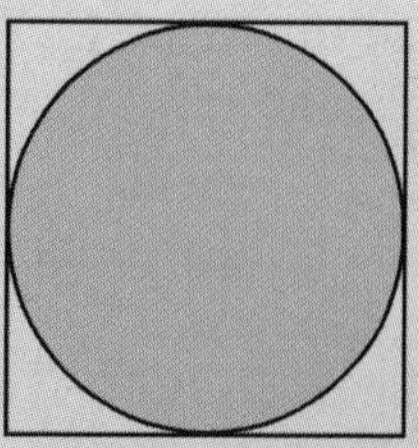

Show that the areas of the square and the disc are in the ratio $4 : \pi$.

7. A circular flower bed has radius 6 m. It is surrounded by a path of width 2 m.

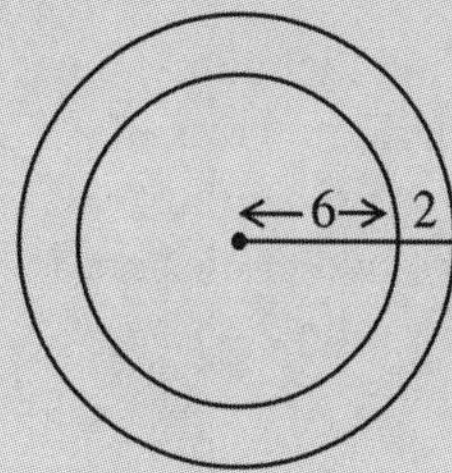

Using $\pi = {}^{22}/_{7}$, find

(i) the area of the path,
(ii) the cost of the path if paving costs €17.25 per square metre.

8. A quarter disc of radius 10 cm has a triangular piece removed, as shown.

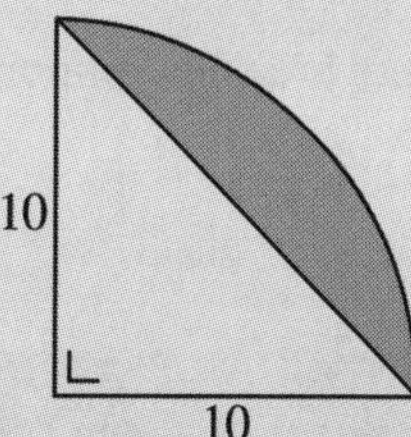

Find the area of the remaining shaded region, using $\pi = 3.14$

9. The sides of a square are each of length $2r$, as shown. Circles are drawn inside and outside the square.

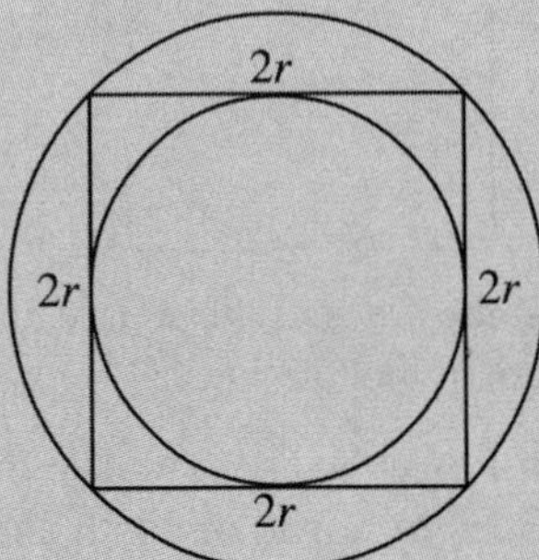

(i) Find the radius of each circle in terms of r.

(ii) Verify that the areas of the two circles are in the ratio 2 : 1.

10. Three athletes, A, B and C run around a track, as shown. The track is rectangular with semi-circular ends. Each athlete runs in a lane which is 1 metre wide.

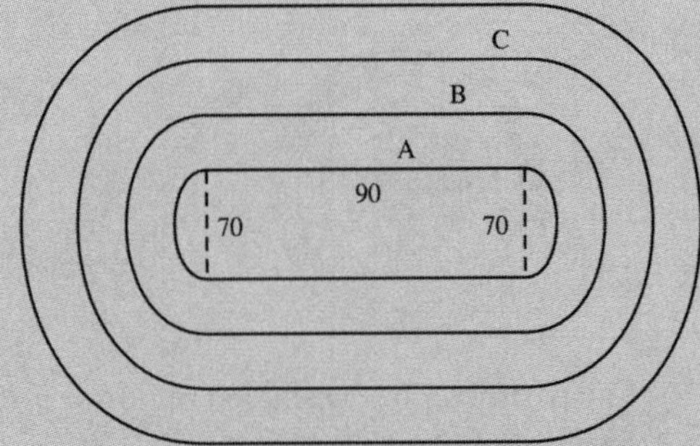

Answer these questions to the nearest metre:

(i) If A runs around the entire track once, how far does she travel?

(ii) If B travels around the entire track once in the next lane, how far does she travel?

(iii) The organisers want the three athletes to compete in a 400 metre race. How much 'stagger' must runners B and C be given? (i.e. How far ahead of A should they start?)

VOLUME

Here are some important formulae:

1. The volume of a sphere $= \frac{4}{3}\pi r^3$

The curved surface area $= 4\pi r^2$

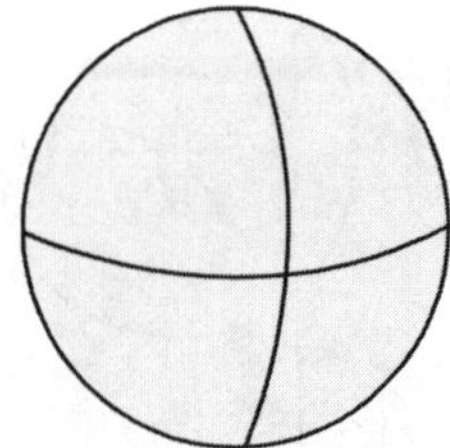

2. The volume of a hemisphere $= \frac{2}{3}\pi r^3$

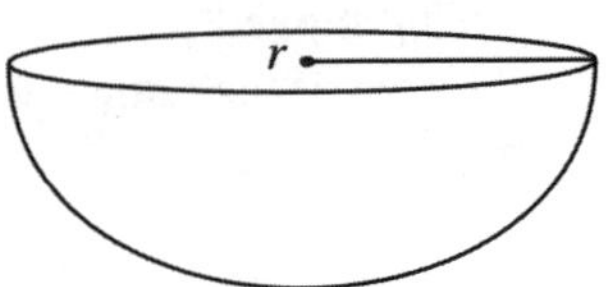

3. The volume of a cylinder = $\pi r^2 h$
Curved surface area = $2\pi rh$
Total surface area = $2\pi rh + 2\pi r^2$

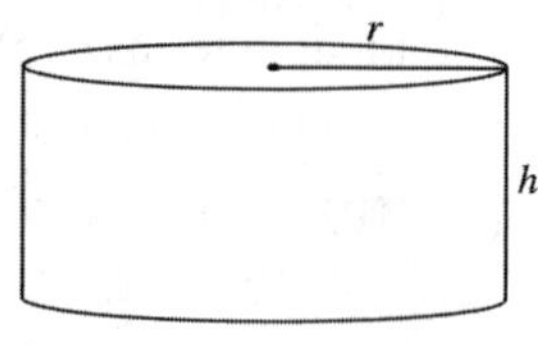

4. The volume of a cone = $\frac{1}{3}\pi r^2 h$

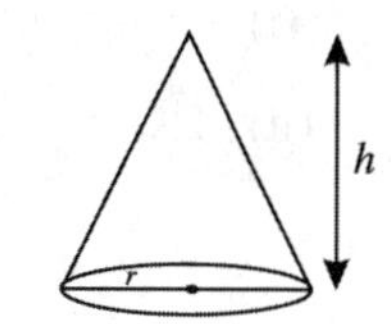

5. The volume of a prism (any shape with a constant cross-section) = Al
[Where A = the area of the cross-section and l = the length]

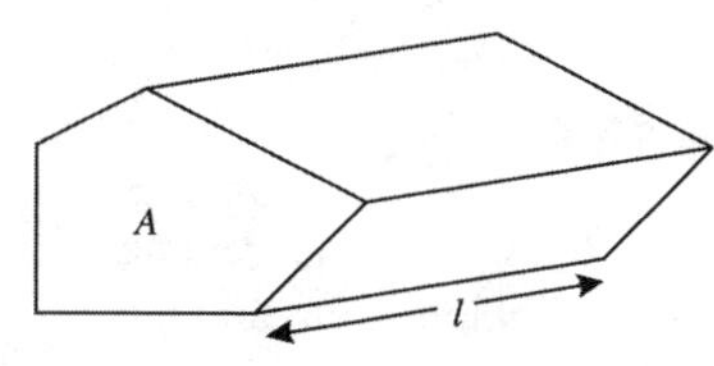

6. The volume of a rectangular box = lbh

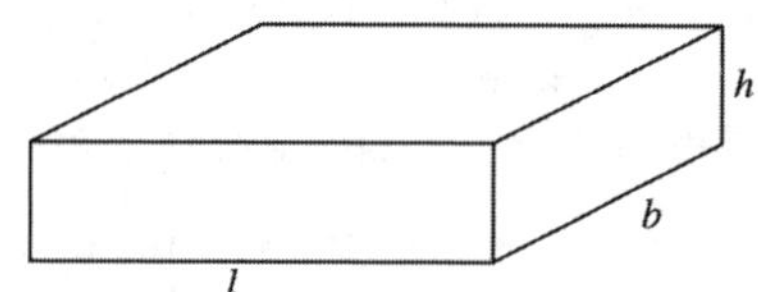

Example 1: Find, in terms of π, the volume of

(i) a sphere of radius 6 cm,
(ii) a hemisphere of radius 3 cm,
(iii) a cylinder of radius 4 cm and height 15 cm,
(iv) a cone of radius 5 cm and height 12 cm,
(v) a rectangular box of length 10 cm, breadth 7 cm and height 4 cm,
(vi) a 'Toblerone' packet of base 4 cm, perpendicular height 3 cm and length 10 cm.

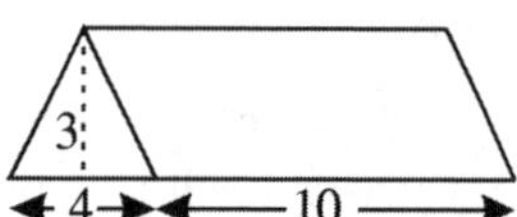

Solution:

(i) $V = \frac{4}{3}\pi r^3 = \frac{4}{3}\cdot\frac{\pi}{1}\cdot\frac{6}{1}\cdot\frac{6}{1}\cdot\frac{6}{1} = 288\pi \text{ cm}^3.$

(ii) $V = \frac{2}{3}\pi r^3 = \frac{2}{3}\cdot\frac{\pi}{1}\cdot\frac{3}{1}\cdot\frac{3}{1}\cdot\frac{3}{1} = 18\pi \text{ cm}^3.$

(iii) $V = \pi r^2 h = \pi(4)^2(15) = 240\pi \text{ cm}^3.$

(iv) $V = \frac{1}{3}\pi r^2 h = \frac{1}{3}\cdot\frac{\pi}{1}\cdot\frac{5}{1}\cdot\frac{5}{1}\cdot\frac{12}{1} = 100\pi \text{ cm}^3.$

(v) $V = lbh = 10(7)(4) = 280 \text{ cm}^3.$

(vi) $V = Al = \left(\frac{1}{2}\cdot 4\cdot 3\right)(10) = 60 \text{ cm}^3.$

Example 2: A solid cylinder has height 10 cm and radius 2 cm.
Find, in terms of π,
(i) the curved surface area,
(ii) the total surface area.

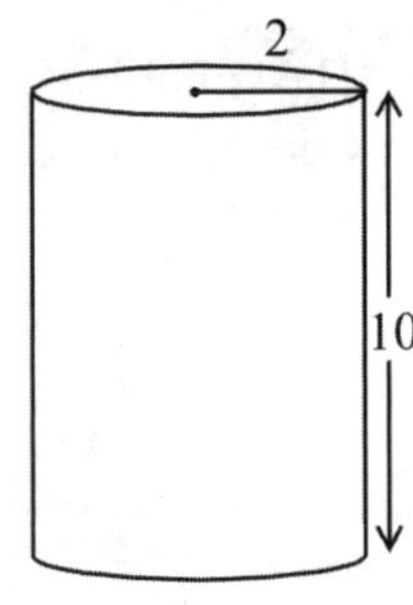

Solution:

(i) $\text{CSA} = 2\pi rh = 2\pi(2)(10) = 40\pi \text{ cm}^2$.

(ii) $\text{TSA} = 2\pi rh + 2\pi r^2 = 2\pi(2)(10) + 2\pi(2)^2$
$= 40\pi + 8\pi$
$= 48\pi \text{ cm}^2$

Exercise 13.C

1. Find, in terms of π, the volume of a cylinder of height 6 cm and radius 2 cm.
2. Find, in terms of π, the volume and curved surface area of a cylinder of height 5 cm and radius 4 cm.
3. Find, in terms of π, the volume of a cone of height 9 cm and radius 5 cm.
4. Find, in terms of π, the volume of a cone of height 5 cm and radius 3 cm.
5. Find, in terms of π, the volume of a sphere of radius 3 m.
6. (i) Find, in terms of π, the volume of a sphere of radius $^3/_2$ m.
   (ii) Find, also, the surface area.
7. Find the volume of a rectangular water-tank which has length 3 m, breadth 2 m and height 1 m.
8. Find the volume of air in a rectangular classroom which has length 8 m, breadth 5 m and height 3 m.
9. The base-radius of a solid cone is 3.5 cm. The height is 12 cm. Find the volume of the cone using $\pi = {}^{22}/_7$.
10. The radius of a hemisphere is 21 cm. Find its volume using $\pi = {}^{22}/_7$.
11. The radius of a cylinder is 5 cm. Its height is 8 cm. Find, using $\pi = 3.14$, the volume of the cylinder.
12. The height of a cylindrical can of beans is 10 cm. The diameter of the base is 7 cm. Find, using $\pi = {}^{22}/_7$, the capacity and total surface area of the can.
13. The length of a 'Toblerone' packet is 8 cm. The length of the base is 2 cm. The perpendicular height is 2 cm. Find its volume.

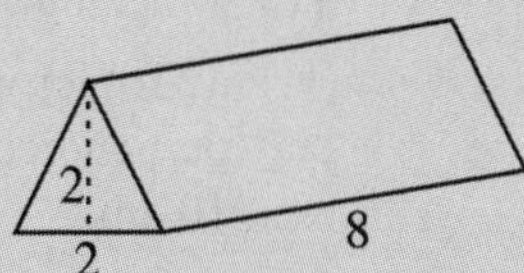

14. A tent has triangular ends, as shown. The height is 2 m, the base is 3 m, the length of the tent is 5 m. Find the volume.

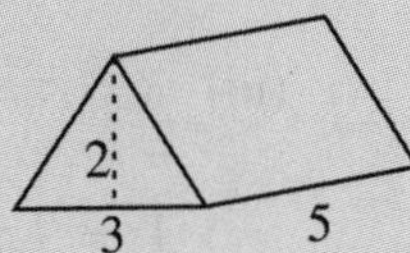

15. A straight tunnel has semi-circular ends as shown. The radius of the tunnel is 7 m; the length is 40 m.

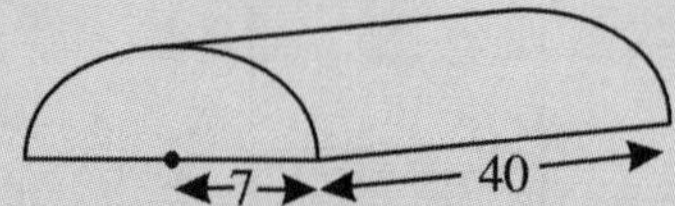

Find

(i) the area of each end, using $\pi = {}^{22}/_{7}$.

(ii) the volume of the tunnel.

16.

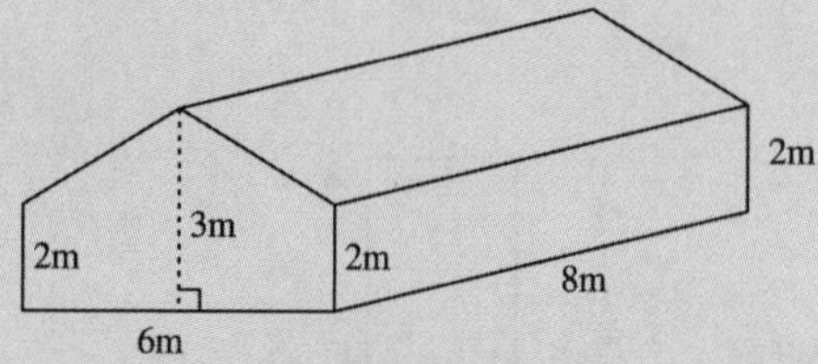

(i) Find the area of the gable wall, as shown in the diagram.

(ii) Find the total volume of the interior of the house.

17. A spinning top consists of a solid cone on a solid hemisphere. The radius of both is 3.5 cm and the height of the cone is 6 cm. Find the total volume of the spinning top to the nearest cubic centimetre.

Take $\pi = {}^{22}/_{7}$.

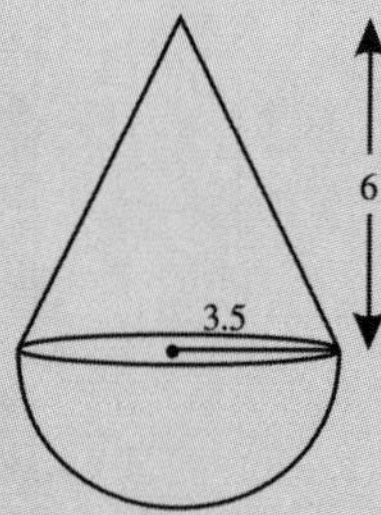

18. A space module consists of a cone on a cylinder. The radius of both is 5 m. The height of the cylindrical part is 8 m; the height of the conical part is 6 m. Find, in terms of π, the total volume.

19. A spherical ball of radius 15 cm fits exactly into a cylindrical can.

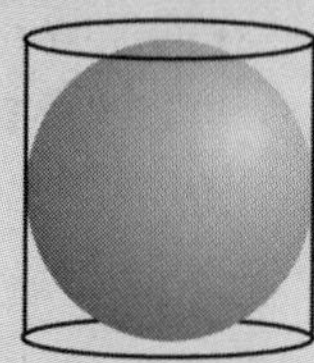

Find

(i) the height and radius of the can,

(ii) the volume of the ball (in terms of π),

(iii) the capacity of the can (in terms of π).

20. A pair of steps are made out of concrete as shown.

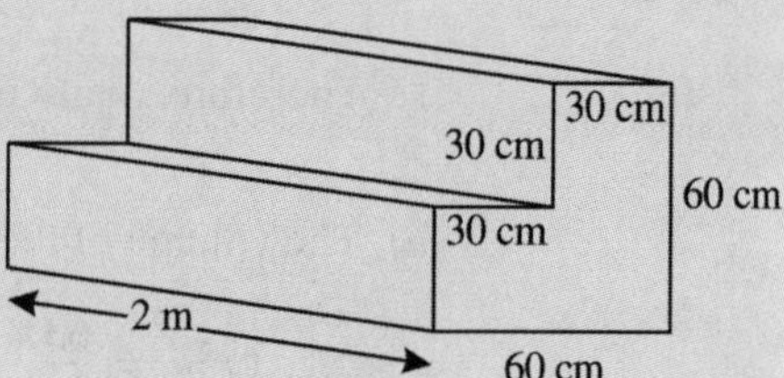

Find (in cubic metres)

(i) the volume of the concrete (in cubic metres),

(ii) the cost of making the steps if concrete costs €88 per cubic metre.

HARDER PROBLEMS

Example 1: A closed test-tube of diameter 3 cm consists of a cylinder on a hemisphere. It is partly filled with water, to a depth of 7½ cm, as shown.

Find the volume of water in terms of π.

If the test-tube is then inverted, find the depth of the water in the cylindrical part.

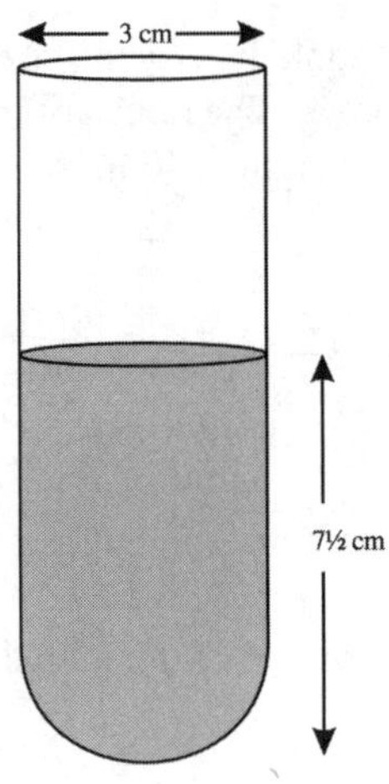

Solution:

(i) The diameter = 3

Therefore $A = 1\frac{1}{2}$, $B = 1\frac{1}{2}$

and $C = 7\frac{1}{2} - 1\frac{1}{2} = 6$

Volume of cylindrical water =

$$\pi r^2 h = \frac{\pi}{1} \times \frac{3}{2} \times \frac{3}{2} \times \frac{6}{1} = \frac{27\pi}{2}$$

Volume of hemispherical part =

$$\frac{2}{3}\pi r^3 = \frac{2}{3} \times \frac{\pi}{1} \times \frac{3}{2} \times \frac{3}{2} \times \frac{3}{2} = \frac{9\pi}{4}$$

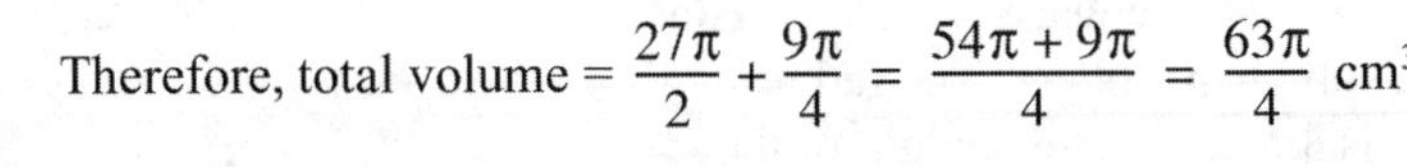

Therefore, total volume $= \frac{27\pi}{2} + \frac{9\pi}{4} = \frac{54\pi + 9\pi}{4} = \frac{63\pi}{4}$ cm^3

(ii) The volume of the water is still the same. It is still $\frac{63\pi}{4}$ cm^3.

$$\therefore \quad \pi r^2 h = \frac{63\pi}{4}$$

$$\therefore \quad r^2 h = \frac{63}{4} \quad \text{[Dividing by } \pi\text{]}$$

$$\therefore \quad \frac{9}{4}h = \frac{63}{4} \quad \left[\text{Since } r^2 = \left(\frac{3}{2}\right)^2 = \frac{9}{4}\right]$$

$$\therefore \quad 9h = 63 \quad \text{[Multiplying by 4]}$$

$$\therefore \quad h = 7 \text{ cm}$$

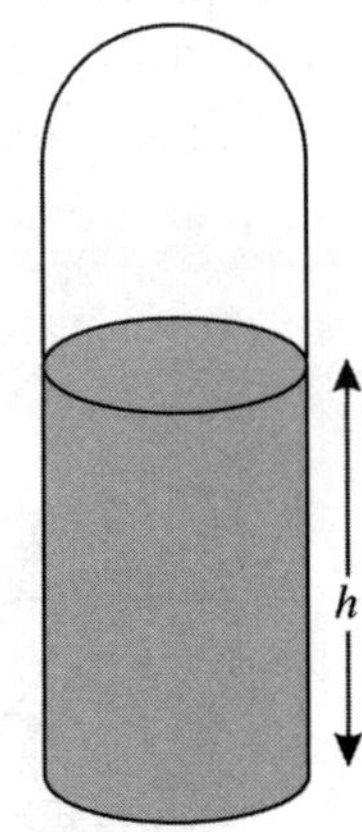

Exercise 13.D

1. A test-tube consists of a hollow cylinder on a hollow hemisphere. The total height is 11 cm. and the tube has diameter 2 cm.

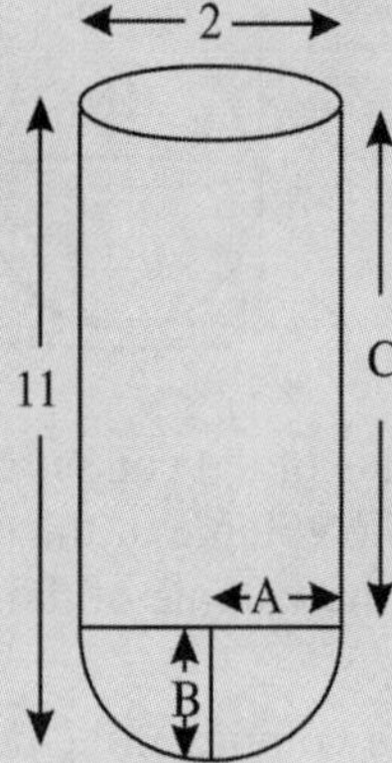

(i) Write down the values of A, B, and C.
(ii) Find the capacity of the test-tube in terms of π.

2. A buoy consists of a cone on a hemisphere. The diameter is 12 cm and the overall height of the buoy is 16 cm.

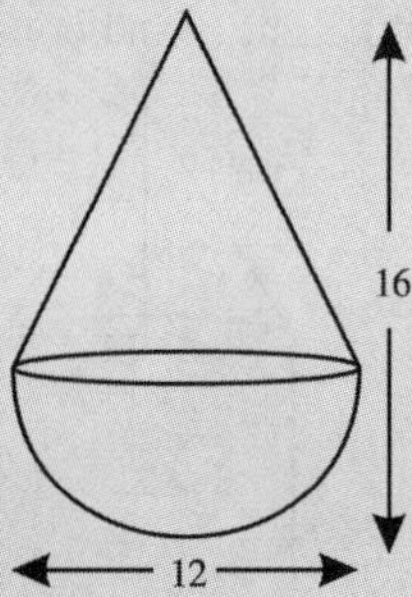

Find
(i) the height of the conical part,
(ii) the volume of the buoy in terms of π.

3. A lighthouse consists of a hemisphere on a cylinder. The diameter is 14 m. The overall height is 37 m.

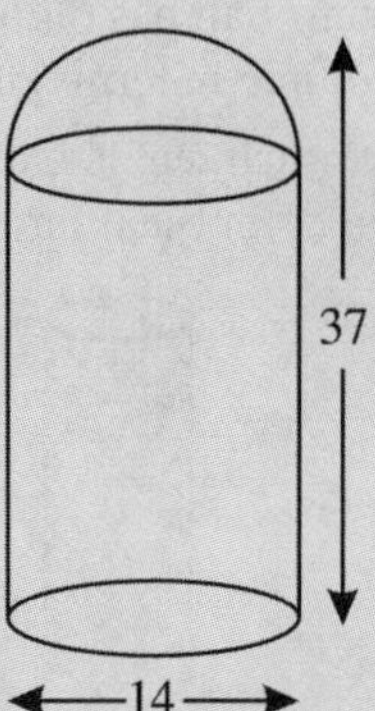

Find, taking $\pi = {}^{22}/_{7}$, the total volume of the lighthouse.

4. A solid metal sphere of radius 6 cm is melted down and remoulded into a solid cone of radius 3 cm.

Find
(i) the volume of the sphere in terms of π,
(ii) the height of the cone.

5. A solid sphere of diameter 18 cm is made of plasticine. It is remoulded to form a cone of height 81 cm. Find the radius of the cone.

6. (a) A tennis ball has radius 3 cm. Find its volume in terms of π.

(b) Three such tennis balls fit exactly into a cylindrical tube.

(i) Write down the radius and the height of the tube.

(ii) Find the capacity (volume) of the tube in terms of π.

(iii) What fraction of the volume of the tube is taken up by the three tennis balls?

7. The volume of a sphere is $\frac{9\pi}{16}$ cubic centimetres. How long is its radius?

8. A candle consists of a cone on a cylinder. The diameter of the candle is 7 cm. The height of the cylindrical part is 8 cm. The height of the conical part is 3 cm.

Find

(i) the volume of each part, using $\pi = {}^{22}/_{7}$,

(ii) the ratio of the volume of the cylindrical part to the volume of the conical part,

(iii) the volume of the smallest rectangular box into which the candle will fit.

9. A toy consists of a solid cone on a solid hemisphere, as shown.

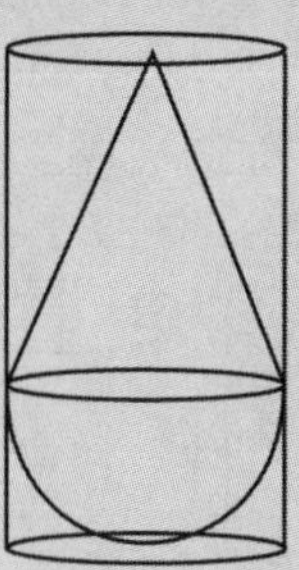

The radius of the cone is of length 6 cm. The volume of the cone is one third of the volume of the hemisphere. Find

(i) the volume of the hemisphere in terms of π,

(ii) the height of the cone,

(iii) the overall height of the toy.

The toy fits exactly into a cylindrical container, as shown. Does the toy take up more or less than half of the capacity of the container?

10. A candle is in the shape of a cone on a cylinder. The cylinder has radius 4 cm. The slant height of the cone is 5 cm.

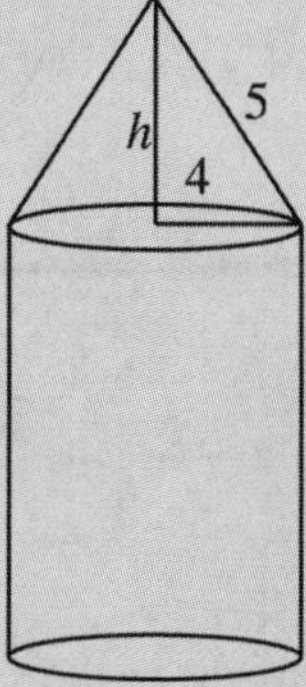

Find

(i) the height, h, of the cone,

(ii) the volume of the cone in terms of π,

(iii) the height of the cylinder, given that its volume is ten times the volume of the cone.

11. A grain silo consists of a cylinder on a cone as shown. The radius of the cylinder is 1.5 m. The slant height of the cone is 2.5 m. The overall height of the grain silo is 20 m.

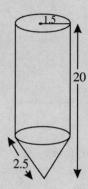

Find
- (i) the height of the cone,
- (ii) the height of the cylinder,
- (iii) the capacity of the silo (when full) in terms of π,
- (iv) the depth of the grain (as measured from the bottommost point of the cone) when the silo is one-seventh full.

12. A space rocket consists of a cone on a cylinder. The diameter is 10 m. The overall height of the rocket is 30 m. If the volume of the rocket is 650π m^3, find the height of the cylindrical part of the rocket.

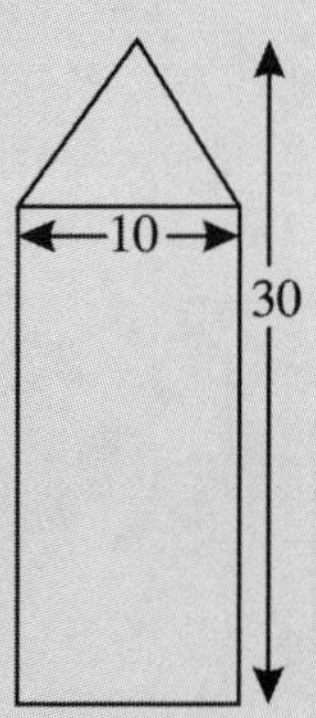

[Hint: let h = the height of the cylindrical part
$\therefore 30 - h$ = height of conical part]

13. A closed plastic container is in the shape of a hollow cylinder on a hollow hemisphere, both of radius-length 3 cm. The container is partly filled with water, to a depth of 10 cm.

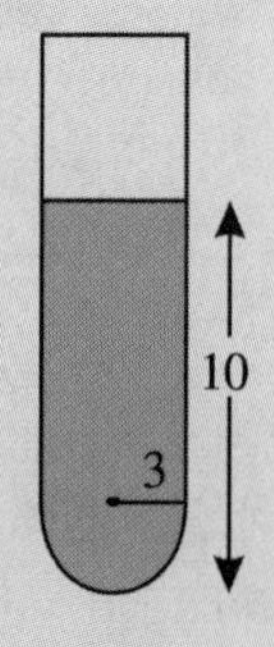

- (i) Find the volume of the water, in terms of π.
- (ii) If the container is turned upside-down, what will the depth of the water be in the cylindrical part?

14. A closed container consists of a cylinder joined to a cone. The height of the cylinder is 10 cm and its diameter is 7 cm.

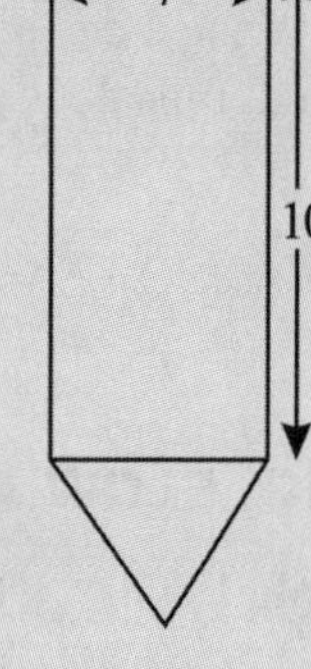

Calculate:
- (i) the capacity of the cylindrical part in terms of π,
- (ii) the vertical height of the cone, given that its capacity is one fifth of the capacity of the cylinder,
- (iii) the volume of the water (in terms of π) in the container when its depth is 13 cm.

What would he height of the water be in the cylinder if the container were inverted?

15. Water is kept cool in a cylindrical container of diameter 28 cm and height 30 cm.

The water is poured into small conical cups, each of diameter 6 cm and height 7 cm.
When the cooler is full, how many cupfulls does it contain?

16. A rectangular block has height 6 cm, length 11 cm and width 8 cm.

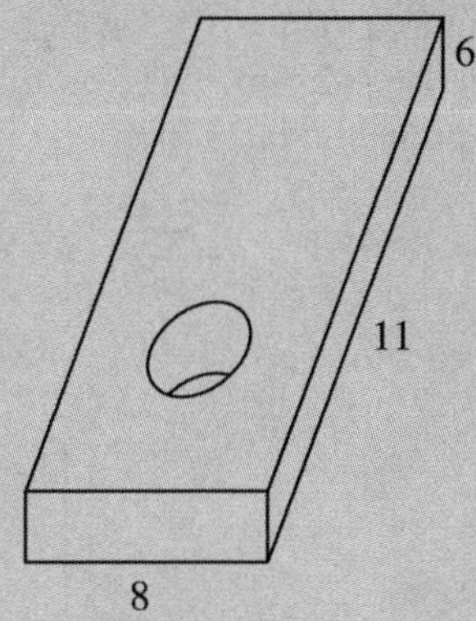

(i) Find its volume.
(ii) A vertical cylindrical hole of radius r centimetres is drilled in the block, as shown. The volume of the remaining piece is 87½% of the original volume. Find r, correct to one decimal place. [Take $\pi = {}^{22}/_{7}$.]

RATIO, FLOW AND OTHER PROBLEMS

Example 1: Two cylinders have radii in the ratio 7 : 5 and heights in the ratio 1 : 2. Which has the greater volume?

Solution: Let $7x$ and $5x$ be the radii.
Let y and $2y$ be the heights.

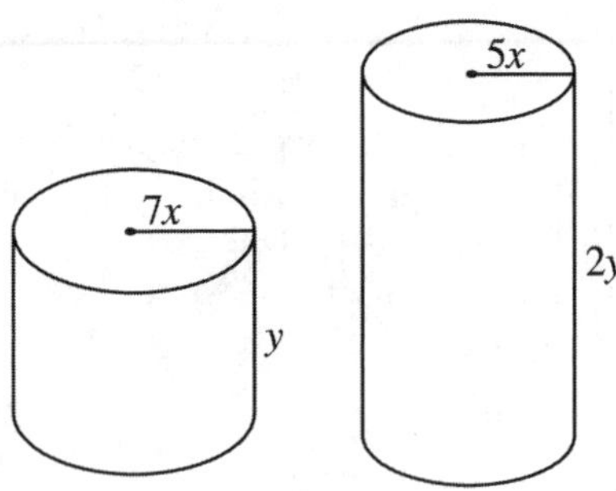

First volume = $\pi r^2 h = \pi(7x)^2(y) = 49\pi x^2 y$

Second volume = $\pi r^2 h = \pi(5x)^2(2y) = 50\pi x^2 y$

$\therefore$ The second cylinder has the greater volume : ***Answer***

Example 2: Water is flowing through a cylindrical pipe at the speed of 35 cm/sec. The radius of the pipe is 5 cm. The water is poured into a cubic tank of side 100 cm. Find the rise in the depth of the water in the tank in 5 minutes.

Use $\pi = {}^{22}/_{7}$.

Solution: This amount of water flows into the tank every second:

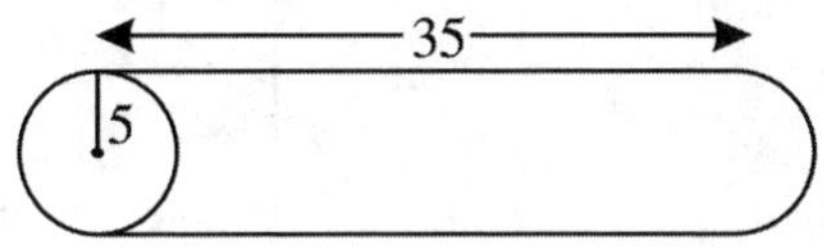

The volume = $\pi r^2 h = \frac{22}{7_1} \times \frac{5}{1} \times \frac{5}{1} \times \frac{35^5}{1} = 2750 \text{ cm}^3$

There are 300 seconds in 5 minutes.

$\therefore$ The volume of water which flows in 5 minutes $= 300 \times 2750$
$= 825\ 000 \text{ cm}^2$

Let x = the increase in depth of the water in the tank.

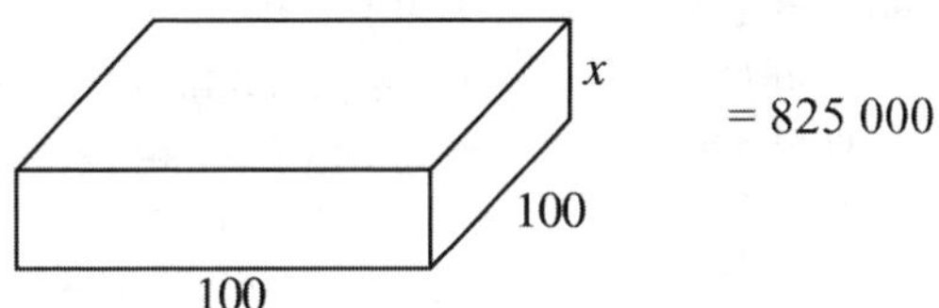

$(100)(100)(x) = 825000$

$\therefore 10000x = 825000$

$\therefore x = 82.5$ cm : ***Answer***

Exercise 13.E

1. Two discs have radii in the ratio 2 : 1. What is the ratio of their areas?
2. Two cylinders have their radii in the ratio 2 : 1 and their heights in the ratio 3 : 1. What is the ratio of their volumes?
3. Two cones have their radii in the ratio 3 : 2 and their heights in the ratio 5 : 12. Which has the greater volume?
4. (a) Two spheres have radii in the ratio 3 : 1. What is the ratio of their volumes?
   (b) The ratio of the volumes of two spheres is 8 : 1. Find the ratio of the lengths of their radii.
5. Three cylinders (*A*, *B* and *C*) have radii in the ratio 5 : 3 : 2 and heights in the ratio 3 : 8 : 19.
   Which has the greatest volume?
6. Two cones have equal volume. Their radii are in the ratio 2 : 1. What is the ratio of their heights?
7. A cone has height 12 cm and radius 10 cm. It is cut half way up (as shown) so that a new cone of height 6 cm and radius 5 cm is formed. Find the ratio original cone's volume : new cone's volume.

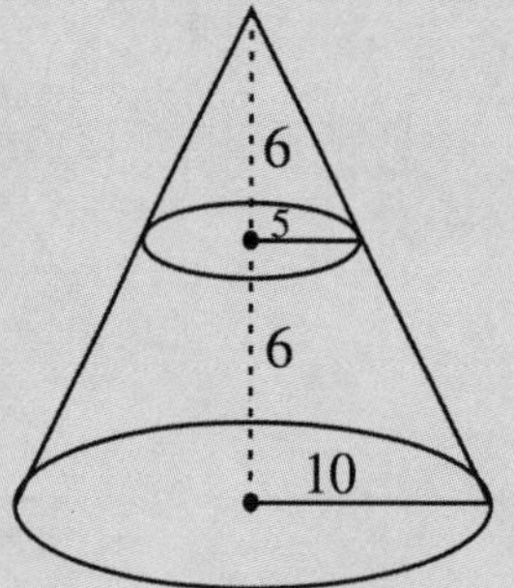

8. A cylindrical tank of radius 12 cm is partly filled with water. A sphere of radius 6 cm is immersed in the water. By how much will the water rise?
9. A cylindrical tank of radius 4 cm is partly filled with water. A cone of radius 2 cm and height 3 cm is immersed in the water. By how much will the water rise?

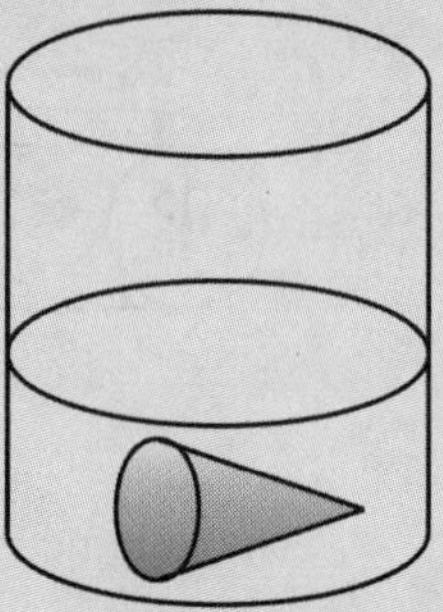

10. Water flows through a cylindrical pipe at a rate of 35 cm per second. The pipe has diameter 4 cm. How long would it take to pour out 22 litres of water? (Use $\pi = {}^{22}/_{7}$)
    [1 litre = 1000 cm^3]
11. Water flows through a cylindrical pipe at a rate of 10 cm per second. The diameter of the pipe is 7 cm. The water is poured into an empty rectangular tank of length 55 cm and width 20 cm.

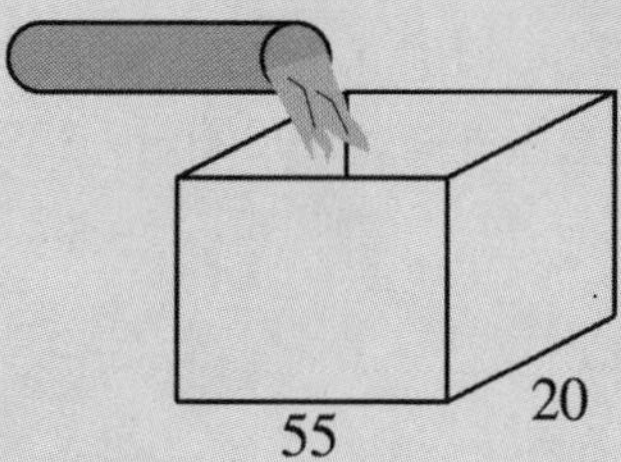

What is the depth of the water after one minute?

12. A ladle is in the shape of a hemisphere of diameter 3 cm. It is used to remove soup from a cylindrical container of radius 6 cm.

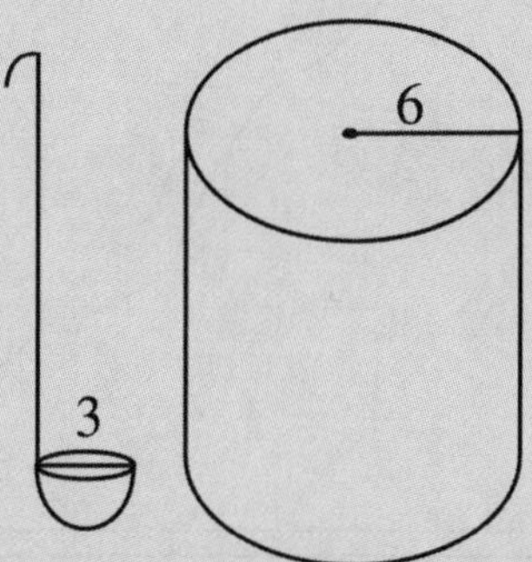

(i) Find the volume of one ladle-full in terms of π.
(ii) How far will the depth of the soup drop if 24 ladle-fulls of soup are removed?
(iii) If the depth of the soup is now $2\frac{1}{2}$ cm, how many more ladle-fulls could still be got?

13. Water pours through a pipe of radius 3 cm at a rate of 15 cm per second. It flows into a conical tank of height 0.9 metres and radius 0.6 metres.

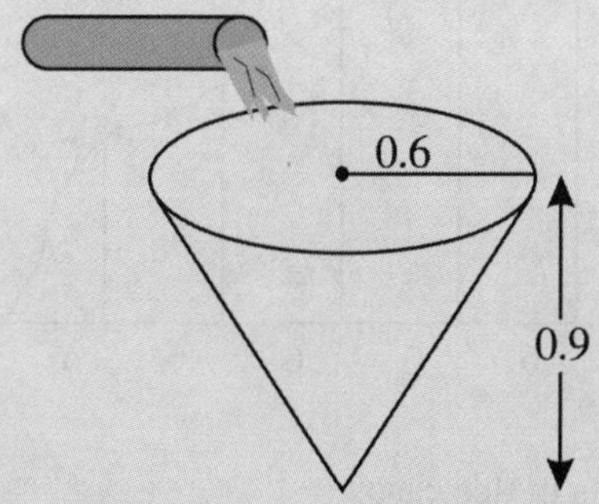

How long will it take to fill the tank?

14. Water flows through a cylindrical pipe of diameter 3.5 cm into a rectangular tank of length 1.1 metres, width 1.4 metres and height 1.5 metres. The tank is filled in 40 minutes. Find (using $\pi = {}^{22}/_{7}$) the rate at which the water flows through the pipe (in cm/s).

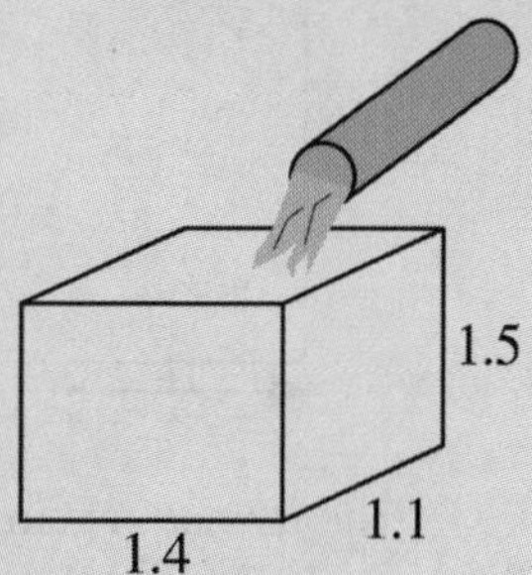

15. A cone has radius 2 cm and height ${}^{27}/_{8}$ cm. It is totally immersed in water inside a cylindrical tank of radius 6 cm.

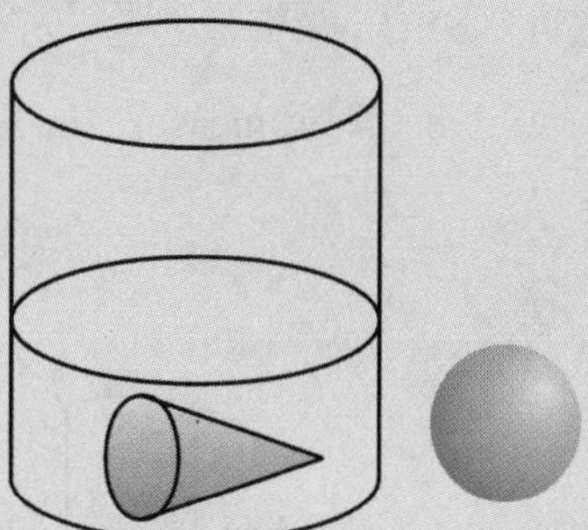

(i) When the cone is removed, calculate the drop in the depth of the water in the tank.
(ii) A sphere of radius r cm is then immersed in the water, which returns to its previous level. Find the value of r.

SIMPSON'S RULE

Example 1: Here is a map of a field which a farmer wants to sell.

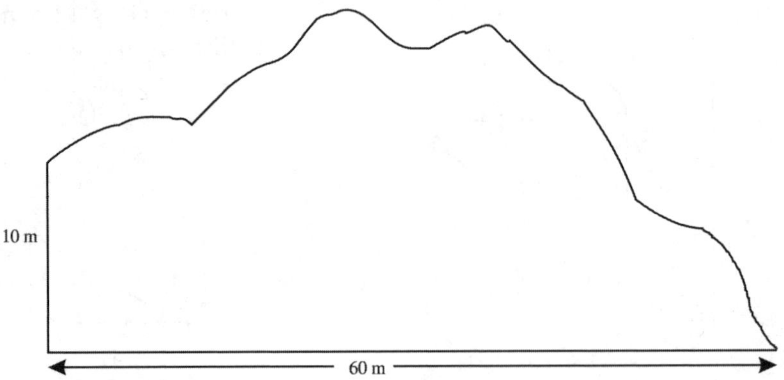

The farmer gets in a surveyor to work out the approximate area of the field. The surveyor uses 'Simpson's Rule' – and here is how it works.

Solution: Divide the area into an EVEN number of strips of equal width. We will divide this field into 10 strips, each of width 6 metres. The letter h is used to denote the width. So, in this case $h = 6$.

Now, measure the length of each 'offset'.

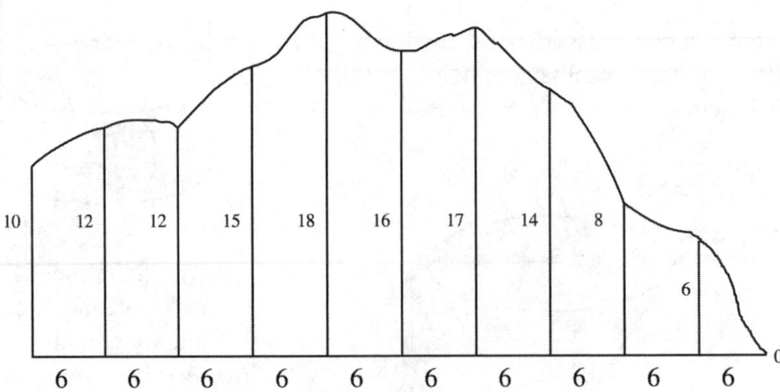

Here are the numbered meaurements in this case:

First	2nd	3rd	4th	5th	6th	7th	8th	9th	10th	Last
10	12	12	15	18	16	17	14	8	6	0

Simpson' Rule, (See Maths Tables p. 42) states that the area is given by the formula:

$$\text{Area} = \frac{h}{3}\{\text{First} + \text{last} + 2(\text{odds}) + 4(\text{evens})\}$$

$$= \frac{6}{3}\{10 + 0 + 2(12 + 18 + 17 + 8) + 4(12 + 15 + 16 + 14 + 6)\}$$

$$= 2\{10 + 2(55) + 4(63)\}$$

$$= 2\{10 + 110 + 252\}$$

$$= 2\{372\}$$

= 744 square metres

To help you remember the formula :

$$\text{Area} = \frac{h}{3}\{\text{First} + \text{last} + 2(\text{odds}) + 4(\text{evens})\}$$

remember **TOFE** which stands for **T**wice the **O**dds and **F**our times the **E**vens. Simpson's rule can then be shortened to

$$\text{Area} = \frac{h}{3}\{\text{First} + \text{last} + \text{TOFE}\}$$

Example 2: Use Simpson's Rule to estimate the area of this irregular figure:

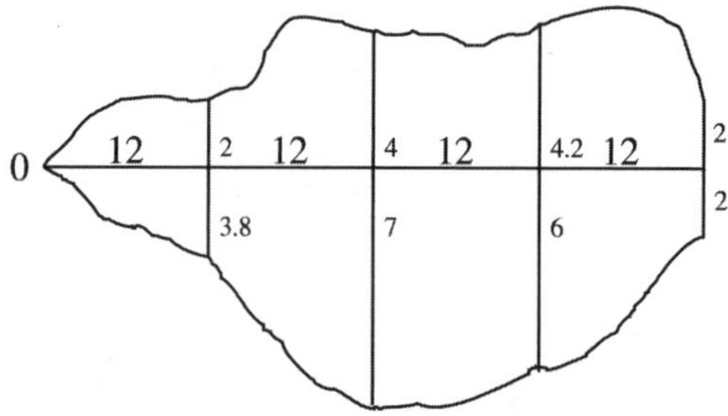

Solution: The ***total*** lengths of the offsets are as follows:

First	2nd	3rd	4th	Last
0	5.8	11	10.2	4

$$\text{Area} = \frac{h}{3}\{\text{First} + \text{last} + 2(\text{odds}) + 4(\text{evens})\}$$

$$= \frac{12}{3}\{0 + 4 + 2(11) + 4(5.8 + 10.2)\}$$

$$= 4\{4 + 22 + 64\} = 4\{90\} = 360 \text{ square units}$$

Example 3:

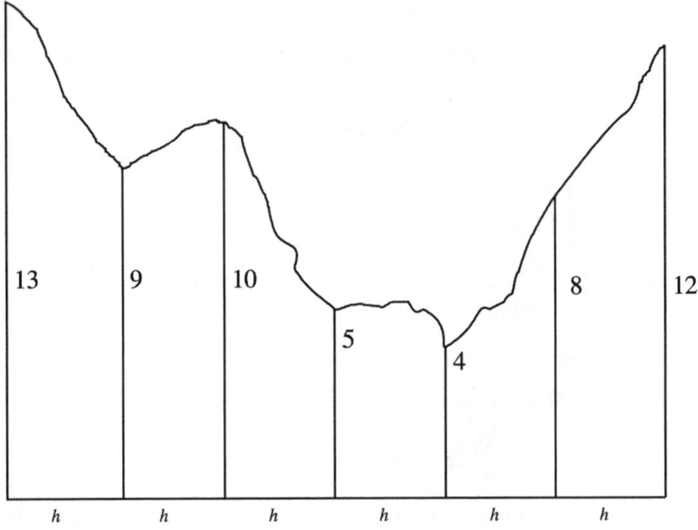

The area of this field is 564 square metres. The offsets are each a distance h apart. Find the value of h.

Solution: The offset lengths are:

First	2nd	3rd	4th	5th	6th	Last
13	9	10	5	4	8	12

$$\text{Area} = \frac{h}{3}\{\text{First} + \text{last} + 2(\text{odds}) + 4(\text{evens})\}$$

$$\therefore\ 564 = \frac{h}{3}\{13 + 12 + 2(10 + 4) + 4(9 + 5 + 8)\}$$

$$\therefore\ 564 = \frac{h}{3}\{13 + 12 + 28 + 88\}$$

$$\therefore\ 564 = \frac{h}{3}\{141\}$$

$$\therefore\ 564 = 47h$$

$$\therefore\ h = 12 \text{ m}$$

Exercise 13.F

1. Use Simpson's Rule to estimate the area of this field, in which each of the offsets are a distance 6 m apart and all measurements are in metres:

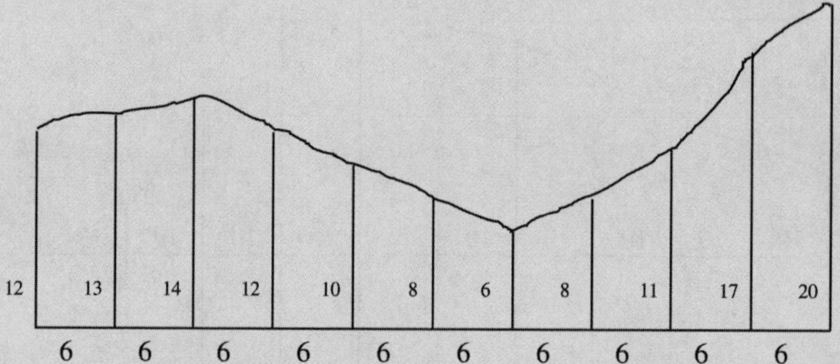

2. Use Simpson's Rule to estimate the area of this field, in which each of the offsets are a distance 10 m apart and all measurements are in metres:

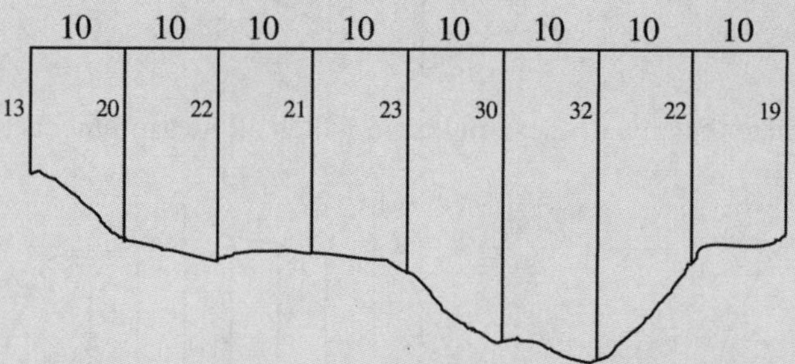

3. Use Simpson's Rule to estimate the area of this field, in which each of the offsets are a distance 50 m apart and all measurements are in metres:

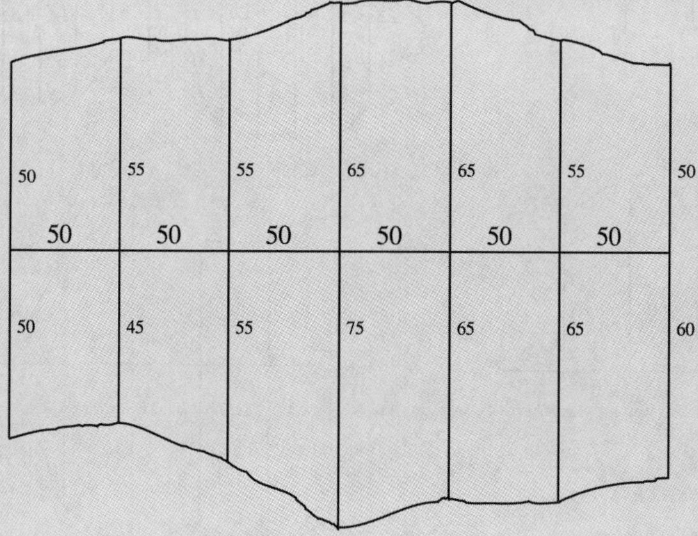

4. Use Simpson's Rule to estimate the area of this field, in which each of the offsets are a distance 10 m apart and all measurements are in metres:

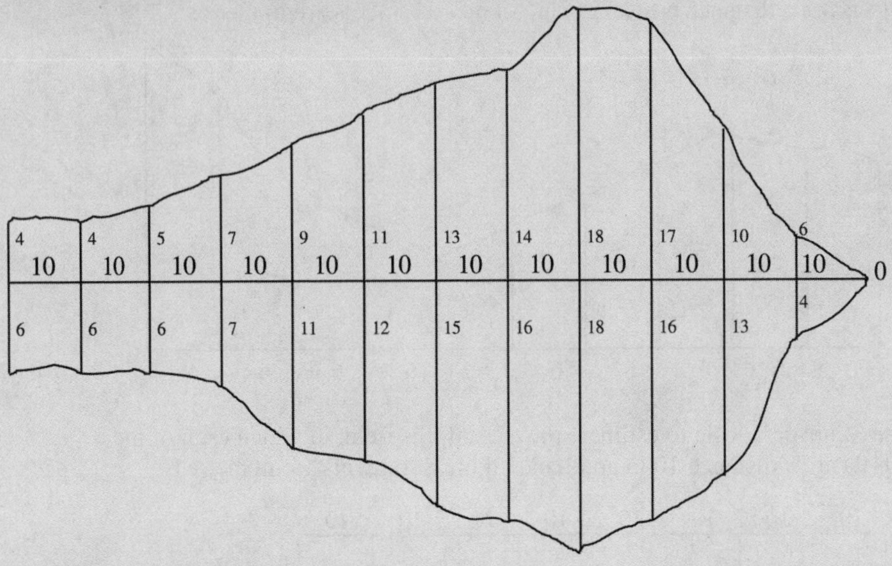

5. Use Simpson's Rule to estimate the area of these fields, in which all measurements are in metres:

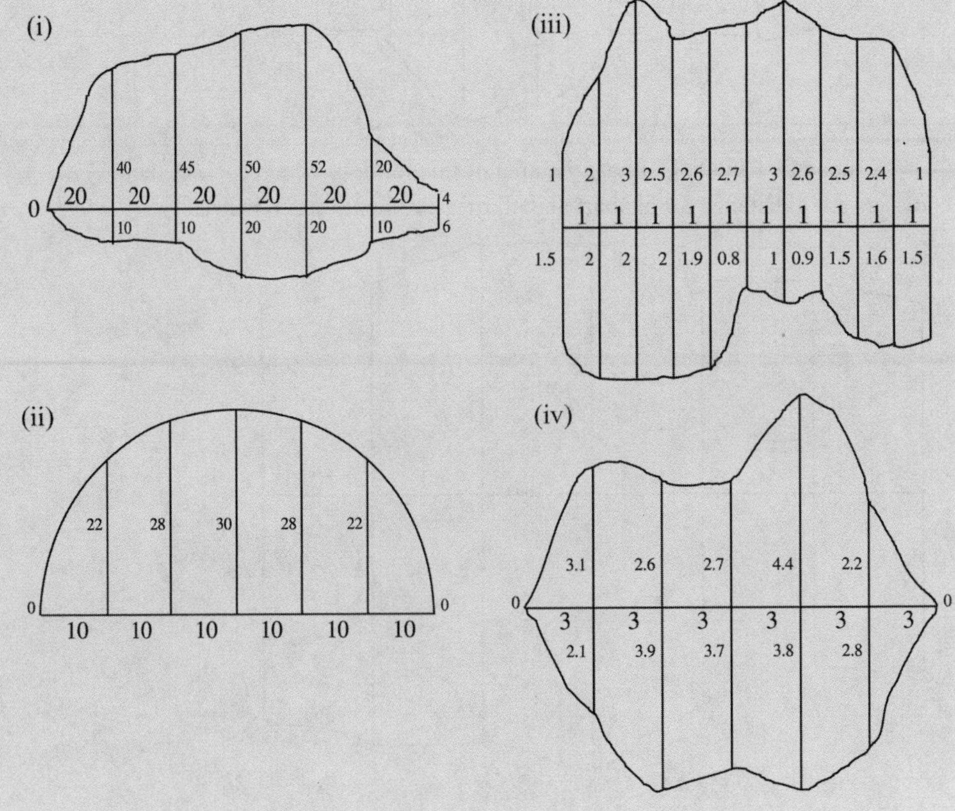

6. Find the area of these plots of land in hectares. [1 hectare = 10 000 m^2]. Measurements are in metres.

(i)

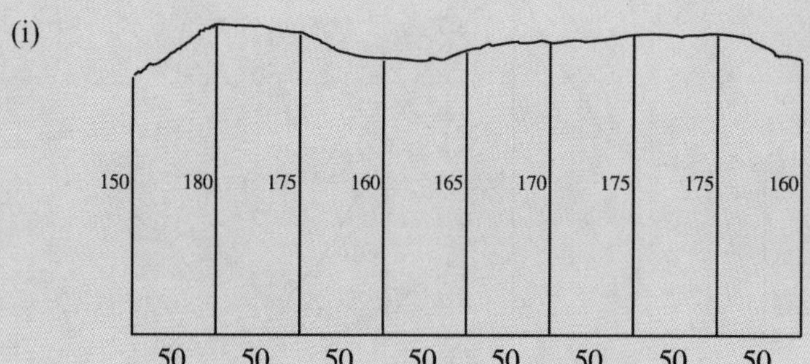

(ii)

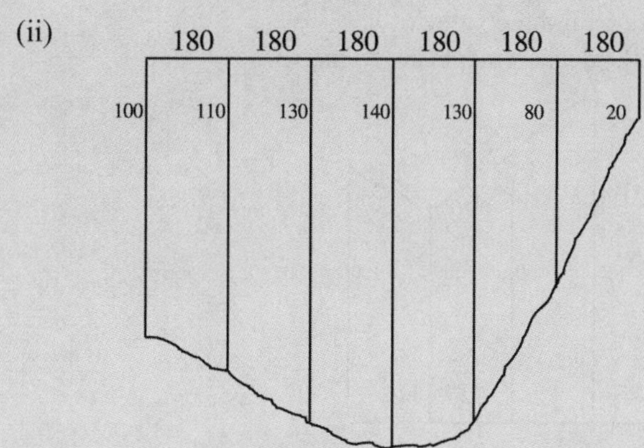

7. The area of this irregular shape is 230 square units. Find the value of x.

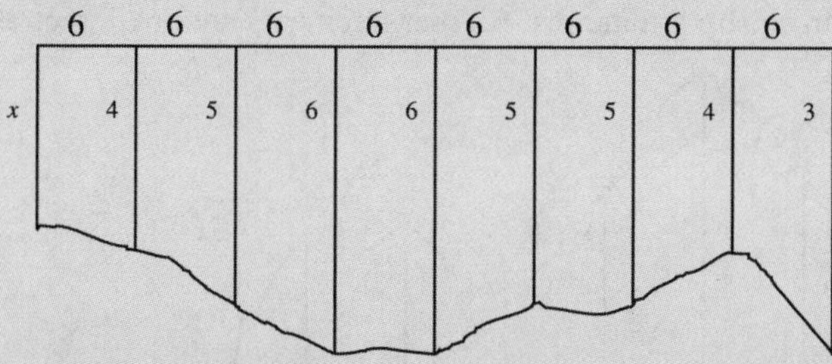

8. The area of this irregular shape is 1200 square units. Find the value of y.

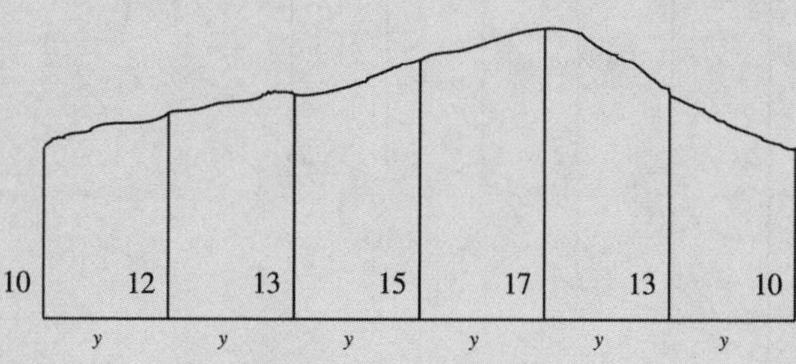

9. The area of this is 40 square units. Find the value of x.

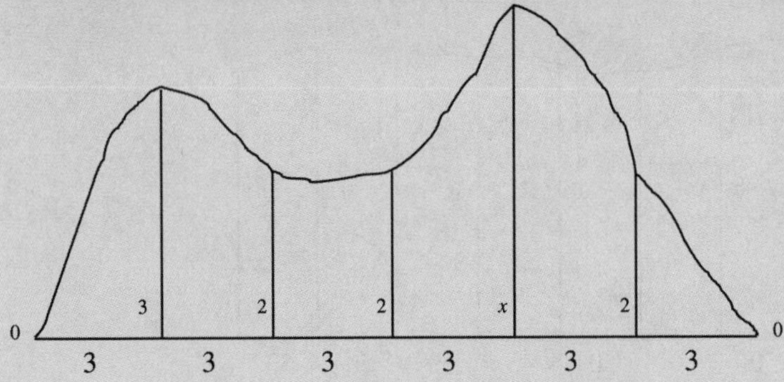

10. The area of this field is 1.5 hectares. Find the value of h.
[1 hectare = 10 000 square metres]. Measurements are in metres.

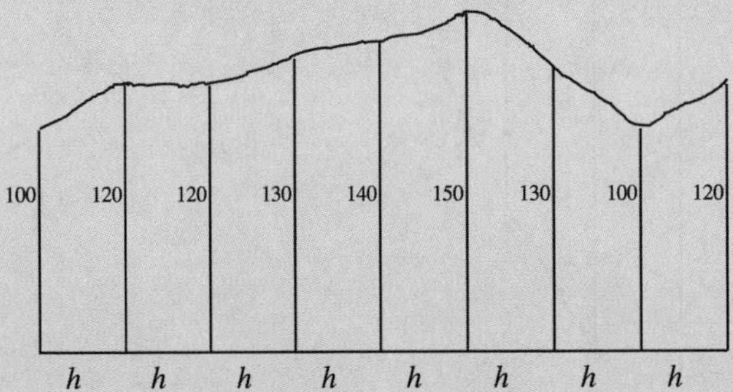

11. Here is a rough drawing of the map of Ireland. Use the diagram to find an approximate value for the area of Ireland in square kilometres. All measurements are in kilometres.

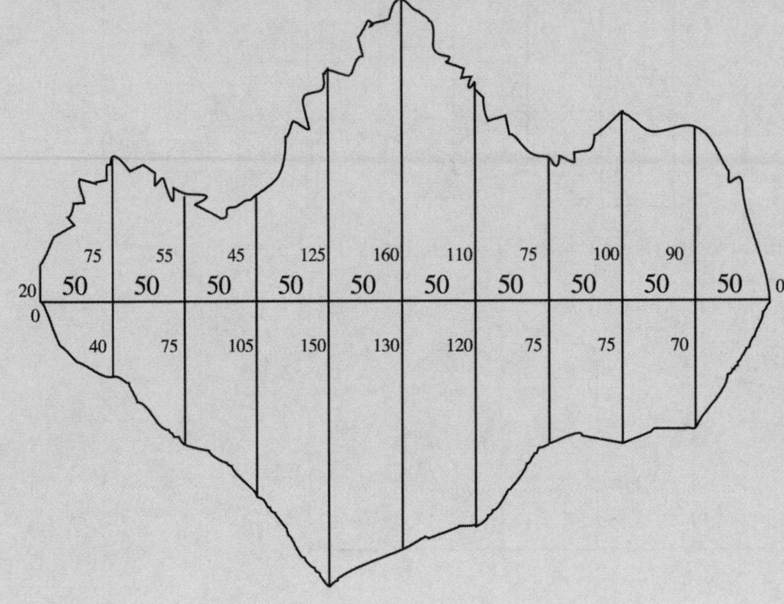

REVISION EXERCISE 13.G

1. (a) Find the area of this sector, using $\pi = 3.14$:

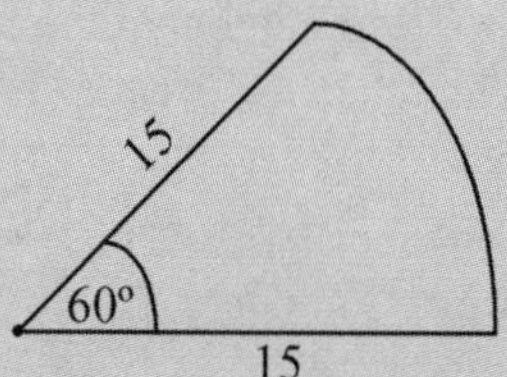

(b) A rectangular box with a lid is 63 cm long, 42 cm wide and 21 cm high. Using $\pi = {}^{22}/_{7}$,

(i) find the capacity of the box,

(ii) find the volume of the biggest sphere which will fit inside the box,

(iii) find the volume of the biggest cylinder which will fit inside the box.

2. (a) Two cylinders have their radii in the ratio 5 : 2 and their heights in the ratio 1 : 6. Which has the greater volume?

(b) A hollow cylindrical pipe has inner radius 3 cm and outer radius 4 cm. The height is 50 cm. Using $\pi = {}^{22}/_{7}$, find the volume.

(c) The slant height of a cone is 17 cm. The height is 15 cm. Find

(i) the radius-length,

(ii) the volume in terms of π.

3. (a) Find the area of this figure, using Simpson's rule:

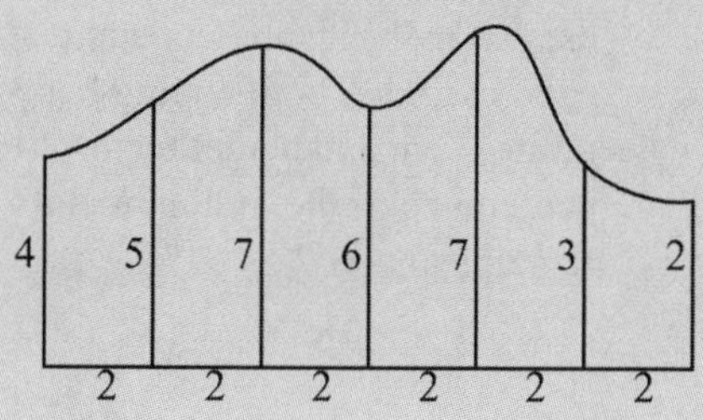

(b) (i) A soup ladle is in the shape of a hemisphere of diameter 9 cm, with a handle attached. Find the volume of one ladle-full in terms of π.

(ii) This ladle is used to remove soup from a cylindrical container of diameter 36 cm. Find the drop in the level of the soup when 24 ladle-fulls are removed.

(iii) If the remaining soup has a depth of 6 cm, how many more ladle-fulls can be got?

4. (a) (i) The diagram shows the plan of a lake. Use Simpson's rule to estimate the area of the lake, given that the offsets are a distance 10 m apart, and all measurements are in metres.

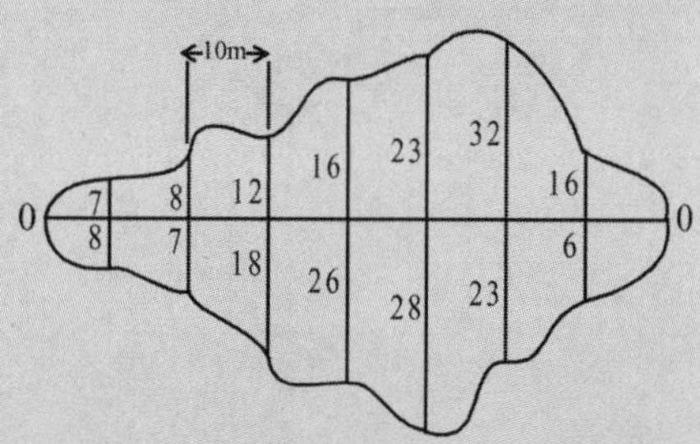

(ii) If the average depth of the lake is 7 m, find the volume of water in the lake.

(b) The volume of a sphere is 4851 cm^3. Taking $\pi = {}^{22}/_{7}$, find the radius.

5. (a) Find the area and perimeter of this sector, using $\pi = 3.14$:

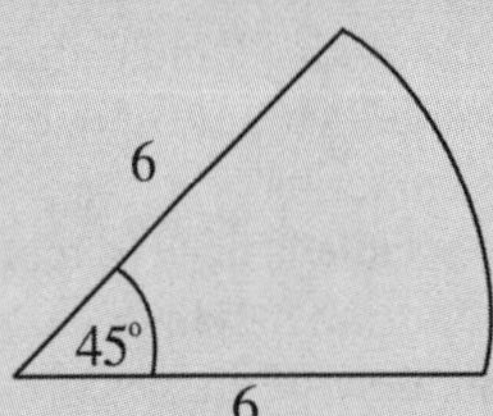

(b) A solid rectangular block of wood measures 6 cm x 8 cm x 10 cm. Find (in terms of π, where necessary) the volume of

(i) the block,
(ii) the biggest sphere which could be cut from the block,
(iii) the biggest cylinder which could be cut from the block.

6. (a) The area of a circular field is 706.5 m^2. Find the length of the radius, taking $\pi = 3.14$.

(b) The area of this field is 500 square metres. Measurements are in metres.

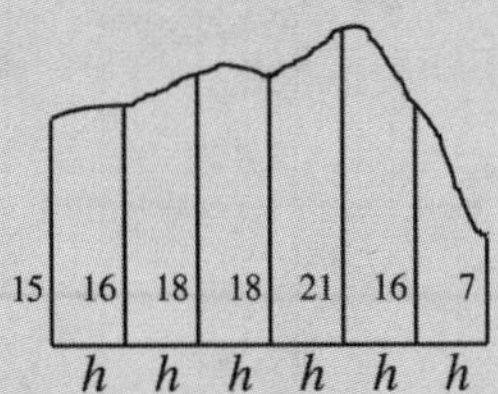

Find the value of h, the width of each strip.

(c) A solid metal sphere of radius 4 cm is melted and reformed into a cone of radius 8 cm. Find the height of the cone.

7. (a) Write 175 ml as a percentage of ½ litre.

(b) Two cylinders have radii in the ratio 11 : 7 and heights in the ratio 2 : 5. Which has the greater volume?

(c) A test-tube consists of a hollow cylinder on a hemisphere. Both have diameter 3 cm. The overall height of the test-tube is 8.5 cm.

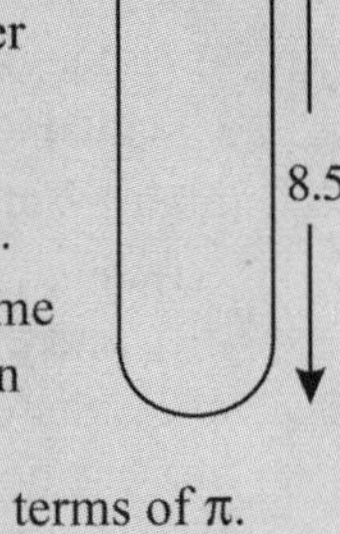

(i) Find the volume of the liquid in the test-tube (when full) in terms of π.
(ii) Find the depth of the liquid in the test-tube when it is half-full.

8. (a) A sphere fits exactly into an open cylindrical container. Show that both have the same curved surface area.

(b) The radius of a solid metal hemisphere is 6 cm. Express its volume in terms of π.
The hemisphere is melted down and some of the molten metal is used to make a solid cone and a solid cylinder, both having base-radius 3 cm and height 6 cm. What percentage of the molten metal remains unused?

1. ***Rectangle:*** Perimeter = $2l + 2b$ Area = lb

2. ***Triangle:*** Perimeter = $a + b + c$ Area = $\frac{1}{2}bh$

3. ***Sphere:*** Curved surface area = $4\pi r^2$ Volume = $\frac{4}{3}\pi r^3$

4. ***Cylinder:*** Curved surface area = $2\pi rh$ Volume = $\pi r^2 h$

5. ***Circle:*** Circumference = $2\pi r$ Area = πr^2

6. ***Cone:*** Volume = $\frac{1}{3}\pi r^2 h$

7. ***Prism:*** Volume = Al [where A = the area of the cross-section and l = the length]

8. ***Rectangular block:*** Volume = lbh

9. ***Simpson's Rule:*** Area = $\frac{h}{3}\{\text{First} + \text{last} + \text{TOFE}\}$

   where **TOFE** stands for
   Twice the **O**dds and **F**our times the **E**vens.

Chapter 14

Plane Geometry: Theorems and Enlargements

Here are the 10 theorems (and their corollaries) which you are required to be able to prove. Applications of these theorems (or 'cuts', as they are commonly called) will not be asked in the Leaving Certificate examination.

THEOREM 1: The sum of the degree-measures of the angles of a triangle is 180°.

Given: A triangle, as shown.

To prove: $A + B + C = 180°$.

Construction: Draw a line through the upper vertex, parallel to the base.

Proof: $A = D$ (Alternate angles)

$C = E$ (Alternate angles)

Now, $D + B + E = 180°$ (Straight angle)

Therefore, $A + B + C = 180°$ (Since $A = D$ and $C = E$)

Q.E.D.

Q.E.D means 'Quod Erat Demonstrandum', which, translated from the Latin, means 'What was to be proved'. It is written to signal the end of a proof.

A ***corollary*** is a consequence of a theorem which is not important enough to earn the name 'theorem' for itself.

Here are two corollaries of theorem 1.

COROLLARY I: The degree-measure of an exterior angle of a triangle is equal to the degree-measure of the sum of the two remote interior angles.

Given: A triangle, as shown.

To prove: $X = B + C$.

Proof:

$$X + A = 180° \text{ (Straight angle)}$$

$$\therefore X = 180° - A$$

$$\text{But } A + B + C = 180°$$

$$\therefore B + C = 180° - A$$

$$\therefore X = B + C \text{ (Since both are equal to } 180° - A\text{)}$$

Q.E.D. (Quite Easily Done!)

COROLLARY II: An exterior angle of a triangle is greater than either remote interior angle.

Given: A triangle, as shown.

To prove: $X > B$ and $X > C$.

Proof: Since $X = B + C$, X must be greater than B alone.
Also X must be greater than C alone. In Maths, $X > B$ and $X > C$.
Q.E.D.

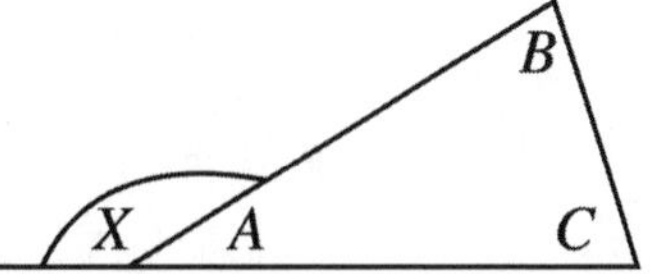

THEOREM 2: Opposite sides of a parallelogram have equal lengths.

Given: A parallelogram *wxyz,* as shown.

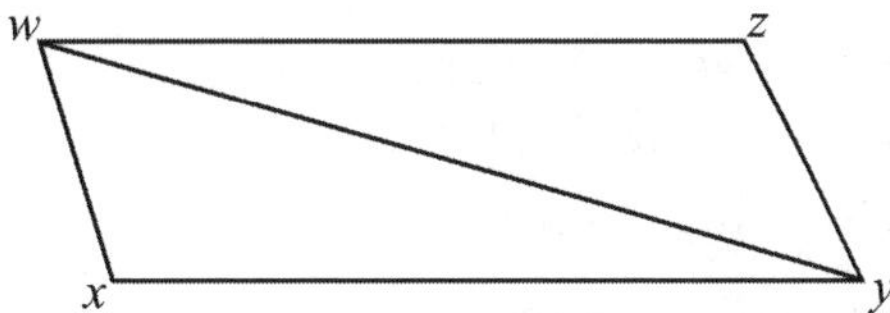

To prove: $|wx| = |zy|$ and $|wz| = |xy|$

Construction: Join [*wy*].

Proof: Δwxy is congruent to Δyzw because

(i) $|<xwy| = |<wyz|$ (Alternate angles)

(ii) $|<xyw| = |<ywz|$ (Alternate angles)

(iii) $|wy| = |wy|$ (Common to both triangles)

which gives congruence by A.S.A.

$\therefore |wx| = |zy|$ and $|wz| = |xy|$ **Q.E.D.**

THEOREM 3: If three parallel lines make intercepts of equal length on a transversal, then they will also make intercepts of equal length on any other transversal.

Given: Three parallel lines L, M, N which make intercepts of equal length on a transversal, as shown.
(i.e. $|pq| = |qr|$)

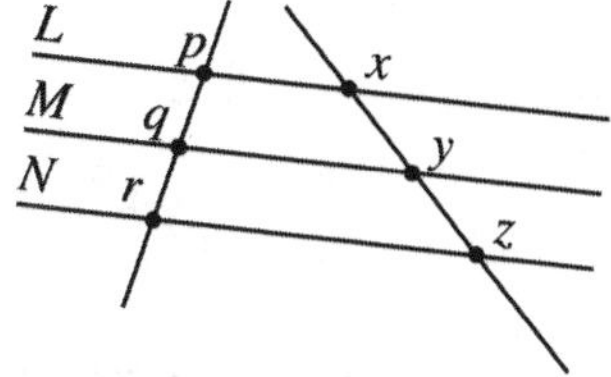

To prove: $|xy| = |yz|$.

Construction: Complete the parallelogram *qpxa* and *yxab*, as shown.

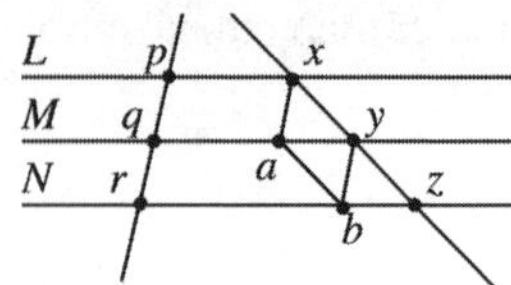

Proof: *yxab* is a parallelogram.

$\therefore |ab| = |xy|$ (by Theorem 2) ... result I.

Furthermore, $ab \parallel yz$ and $M \parallel N$.

$\therefore$ *abzy* is a parallelogram

$\therefore |ab| = |yz|$ (by Theorem 2) ... result II.

$\therefore |xy| = |yz|$ (combining results I and II) **Q.E.D.**

THEOREM 4: A line which is parallel to one side-line of a triangle, and cuts a second side, will cut the third side in the same proportion as the second.

Given: A triangle *abc* and a line *de* parallel to *bc* which cuts [*ab*] in the ratio $n : m$.

To prove: $|ae| : |ec| = n : m$.

Construction: Divide [*ad*] into *n* equal parts and [*db*] into *m* parts. Through each point of division draw a line parallel to *bc*.

Proof: According to the previous theorem the parallel lines make intercepts of equal length along [*ac*]. Let *k* be the length of each of these intercepts.

$\therefore |ae| = nk$ and $|ec| = mk$

$\therefore |ae| : |ec| = nk : mk = n : m$ **Q.E.D.**

THEOREM 5: If the three angles of one triangle have degree-measures equal, respectively, to those of a second triangle, then the lengths of the corresponding sides of the two triangles are proportional.

Given: Triangles Δabc and Δxyz with equal angles, as shown.

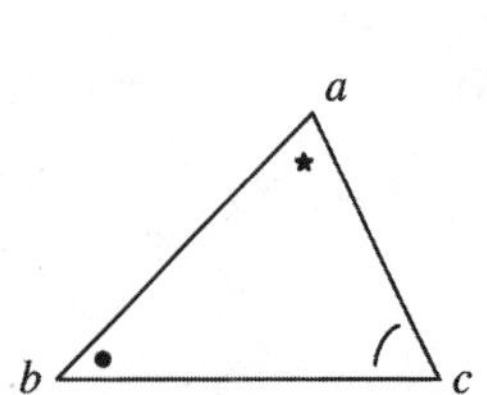

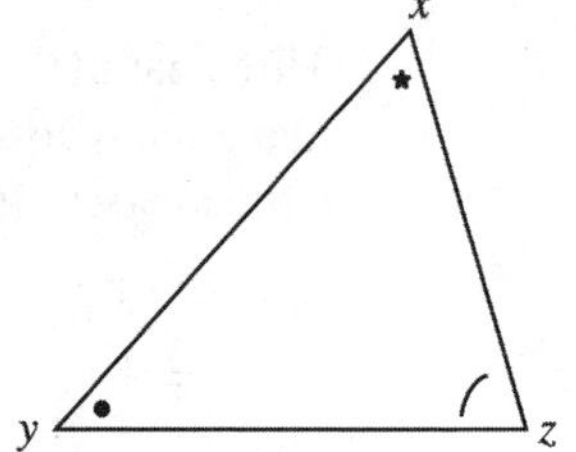

To prove: $\frac{|ab|}{|xy|} = \frac{|ac|}{|xz|} = \frac{|bc|}{|yz|}$

Construction: Map Δabc onto Δxyz, as shown, without changing any lengths or angles.

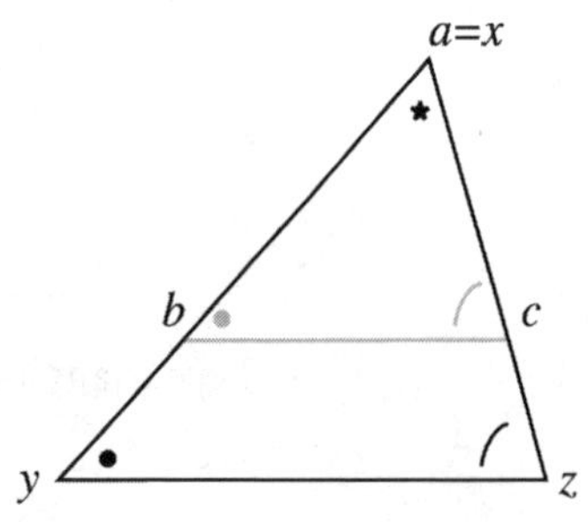

Proof: bc is parallel to yz

(Corresponding angles are equal)

$\therefore \frac{|ab|}{|xy|} = \frac{|ac|}{|xz|}$ (Theorem 4)

Similarly, it can be proved that

$\frac{|ab|}{|xy|} = \frac{|bc|}{|yz|}$

Therefore $\frac{|ab|}{|xy|} = \frac{|ac|}{|xz|} = \frac{|bc|}{|yz|}$ **Q.E.D.**

THEOREM 6: *The theorem of Pythagoras*: In a right-angled triangle, the square of the length of the side opposite the right-angle is equal to the sum of the squares of the lengths of the other two sides.

Given: A triangle Δabc such that $|\angle bac| = 90°$.

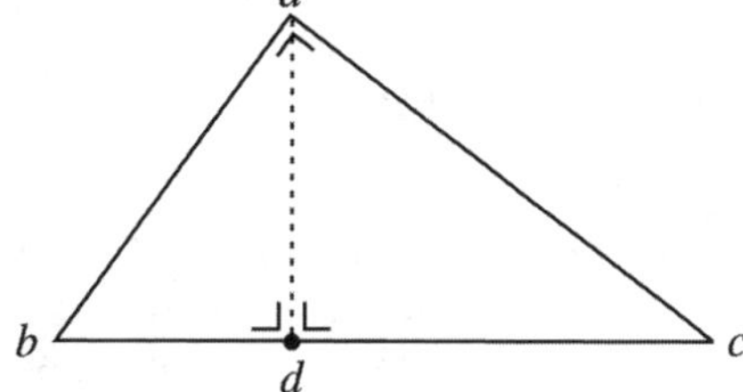

To prove: $|bc|^2 = |ab|^2 + |ac|^2$

Construction: Drop a perpendicular $[ad]$ onto $[bc]$.

Proof: Take Δabd and Δabc.

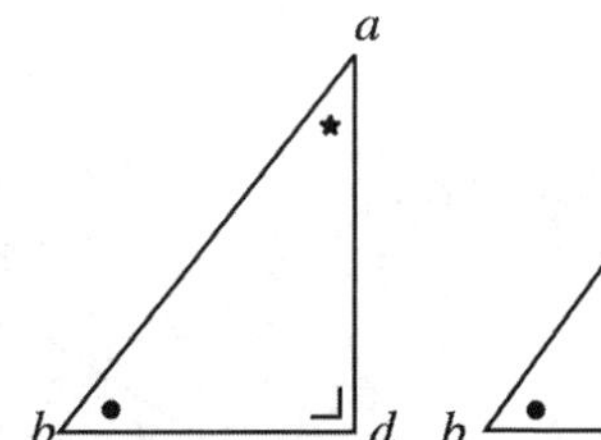

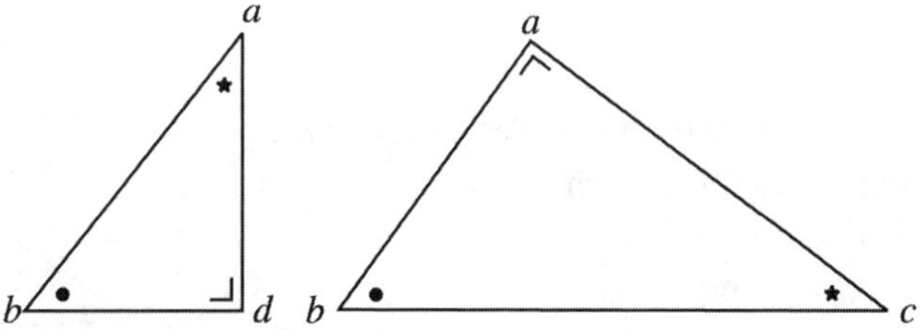

These triangles have equal angles, because

(i) $|\angle abd| = |\angle abc|$ (common)

(ii) $|\angle bda| = |\angle bac|$ (both 90°) and hence

(iii) $|\angle bad| = |\angle bca|$ (remaining angle out of 180°)

$\therefore \frac{|ab|}{|bc|} = \frac{|bd|}{|ab|}$ (Theorem 5)

$\therefore |ab|^2 = |bc|\,|bd|$ ... result I

Now take Δadc and Δabc.

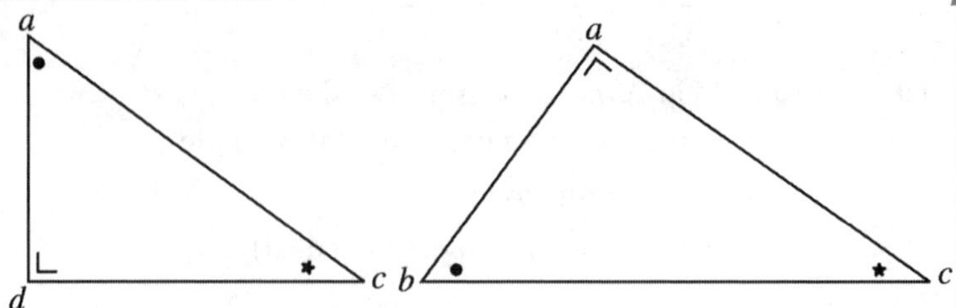

These triangles have equal angles because

(i) $|\angle acd| = |\angle acb|$ (common)

(ii) $|\angle adc| = |\angle bac|$ (both 90°) and hence

(iii) $|\angle cad| = |\angle abc|$ (remaining angle)

$$\therefore \frac{|ac|}{|bc|} = \frac{|dc|}{|ac|} \quad \text{(Theorem 5)}$$

$$\therefore |ac|^2 = |bc|\;|dc| \quad \text{... result II}$$

Add results I and II, which gives

$$\begin{aligned} |ab|^2 + |ac|^2 &= |bc|\;|bd| + |bc|\;|dc| \\ &= |bc|\;(|bd| + |dc|) \\ &= |bc|\;|bc| \quad (\text{Since } |bd| + |dc| = |bc|) \\ &= |bc|^2 \end{aligned}$$

In conclusion, $|ab|^2 + |ac|^2 = |bc|^2$ **Q.E.D.**

THEOREM 7: (*Converse of Pythagoras' theorem*): If the square of the length of one side of a triangle is equal to the sum of the squares of the lengths of the other two sides, then the triangle has a right-angle and this is opposite the longest side.

Given: A triangle Δabc, with sides of lengths x, y and z (as shown) such that $z^2 = x^2 + y^2$

To prove: $|\angle bac| = 90°$.

Construction: Draw another triangle pqr, such that $|\angle qpr| = 90°$ and $|pq| = x$ and $|pr| = y$ and $|qr| = w$.

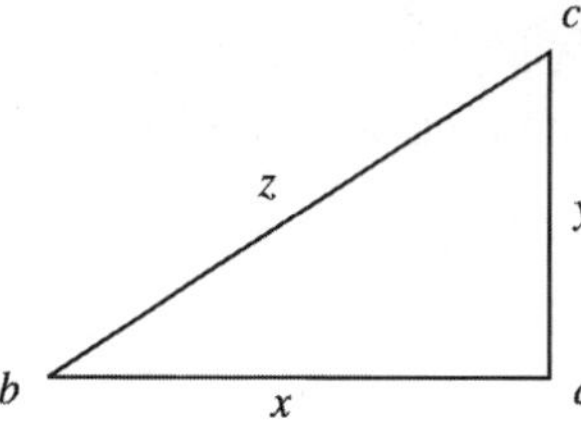

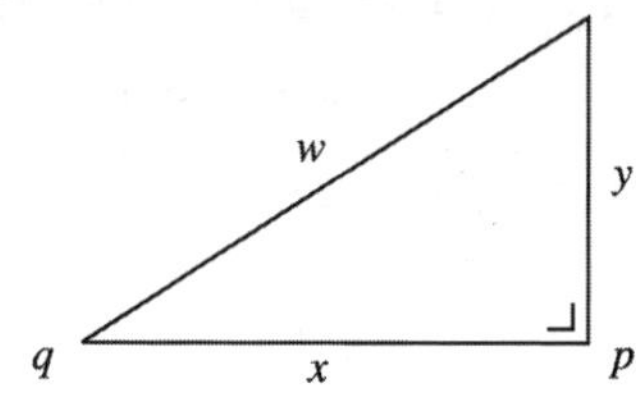

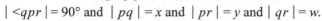

Proof: By Pythagoras' Theorem, $w^2 = x^2 + y^2$ (since $|\angle qpr| = 90°$)

But $z^2 = x^2 + y^2$ (given)

Therefore $w = z$

Now, Δabc and Δpqr must be congruent, since they have three sides equal in length.

Hence, $|\angle bac| = |\angle qpr| = 90°$. **Q.E.D.**

THEOREM 8: The products of the lengths of the sides of a triangle by the corresponding altitudes are equal.

Given: A triangle Δabc with altitudes $[ad]$, $[be]$ and $[cf]$.

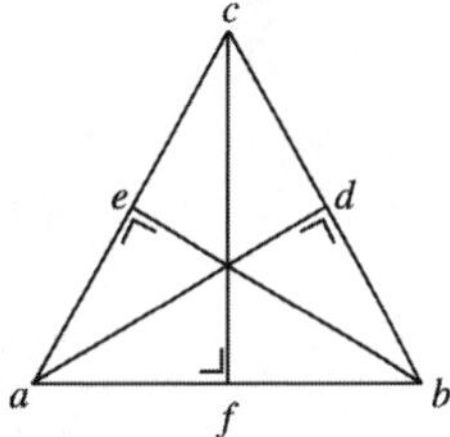

To prove: $|ab|.|cf| = |bc|.|ad| = |ac|.|be|$

Proof: Take triangles Δabd and Δbcf.

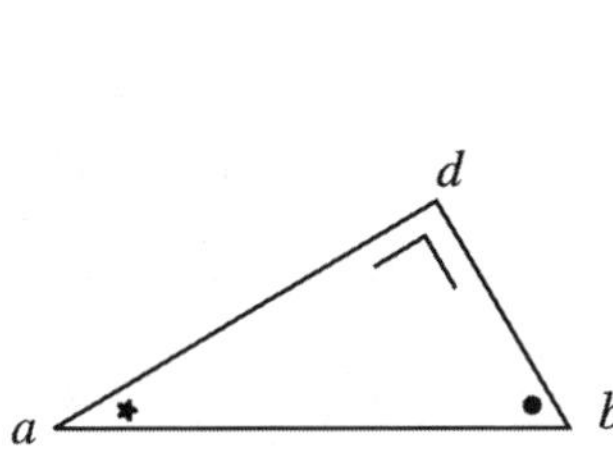

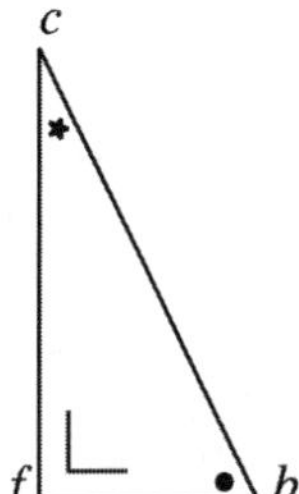

These triangles are equiangular because

(i) $|\angle dba| = |\angle cbf|$ (common to both)

(ii) $|\angle bda| = |\angle bfc|$ (both are 90°)

(iii) $|\angle bad| = |\angle bcf|$ (remaining angle from 180°)

Hence, in accordance with Theorem 5,

$$\frac{|ab|}{|bc|} = \frac{|ad|}{|cf|}$$

$\Rightarrow |ab|.|cf| = |bc|.|ad|$

This result can be similarly extended to prove that

$|ab|.|cf| = |bc|.|ad| = |ac|.|be|$ **Q.E.D.**

THEOREM 9: If the lengths of the two sides of a triangle are unequal, then the degree-measures of the angles opposite to them are unequal, with the greater angle opposite to the longer side.

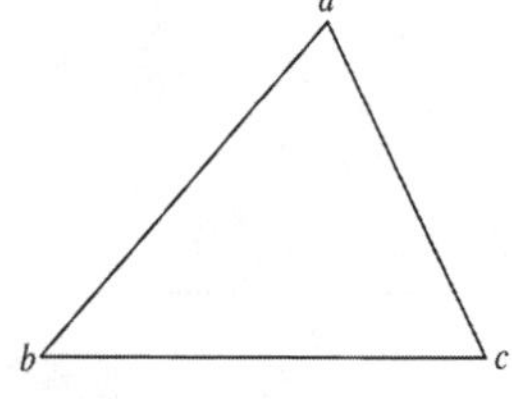

Given: A triangle Δabc such that $|ab| > |ac|$.

To prove: $|<abc| < |<acb|$.

Construction: Let p be the point on $[ab]$ such that $|ap| = |ac|$. Join p to c.

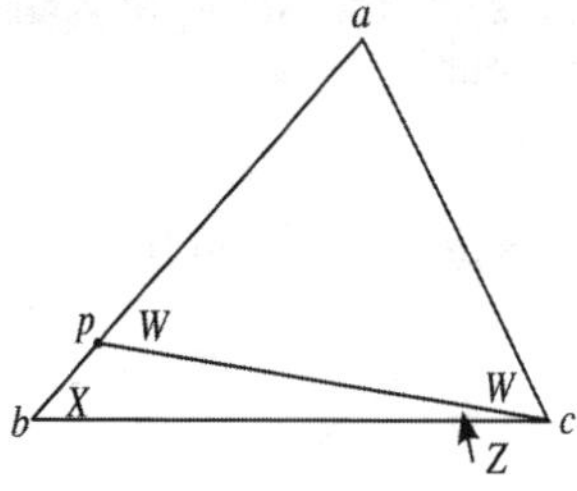

Proof: Δapc is isosceles (since $|ap| = |ac|$)

$\therefore$ $|<apc| = |<acp|$ (We'll call this angle-measure $= W$)

Now $W = X + Z$ (Theorem 2)

$\therefore$ $X = W - Z$

i.e. $|<abc| = W - Z$ ... result I

Furthemore $|<acb| = W + Z$ ... result II

Combining results I and II gives $|<abc| < |<acb|$ **Q.E.D.**

THEOREM 10: The sum of the lengths of any two sides of a triangle is greater than that of the third side.

Given: A triangle Δabc

To prove: $|ac| < |ab| + |bc|$

Construction: Drop a perpendicular $[bd]$ onto $[ac]$.

Proof: $W + X = 90°$ (Consequence of Theorem I)

$\therefore$ $X < 90°$

$\therefore$ $|ad| < |ab|$ (Theorem 9) ... result I

Similarly, $Y + Z = 90°$

$\therefore$ $Y < 90°$

$\therefore$ $|dc| < |bc|$ ... result II

Adding results I and II gives $|ad| + |dc| < |ab| + |bc|$

$\Rightarrow$ $|ac| < |ab| + |bc|$ (since $|ad| + |dc| = |ac|$) **Q.E.D**

Exercise 14.A

1. (a) Prove that the sum of the degree-measures of the angles of a triangle is 180°.

(b) Write down the value of x in each case:

(i)

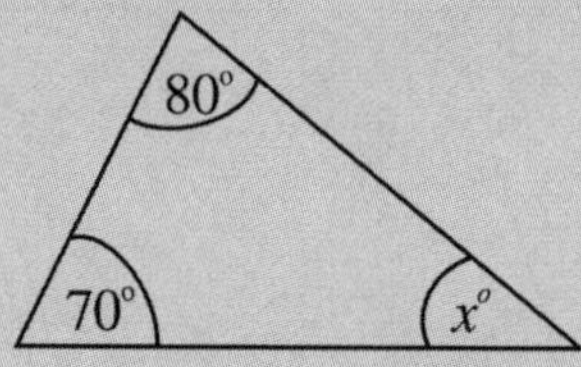

(ii)

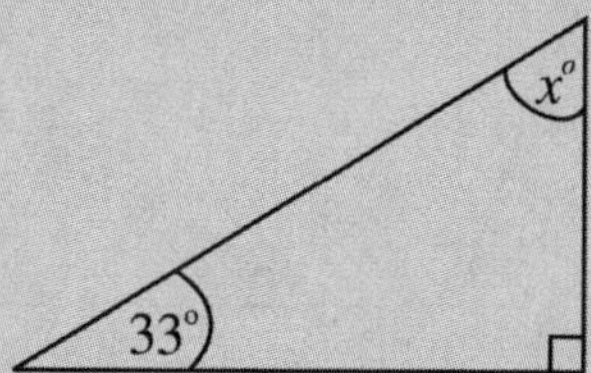

(iii)

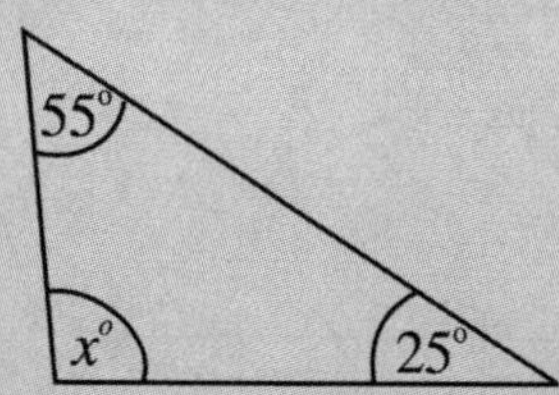

(iv)

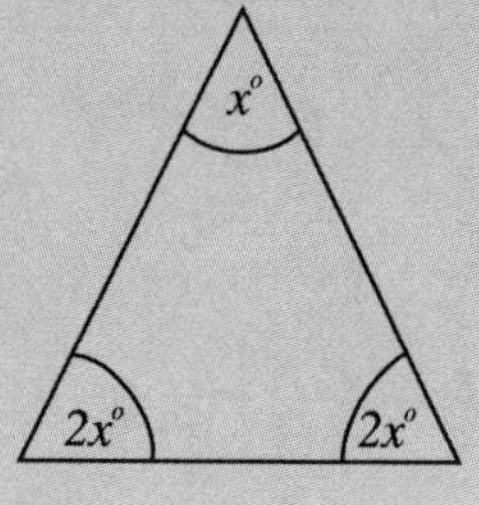

2. (a) Prove that the degree-measure of an exterior angle of a triangle is equal to the degree-measure of the sum of the two remote interior angles.

(b) Write down the value of x in each case:

(i)

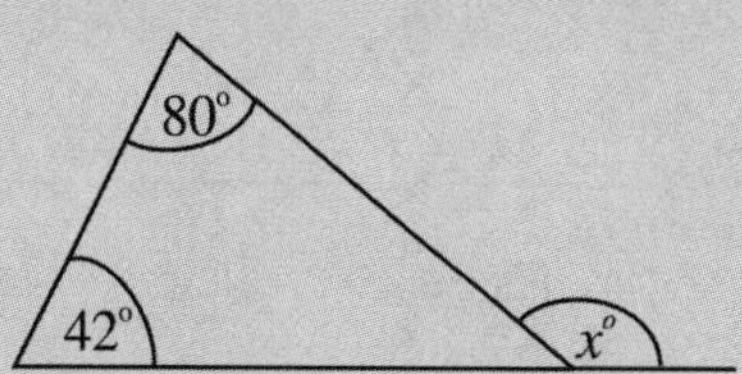

(ii)

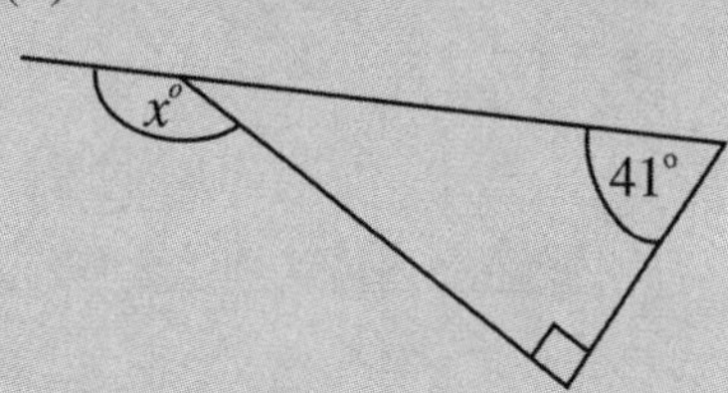

(iii)

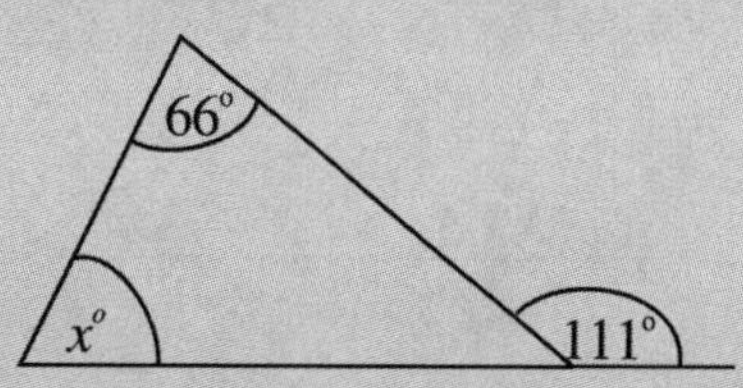

(iv)

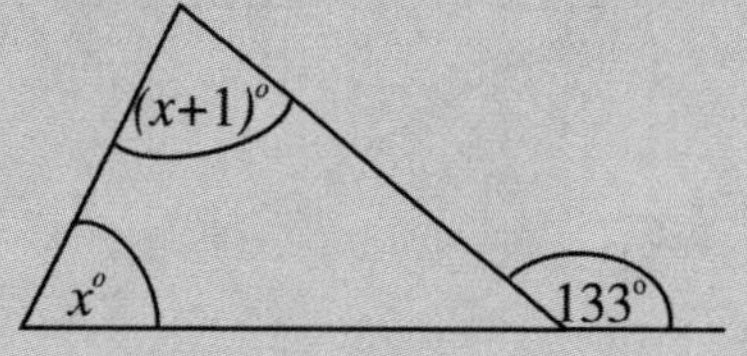

3. (a) Prove that an exterior angle of a triangle is greater than either remote interior angle.

(b) In each case, write down two inequalities involving the exterior angle X. For example

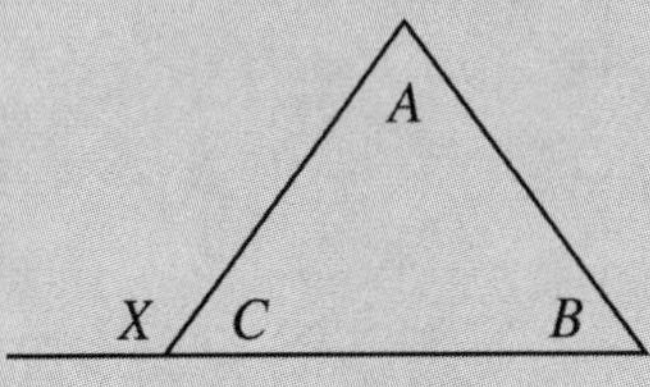

in this case, $X > A$ and $X > B$.

(i)

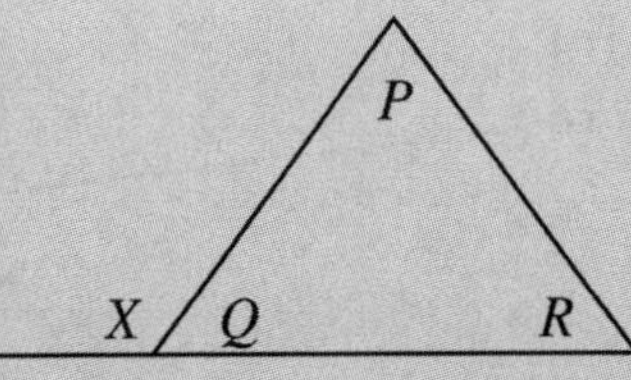

(ii)

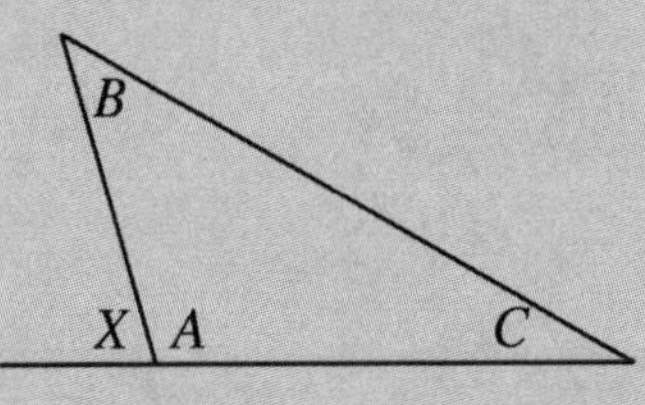

(iii)

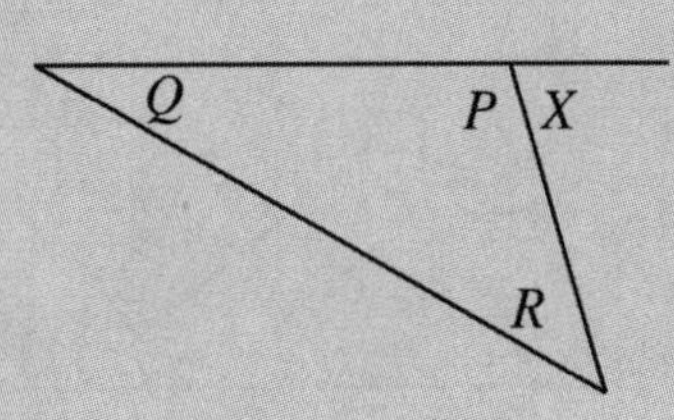

4. (a) Prove that the opposite sides of a parallelogram have equal lengths.

(b) Write down the values of x and y in each case, and find the areas of these parallelograms: (see Maths Tables p.6).

(i)

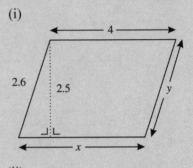

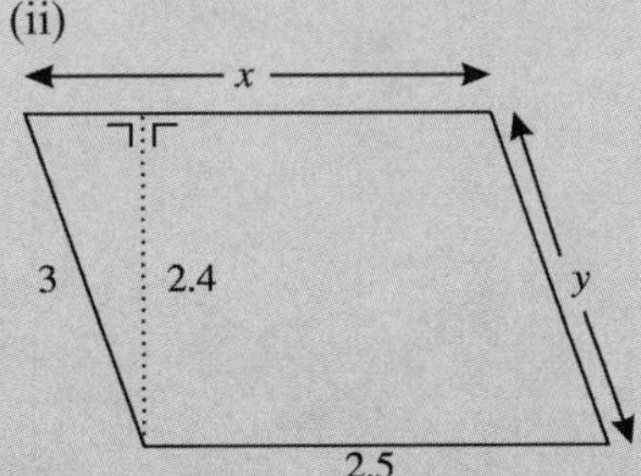

(ii)

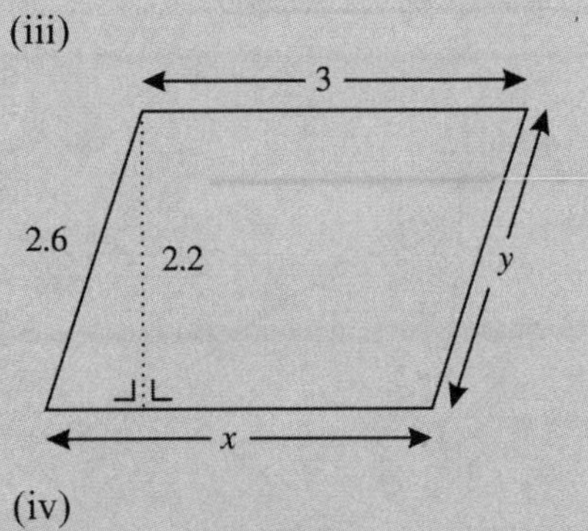

(iii)

(iv)

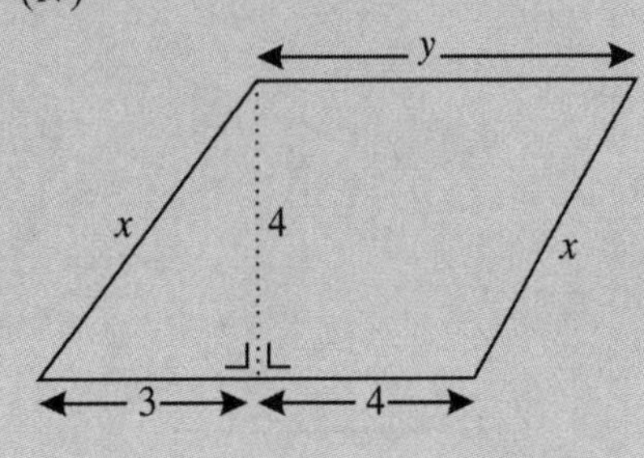

5. (a) Prove that if three parallel lines make intercepts of equal length on a transversal, then they will also make equal intercepts on any other transversal.

(b) Deduce that a line which is parallel to one side of a triangle, and cuts a second side, will cut the third side in the same proportion as the second.

(c)

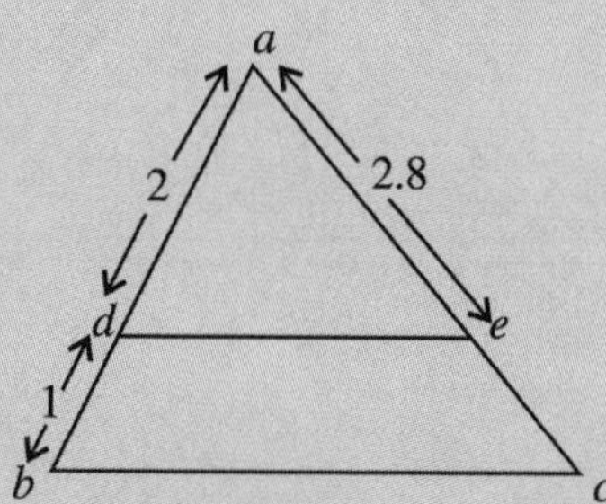

In the diagram, $de \parallel bc$. Find the length $|ec|$.

6. (a) Prove that if the three angles of one triangle have degree-measures equal, respectively, to the degree measures of the angles of a second triangle, then the lengths of the corresponding sides of the two triangles are proportional.

(b) The angles in these triangles are equal. Find $|ac|$ and $|yz|$.

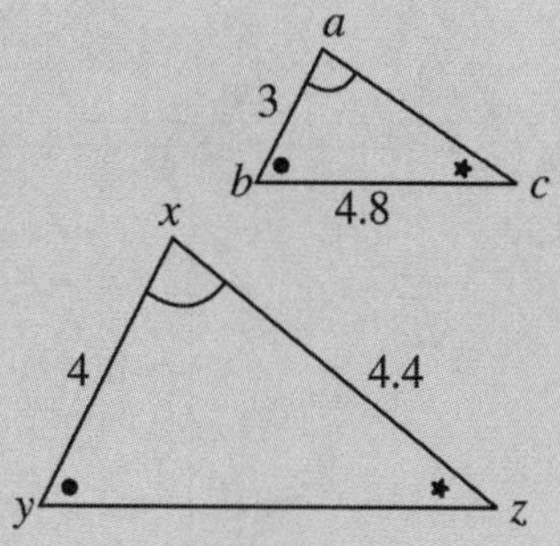

7. (a) Prove that in a right-angled triangle, the square of the length of the side opposite the right-angle is equal to the sum of the squares of the lengths of the other two sides.

(b) Find the value of x and y in each case:

(i)

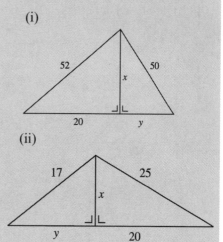

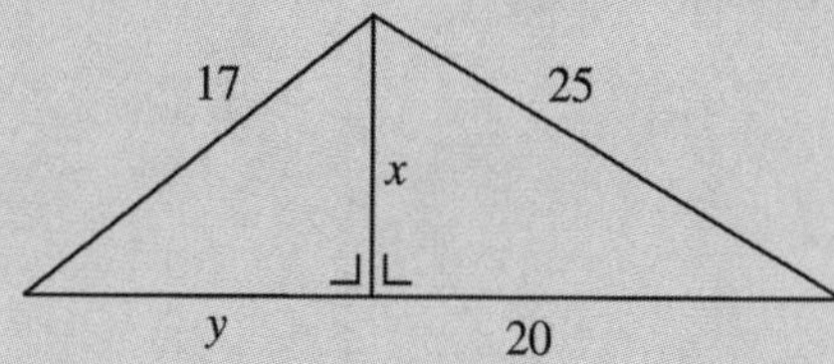

(ii)

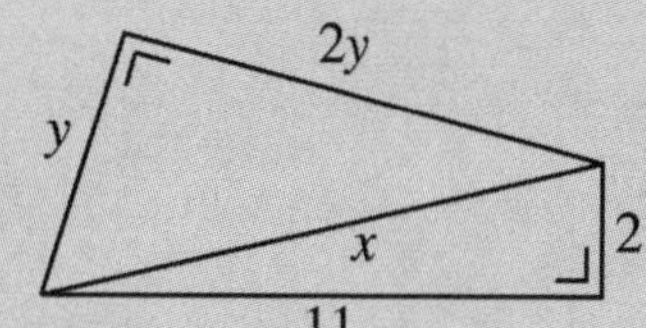

(iii)

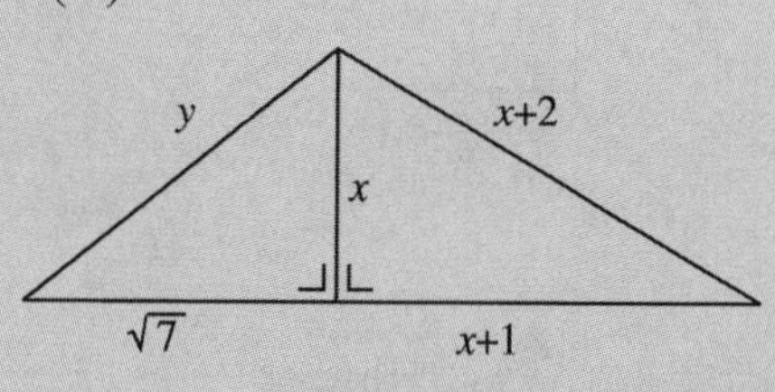

(iv)

y

x+2

x

√7

x+1

8. (a) Prove that if the square of the length of one side of a triangle is equal to the sum of the lengths of the squares of the other two sides, then the triangle has a right angle and it is opposite the longest side.

(b) Investigate if these triangles are right-angled or not:

(i)

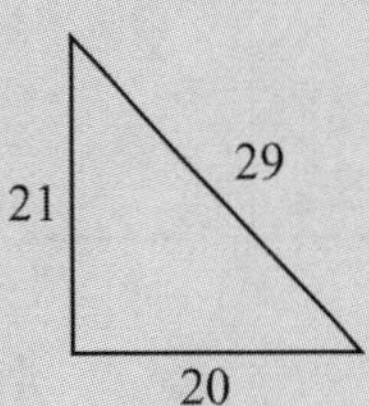

(ii)

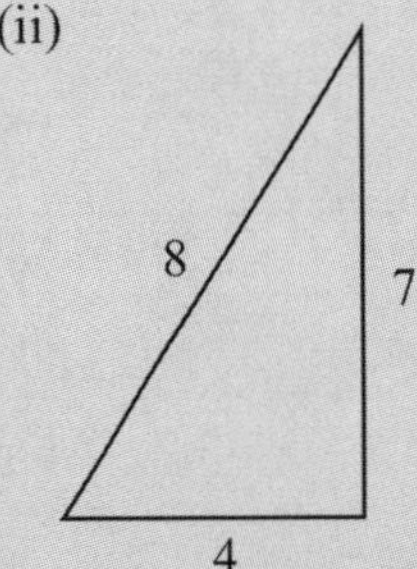

(iii)

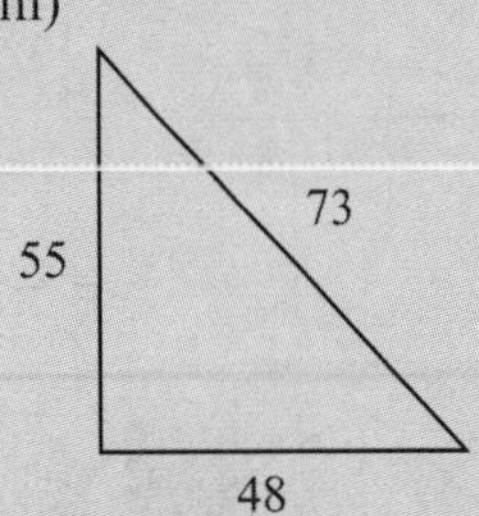

(iv)

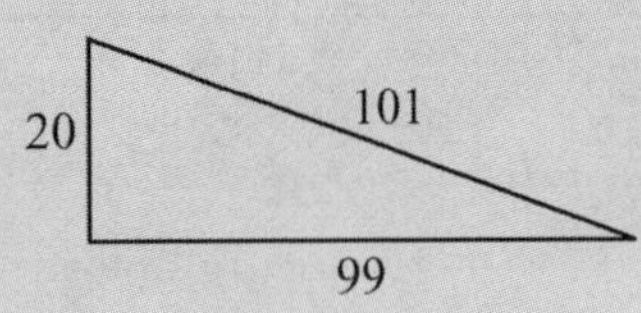

9. (a) Prove that the products of the lengths of the sides of a triangle by the corresponding altitudes are equal.

(b) Find the length x in each case:

(i)

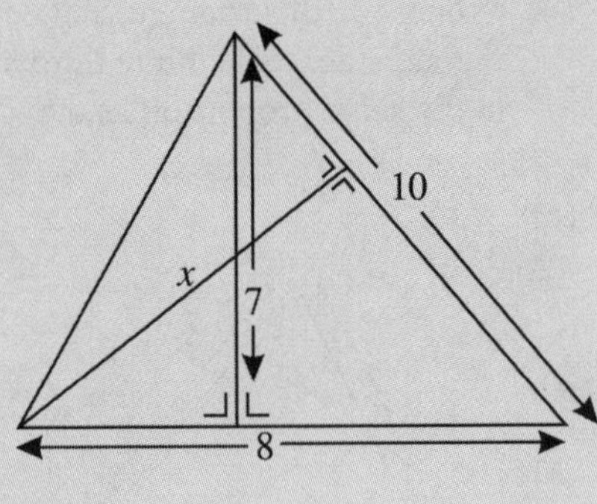

(ii)

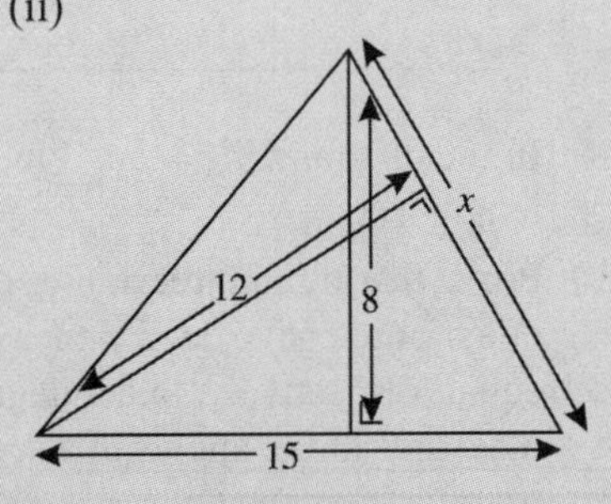

(iii)

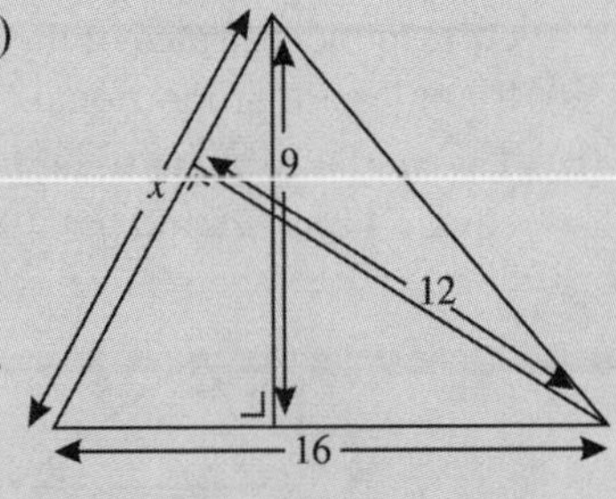

(iv)

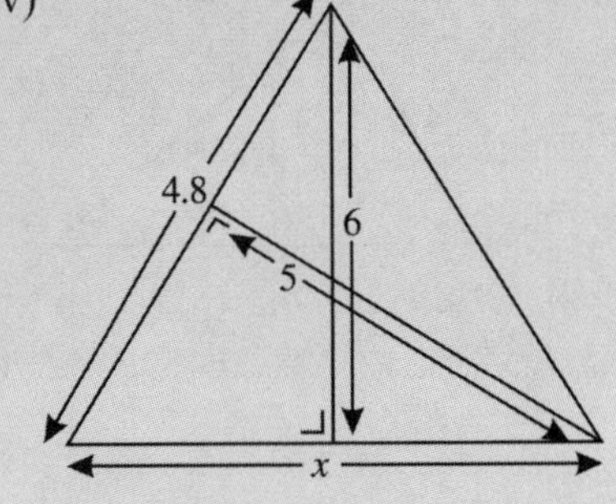

10. (a) Prove that if the lengths of the two sides of a triangle are unequal, then the degree-measures of the angles opposite them are unequal, with the greater angle opposite the longer side.

(b) Which is the greatest angle in this triangle?

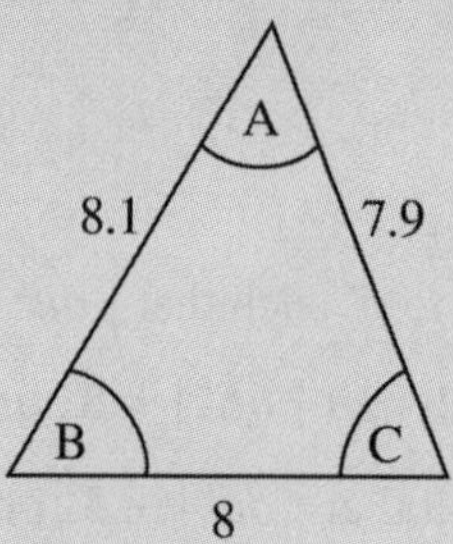

(c) Which is the smallest angle in this triangle?

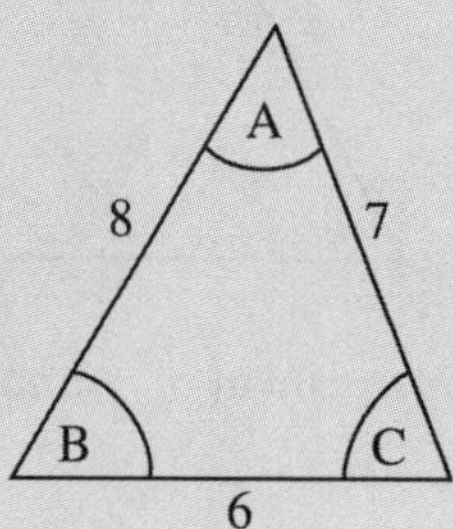

(d) Which side of the Δabc is the greatest?

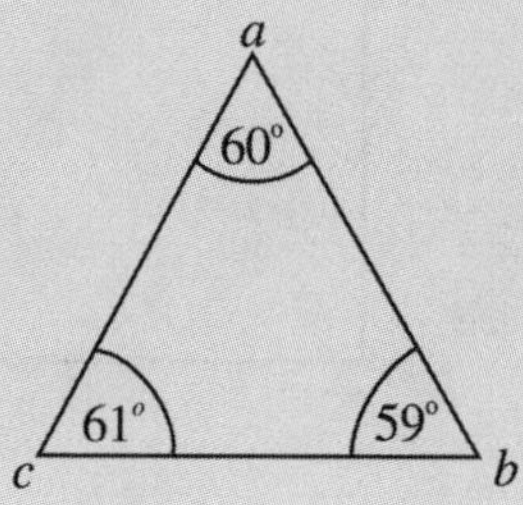

11. (a) Prove that the sum of the lengths of any two sides of a triangle is greater than that of the third side.

(b) Δpqr is a triangle. Replace the question marks with letters in the following three inequalities:

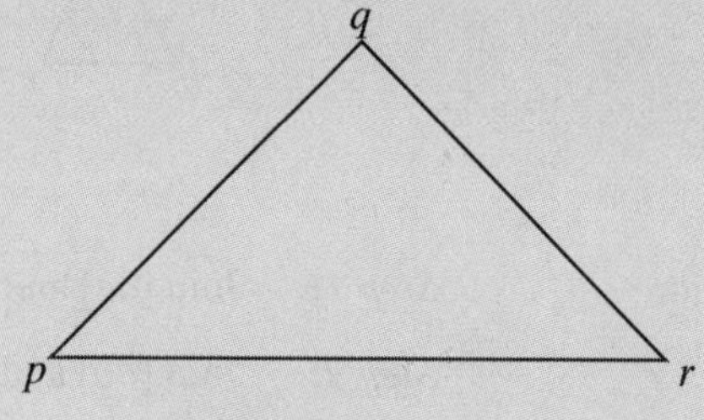

(i) $|pq| < |??| + |??|$

(ii) $|pr| < |??| + |??|$

(iii) $|qr| < |??| + |??|$

(c) State why it is impossible to construct a triangle whose sides have lengths 10 cm, 6 cm and 3 cm.

(d) Is it possible to construct a triangle whose sides are 21 cm, 12 cm and 8 cm?

(e) (i) Use Pythagoras' Theorem to find the missing side, x, in this right-angled triangle.

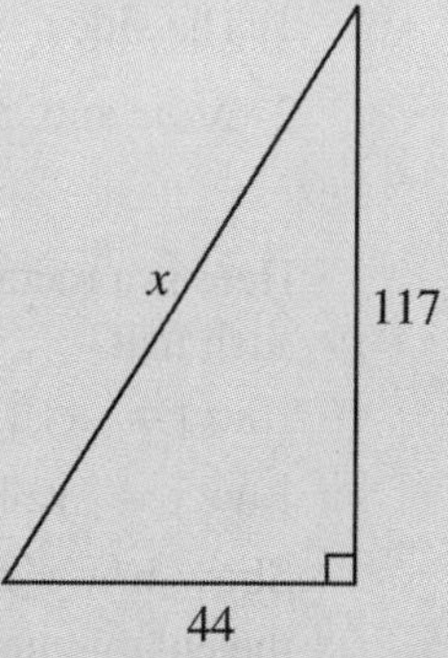

(ii) Verify that $117 + 44 > x$

ENLARGEMENTS

Example 1: Here is Δabc. Draw the enlargement of Δabc, centre o, of scale factor 3.

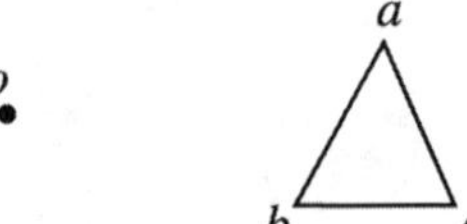

Solution:

Step 1: Join $[oa]$ and produce (extend) to a' such that $|oa'| = 3|oa|$.

Step 2: Join $[ob]$ and produce to b' such that $|ob'| = 3|ob|$.

Step 3: Join $[oc]$ and produce to c' such that $|oc'| = 3|oc|$.

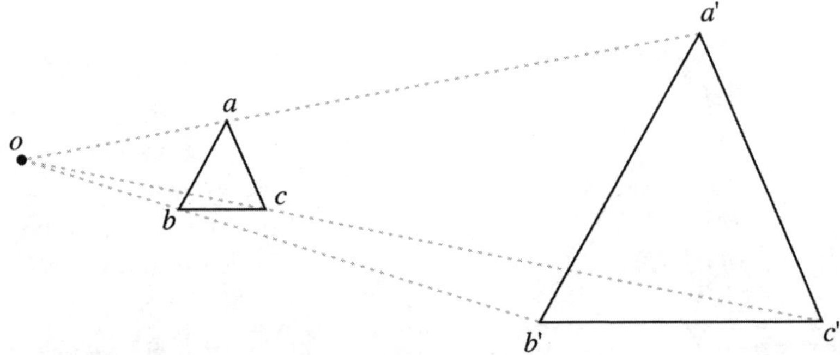

The new triangle $\Delta a'b'c'$ is the desired enlargement of Δabc.
Two things are worth noting:

1. The sides $\Delta a'b'c'$ are three times as long as the sides of Δabc.
2. Δabc and $\Delta a'b'c'$ are equilangular (or similar).

Example 2: Here is a rectangle $wxyz$ such that $|wz| = |xy| = 3$ and $|wx| = |yz| = 4$. Show $w'x'y'z'$, the enlargement of $wxyz$, centre p, of scale factor 2.
Find, by measuring, the ratios

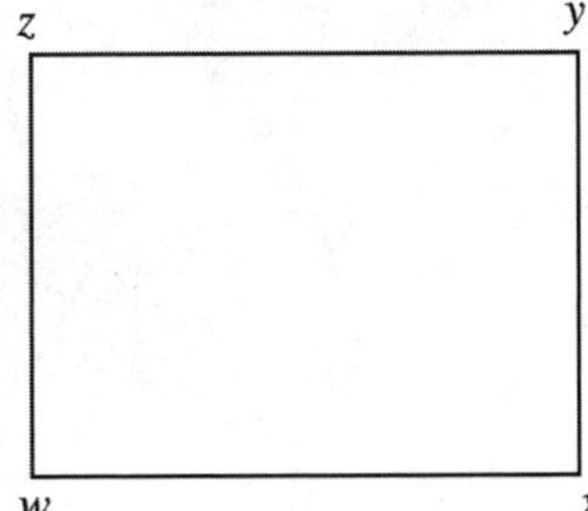

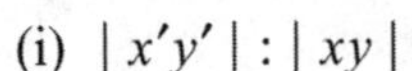

(i) $|x'y'| : |xy|$.

(ii) Area $w'x'y'z'$: Area $wxyz$.

Solution: $|pw'| = 2|pw|$; $|px'| = 2|px|$; $|py'| = 2|py|$; $|pz'| = 2|pz|$.

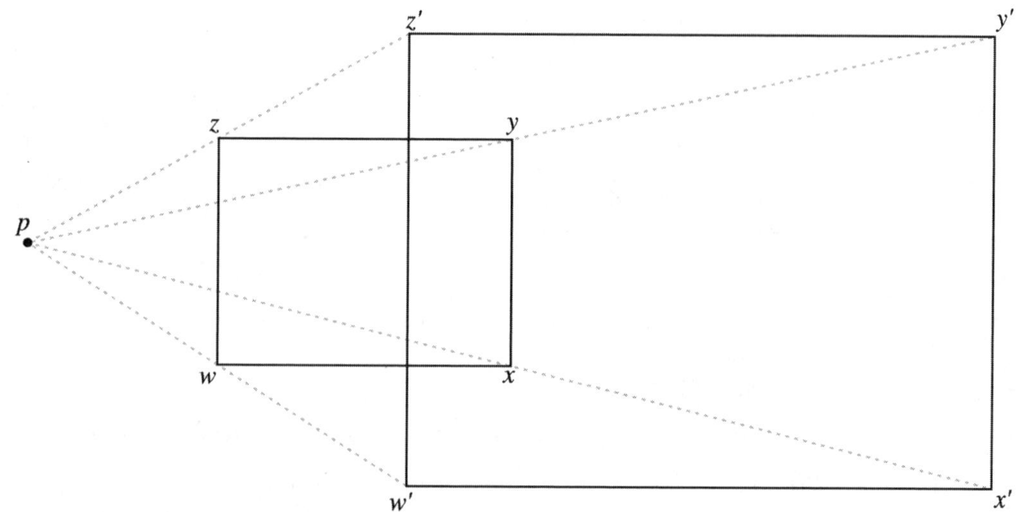

By measuring, it is found that $|x'y'| = 6$ and $|w'x'| = 8$.

Hence, the area of $w'x'y'z'$ is $6 \times 8 = 48$.
The area of the original rectangle $wxyz$ was $3 \times 4 = 12$.

(i) $|x'y'| : |xy| = 6 : 3 = 2 : 1$.

(ii) Area $w'x'y'z'$: Area $wxyz = 48 : 12 = 4 : 1$.

ENLARGEMENT AND REDUCTION

Let k be the scale factor.

Enlargement:	If $k > 1$, then the image will be larger than the original object.
Reduction:	If $0 < k < 1$, then the image will be smaller than the original object, as in the next example.

Example 3:

(i) Draw Δabc, where $a = (2, 6)$, $b = (8, 4)$, $c = (4, 0)$ and find its area.

(ii) Draw $\Delta a'b'c'$, the image of Δabc under the enlargement, centre $o(0, 0)$ of scale factor ½.

(iii) Find the ratio $\dfrac{\text{Area } \Delta a'b'c'}{\text{Area } \Delta abc}$.

Solution: (i) Here is Δabc.

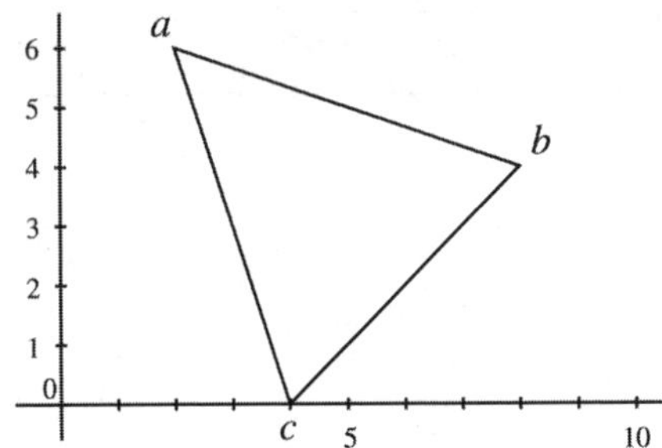

To find the area: Let $(2, 6) \to (0, 0)$ (Down 2, down 6).
Hence $(8, 4) \to (6, -2)$
and$(4, 0) \to (2, -6)$

The area is $= \frac{1}{2}|\, x_1 y_2 - x_2 y_1 \,| = \frac{1}{2}|\, (6)(-6) - (2)(-2) \,| = 16$ units^2.

(ii) Join $[oa]$. Mark a' such that $|\, oa' \,| = \frac{1}{2}|\, oa \,|$. $a' = (1, 3)$
Join $[ob]$. Mark b' such that $|\, ob' \,| = \frac{1}{2}|\, ob \,|$. $b' = (4, 2)$
Join $[oc]$. Mark c' such that $|\, oc' \,| = \frac{1}{2}|\, oc \,|$. $c' = (2, 0)$

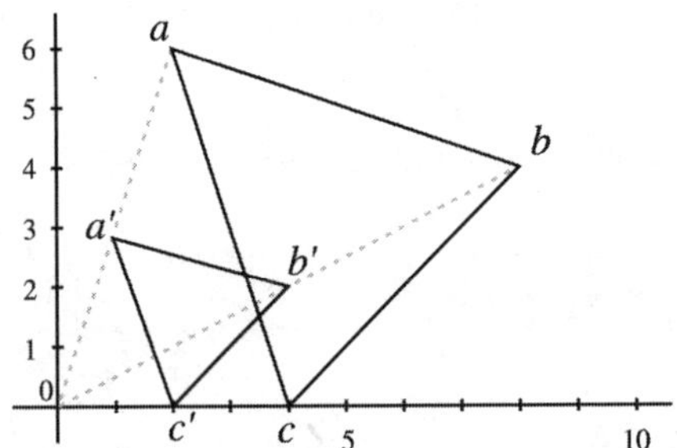

(iii) To find the area of $\Delta a'b'c'$: Let $(1, 3) \to (0, 0)$ (Down 1, down 3)
Hence $(4, 2) \to (3, -1)$ and $(2, 0) \to (1, -3)$.

Area $\Delta a'b'c'$, $= \frac{1}{2}|\, (3)(-3) - (1)(-1) \,| = 4$ units^2.

$$\therefore \quad \frac{\text{Area } \Delta a'b'c'}{\text{Area } \Delta abc} = \frac{4}{16} = \frac{1}{4}$$

Length and Area

For any enlargement (or reduction) of scale factor k.

$$\frac{\text{Image length}}{\text{Object length}} = \frac{k}{1} \quad \text{and} \quad \frac{\text{Image area}}{\text{Object area}} = \frac{k^2}{1}$$

Exercise 14.B

1. Here is a line segment $[ab]$ of length 3 cm. Copy the diagram and show $[a'b']$ the enlargement of $[ab]$, centre o, of scale factor 2.

   How long is the image $[a'b']$?

2. The diagram shows a line segment $[pq]$ of length 5 cm. Show the image of $[pq]$ under the enlargement, centre o, of scale factor 3.

   How long is the line segment $[p'q']$, the image of $[pq]$ under the enlargement?

3. Copy this diagram and show the image of Δabc under the enlargement, centre o, scale factor 2.

4. Show the enlargement of Δxyz if the centre of enlargement is p and the scale factor is 3.

5. (a) The diagram shows a square of side 4 cm. Copy this diagram and illustrate $p'q'r's'$, the image of the square $pqrs$ under the enlargement of scale factor 1.5, centre o.

   (b) Find

   (i) the length $|p'q'|$.

   (ii) the area $p'q'r's'$.

   (c) Write down the ratios:

   (i) $\dfrac{|p'q'|}{|pq|}$ (ii) $\dfrac{\text{Area } p'q'r's'}{\text{Area } pqrs}$

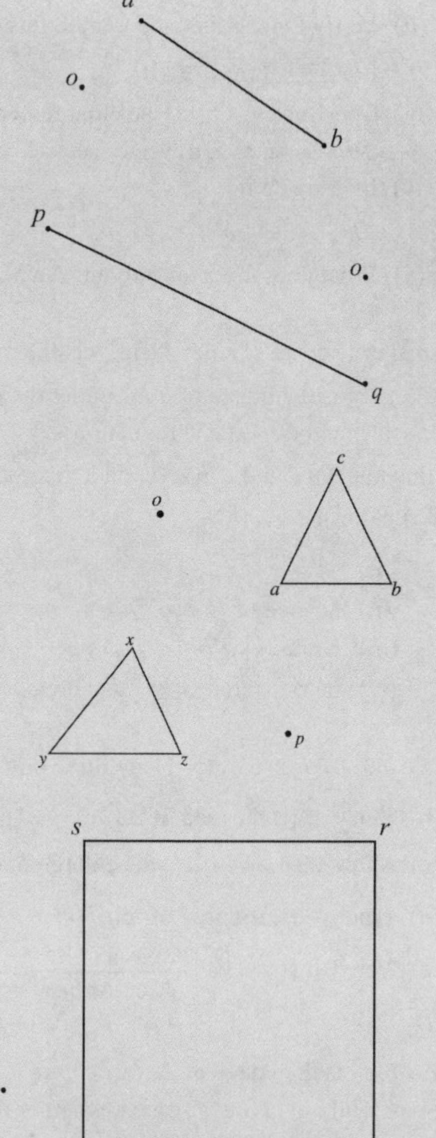

6. Draw a square $opqr$ of side 5 cm.

   Illustrate its image under the reduction, centre o, of scale factor 0.8.

   What is the ratio of the image area to the original area?

7. (i) Draw a right-angled triangle abc such that $|\angle bac| = 90°$, $|ac| = 6$ cm, $|ab| = 2.5$ cm and $|bc| = 6.5$ cm.

(ii) Verify Pythagoras' theorem in this case $|bc|^2 = |ab|^2 + |ac|^2$.

(iii) Construct $\Delta a'b'c'$, the enlargement of Δabc, centre a, of scale factor 2.

(iv) Investigate if $|b'c'|^2 = |a'b'|^2 + |a'c'|^2$.

(v) What does this prove about $\Delta a'b'c'$?

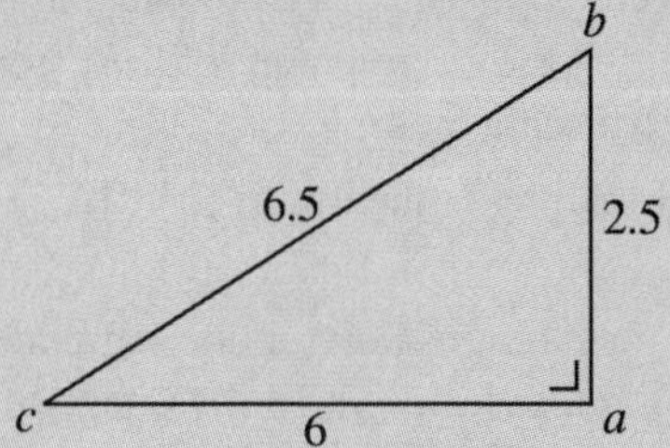

8. $abcd$ is a square of side 10 cm. p is the midpoint of $[ab]$.
$a'b'c'd'$ is the image of $abcd$ under the enlargement, centre p, of scale factor 0.4 (i.e. a reduction).
Illustrate $abcd$ and $a'b'c'd'$ on a diagram.
Write down

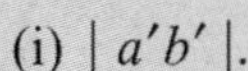

(i) $|a'b'|$.

(ii) the area of $a'b'c'd'$.

(iii) the ratio $|a'b'| : |ab|$.

(iv) the ratio area $a'b'c'd'$: area $abcd$.

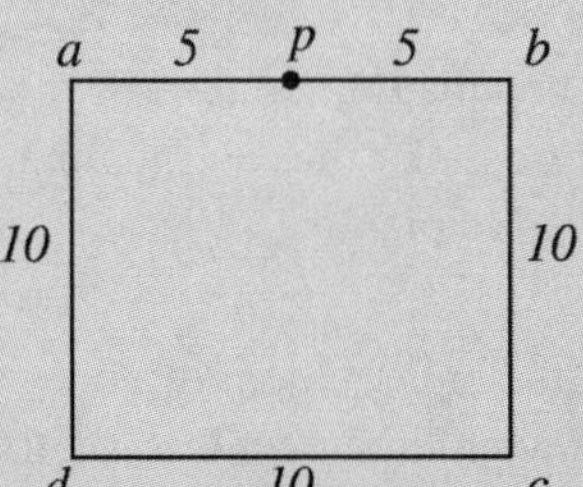

9. (a) $a(1, 0)$, $b(2, 5)$, $c(5, 1)$ are three points. Show the triangle abc on the x-y plane.

(b) Find (i) the area of Δabc, (ii) $|bc|$.

(c) Show, also, $\Delta a'b'c'$, the enlargement of Δabc centre $(0, 0)$ of scale factor $k = 2$.

(d) Find (i) the area of $\Delta a'b'c'$, (ii) $|b'c'|$.

(e) Verify that (i) $\dfrac{\text{Area } \Delta a'b'c'}{\text{Area } \Delta abc} = k^2$, (ii) $\dfrac{|b'c'|}{|bc|} = k$

10. $\Delta a'b'c'$ is the image of Δabc, centre a, of scale factor 2.
State, without giving a reason, whether these are true or false:

(i) $\dfrac{|a'b'|}{|ab|} = 2$ (ii) $\dfrac{|bc|}{|b'c'|} = \dfrac{1}{2}$

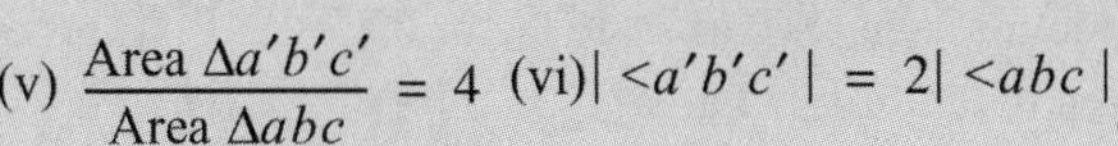

(iii) $|a'c'| = ½|ac|$ (iv) $\dfrac{\text{Area } \Delta a'b'c'}{\text{Area } \Delta abc} = 2$

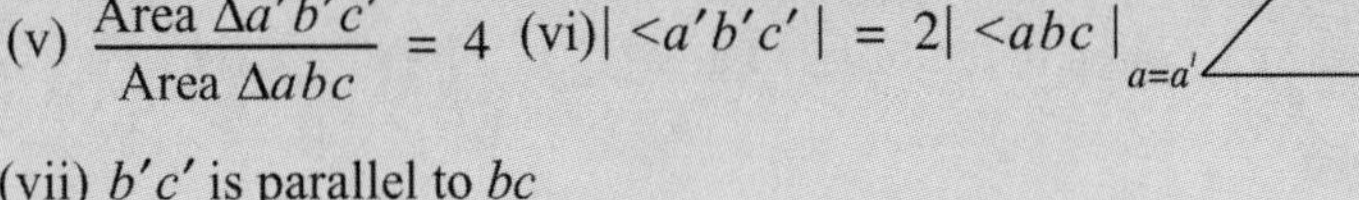

(v) $\dfrac{\text{Area } \Delta a'b'c'}{\text{Area } \Delta abc} = 4$ (vi) $|\angle a'b'c'| = 2|\angle abc|$

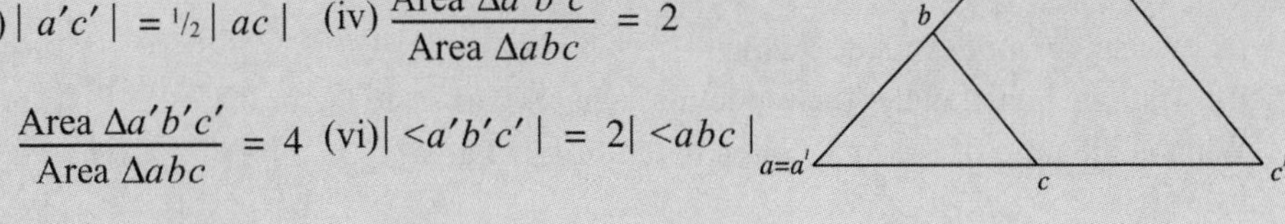

(vii) $b'c'$ is parallel to bc

11. $a(0, 2)$, $b(4, 0)$, $c(2, -2)$ and $d(-2, 0)$ are four points.
   (a) Illustrate these points on the x-y co-ordinate plane.
   (b) Show that *abcd* is a parallelogram by showing that *ab* is parallel to *cd* and that *ad* is parallel to *bc*.
   (c) Show the enlargement of *abcd* of scale factor 1.5, centre the origin.
   (d) Investigate if the enlargement is also a parallelogram.

12. Draw any triangle Δpqr. Show $\Delta p'q'r'$, the enlargement of Δpqr, centre p, of scale factor 3.

With reference to one of the theorems earlier in the chapter, say why $p'q'$ is parallel to pq.

FINDING OUT

Example 1: If Δxyz is the enlargement of Δabc, find
  (i) the centre of the enlargement (o),
  (ii) the scale factor (k).
  (iii) the ratio Area Δxyz : Area Δabc.

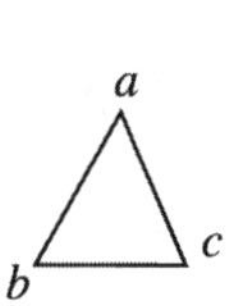

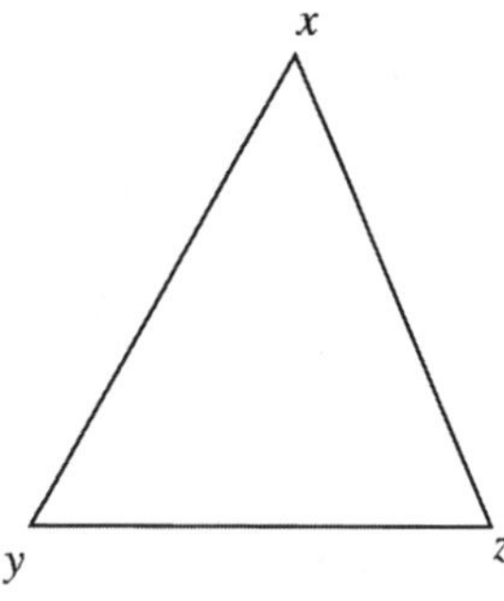

Solution:
  (i) Join x to a and produce.
  Join y to b and produce.
  Join z to c and produce.
  Where these three lines meet is o, the centre of the enlargement.

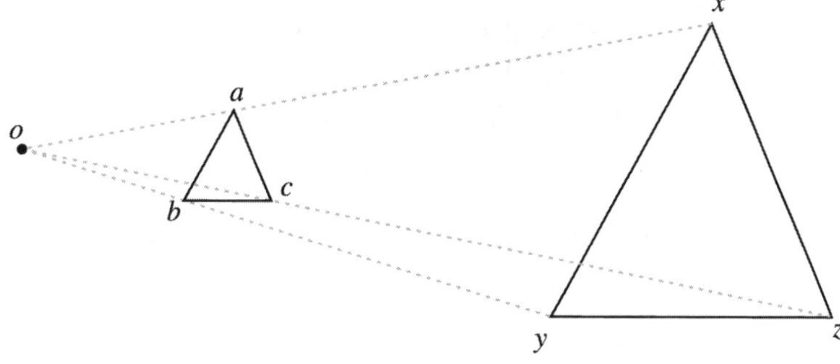

(ii) Measure $|ox|$ and $|oa|$.

$|ox| = 8.5$ and $|oa| = 2.5$

$$\therefore\ k = \frac{|ox|}{|oa|} = \frac{8.5}{2.5} = \frac{17}{5} = 3.4$$

(iii) Area Δxyz : Area $\Delta abc = k^2 : 1 = (3.4)^2 : 1 = 11.56 : 1$

Example 2: $\Delta A'B'C'$ is the image of ΔABC under an enlargement, of centre o, and scale factor k.

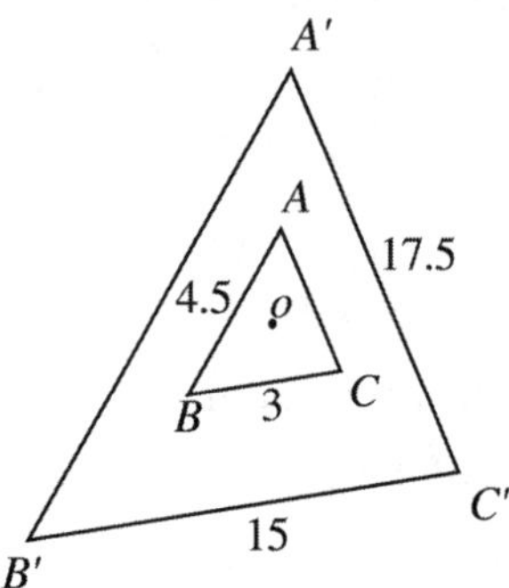

Find (i) k, (ii) $|A'B'|$, (iii) $|AC|$,

(iv) The ratio Perimeter of $\Delta A'B'C'$: Perimeter of ΔABC,

(v) The ratio Area of $\Delta A'B'C'$: Area of ΔABC.

Solution:

(i) $k = \dfrac{|B'C'|}{|BC|} = \dfrac{15}{3} = 5$

(ii) $|A'B'| = k|AB| = 5|AB| = 5 \times 4.5 = 22.5$

(iii) $|A'C'| = k|AC| \Rightarrow 17.5 = 5|AC| \Rightarrow |AC| = 17.5 \div 5 = 3.5$

(iv) Perimeter $\Delta A'B'C'$: Perimeter $\Delta ABC = 55 : 11 = 5 : 1$

(v) Area $\Delta A'B'C'$: Area $\Delta ABC = k^2 : 1 = 25 : 1$

Exercise 14.C

1. Copy this diagram exactly:

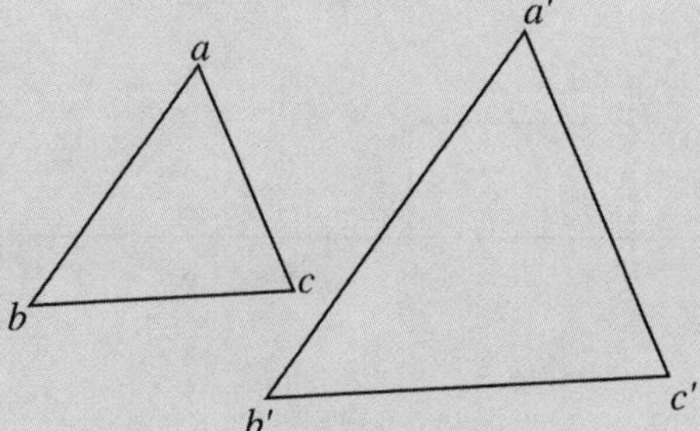

$\Delta a'b'c'$ is an enlargement of Δabc.

(i) Show the centre of the enlargement.
(ii) Find the scale factor.

2. Copy this diagram of 2 rectangles exactly:

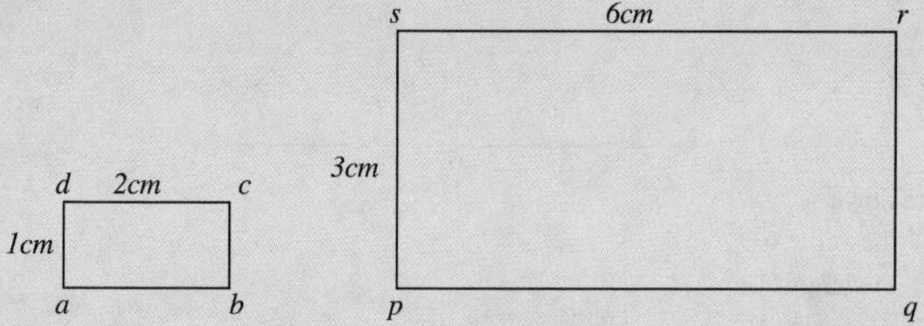

(i) If *pqrs* is the image of *abcd* under an enlargement of scale factor *k* and centre *o*, find the point *o* and the value of *k*.
(ii) Verify that area *pqrs* : area *abcd* = k^2 : 1.

3.

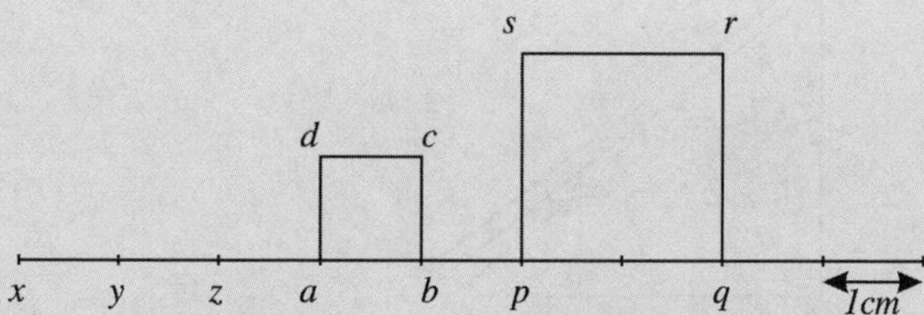

Square *pqrs* is the image of *abcd* under an enlargement.

(i) Name the centre of the enlargement.
(ii) Find the scale factor.
(iii) Find the ratio area *pqrs* : area *abcd*.

4. Rectangle *abcd* is the image of *nmos* under an enlargement.

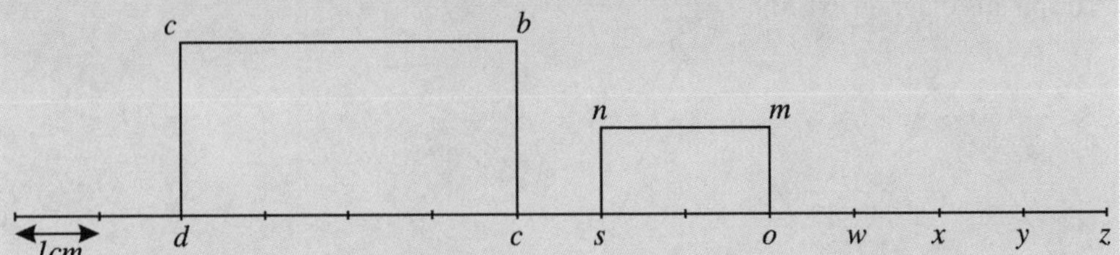

(i) Name the centre of the enlargement.
(ii) Write down the scale factor.

5. Δabc is the image of Δxyz under an enlargement of scale factor k and centre o.

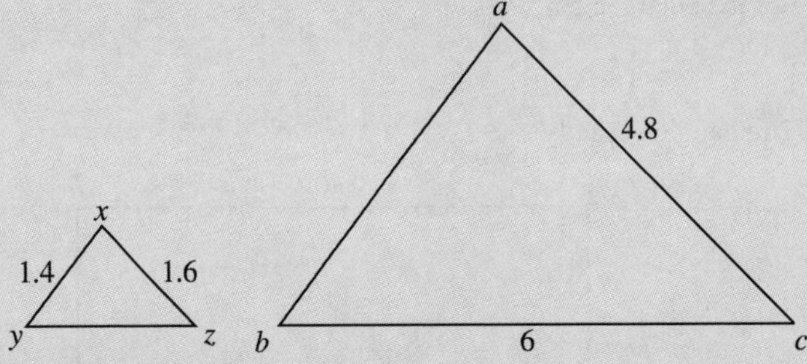

Write down
(i) the value of k,
(ii) the length $|ab|$,
(iii) the length $|yz|$.

6. Δpqr is an enlargement of Δxyr. Both triangles are right-angled, as shown.

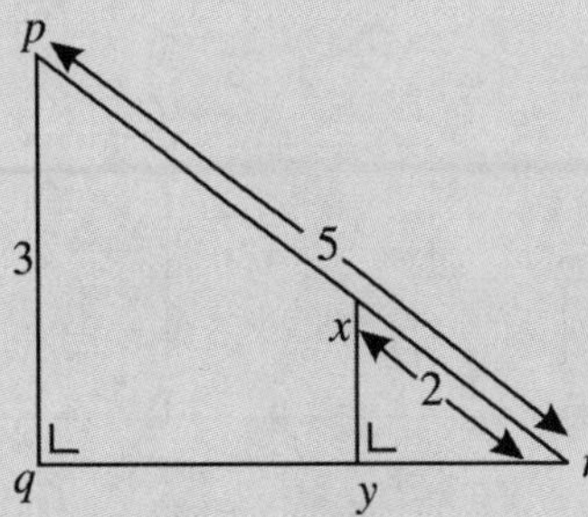

(i) Name the centre of the enlargement.
(ii) Write down the value of k, the scale factor.
(iii) Find the length $|qr|$, using Pythagoras' theorem.
(iv) Find the lengths $|xy|$ and $|yr|$.
(v) Calculate the ratio area Δpqr : area Δxyr.

7. $o(0, 0)$, $a(0, 1)$, $b(2, 0)$ are the vertices of Δoab
$p(-7, -1)$, $q(-7, 2)$, $r(-1, -1)$ are the vertices of Δpqr.

(i) Show these two triangles on the *x-y* co-ordinate plane.
(ii) If Δpqr is the image of Δoab under an enlargement, centre *c* and of scale factor *k*, find the co-ordinates of *c* and the value of *k*.

8. Square *abcd* is the image of square *nmsd* under an enlargement $|ds| = |sc|$.

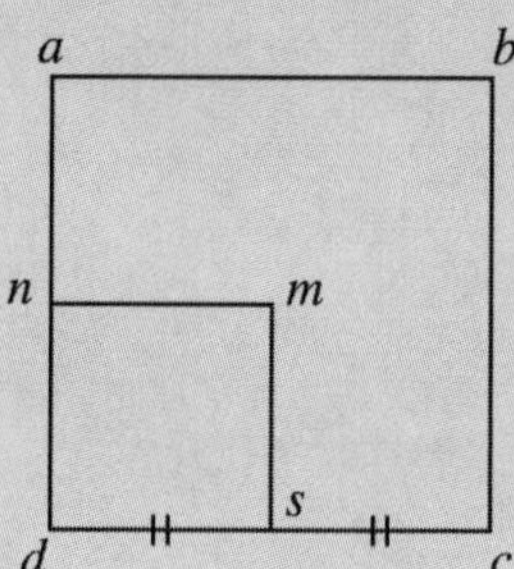

(i) What point is the centre of this enlargement?
(ii) What is the scale factor of the enlargement?
(iii) What is the ratio of the area of *abcd* : the area of *nmsd*?

9. *abcd* is a square of side 6 units. *wxyz*, as shown, is a square of side 2 units.

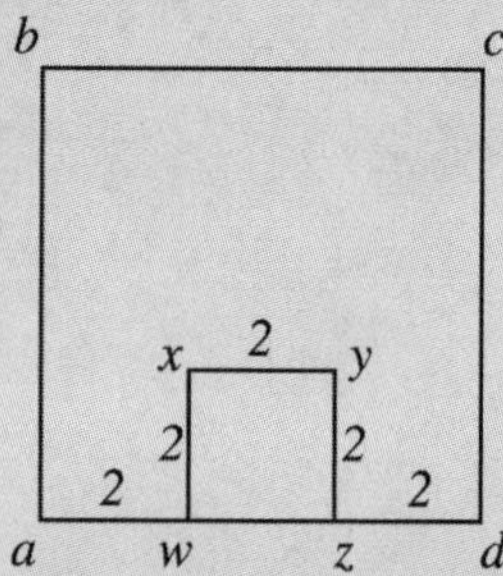

If *abcd* is an enlargement of *wxyz*, write down

(i) the scale factor of the enlargement,
(ii) the location of the centre of the enlargement,
(iii) the ratio $|bd| : |xz|$,
(iv) the ratio area *abcd* : area *wxyz*,
(v) the ratio perimeter *abcd* : perimeter *wxyz*.

10. Δade is the enlargement of Δabc, centre a, of scale factor k.

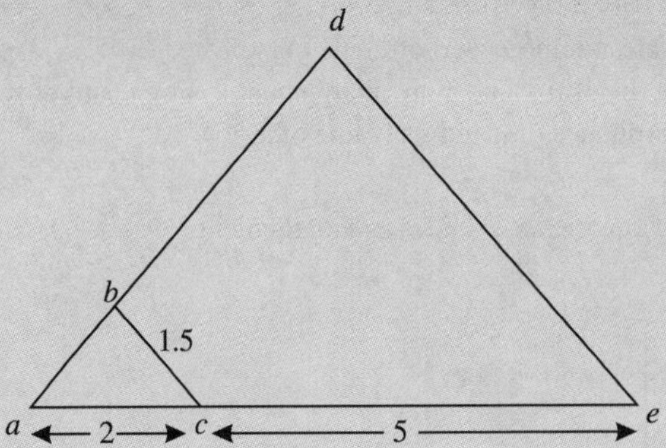

(i) Write down the value of k.

(ii) If $|bc| = 1.5$, find $|de|$.

(iii) If $|bd| = 3.5$ and $|ab| = x$, find the value of x.

(iv) Write down the ratio area Δade : area Δabc

REVISION EXERCISE 14.D

1. (a) Prove that the sum of the degree-measures of the angles of a triangle is 180°.

(b) Write down the value of x and of y:

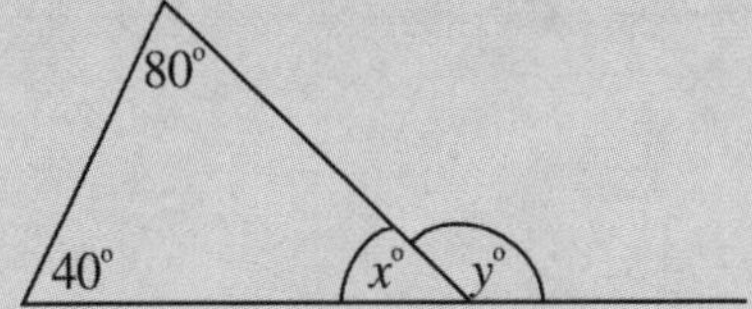

(c) Copy this diagram and construct $\Delta a'b'c'$, the image of Δabc under the enlargement, centre o of scale factor 2.

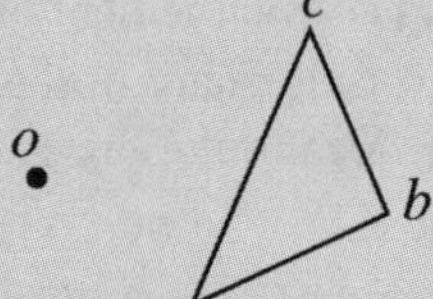

What is the ratio of

(i) $|ab| : |a'b'|$

(ii) Area $\Delta a'b'c'$: Area Δabc

2. (a) $|pr| = |qr| = |rs|$ and $|\angle prq| = 44°$.

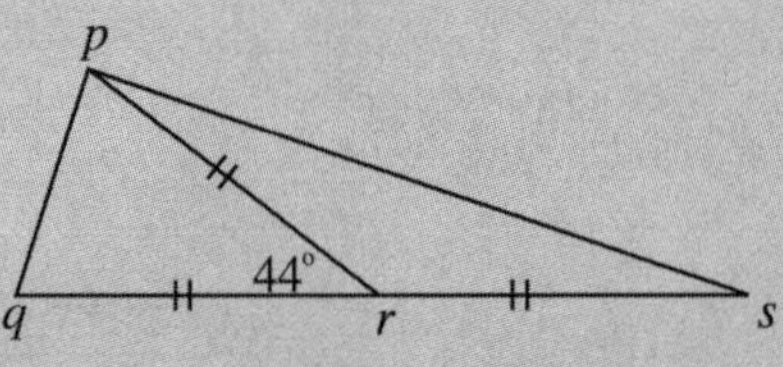

(i) Find $|\angle pqr|$.

(ii) Find $|\angle psr|$.

(b) Prove that the degree-measure of an exterior angle of a triangle is equal to the degree-measure of the sum of the two remote interior angles.

(c) The triangle *xyz* is the image of the triangle *abc* under the enlargement, centre *o*, with $|ab| = 4.4$ and $|xz| = 15$. The scale factor of the enlargement is 1.5.

(i) Find $|ac|$.

(ii) Find $|xy|$.

(iii) If the area of the triangle *abc* is 14.4 square units, find the area of triangle *xyz*.

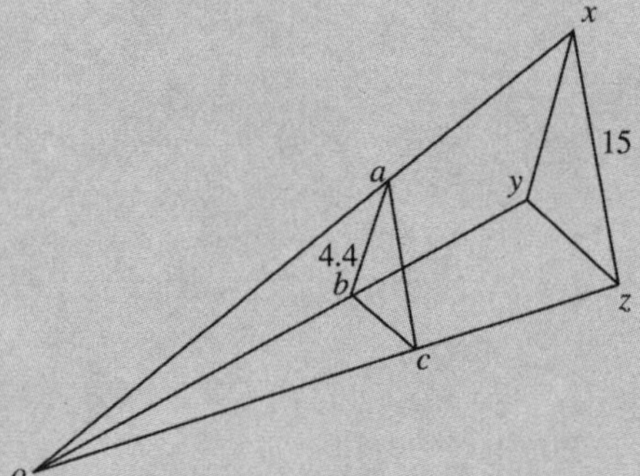

3. (a) Find the length *x* correct to two decimal places:

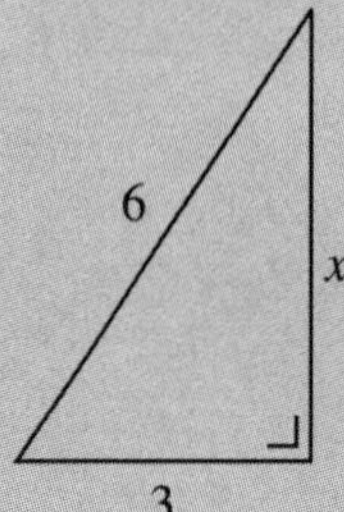

(b) Prove that an exterior angle of a triangle is greater than either remote interior angle.

(c) The triangle $pq'r'$ is the image of triangle *pqr* by an enlargement, centre *p*, as shown.

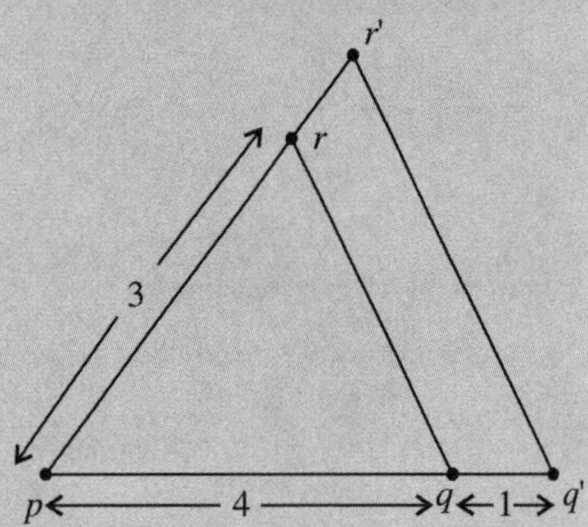

Calculate

(i) the scale factor,

(ii) $|rr'|$,

(iii) $|rq| : |r'q'|$,

(iv) Area $pq'r'$: Area pqr.

4. (a) $tp \parallel qr$. $|qp| = |pr|$ and $|\angle prs| = 128°$. Find

(i) $|\angle qpr|$

(ii) $|\angle qpt|$

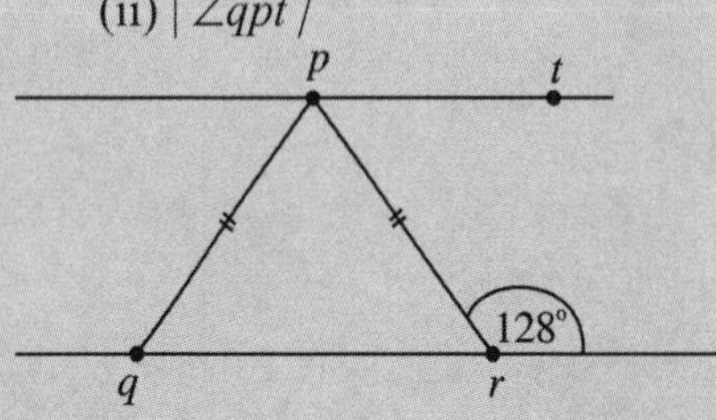

(b) Prove that opposite sides of a parallelogram have equal lengths.

(c) The triangle *ocd* is the image of triangle *oab* under an enlargement, centre *o*, with $|oa| = 4$ and $|ac| = 6$.

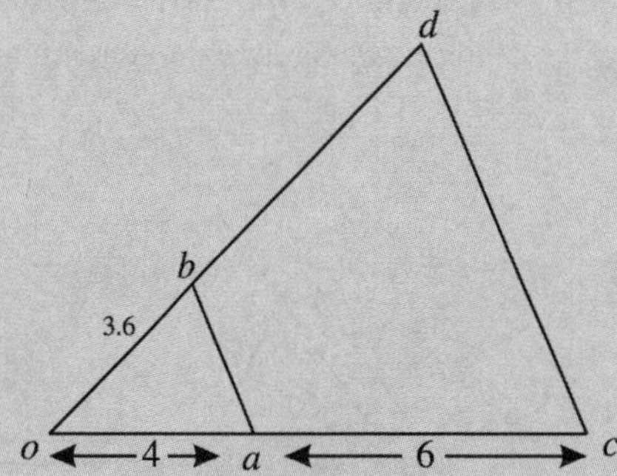

(i) Find the scale factor of the enlargement.

(ii) If $|ob| = 3.6$, find $|bd|$.

(iii) Calculate $|ab| : |cd|$.

(iv) If the area of the triangle *ocd* is 21 square units, find the area of the triangle *oab*.

5. (a) Prove that if three parallel lines make intercepts of equal length on a transversal, then they will also make equal intercepts on any other transversal.

(b) Deduce that a line which is parallel to one side of a triangle, and cuts a second side, will cut the third side in the same proportion as the second.

(c) *abcd* is a rectangle such that $|ab| = |cd| = 5$ cm and $|bc| = |ad| = 10$ cm. Construct *abcd* and construct its image $a'b'c'd'$ under the enlargement, centre *c*, of scale factor 0.6. Find

(i) $|a'b'|$ (ii) $|a'd'|$

(iii) $|bb'|$ (iv) $\dfrac{\text{Area } a'b'c'd'}{\text{Area } abcd}$

6. (a) Find, in terms of π, the area of the circle inscribed in the square *ptwq*, given that $|pr| = \sqrt{20}$ cm and $|rq| = 4$ cm and $|\angle qrp| = 90°$.

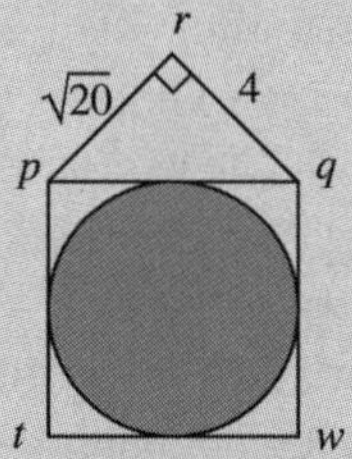

(b) Prove that if the three angles of one triangle have degree-measures equal, respectively, to the degree measures of the angles of a second triangle, then the lengths of the corresponding sides of the two triangles are proportional.

(c) The triangle *opq* is the reduction of triangle *ors*, of scale factor *k* and centre *o*. $|op| = 2$ and $|pr| = 7$.

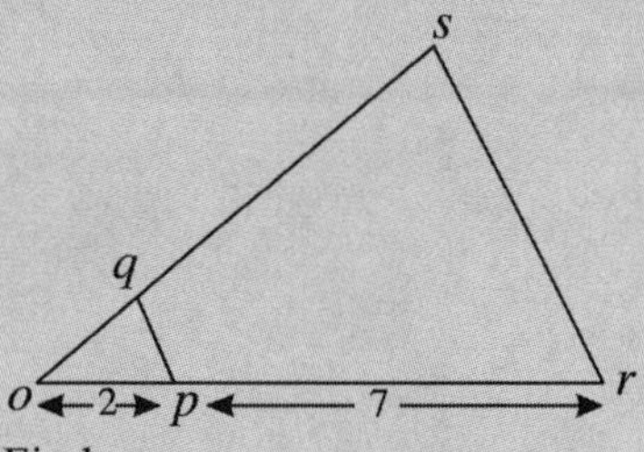

Find

(i) the value of *k*,

(ii) the ratio $|oq| : |os|$,

(iii) Area Δopq : Area Δors,

(iv) the area of the quadrilateral *prsq*, given that the area of triangle *ors* is 20¼ square units.

7. (a) Find the length $|ac|$ in the diagram, where $ac \perp bd$.

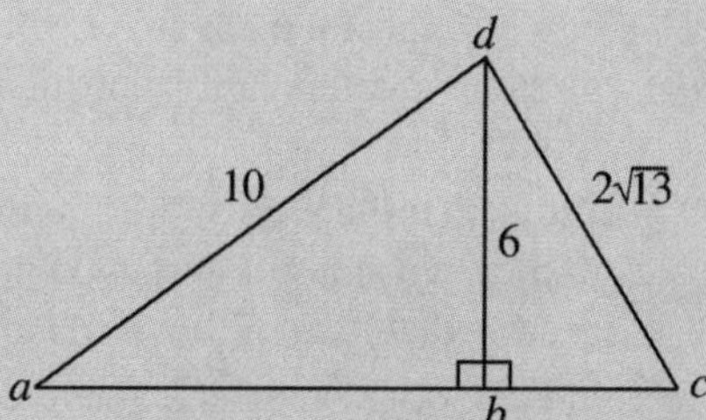

(b) Prove that in a right-angled triangle, the square of the length of the side opposite the right-angle is equal to the sum of the squares of the lengths of the other two sides.

(c) Triangle *abc* has a right angle at *b*. $|ab| = 7\frac{1}{2}$ cm and $|bc| = 4$ cm.

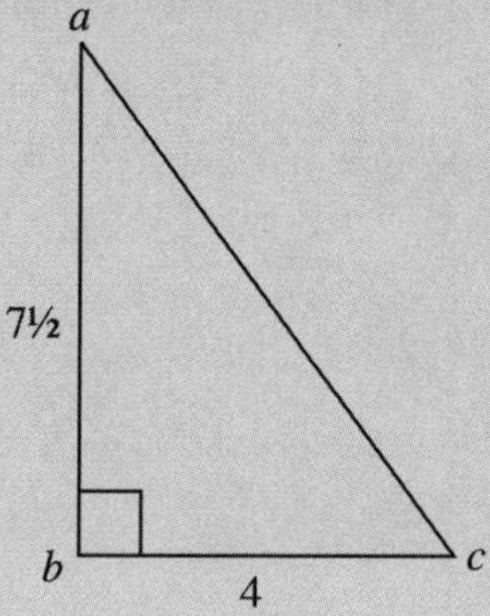

(i) Find $|ac|$.

(ii) Construct triangle $a'b'c'$, the image of triangle *abc* under a reduction, centre *b*, of scale factor 0.75.

(iii) Find $|a'b'|$.

(iv) Find area $\Delta a'b'c'$.

8. (a) Prove that if the square of the length of one side of a triangle is equal to the sum of the lengths of the squares of the other two sides, then the triangle has a right angle and is opposite the longest side.

(b) Investigate if a triangle, whose sides are of lengths 65, 56 and 33, is a right-angled triangle.

(c) Triangle *abc* has sides x, $x - 1$ and $x + 1$ as shown. If $|\angle abc| = 90°$, find the value of x.

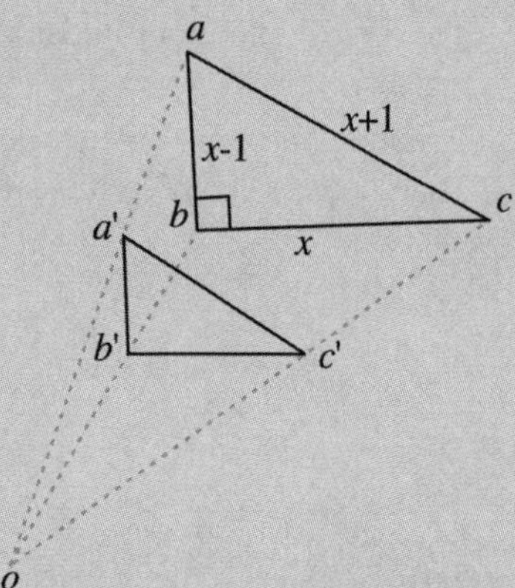

Triangle $a'b'c'$ is the image of triangle *abc* under a reduction, centre *o*, of scale factor $^4/_5$.

Find the lengths of the sides of triangle $a'b'c'$ and verify that it is also right-angled.

9. (a) Find the value of x, as in the diagram.

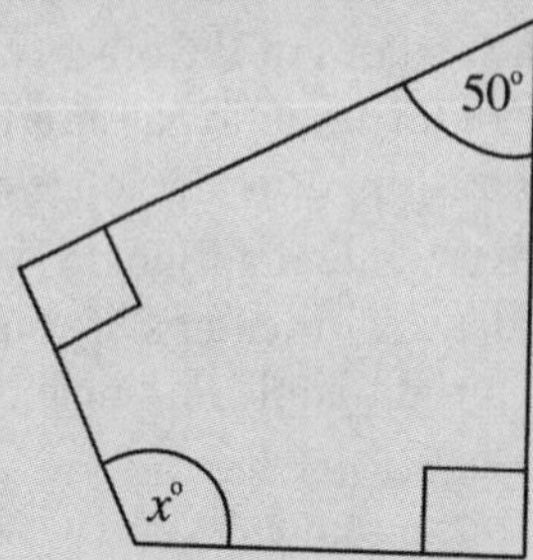

(b) Prove that the products of the lengths of the sides of a triangle by the corresponding altitudes are equal.

(c) Triangle abc is an enlargement of triangle pqr, centre o, of scale factor k.

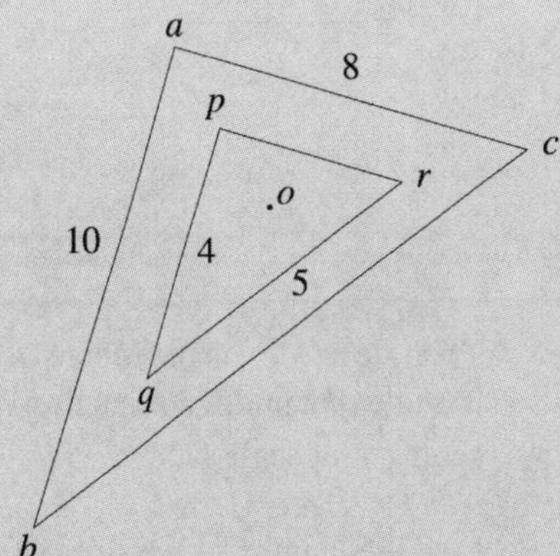

Write down

(i) the value of k,

(ii) the length $|bc|$,

(iii) the length $|pr|$,

(iv) the ratio
Area Δabc : Area Δpqr.

10. (a) Prove that if the lengths of the two sides of a triangle are unequal, then the degree-measures of the angles opposite them are unequal, with the greater angle opposite the longer side.

(b) Prove that the sum of the lengths of any two sides of a triangle is greater than that of the third side.

(c) $a(2, 2)$, $b(4, 1)$ and $c(3, 5)$ are the vertices of a triangle abc. $p(8, 5)$, $q(16, 1)$ and $r(x, y)$ are the vertices of triangle pqr. Triangle pqr is the enlargement of triangle abc, centre d and of scale factor k.

(i) Find the co-ordinates of d.

(ii) Find the value of k.

(iii) Find (x, y), the co-ordinates of r.

(iv) Verify, using the formula

$$A = \frac{1}{2}|x_1y_2 - x_2y_1|, \text{ that}$$

area pqr : area abc = k^2 : 1.

(v) Verify that $|ab| : |pq| = 1 : k$

1. The ten theorems and the two corollaries:

Theorem 1: The sum of the degree-measures of the angles of a triangle is 180°.

Corollary I: The degree-measure of an exterior angle of a triangle is equal to the degree-measure of the sum of the two remote interior angles.

Corollary II: An exterior angle of a triangle is greater than either remote interior angle.

Theorem 2: Opposite sides of a parallelogram have equal lengths.

Theorem 3: If three parallel lines make intercepts of equal length on a transversal, then they will also make intercepts of equal length on any other transversal.

Theorem 4: A line which is parallel to one side-line of a triangle, and cuts a second side, will cut the third side in the same proportion as the second.

Theorem 5: If the three angles of one triangle have degree-measures equal, respectively, to the degree-measures of the angles of a second triangle, then the lengths of the corresponding sides of the two triangles are proportional.

Theorem 6: **The Theorem of Pythagoras**: In a right-angled triangle, the square of the length of the side opposite the right-angle is equal to the sum of the squares of the lengths of the other two sides.

Theorem 7: (Converse of Pythagoras' Theorem): If the square of the length of one side of a triangle is equal to the sum of the squares of the lengths of the other two sides, then the triangle has a right-angle and this is opposite the longest side.

Theorem 8: The products of the lengths of the sides of a triangle by the corresponding altitudes are equal.

Theorem 9: If the lengths of the two sides of a triangle are unequal, then the degree-measures of the angles opposite to them are unequal, with the greater angle opposite to the longer side.

Theorem 10: The sum of the lengths of any two sides of a triangle is greater than that of the third side.

2. When an enlargement of scale factor k takes place,
   (i) Image length : Object length = $k : 1$
   (ii) Image area : Object area = $k^2 : 1$

Chapter 15

Trigonometry

DEGREES AND PARTS OF DEGREES

A full turn is divided into 360 parts called degrees, as you know. A degree may be divided into 60 smaller parts called minutes. So, 37½° may be written as 37°30′ (37 degrees and 30 minutes) or as 37.5°. Similarly, 3¼° may be written as 3°15′ or as 3.25°. A minute can be further divided into sixty parts, called seconds, but we never deal with these, since they are so small.

You can enter 3°15′ on your calculator by pressing these buttons:

DMS stands for Degrees-Minutes-Seconds. On some calculators this button appears as [°′″]

You can use your calculator to ***convert*** angles from decimals (like 34.6°) to degrees-and-minutes (like 34° 36′), by pressing [3] [4] [.] [6] [DMS].

Example 1: Find the value of A:

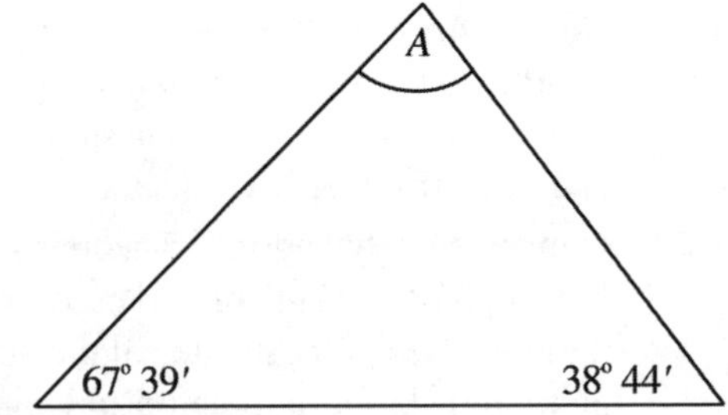

Solution: The sum of the angles = 180°

Therefore, A = 180° – 67° 39′ – 38° 44′ = 73° 37′

[On a calculator:

[1] [8] [0] [°′″] [-] [6] [7] [°′″] [3] [9] [-] [3] [8] [°′″] [4] [4] [=]].

SINE, COSINE AND TANGENT

You can find the sine, cosine or tan of any angle on your calculator, by pressing the buttons [sin] or [cos] or [tan]. We usually correct values of these functions to four decimal places, but not always.

Example 2:

(i) Find cos 56° correct to four decimal places.

(ii) Find sin 53° 8′ correct to one decimal place.

(iii) If tan A = 0.34, find A to the nearest degree.

Solution:

(i) 1. Make sure that your calculator is in 'Degree Mode'. Press the DRG button until you see DEG on the screen. The calculator is now ready.

2. Press cos 5 6 = on your calculator.

3. You will get 0.559192903 = 0.5592 (correct to four decimal places).

(ii) Press sin 5 3 DMS 8 =

You will get 0.800033833 = 0.8 (to one decimal place).

(iii) Press 2nd F tan 0 . 3 4 =

You get 18.77803322° = 19° to the nearest degree.

Exercise 15.A

1. Find the value of A:

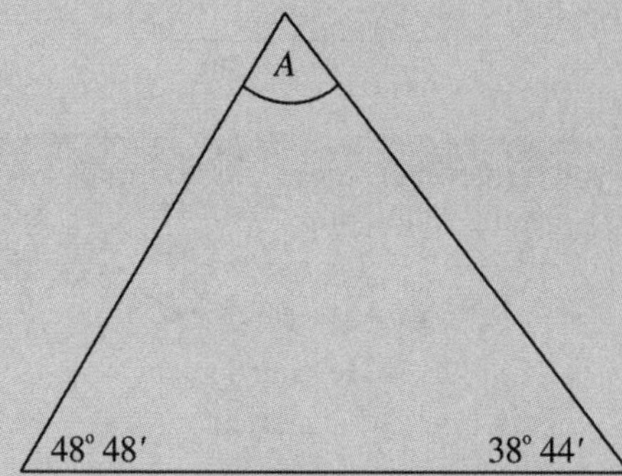

2. Two of the angles of a triangle are 56° 46′ and 39° 56′. Find the third angle.

3. Two of the angles of a triangle are 19° 12′ and 109° 55′. Find the third angle.

4. Find the value of A:

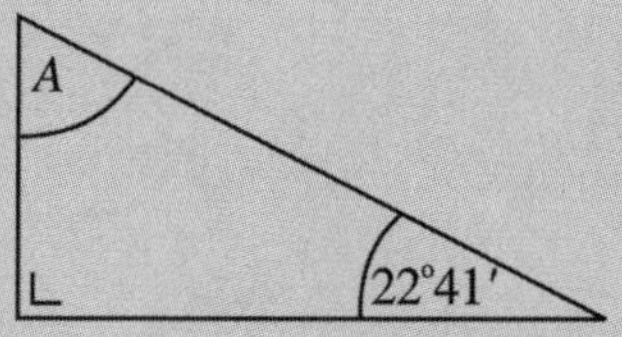

5. Find the value of A:

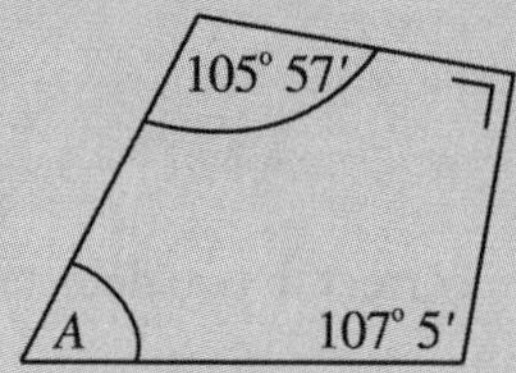

6. Use your calculator to evaluate the following (correct to four decimal places):

(i) sin 66°
(ii) cos 49°
(iii) tan 64°
(iv) sin 33° 54′
(v) cos 12° 41′
(vi) tan 7° 7′

7. Use your calculator to evaluate the following (correct to one decimal place):

(i) sin 44°
(ii) cos 60°
(iii) tan 21° 48′
(iv) sin 64° 9′
(v) cos 72° 32′
(vi) tan 26° 34′

8. Use your calculator to evaluate the following (correct to one decimal place):

(i) sin 23½°
(ii) cos 36.87°
(iii) tan 66½°
(iv) sin 5¾°
(v) cos 78.46°
(vi) tan 81¼°

9. Find the value of A in each case, to the nearest degree:

(i) $\sin A = 0.5$
(ii) $\cos A = 0.9$
(iii) $\tan A = 1$
(iv) $\sin A = 0.6$
(v) $\cos A = 0.53$
(vi) $\tan A = 4$

10. Find the value of A (where A is an acute angle) in each case, to the nearest minute:

(i) $\sin A = 0.4$
(ii) $\cos A = 0.9$
(iii) $\tan A = \frac{1}{2}$
(iv) $\sin A = \frac{1}{4}$
(v) $5 \cos A = 4$
(vi) $2 \tan A = 3$

SOLVING RIGHT-ANGLED TRIANGLES

Here is a right-angled triangle.

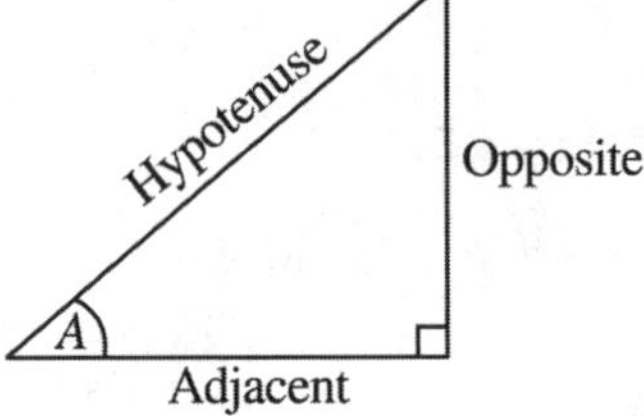

The sine, cosine and tangent of the angle A are defined in the following way:

$$\sin A = \frac{\text{Opposite}}{\text{Hypotenuse}}$$

$$\cos A = \frac{\text{Adjacent}}{\text{Hypotenuse}}$$

$$\tan A = \frac{\text{Opposite}}{\text{Adjacent}}$$

To help you remember these three important formulae, learn the mnemonic:

'**S**illy **O**ld **H**arry -
Caught **A** **H**erring -
Trawling **O**ff **A**merica'

Example 1: Find the values of x in the diagram, correct to two decimal places.

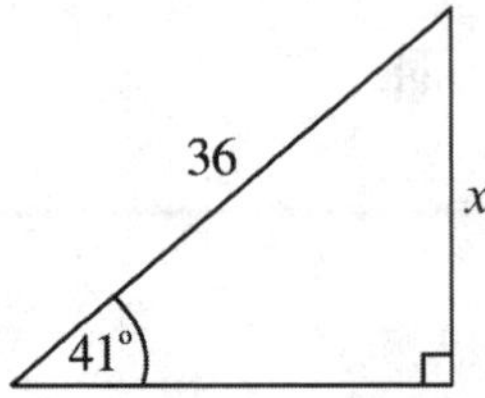

Solution:

$$\sin A = \frac{\text{Opposite}}{\text{Hypotenuse}}$$

$$\therefore \ \sin 41° = \frac{x}{36}$$

$$\therefore \ 0.6561 = \frac{x}{36}$$

$$\therefore x = 0.6561(36) = 23.618 = 23.62$$ correct to two decimal places

Example 2: Find the value y as in the diagram.

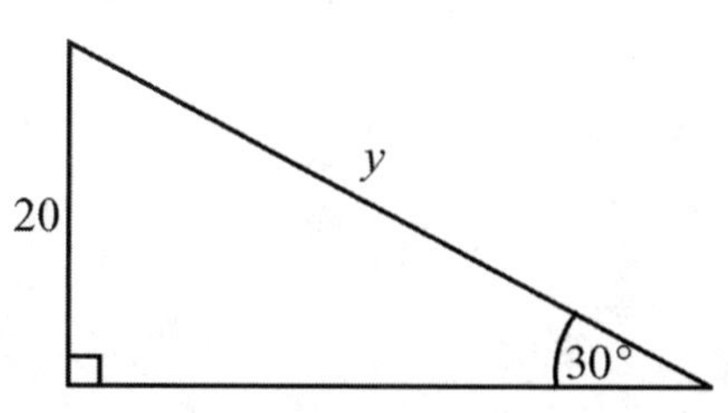

$$\sin A = \frac{\text{Opposite}}{\text{Hypotenuse}}$$

$$\therefore \sin 30° = \frac{20}{y}$$

$$\therefore 0.5 = \frac{20}{y}$$

$$\therefore 0.5y = 20$$

$$\therefore y = \frac{20}{0.5} = 40$$

Example 3: Find the values of x and y in the diagram, correct to the nearest integer (whole number).

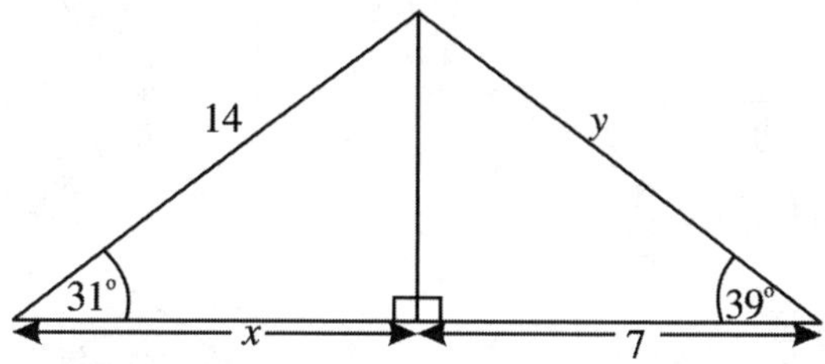

Solution:

$$\cos A = \frac{\text{Adjacent}}{\text{Hypotenuse}}$$

$$\therefore \cos 31° = \frac{x}{14}$$

$$\therefore 0.8572 = \frac{x}{14}$$

$$\therefore x = 0.8572(14) = 12 \text{ (to the nearest integer)}$$

$$\cos A = \frac{\text{Adjacent}}{\text{Hypotenuse}}$$

$$\therefore \cos 39° = \frac{7}{y}$$

$$\therefore 0.7771 = \frac{7}{y}$$

$$\therefore 0.7771y = 7$$

$$\therefore y = \frac{7}{0.7771} = 9 \text{ (to the nearest integer)}$$

Example 3: Find the value of x to the nearest integer.
Hence find A to the nearest degree.

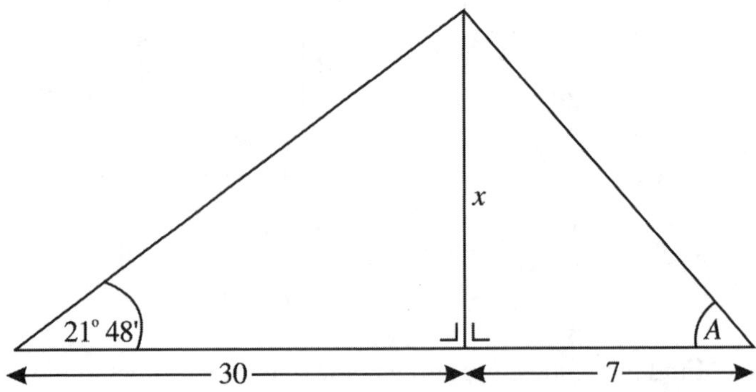

Solution:

$\tan A = \dfrac{\text{Opposite}}{\text{Adjacent}}$

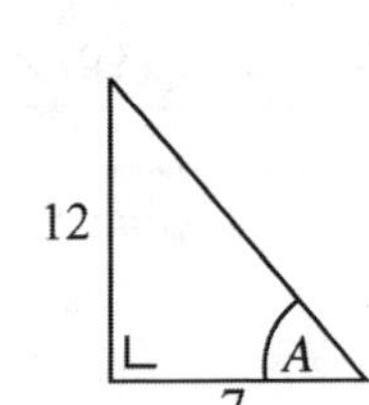

$\therefore \tan 21°48' = \dfrac{x}{30}$

$\therefore 0.4 = \dfrac{x}{30}$

$\therefore x = 0.4(30) = 12$ (to the nearest integer)

$\tan A = \dfrac{\text{Opposite}}{\text{Adjacent}}$

$\therefore \tan A = \dfrac{12}{7}$

$\therefore \tan A = 12 \div 7 = 1.7143$

$\therefore A = 59.74° = 60°$ (to the nearest degree)

12
A
7

Exercise 15.B

1. Solve for x to the nearest unit:

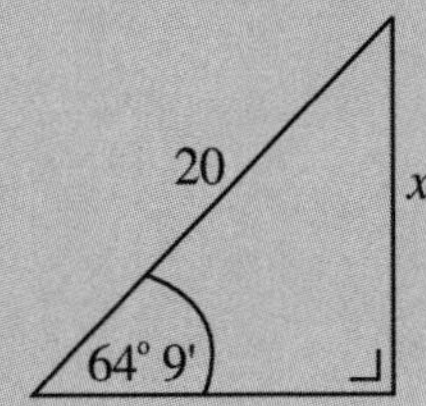

2. Solve for x to the nearest unit:

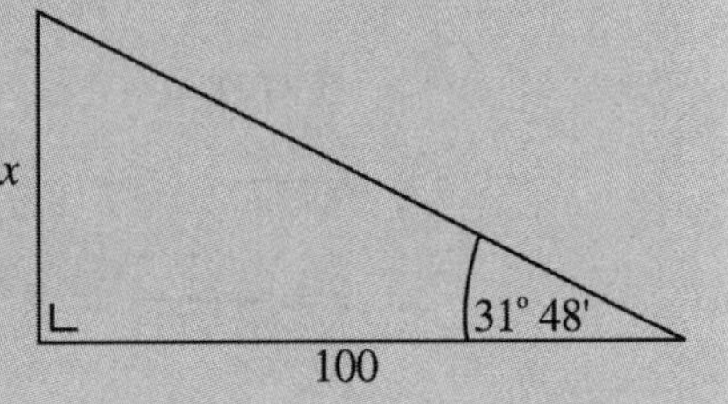

3. Solve for x to the nearest unit:

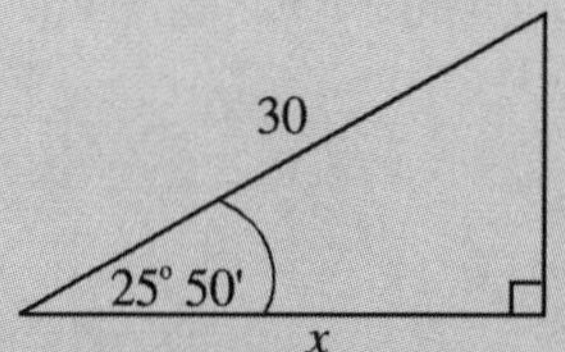

4. Solve for x to the nearest unit:

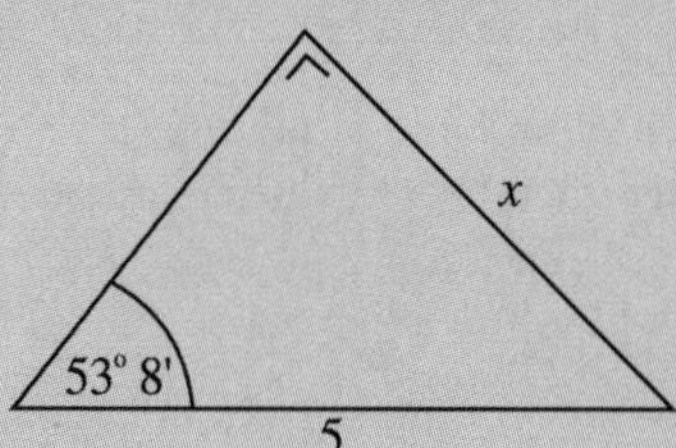

5. Solve for x to the nearest unit:

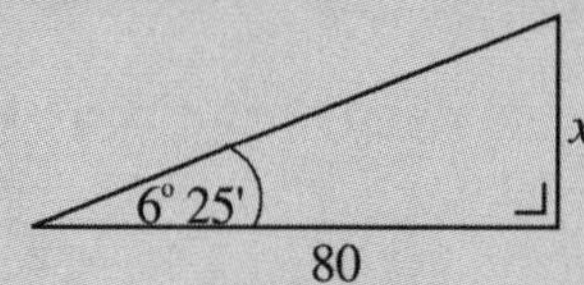

6. Solve for x to the nearest unit:

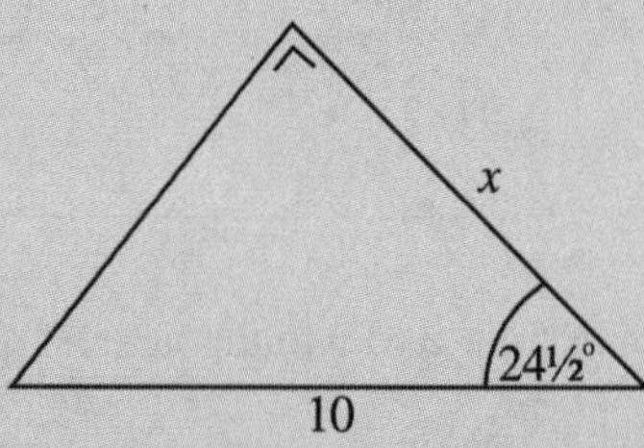

7. Solve for x to the nearest minute:

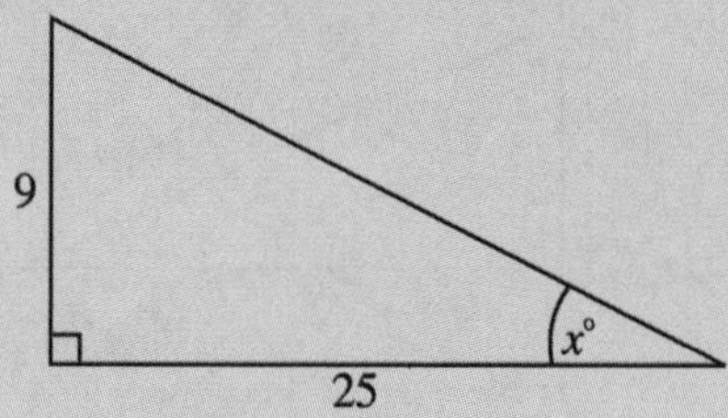

8. Solve for x to the nearest unit:

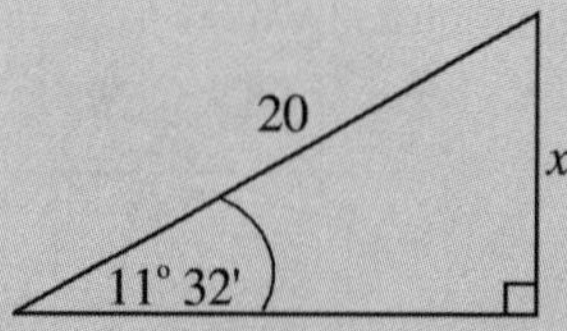

9. Solve for x to the nearest minute:

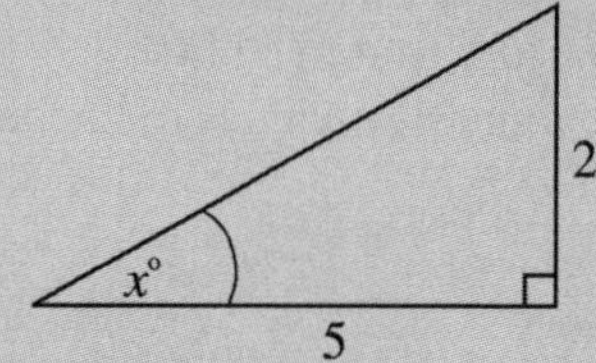

10. Solve for x to the nearest unit:

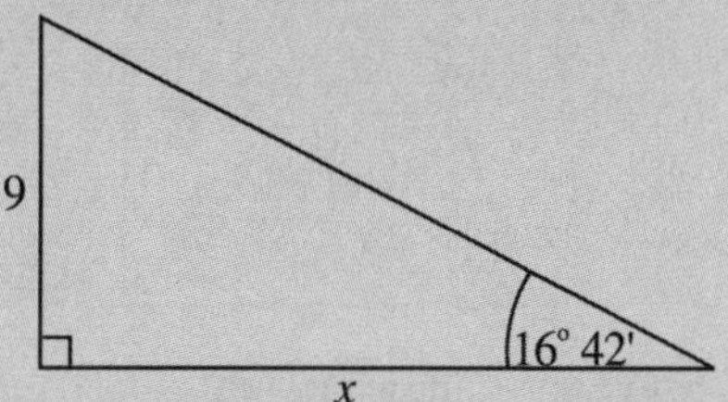

11. Solve for x and y (taking trigonometrical values to one decimal place. e.g. $\tan 31° = 0.6$):

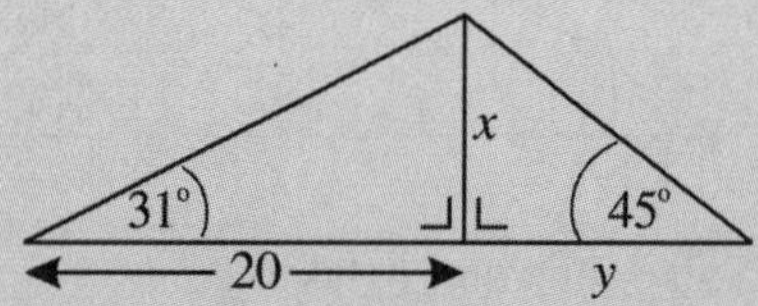

12. Solve for x and y (taking trigonometrical values to one decimal place):

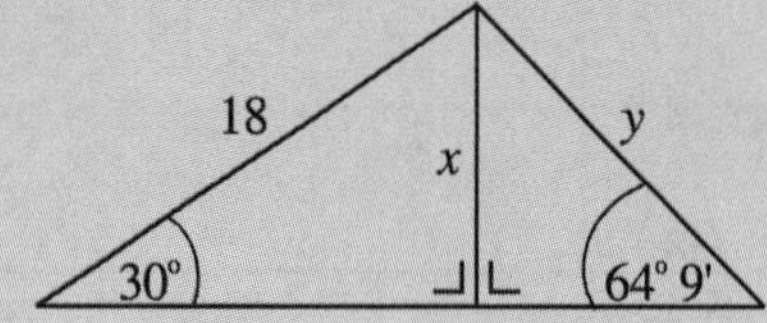

13. Solve for x and y (taking trigonometrical values to one decimal place):

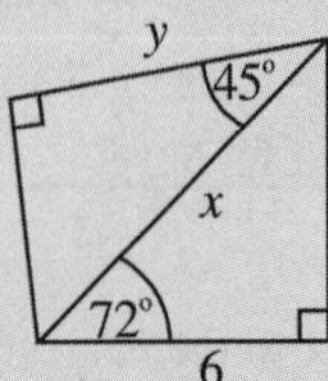

14. Solve for x and y (taking trigonometrical values to one decimal place):

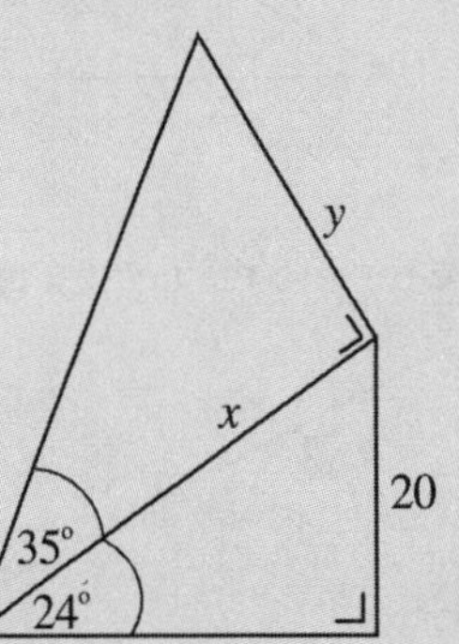

15. Solve for x and y (taking trigonometrical values to one decimal place):

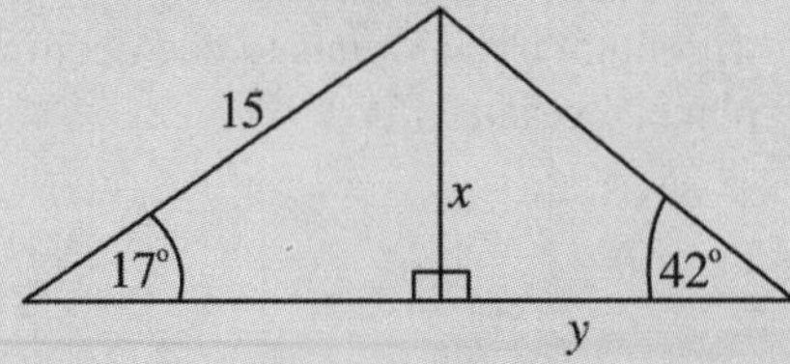

16. Solve for x and y (taking trigonometrical values to one decimal place):

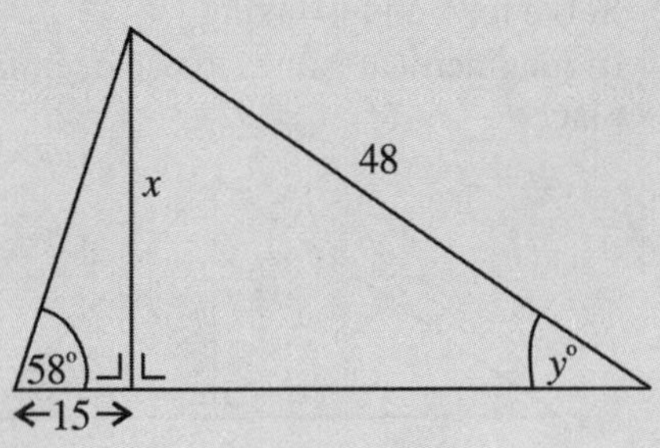

17. Solve for x and y (taking trigonometrical values to one decimal place):

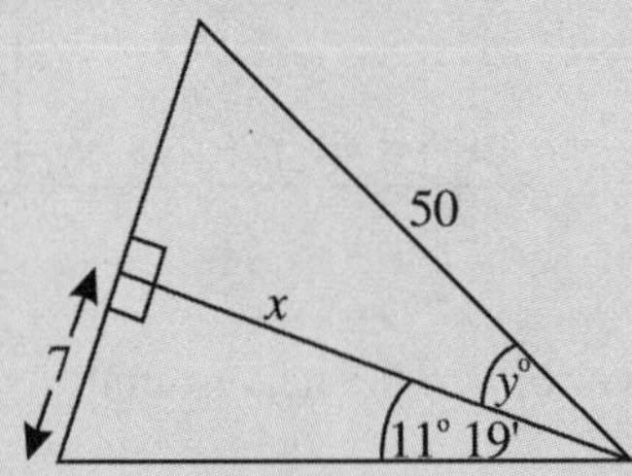

18. Solve for x and y (taking trigonometrical values to one decimal place):

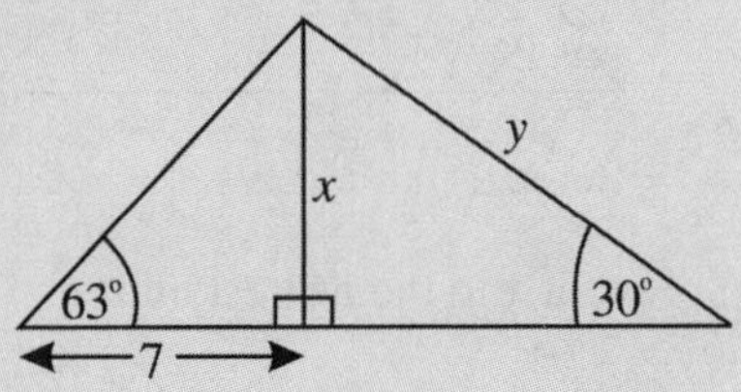

19. Solve for x and y to the nearest unit:

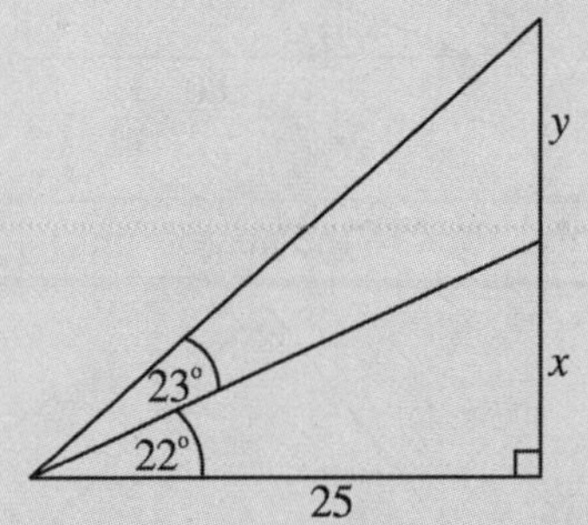

20. Solve for x and y to the nearest unit:

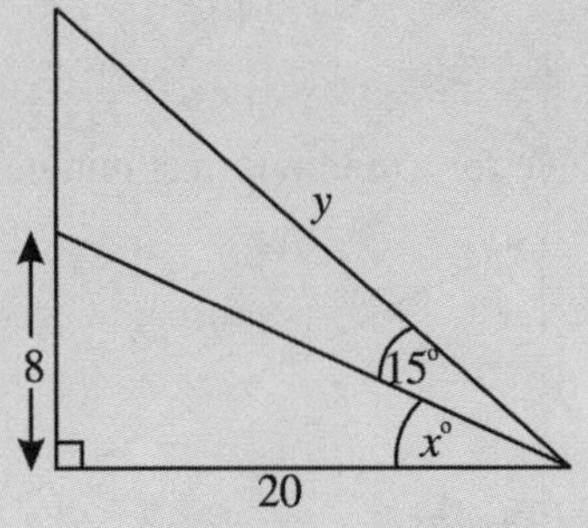

21. A 10 m ladder leans against a vertical wall. The ladder makes an angle of 63° with the horizontal ground. How far is the foot of the ladder from the foot of the wall?

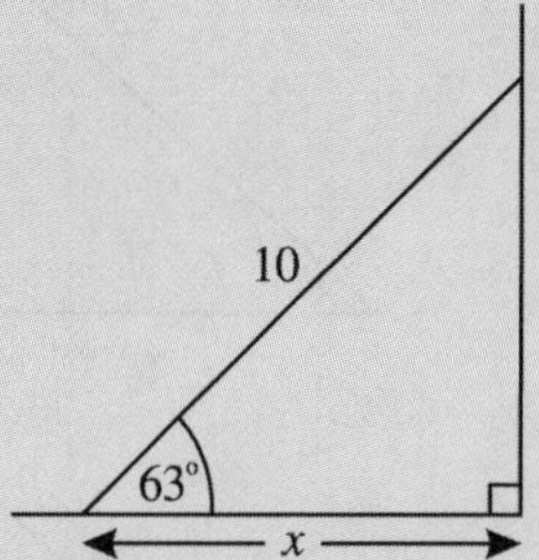

22. A person stands on level ground when the sun's elevation is 52°. The person casts a shadow of length 1.5 metres. Find the person's height to the nearest centimetre.

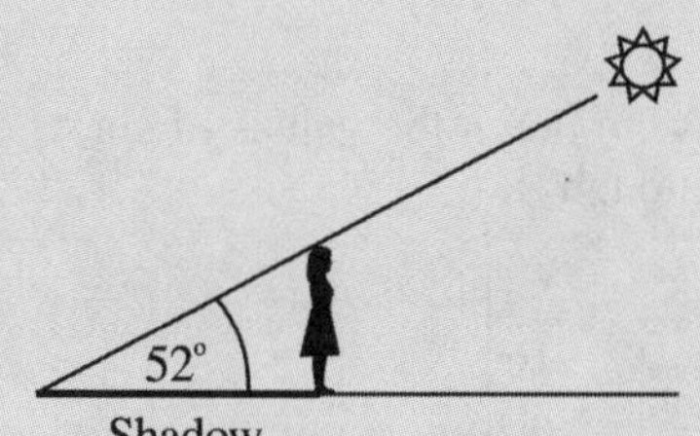

23. An aeroplane takes off from level ground and travels at a constant angle A to the ground at a speed of 50 m/s. After 8 seconds the aeroplane is 90 metres above the ground. Find A to the nearest degree.

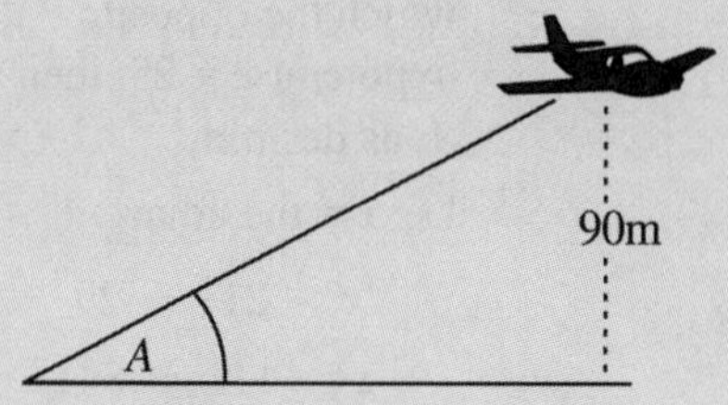

24. This vertical pole is tied to the horizontal ground by means of two wires. The longer wire is 22 m long and makes an angle of 47° with the ground. The shorter wire makes an angle of 62° with the ground.

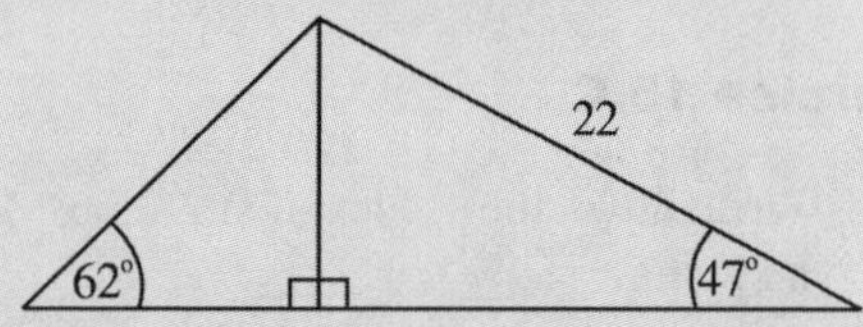

Find, to the nearest metre,

(i) the height of the pole,

(ii) the length of the shorter wire.

FINDING SIN, COS, TAN WITHOUT A CALCULATOR

Example 1: Write down the values of sin A, cos A and tan A, as in the diagram.

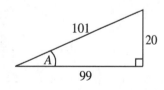

Solution:

$$\sin A = \frac{\text{Opposite}}{\text{Hypotenuse}} = \frac{20}{101}$$

$$\cos A = \frac{\text{Adjacent}}{\text{Hypotenuse}} = \frac{99}{101}$$

$$\tan A = \frac{\text{Opposite}}{\text{Adjacent}} = \frac{20}{99}$$

Example 2: A is an acute angle such that $\sin A = \frac{21}{29}$.

Find $\cos A$ and $\tan A$.

Solution: $\sin A = \frac{\text{Opposite}}{\text{Hypotenuse}} = \frac{21}{29}$

If we draw a right-angled triangle, in which the opposite = 21 and the hypotenuse = 29, then the angle will be A, as desired.

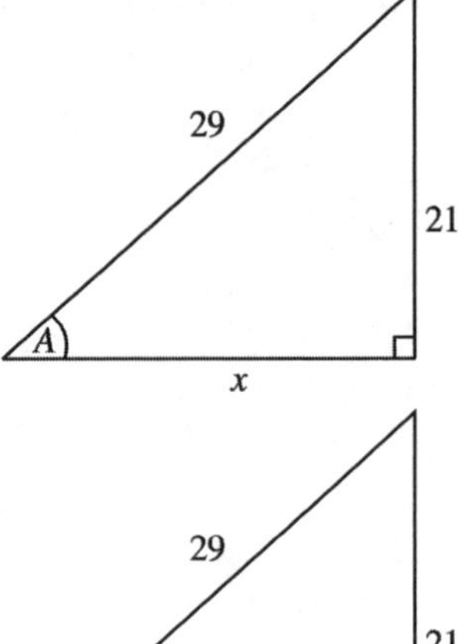

Let x = the adjacent.

$$x^2 + 21^2 = 29^2$$

$$\therefore\ x^2 + 441 = 841$$

$$\therefore\ x^2 = 400$$

$$\therefore\ x = 20$$

$$\therefore\ \cos A = \frac{\text{Adjacent}}{\text{Hypotenuse}} = \frac{20}{29}$$

$$\text{and}\ \tan A = \frac{\text{Opposite}}{\text{Adjacent}} = \frac{21}{20}$$

Exercise 15.C

1. Write down the values of $\sin A$, $\cos A$, and $\tan A$:

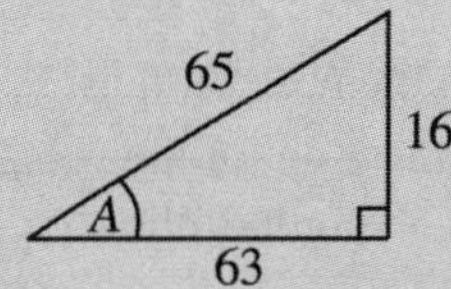

2. Write down the values of $\sin A$, $\cos A$, and $\tan A$:

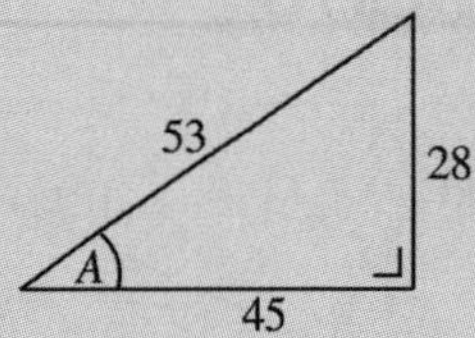

3. Write down the values of $\sin A$, $\cos A$, and $\tan A$:

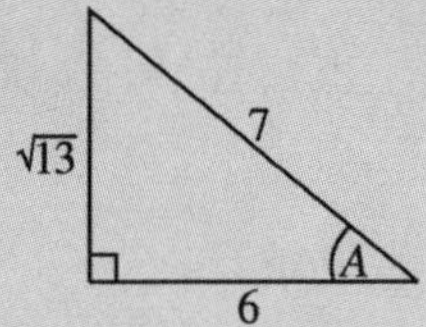

4. Write down the values of $\sin A$, $\cos A$, and $\tan A$:

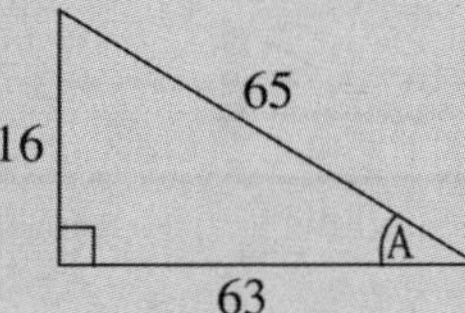

5. Write down the values of $\sin B$, $\cos B$, and $\tan B$:

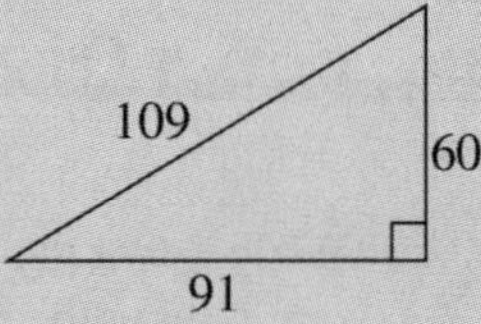

6. Write down the values of $\sin \theta$, $\cos \theta$, and $\tan \theta$:

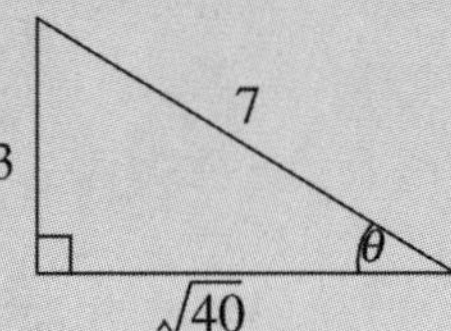

7. If $\tan A = \frac{3}{4}$, find the values of $\cos A$ and $\sin A$.

8. If $\cos A = \frac{12}{13}$, find the values of $\sin A$ and $\tan A$.

9. If $\sin A = \frac{15}{17}$, find the values of $\cos A$ and $\tan A$.

10. If $\cos A = \frac{24}{25}$, find the values of $\sin A$ and $\tan A$.

11. If $\tan A = \frac{\sqrt{7}}{3}$, find the values of $\cos A$ and $\sin A$.

12. If $\sin A = \frac{3}{\sqrt{10}}$, find the values of $\cos A$ and $\tan A$.

13. If $\cos A = \frac{\sqrt{5}}{3}$, find the values of $\sin A$ and $\tan A$.

14. If $\tan B = 2$, find the values of $\cos B$ and $\sin B$ in surd form.

15. If $\sin A = \frac{77}{85}$, find the values of $\cos A$ and $\tan A$.

16. If $\tan B = 4$, find the value of $(\cos B + \sin B)$ in surd form.

17. If $\cos \theta = \frac{1}{4}$, find $\sin \theta$ and $\tan \theta$ in surd form. Find, also, the value of θ to the nearest ½-degree.

THREE SPECIAL ANGLES: 45°, 60° & 30°

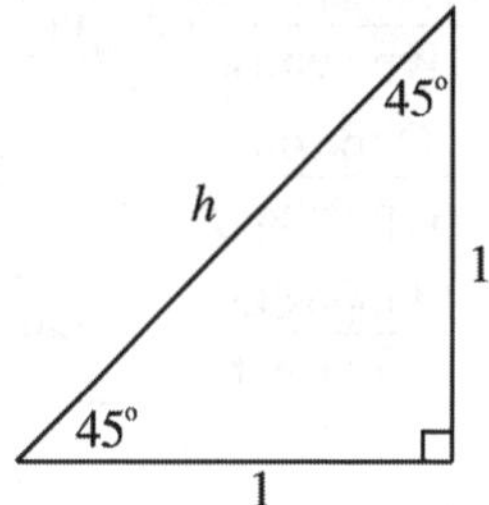

If you were on a desert island and wanted to create an angle of 45°, how would you do it? You could put two sticks of length 1 unit at right angles to each other.

Now complete the triangle with a third stick.

The angles in the other corners must be both 45° (since the triangle is isosceles).

Let h = the length of the hypotenuse.

By Pythagoras' theorem,
$$h^2 = 1^2 + 1^2$$
$$\therefore h^2 = 2$$
$$\therefore h = \sqrt{2}$$

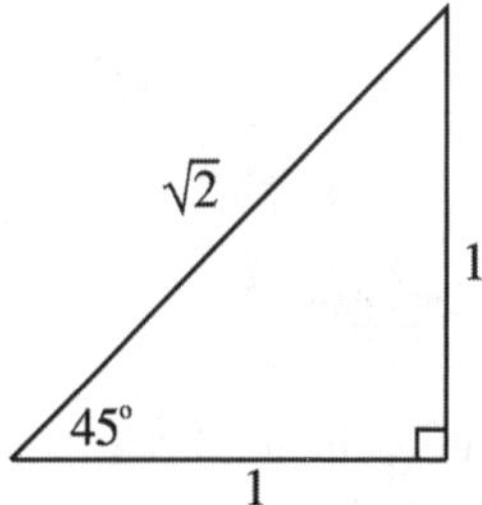

$$\cos A = \frac{\text{Adjacent}}{\text{Hypotenuse}} \quad \therefore \quad \cos 45° = \frac{1}{\sqrt{2}}$$

$$\sin A = \frac{\text{Opposite}}{\text{Hypotenuse}} \quad \therefore \quad \sin 45° = \frac{1}{\sqrt{2}}$$

$$\tan A = \frac{\text{Opposite}}{\text{Adjacent}} \quad \therefore \quad \tan 45° = \frac{1}{1} = 1$$

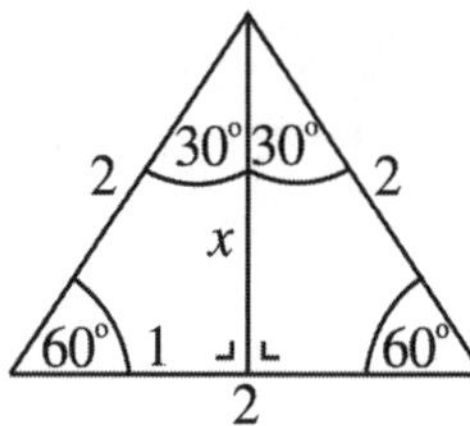

On a desert island, how would you create angles of 60° and 30°? You could get three sticks, each of length 2 units and form them into a triangle.

Since the triangle is equilateral, each angle is 60°.

Now if you bisect the triangle, you get a right-angled triangle with other angles of 60° and 30°.

Let x = the side opposite 60°.
By Pythagoras' theorem,

$$2^2 = 1^2 + x^2$$

$$\therefore 4 = 1 + x^2$$

$$\therefore 3 = x^2$$

$$\therefore x = \sqrt{3}$$

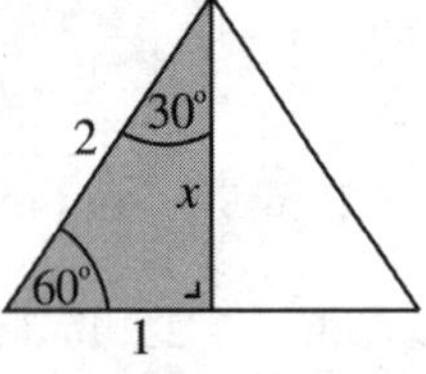

$$\cos A = \frac{\text{Adjacent}}{\text{Hypotenuse}} \quad \therefore \quad \cos 60° = \frac{1}{2}$$

$$\sin A = \frac{\text{Opposite}}{\text{Hypotenuse}} \quad \therefore \quad \sin 60° = \frac{\sqrt{3}}{2}$$

$$\tan A = \frac{\text{Opposite}}{\text{Adjacent}} \quad \therefore \quad \tan 60° = \frac{\sqrt{3}}{1} = \sqrt{3}$$

$$\cos A = \frac{\text{Adjacent}}{\text{Hypotenuse}} \quad \therefore \quad \cos 30° = \frac{\sqrt{3}}{2}$$

$$\sin A = \frac{\text{Opposite}}{\text{Hypotenuse}} \quad \therefore \quad \sin 30° = \frac{1}{2}$$

$$\tan A = \frac{\text{Opposite}}{\text{Adjacent}} \quad \therefore \quad \tan 30° = \frac{1}{\sqrt{3}}$$

Here is a table of all these results as they appear on page 9 of the maths tables:

A	**0**	π	$\frac{\pi}{2}$	$\frac{\pi}{3}$	$\frac{\pi}{4}$	$\frac{\pi}{6}$
cos A	1	−1	0	$\frac{1}{2}$	$\frac{1}{\sqrt{2}}$	$\frac{\sqrt{3}}{2}$
sin A	0	0	1	$\frac{\sqrt{3}}{2}$	$\frac{1}{\sqrt{2}}$	$\frac{1}{2}$
tan A	0	0	undefined	$\sqrt{3}$	1	$\frac{1}{\sqrt{3}}$

Unfortunately the angles are given in radians, not degrees. In order to make sense of this, you need to know that π radians = 180°.

So, $\pi = 180°$, $\frac{\pi}{2} = \frac{180°}{2} = 90°$, $\frac{\pi}{3} = \frac{180°}{3} = 60°$, $\frac{\pi}{4} = \frac{180°}{4} = 45°$, $\frac{\pi}{6} = \frac{180°}{6} = 30°$.

For example, $\sin 30° = \sin \frac{\pi}{6} = \frac{1}{2}$ (from the table).

Example 1: Find x, as in the diagram.

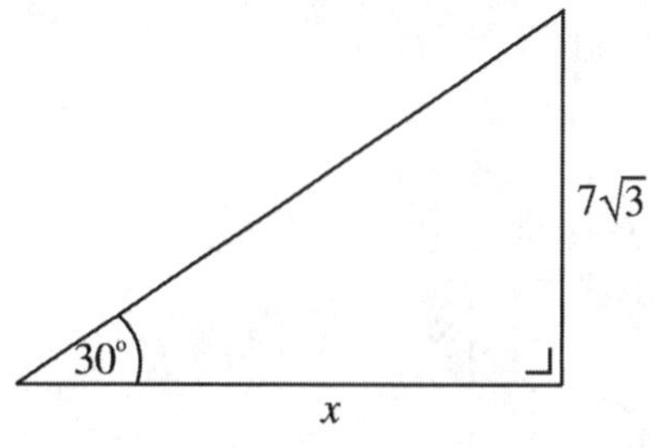

Solution:

$$\tan A = \frac{\text{Opposite}}{\text{Adjacent}}$$

$$\therefore \tan 30° = \frac{7\sqrt{3}}{x}$$

$$\therefore \frac{1}{\sqrt{3}} = \frac{7\sqrt{3}}{x}$$

$$\therefore 1x = 7(\sqrt{3})^2 = 7(3) = 21:$$ ***Answer***

Exercise 15.D

1. (a) Copy and complete the table (in surd form):

cos 45°	sin 45°	tan 45°

(b) Find x, as in the diagram.

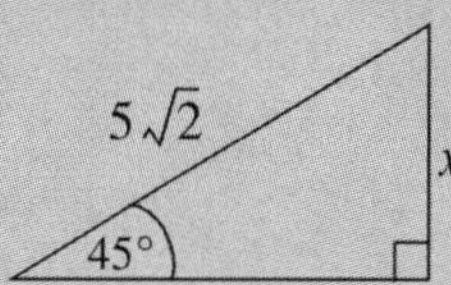

2. (a) Copy and complete the table (in surd form):

cos 30°	sin 30°	tan 30°

(b) Find x, as in the diagram.

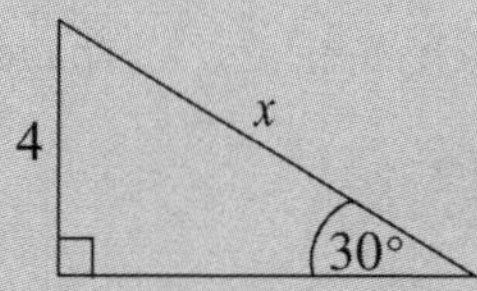

3. (a) Copy and complete the table (in surd form):

cos 60°	sin 60°	tan 60°

(b) Find x, as in the diagram.

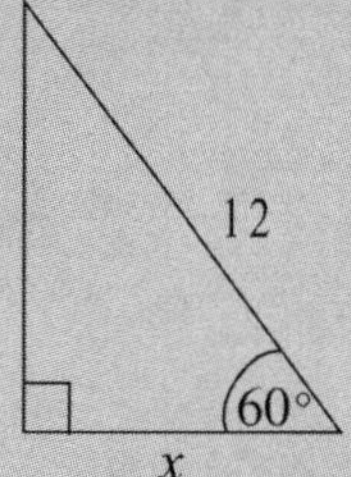

4. Find h, the perpendicular height of Δabc.

Hence find the area of Δabc.

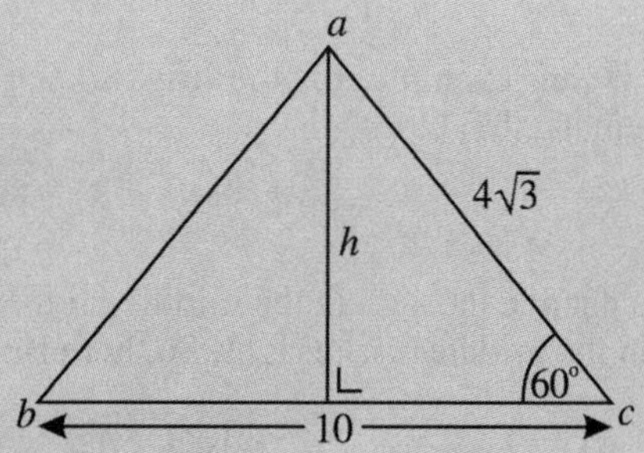

5. Find
(i) $|ab|$,
(ii) $|bc|$,
(iii) area Δabc.

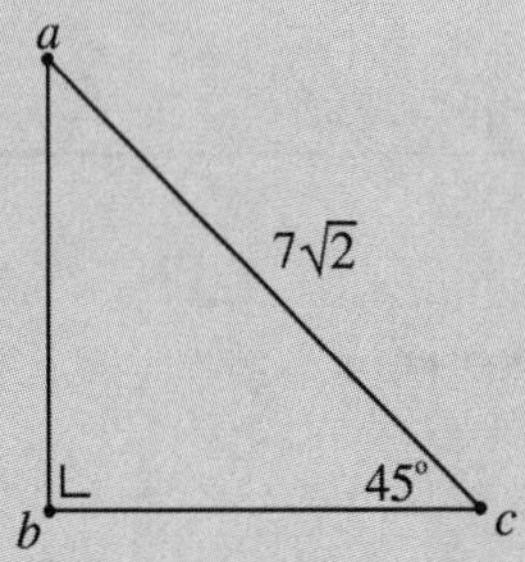

6. Find the value of x and the value of y (in surd form):

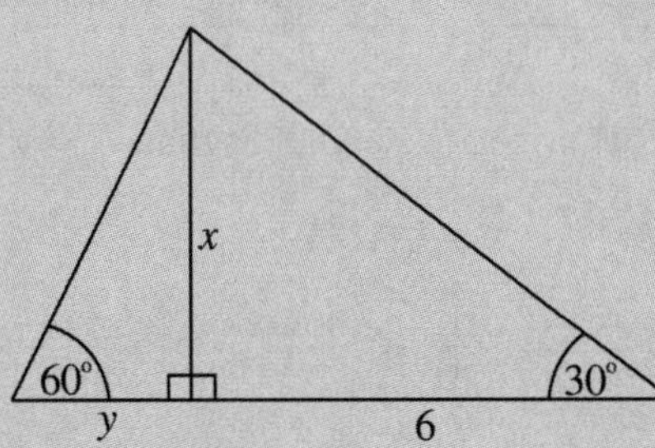

7. If $A = 45°$, evaluate $\sin^2 A + \cos^2 A$.
[Hint: $\text{Sin}^2 A$ is shorthand for $(\text{Sin } A)^2$]

8. Evaluate $\sin^2 60° + \cos^2 60° + \tan^2 60°$.

9. Evaluate $\tan^2 60° + \tan^2 45° + \tan^2 30°$.

10. If $A = 45°$, verify that $\dfrac{\sin A}{\cos A} = \tan A$.

11. If $A = 30°$, verify that
(i) $\cos 2A = \cos^2 A - \sin^2 A$,
(ii) $\sin 2A = 2 \sin A \cos A$.

12. If $\theta = 60°$, verify that
(i) $\dfrac{\sin\theta}{\cos\theta} = \tan\theta$,
(ii) $\sin^2\theta + \cos^2\theta = 1$

COMPOUND ANGLES

Is it true that $\cos 30° = \cos 20° + \cos 10°$?
The answer is an emphatic ***NO!***, since $0.8660 \neq 0.9397 + 0.9848$
But you may be surprised to learn that $\cos 30° = \cos 20° \cos 10° - \sin 20° \sin 10°$
[Verify it with a calculator if you don't believe it.]

This is an example of the trigonometrical identity, which appears on page 9 of the Mathematical Tables:

$$\cos(A + B) = \cos A \cos B - \sin A \sin B$$

If you change the sign in the middle on the left-hand side of this formula, you must change the sign in the middle on the right. So, here is another formula (which does ***not*** appear on page 9):

$$\cos(A - B) = \cos A \cos B + \sin A \sin B$$

Here are another two, the first of which appears on page 9 of the Mathematical Tables:

$$\sin(A + B) = \sin A \cos B + \cos A \sin B$$
$$\sin(A - B) = \sin A \cos B - \cos A \sin B$$

Example 1: Write sin 15° in surd form.

Solution:

$$\sin 15^\circ = \sin(45^\circ - 30^\circ)$$
$$= \sin 45^\circ \cos 30^\circ - \cos 45^\circ \sin 30^\circ$$
$$= \frac{1}{\sqrt{2}} \cdot \frac{\sqrt{3}}{2} - \frac{1}{\sqrt{2}} \cdot \frac{1}{2} = \frac{\sqrt{3}}{2\sqrt{2}} - \frac{1}{2\sqrt{2}} = \frac{\sqrt{3}-1}{2\sqrt{2}}$$

Example 2: If $\cos A = \frac{3}{5}$ and $\cos B = \frac{12}{13}$, write $\cos(A + B)$ as a fraction.

Solution:

$$\cos A = \frac{3}{5} = \frac{\text{Adjacent}}{\text{Hypotenuse}}$$

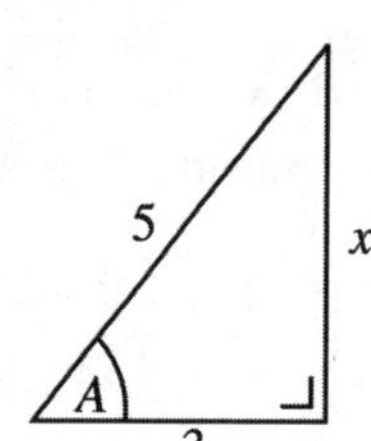

Draw a triangle with the adjacent = 3 and the hypotenuse = 5.
Let x = the opposite.
By Pythagoras' theorem,

$$x^2 + 3^2 = 5^2$$
$$\therefore \quad x^2 + 9 = 25$$
$$\therefore \quad x^2 = 16$$
$$\therefore \quad x = 4$$

$$\therefore \quad \sin A = \frac{\text{Opposite}}{\text{Hypotenuse}} = \frac{4}{5}$$

$$\cos B = \frac{12}{13} = \frac{\text{Adjacent}}{\text{Hypotenuse}}$$

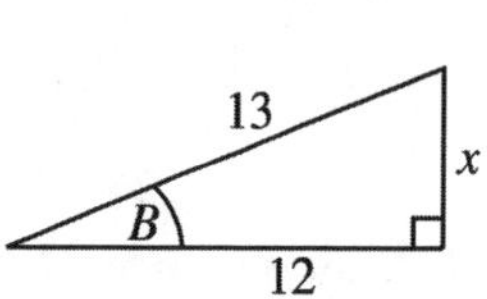

Draw a triangle with the adjacent = 12 and the hypotenuse = 13. Let x = the opposite.
By Pythagoras' theorem,

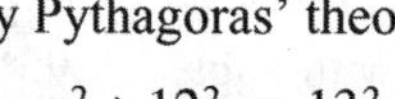

$$x^2 + 12^2 = 13^2$$
$$\therefore \quad x^2 + 144 = 169$$
$$\therefore \quad x^2 = 25$$
$$\therefore \quad x = 5$$

$$\therefore \sin B = \frac{\text{Opposite}}{\text{Hypotenuse}} = \frac{5}{13}$$

Now, $\cos(A + B) = \cos A \cos B - \sin A \sin B$

$$= \frac{3}{5} \cdot \frac{12}{13} - \frac{4}{5} \cdot \frac{5}{13} = \frac{16}{65}$$

Exercise 15.E

1. Write cos 15° in surd form, by writing it as cos(45° – 30°).
2. Write sin 105° in surd form, by writing it as sin(45° + 60°).
3. Write cos 75° in surd form, by writing it as cos(45° + 30°).
4. Write $\sin 75°$ in surd form by writing it as $\sin(45° + 30°)$.
5. Write $\cos 105°$ in surd form by writing it as $\cos(60° + 45°)$.
6. By writing $\sin 15°$ as $\sin(60° - 45°)$, find $\sin 15°$ in surd form.
7. If $\sin A = \frac{3}{5}$ and $\sin B = \frac{5}{13}$, write these as fractions:
   (i) cos A,
   (ii) cos B,
   (iii) sin($A + B$).
8. If $\cos A = \frac{4}{5}$ and $\cos B = \frac{15}{17}$, write these as fractions:
   (i) sin A,
   (ii) sin B,
   (iii) cos($A + B$).
9. If $\cos A = \frac{3}{5}$ and $\cos B = \frac{21}{29}$, write these as fractions:
   (i) sin A,
   (ii) sin B,
   (iii) cos($A - B$).
10. If $\sin A = \frac{24}{25}$ and $\sin B = \frac{4}{5}$, find $\sin(A + B)$ as a fraction.
11. If $\cos A = \frac{5}{13}$ and $\cos B = \frac{12}{37}$, find $\cos(A + B)$ as a fraction.
12. If $\sin A = \frac{8}{\sqrt{65}}$ and $\cos B = \frac{7}{\sqrt{65}}$ find $\sin(A + B)$.
13. If $\sin A = \frac{\sqrt{5}}{3}$ and $\sin B = \frac{\sqrt{7}}{4}$, write these as fractions:
   (i) cos A,
   (ii) cos B,
   (iii) sin($A - B$).
14. If $\cos A = \frac{4}{5}$ find the value of
   (i) sin A,
   (ii) sin $2A$.
   [Hint: Sin $2A = \sin(A + A)$]

NON-ACUTE ANGLES

Supposing you want to know the cosine of 135°. The Maths tables will not give you the answer. And, worse still, you cannot draw a right angled triangle with angles of 90° and 135°, because 90° + 135° > 180°. So, we need a new, improved definition of cosine (and sine and tangent).

Definition

Draw a circle with centre (0, 0) and radius one unit in length (called a ***unit circle***). Draw a radius along the positive sense of the x-axis. Now draw another radius, at an angle A to the first radius (turning anti-clockwise). If (x, y) is the point where this radius meets the circle, then

$$\cos A = x,\ \sin A = y,\ \tan A = \frac{y}{x} = \frac{\sin A}{\cos A}$$

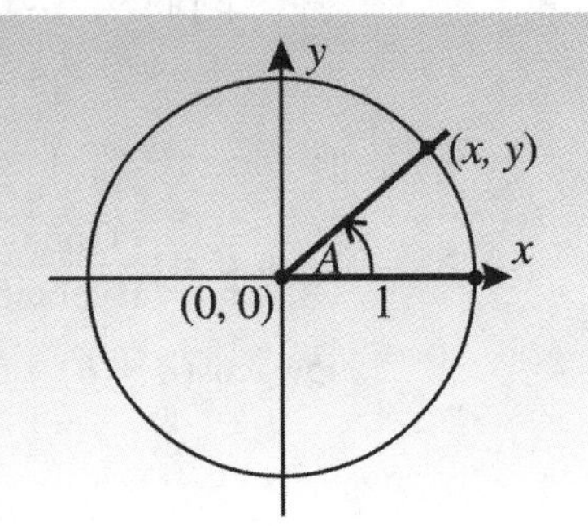

For example, when $A = 53°$, we find that the point $(x, y) = (0.6, 0.8)$

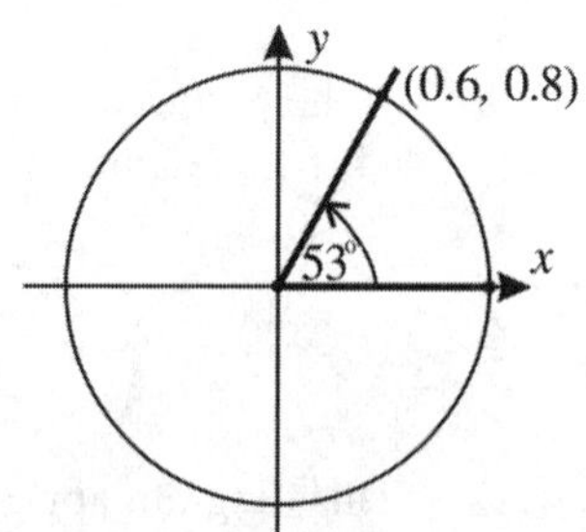

$\therefore\ \cos 53° = 0.6$

$\sin 53° = 0.8$

$\tan 53° = \frac{0.8}{0.6} = \frac{4}{3}$

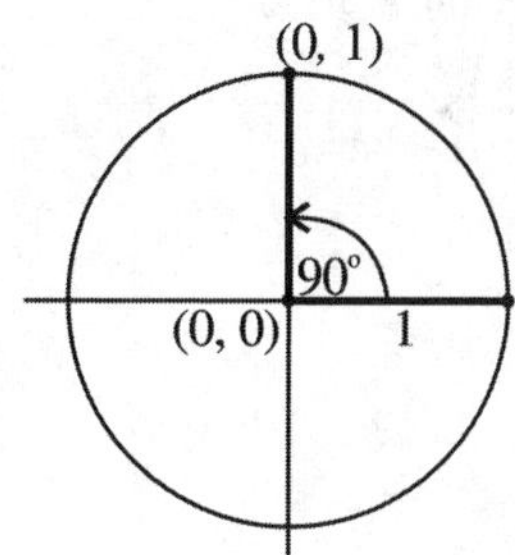

Also, if $A = 90°$, the point $(x, y) = (0, 1)$.

$\therefore\ \cos 90° = 0$ and $\sin 90° = 1$

and $\tan 90° = {}^1/_0$ = undefined

[Because you cannot divide by zero].

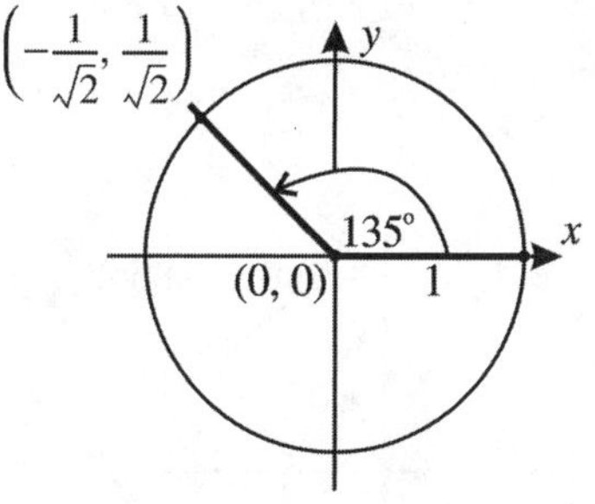

Now, if $A = 135°$, then $(x, y) = \left(-\frac{1}{\sqrt{2}}, \frac{1}{\sqrt{2}}\right)$.

$\therefore\ \cos 135° = -\frac{1}{\sqrt{2}}$

$\sin 135° = \frac{1}{\sqrt{2}}$

$\tan 135° = \frac{\sin 135°}{\cos 135°} = -1$

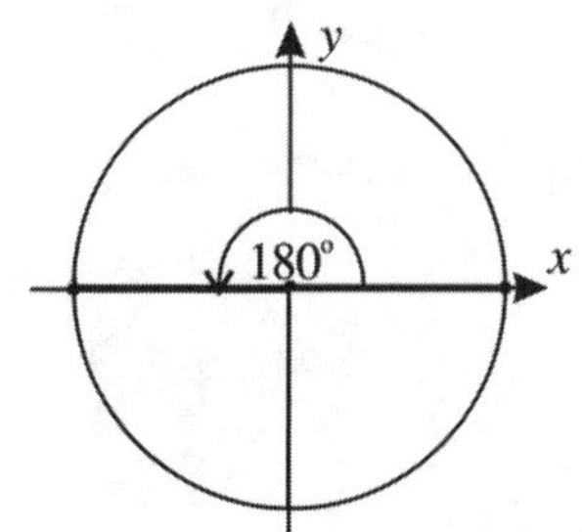

If $A = 180°$, then $(x, y) = (-1, 0)$

$\therefore\ \cos 180° = -1$

$\sin 180° = 0$

$\tan 180° = \frac{0}{-1} = 0$

Finally, if $A = 270°$, then $(x, y) = (0, -1)$.

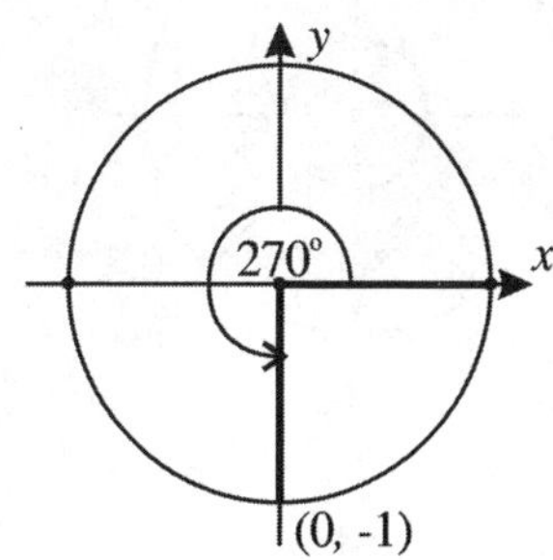

$\therefore\ \cos 270° = 0$

$\sin 270° = -1$

$\tan 270° = \frac{-1}{0}$ = undefined

1. To help you remember that $(x, y) = (\cos A, \sin A)$, remember that the Christian name comes before the Surname.

$\therefore$ $(x, y) =$ (**C**hristian name, **S**urname)
(**C**osine, **S**ine)

2. This diagram appears on page 9 of the Maths Tables:

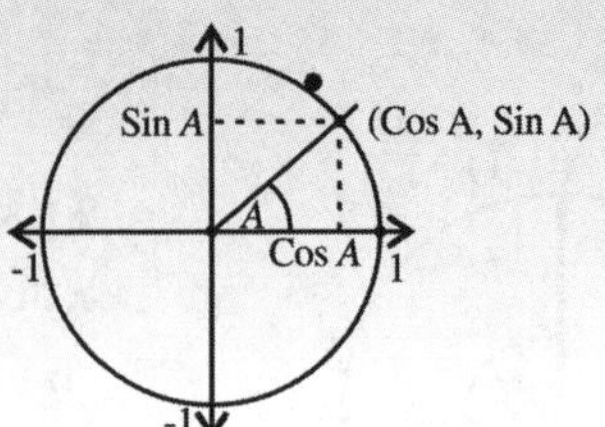

Exercise 15.F

1. Use the diagram to write down the values of
   (i) cos 60°,
   (ii) sin 60°.

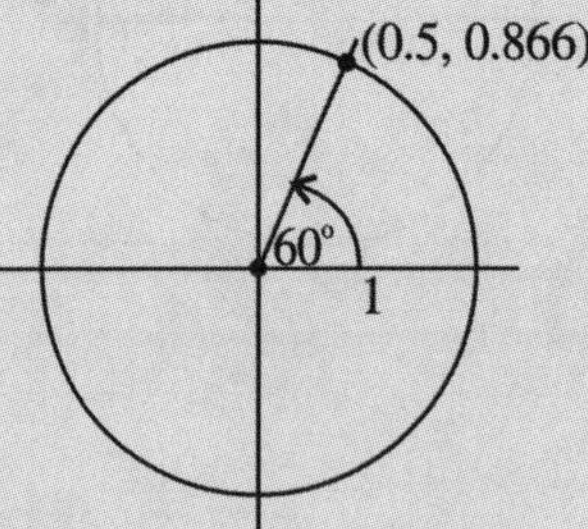

2. Use the diagram to estimate the values of
   (i) cos 315°,
   (ii) sin 315°,
   (iii) tan 315°.

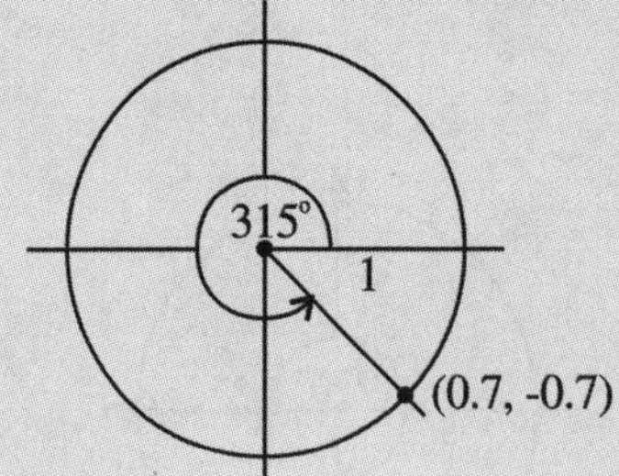

3. (a) Use the diagram to estimate the values of
   (i) cos 150°,
   (ii) sin 150°.

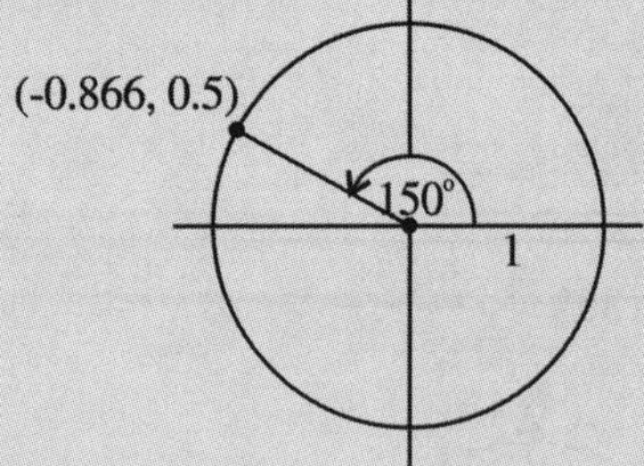

   (b) Use the diagram to estimate the values of
   (i) cos 240°,
   (ii) sin 240°.

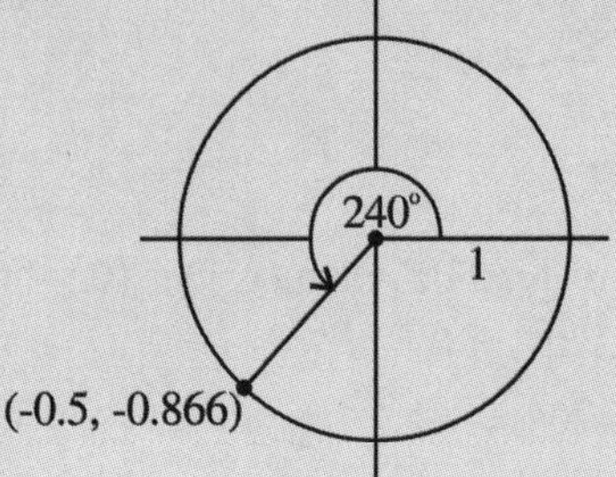

4. Use the diagram to complete the table below:

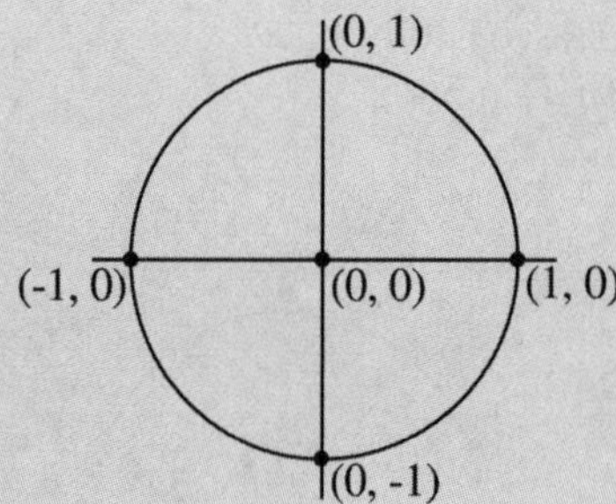

A	0°	90°	180°	270°	360°
cos A					1
sin A					
tan A		undefined		undefined	

5. (i) Write down two values of A (where $0° \leq A \leq 360°$) such that $\cos A = 0$.

(ii) Write down one value of A (where $0° \leq A \leq 360°$) such that $\sin A = -1$.

(iii) Write down one value of A (where $0° \leq A \leq 360°$) such that $\cos A = -1$.

(iv) Write down three values of A (where $0° \leq A \leq 360°$) such that $\sin A = 0$.

(v) Write down two values of A (where $0° \leq A \leq 360°$) such that $\cos A = 1$.

(vi) If $\tan \theta = 0$ find three values of θ in the range $0° \leq \theta \leq 360°$.

(vii) Solve for B (where $0° \leq B \leq 360°$) $\text{sine } B - 1 = 0$

6. Use your calculator to find the value of θ (to the nearest degree) in each case:

(i)

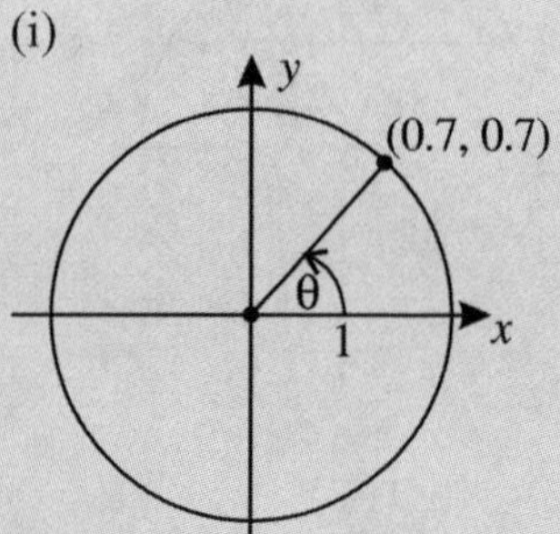

(ii)

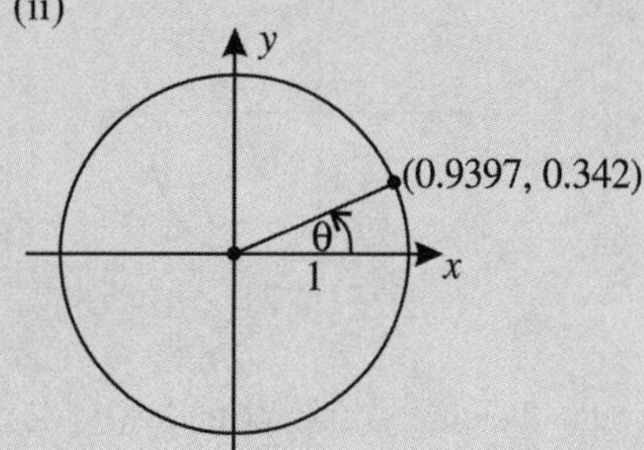

(iii)

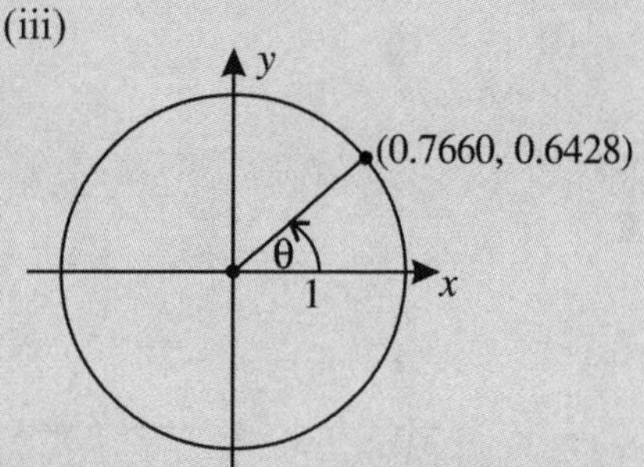

(iv)

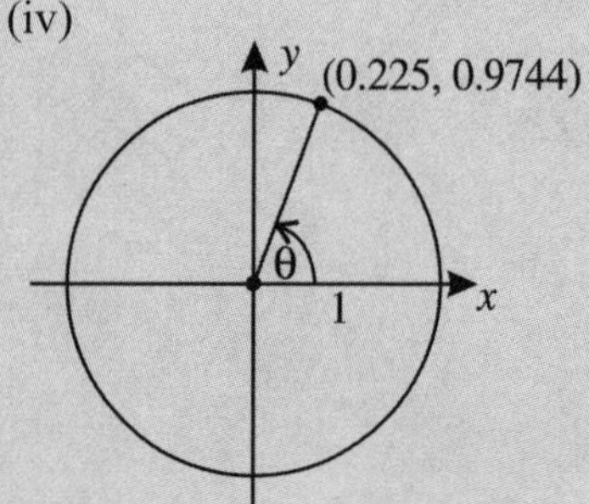

(continued over→)

(v)

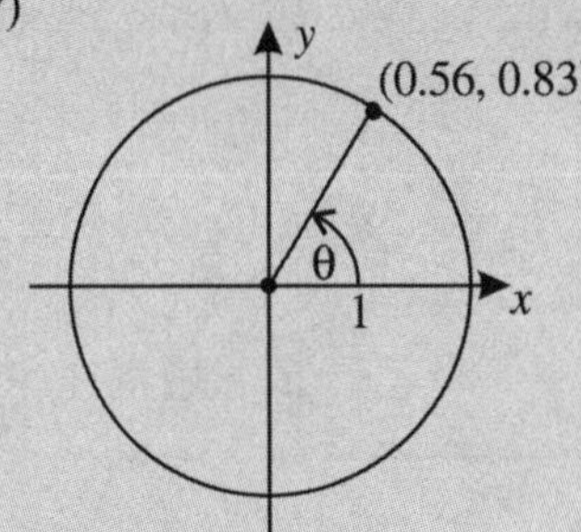

(vi)

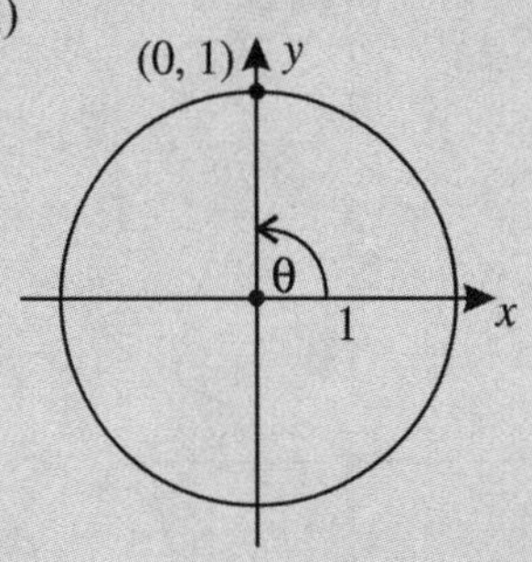

7. Use the diagram to write down approximations for
(i) cos 216°,
(ii) sin 216°,
(iii) tan 216°.

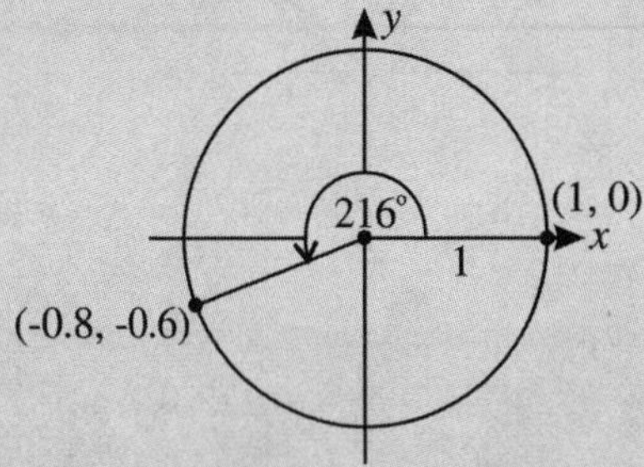

8. Use the diagram to write down the values of
(i) cos 300°,
(ii) sin 300°,
(iii) tan 300°.

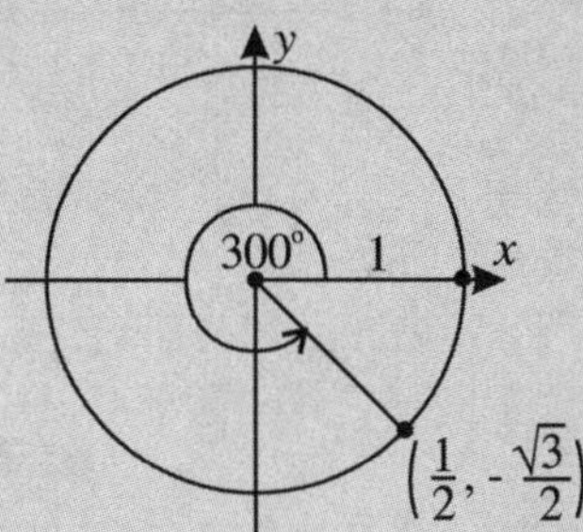

9. The diagram shows a line segment [*oa*] such that | *oa* | = 1 unit.
Use your protractor to find a point *p* on [*oa*] such that | *op* | = cos 36°.

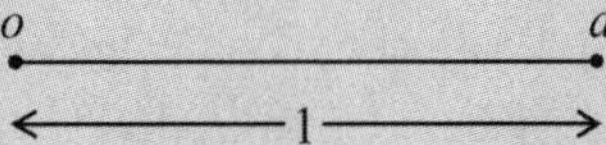

[Hint: Start by drawing a unit circle with *o* as its centre.

10. The diagram shows a line segment [*ok*] such that | *ok* | = 1 unit.
Use your protractor to find a point *p* on [*ok*] such that | *op* | = cos 55°.

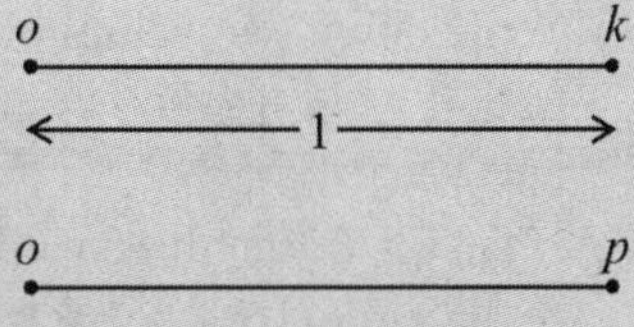

11.

op is a line segment of length 1 unit. Construct a point *k* on [*op*] such that | *ok* | = sin 70°.

THE FOUR QUADRANTS

Let us divide the unit circle into four quadrants.
The 1st quadrant is for angles in the range:
$0^\circ - 90^\circ$.
The 2nd quadrant is for angles in the range:
$90^\circ - 180^\circ$.
The 3rd quadrant is for angles in the range:
$180^\circ - 270^\circ$.
The 4th quadrant is for angles in the range:
$270^\circ - 360^\circ$.

90°, 2nd quadrant $(-x, y)$, 1st quadrant (x, y), 0° (360°), 180°, 3rd quadrant $(-x, -y)$, 4th quadrant $(x, -y)$, 270°

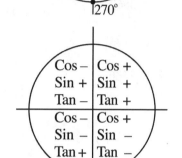

Your experience should, by now, have shown you that in the 1st quadrant, all values of cos, sin and tan are positive.
In the 2nd quadrant, cosines are negative, sines are positive and tangents are negative.

(since $\tan = \frac{\sin}{\cos} = \frac{\text{positive}}{\text{negative}} = \text{negative}$)

In the 3rd quadrant, cosines and sines are both negative. Hence tangents are positive.

(since $\tan = \frac{\sin}{\cos} = \frac{\text{negative}}{\text{negative}} = \text{positive}$)

2nd quadrant	1st quadrant
Cos – Sin + Tan –	Cos + Sin + Tan +
Cos – Sin – Tan +	Cos + Sin – Tan –

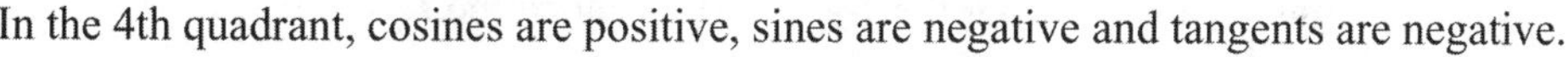

In the 4th quadrant, cosines are positive, sines are negative and tangents are negative.

(since $\tan = \frac{\sin}{\cos} = \frac{\text{negative}}{\text{positive}} = \text{negative}$)

Here, in summary, are the quadrants where the functions are POSITIVE:

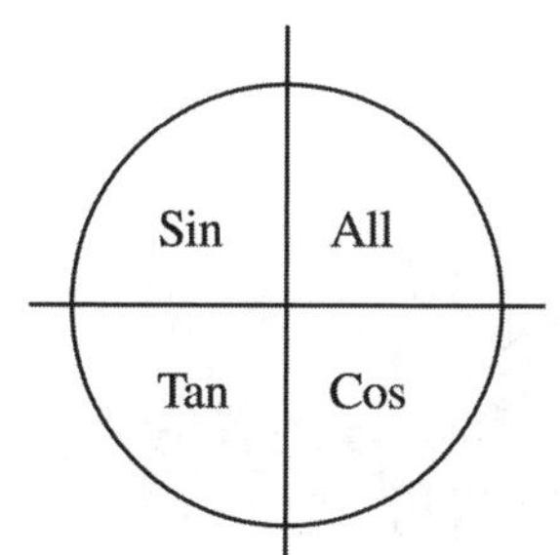

which is written in short as

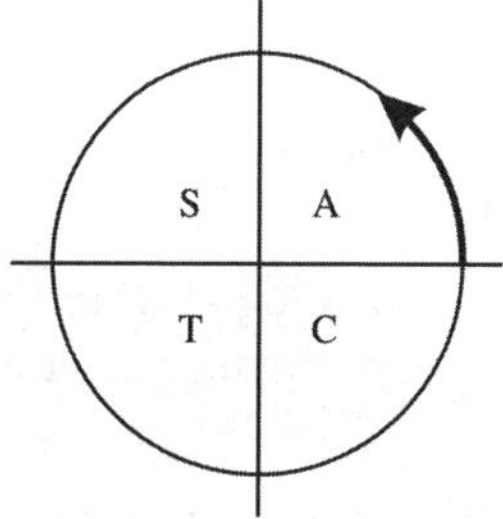

To remember **A–S–T–C**
remember
Alfie **S**tole **T**wo **C**hickens

For example,

cos 30° = + 0.8660
sin 30° = + 0.5
tan 30° = + 0.5774

cos 150° = – 0.8660
sin 150° = + 0.5
tan 150° = – 0.5774

cos 210° = – 0.8660
sin 210° = – 0.5
tan 210° = + 0.5774

cos 330° = + 0.8660
sin 330° = – 0.5
tan 330° = – 0.5774

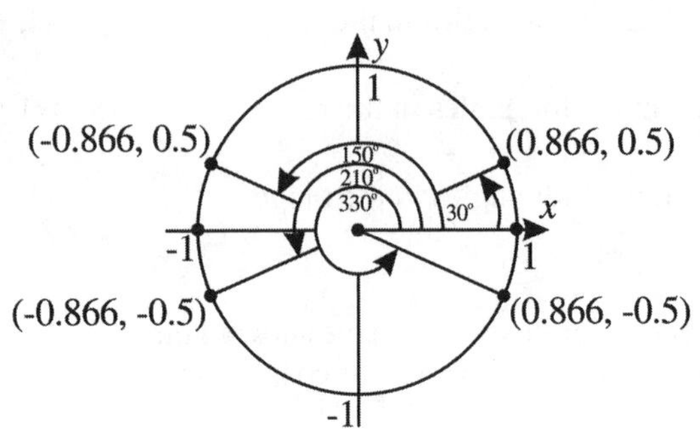

Note that the values of these functions are all the same (except for their signs). This is because all of the above angles are 30° from the x-axis. 30° is called the ***reference angle*** for these angles.

So, when we want to find the cos, sin or tan of a non-acute angle, we follow these four steps:

Step 1: Draw a rough sketch of the angle.

Step 2: Use A-S-T-C to find the ***sign*** (positive or negative).

A

x - axis

Reference angle

Step 3: Look up the tables to find the cos, sin or tan of the ***reference angle*** (i.e. the angle to the nearest x-axis).

Step 4: Put these together to form your answer.

Example 1: Write these in surd form: (i) cos 135° (ii) tan 330° (iii) sin 120°

Solution:

(i) ***Step 1:***
Draw 135°

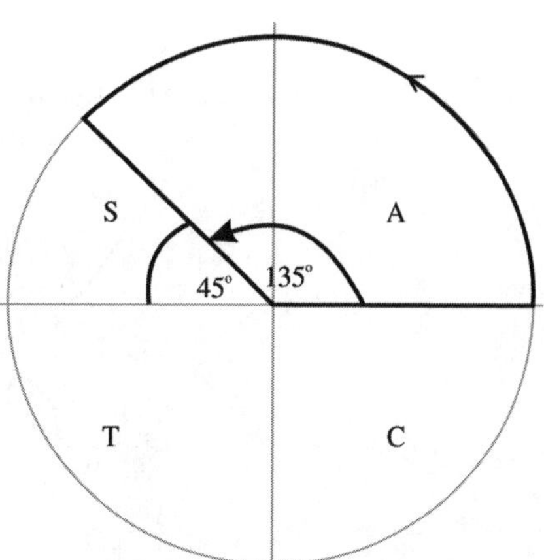

Step 2:
In the second quadrant, cosine is negative.

Step 3:
The reference angle is 45°.

cosine 45° = $\frac{1}{\sqrt{2}}$

Step 4:

$\therefore$ cos 135° = $-\frac{1}{\sqrt{2}}$

(ii) ***Step 1:***
Draw 330°

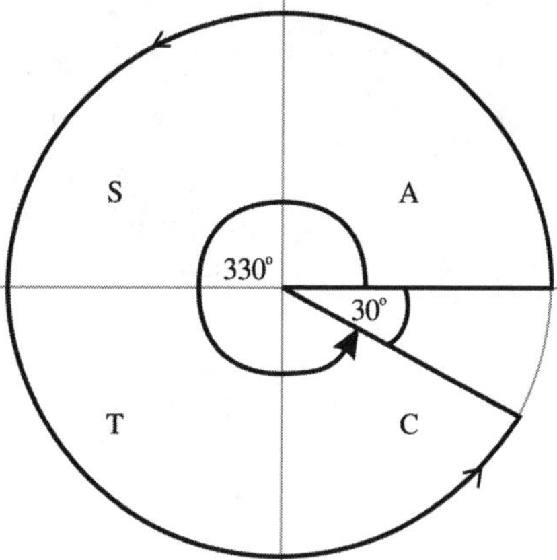

Step 2:
In the fourth quadrant, tan is negative.

Step 3:
The reference angle is 30°.

tan 30° = $\frac{1}{\sqrt{3}}$

Step 4:

$\therefore$ tan 330° = $-\frac{1}{\sqrt{3}}$

(iii) ***Step 1:***
Draw 120°

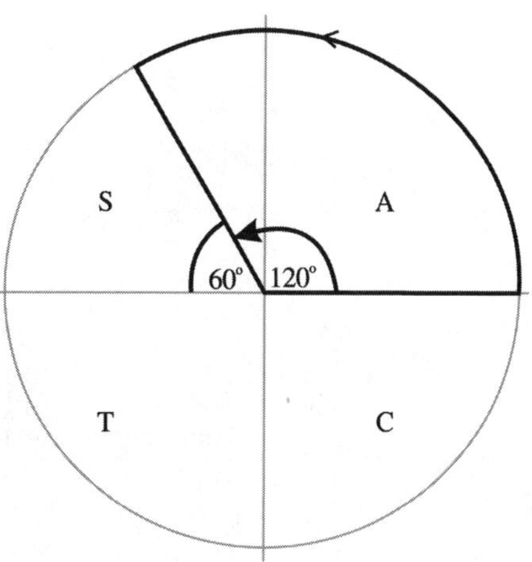

Step 2:
In the second quadrant, sine is positive.

Step 3:
The reference angle is 60°.

sine 60° = $\frac{\sqrt{3}}{2}$

Step 4:

$\therefore$ sin 120° = $\frac{\sqrt{3}}{2}$

Example 2:

(i) Find two values of A such that $\tan A = -\sqrt{3}$, $0^\circ < A < 360^\circ$.

(ii) Find two values of θ such that $2\cos\theta - 1 = 0$, $0^\circ < \theta < 360^\circ$.

Solution:

(i) There are two quadrants where tan is negative: the second and the fourth.

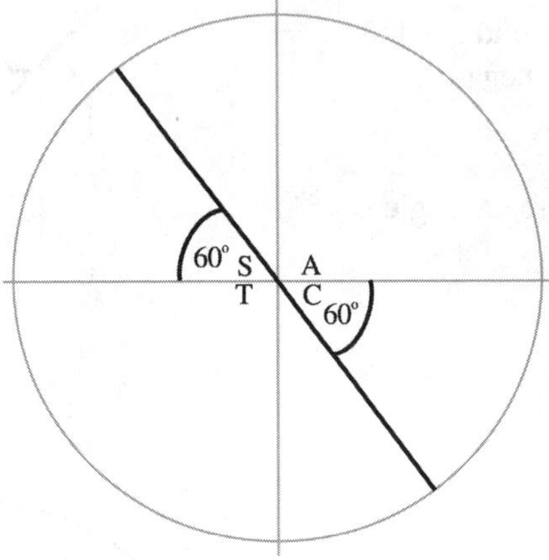

Tan $60^\circ = \sqrt{3}$, so the reference angle must be 60°.
Therefore, the two values of A are $180^\circ - 60^\circ = 120^\circ$ and $360^\circ - 60^\circ = 300^\circ$.
Answer: 120° and 300°.

(ii) $2\cos\theta - 1 = 0$
$\Rightarrow 2\cos\theta = 1$
$\Rightarrow \cos\theta = \frac{1}{2}$

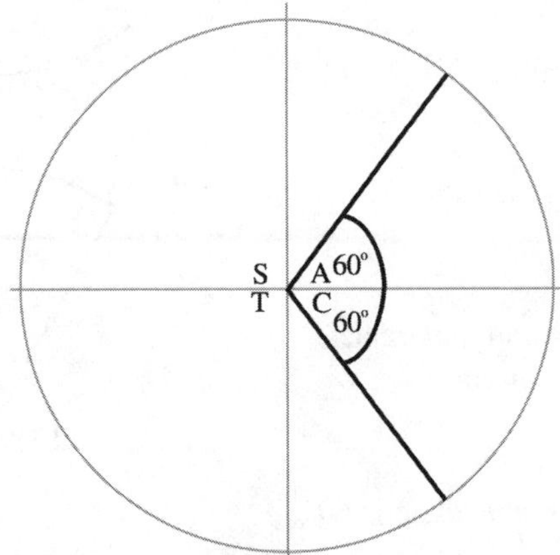

There are two quadrants where cosine is positive: the first and the fourth.
Cos $60^\circ = \frac{1}{2}$, so the reference angle must be 60°.
Therefore, the two values of θ are 60° and $360^\circ - 60^\circ = 300^\circ$.
Answer: 60° and 300°.

Exercise 15.G

1. Use the table on page 9 of the Maths Tables to find these:

(i) sin 135°
(ii) tan 315°
(iii) cos 330°
(iv) sin 210°
(v) tan 300°
(vi) sin 330°
(vii) cos 150°
(viii) tan 225°
(ix) sin 315°
(x) cos 300°

2. Find two possible values of x in each case, where $0° < x < 360°$:

(i) $\tan x = 1$
(ii) $\sin x = -\frac{1}{2}$
(iii) $\cos x = -\frac{\sqrt{3}}{2}$
(iv) $\tan x = -\sqrt{3}$
(v) $\sin x = \frac{1}{\sqrt{2}}$
(vi) $\cos x = \frac{1}{\sqrt{2}}$
(vii) $\tan x = -1$
(viii) $\sin x = \frac{\sqrt{3}}{2}$
(ix) $\cos x + \frac{1}{2} = 0$
(x) $\tan x = \sqrt{3}$

3. Find two values of A (to the nearest degree) in each case, where $0° < A < 360°$:

(i) $\sin A = 0.342$
(ii) $\cos A = 0.82$
(iii) $\tan A = 0.84$
(iv) $\cos A = -0.9848$
(v) $\sin A = -0.3746$
(vi) $\tan A = -1.6$

4. Find all values of A (to the nearest degree) in each case, where $0° \leq A \leq 360°$:

(i) $5 \sin A = 2$
(ii) $4 \cos A = 3$
(iii) $\tan A + 2 = 0$
(iv) $10 \cos A + 7 = 0$
(v) $3 \sin A + 2 = 0$
(vi) $2 \tan A - 7 = 0$
(vii) $\sin A = 0$
(viii) $\cos A = 0$
(ix) $\cos A + 1 = 0$
(x) $\tan A = 0$

5. (a) Find the only value of x, to the nearest degree, where $0° < x < 360°$, such that $\cos x = -0.8$ and $\sin x = -0.6$

(b) Find the only value of θ, to the nearest degree, where $0° < \theta < 360°$, such that $\cos \theta = {}^{12}/_{13}$ and $\sin \theta = -{}^{5}/_{13}$. Find, also, the value of tan θ as a fraction.

(c) Find the only value of ϕ, where $0° < \phi < 360°$, such that $\sin \phi = 1$ and $\cos \phi = 0$.

6. Find the only value of θ, to the nearest degree, where $0° < \theta < 360°$, such that $\sin \theta = {}^{24}/_{25}$ and $\tan \theta = -{}^{24}/_{7}$. Find, also, the value of cos θ as a fraction.

NON-RIGHT-ANGLED TRIANGLES

Page 9 of the Mathematical Tables contains two formulae for solving non-right-angled triangles.
Here they are:

Sine formula: $\dfrac{a}{\text{Sin } A} = \dfrac{b}{\text{Sin } B} = \dfrac{c}{\text{Sin } C}$

Cosine formula: $a^2 = b^2 + c^2 - 2bc \text{ Cos } A$

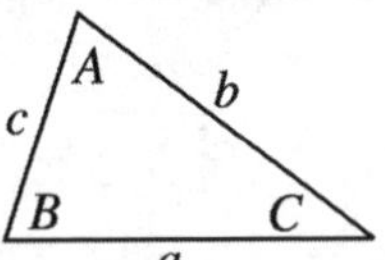

1. The angle A is always opposite side a. B is opposite b etc.
2. If you know an angle and the opposite side, use Sine formula. Otherwise, use Cosine formula.
3. Remember that the sum of the angles in any triangle is 180º.

To find x, you would use Sine formula because you DO KNOW an angle and the side opposite.

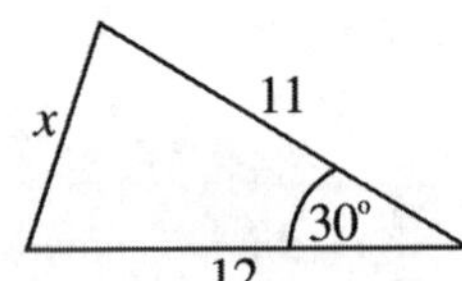

To find x, use Cosine formula because you DON'T KNOW an angle and the side opposite.

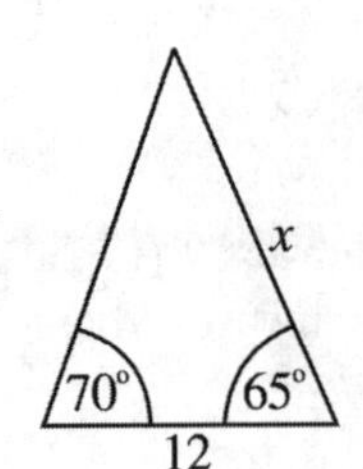

The third angle is 180º – 70º – 65º = 45º, so now you DO KNOW an angle and the side opposite. Use Sine formula.

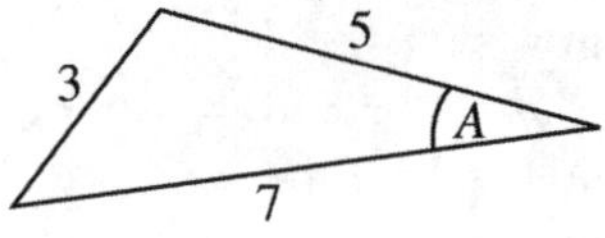

You DON'T KNOW any angle at all! So you certainly DON'T KNOW an angle and the opposite side. Use the Cosine formula to find A.

4. The Sine formula really means
$$\frac{\text{any side}}{\text{Sin of opposite angle}} = \frac{\text{any other side}}{\text{Sin of opposite angle}}$$

5. When you use the Cosine formula, the angle MUST be labelled A, and so the opposite side MUST be a. The other sides are b and c; it doesn't matter which is which.

Example 1:

(i) Find $|qs|$ correct to one decimal place.

(ii) Hence find $|qr|$ correct to one decimal place.

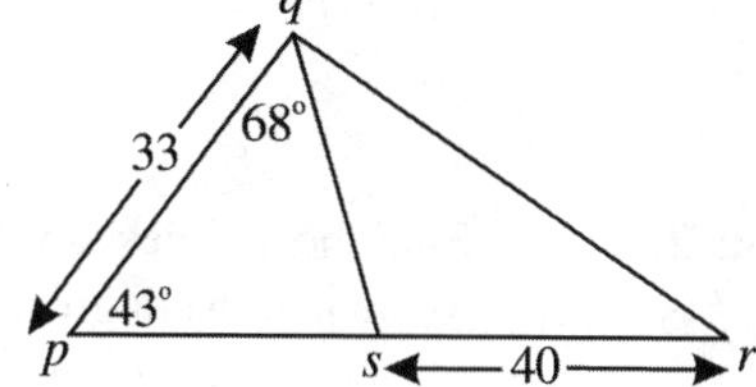

Solution:

(i) Firstly, $|\angle psq| = 180° - 43° - 68° = 69°$.

$\therefore \; |\angle qsr| = 180° - 69° = 111°$.

Take Δpqs. We DO KNOW an angle and the opposite side (69° opposite 33), so we use Sine formula.

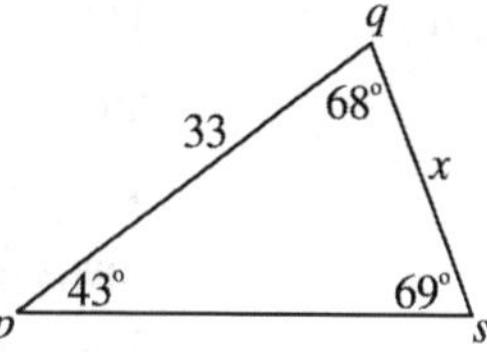

$$\frac{\text{side}}{\text{Sin of opposite angle}} = \frac{\text{other side}}{\text{Sin of opposite angle}}$$

$$\Rightarrow \frac{x}{\text{Sin } 43°} = \frac{33}{\text{Sin } 69°}$$

$$\Rightarrow \frac{x}{0.6820} = \frac{33}{0.9336}$$

$$\Rightarrow 0.9336x = 22.506$$

$$\Rightarrow \quad x = \frac{22.506}{0.9336} = 24.1$$

(ii) Now look at Δqsr.

In this case, you DO NOT KNOW an angle and the opposite side.

Use Cosine formula.

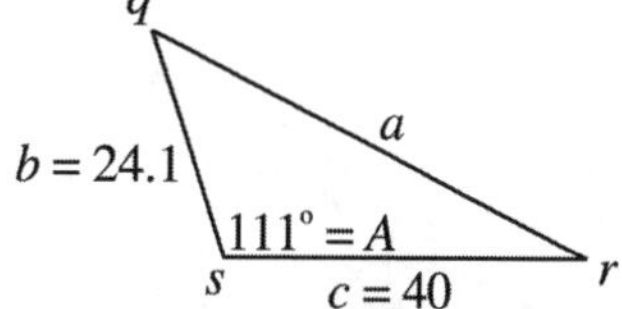

$a^2 = b^2 + c^2 - 2bc \text{ Cos } A$

The angle (111°) MUST be labelled A. The side opposite 111° MUST be a. The other two are b and c (it doesn't matter which).

Let $b = 24.1$, $c = 40$.

(continued over→)

$$\Rightarrow a^2 = b^2 + c^2 - 2bc \text{ Cos } A$$

$$\Rightarrow a^2 = (24.1)^2 + (40)^2 - 2(24.1)(40)(\text{Cos } 111°)$$

$$\Rightarrow a^2 = 580.81 + 1600 - 2(24.1)(40)(-0.3583679)$$

$$\Rightarrow a^2 = 580.81 + 1600 + 690.93341$$

$$\Rightarrow a^2 = 2871.7434$$

$$\Rightarrow a = \sqrt{2871.7434}$$

$\Rightarrow a = 53.6$ correct to one decimal place.

Answer: $|qs| = 24.1$; $|qr| = 53.6$

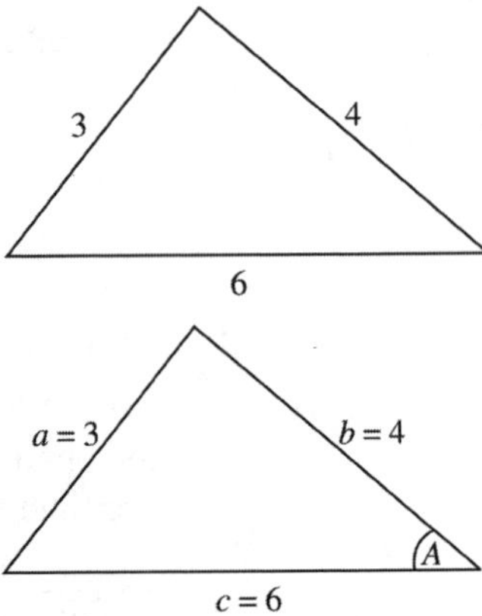

Example 2: Find the smallest angle in this triangle to the nearest degree.

Solution: The smallest angle will be opposite 3, the smallest side. Call this angle A.
The side opposite A must be a.
Therefore $a = 3$.
The other sides are b and c.
Let $b = 4$ and $c = 6$.
We will use the Cosine Formula since we ***do not*** know an angle and the opposite side.

$$a^2 = b^2 + c^2 - 2bc \cos A$$

$$\therefore 3^2 = 4^2 + 6^2 - 2(4)(6) \cos A$$

$$\therefore 9 = 16 + 36 - 48 \cos A$$

$$\therefore 9 = 52 - 48 \cos A$$

$$\therefore 48 \cos A = 52 - 9$$

$$\therefore 48 \cos A = 43$$

$$\therefore \cos A = \frac{43}{48} = 0.8958333$$

$\therefore A = 26°$ to the nearest degree.

Exercise 15.H

1. Use the ***Sine Formula*** to find x to the nearest natural number:

(i)

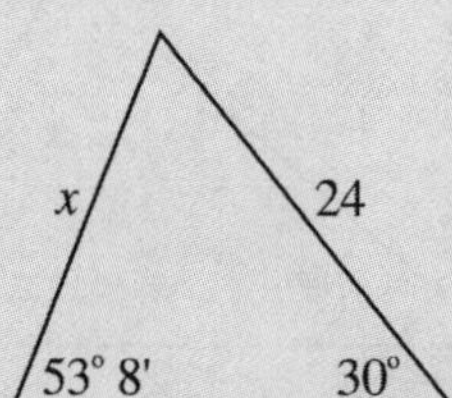

(ii)

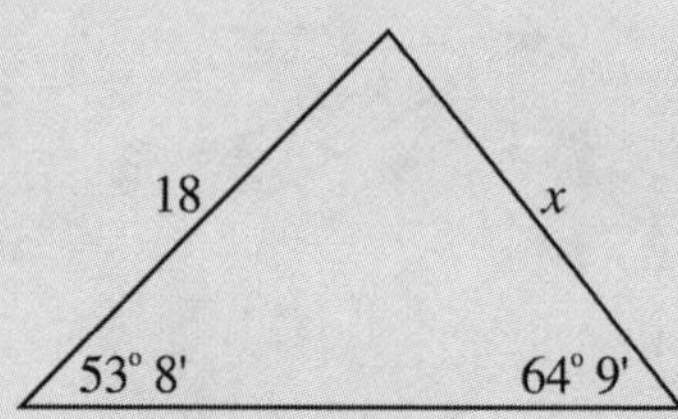

(iii)

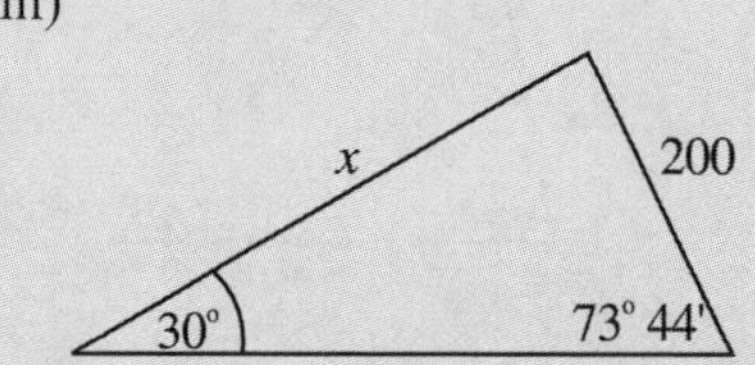

(iv)

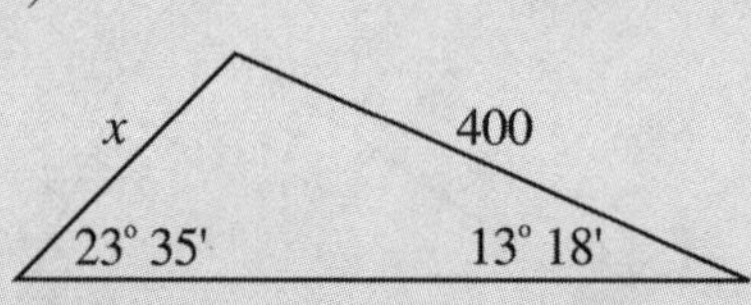

(v)

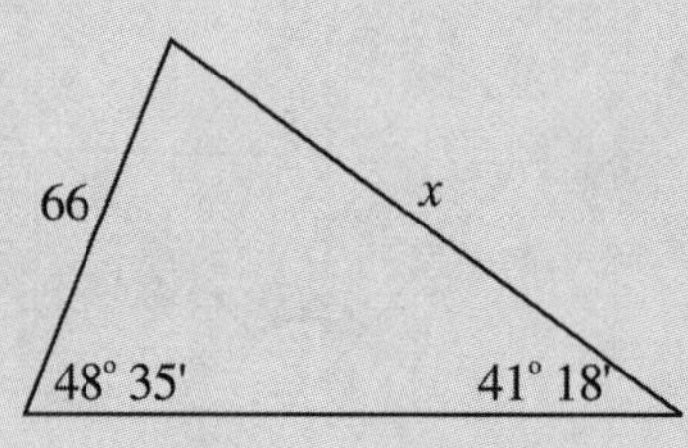

2. Use the ***Sine Formula*** to find A to the nearest degree:

(i)

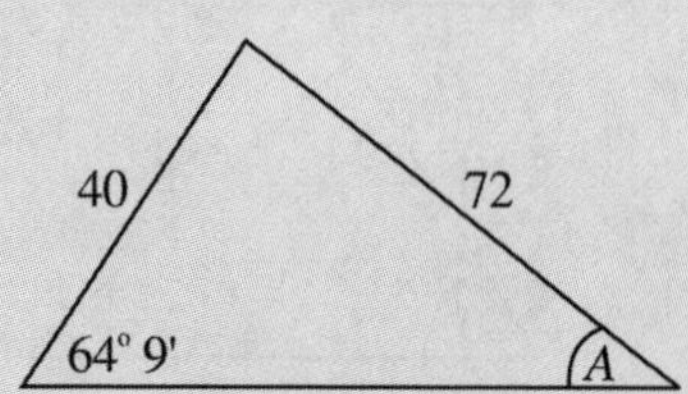

(ii)

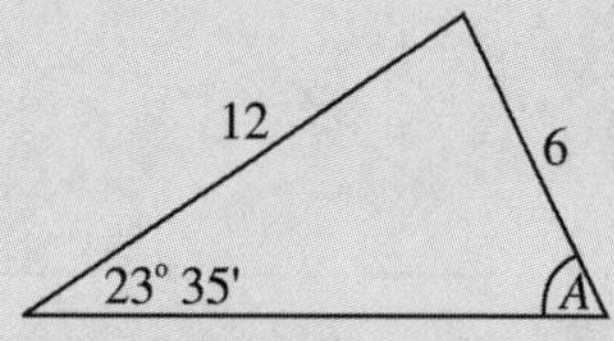

(iii)

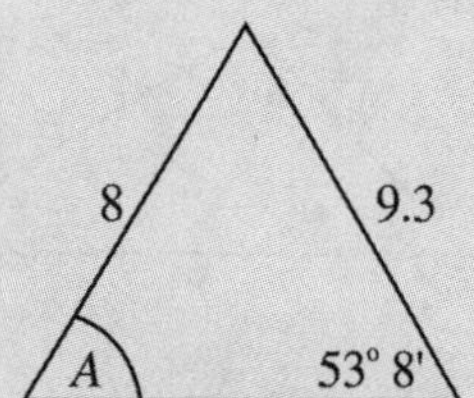

(iv)

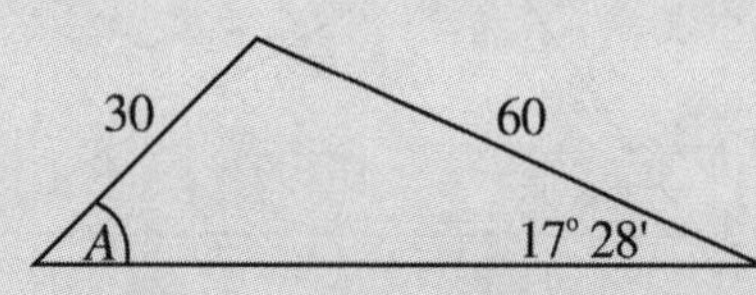

(v)

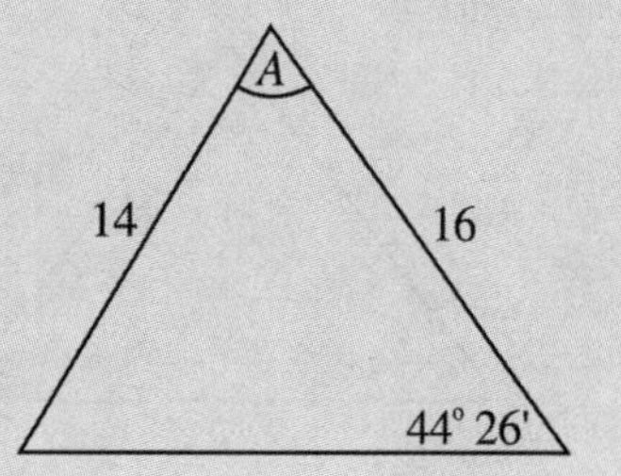

3. Use the ***Cosine Formula*** to find a in the form $\sqrt{n}$, where $n \in N$. Use cosine values to ***one decimal place***

(i)

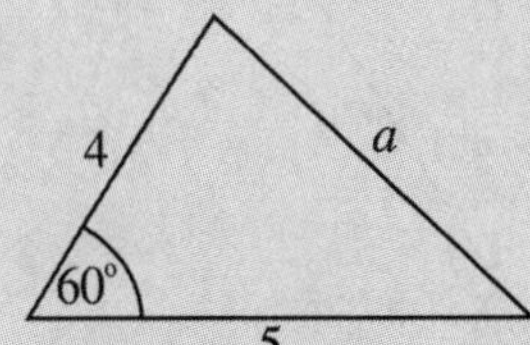

(ii)

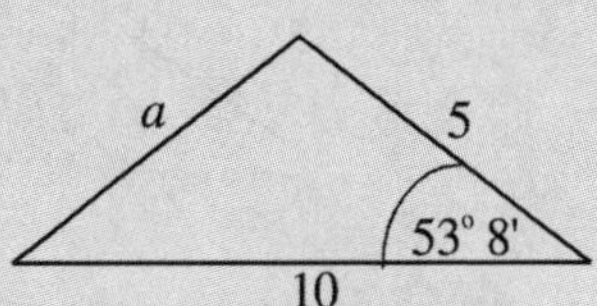

(iii)

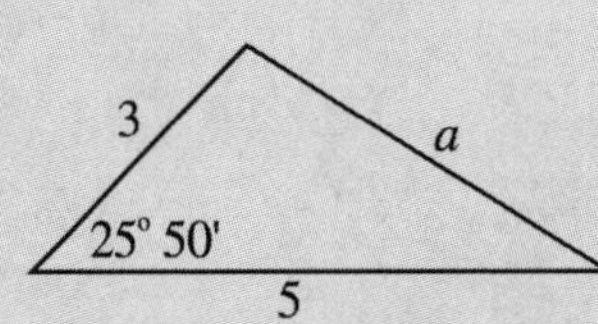

(iv)

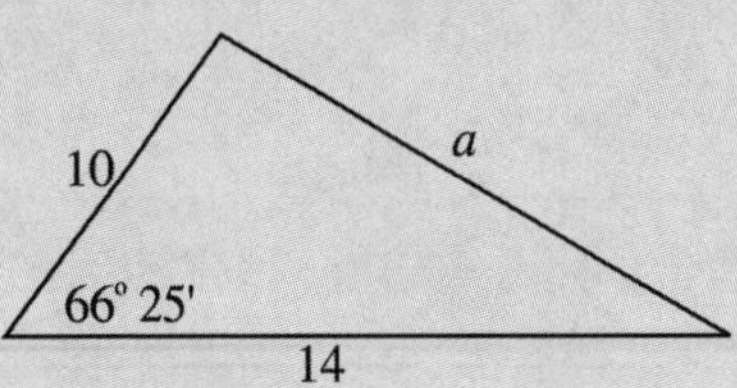

(v)

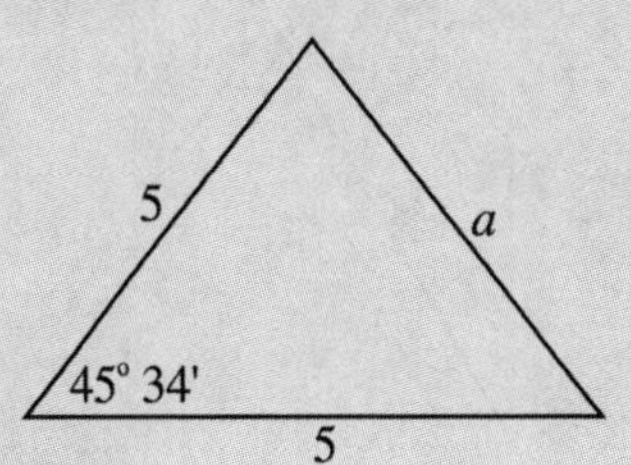

4. Use the ***Cosine Formula*** to find A to the nearest degree:

(i)

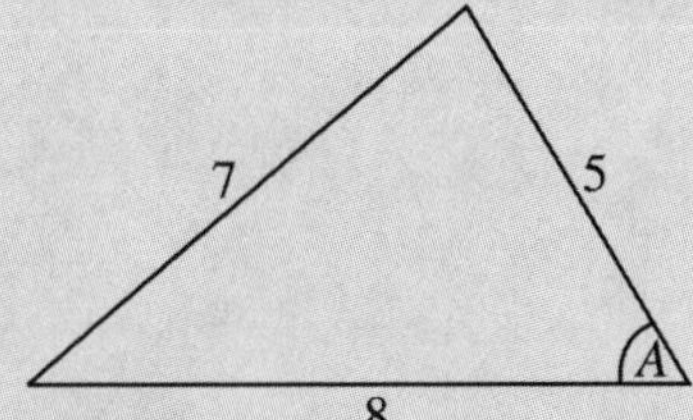

(ii)

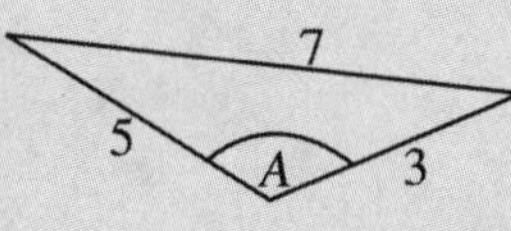

(iii)

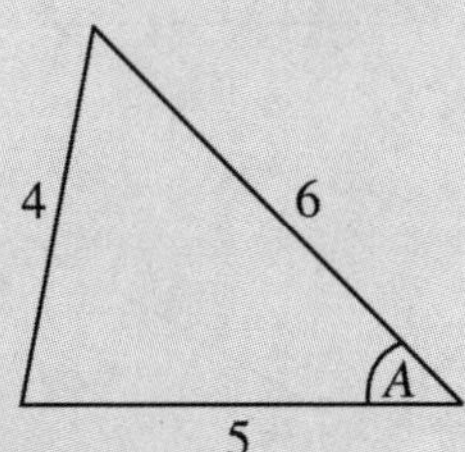

(iv)

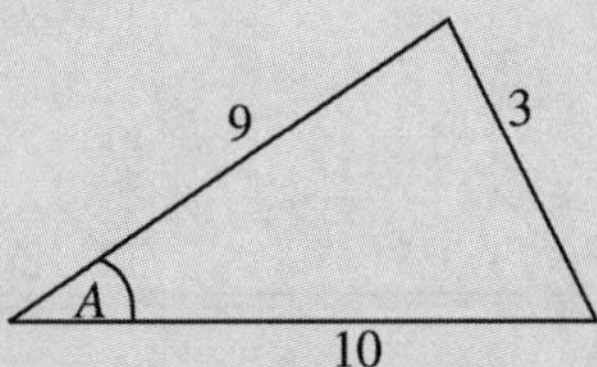

(v)

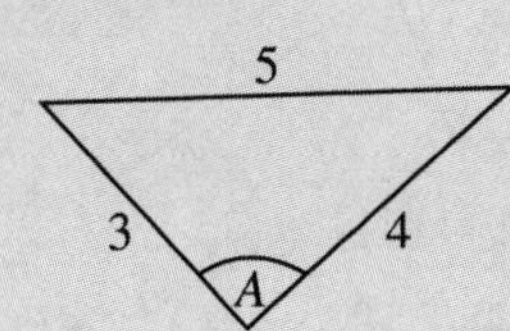

5. Find, correct to one decimal place,
(i) $|bd|$,
(ii) $|cd|$.

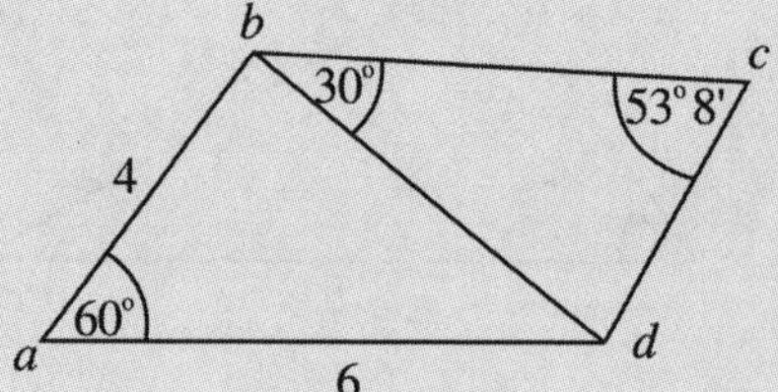

6. Find, to the nearest integer, $|ac|$ and $|ad|$.

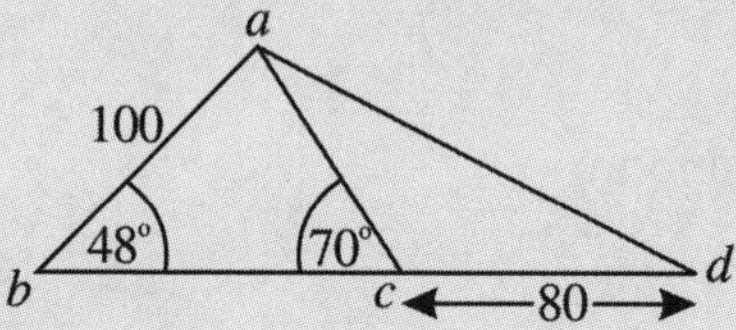

7. The sides of a triangle have lengths 9 cm, 5 cm and 7 cm. Find the measure of the smallest angle to the nearest degree.

8. If $|\angle sqr| = 110°$, find
(i) $|pq|$,
(ii) $|pr|$ (to two decimal places).

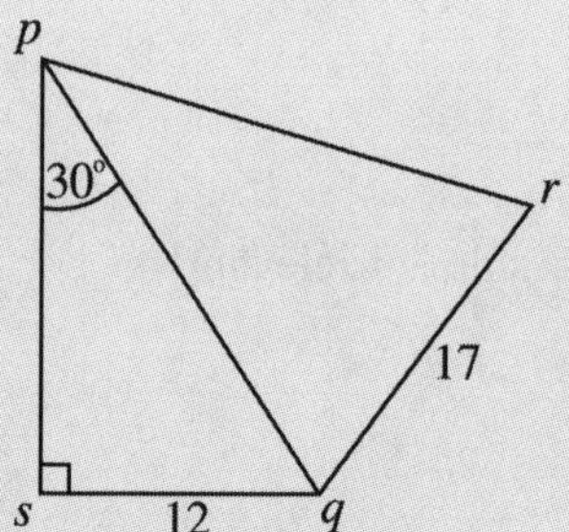

9. $pqrs$ is a quadrilateral (see diagram).
(i) Find $|pr|$ to the nearest integer,
(ii) Hence find $|\angle psr|$ to the nearest degree.

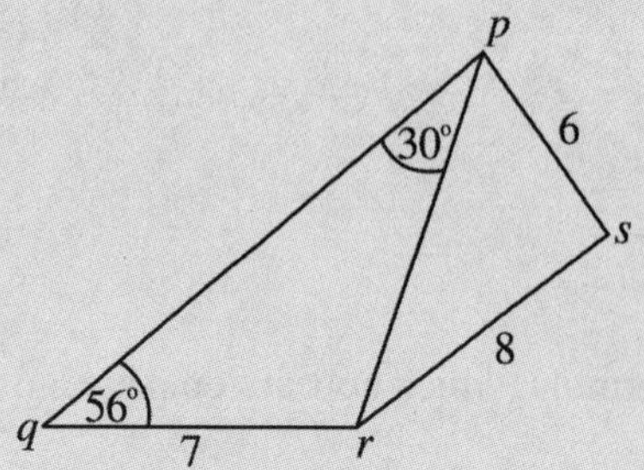

10. Find, correct to three significant figures, the values of a, B and C.

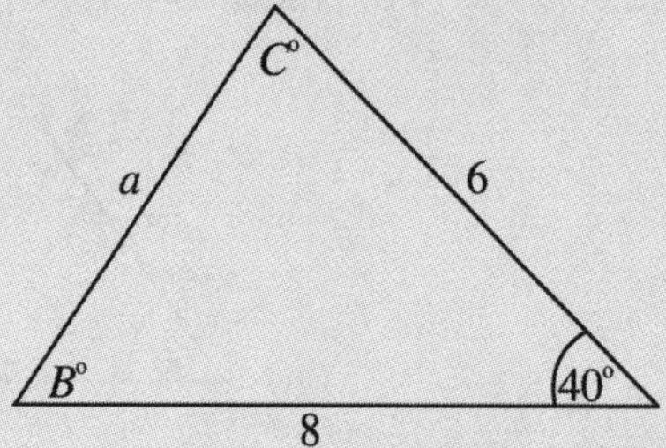

11. Find $|pq|$ to the nearest metre.

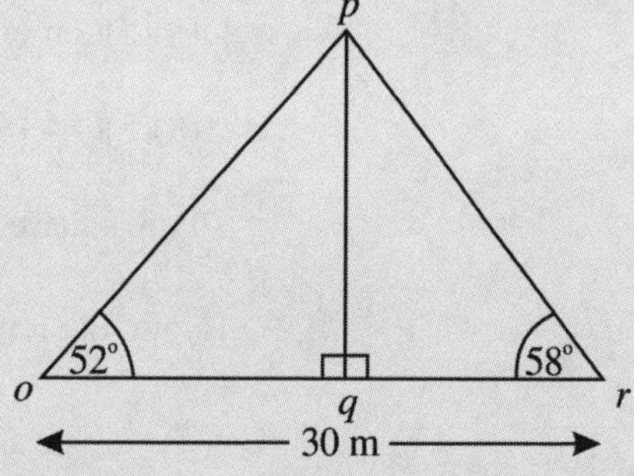

12. Two ships, H and K leave Cobh harbour at the same time.
H sails at 20 km/h in a direction W 43° S.
K sails at 32 km/h in a direction E 65° S. How far apart (to the nearest kilometre) will they be in 2½ hours?

AREA OF A TRIANGLE

There is a trigonometric formula for the area of a triangle. It is:

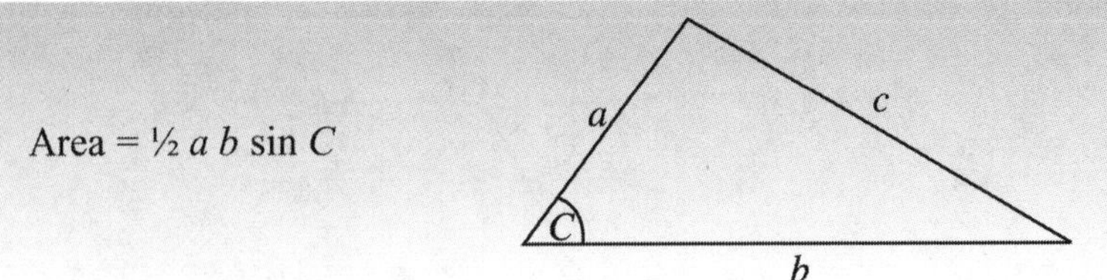

This formula, which appears on page 6 of the Mathematical Tables, means

Area = ½(one side)(another side)(sine of the angle between them)

Example 1: Find the area of this triangle in surd form:

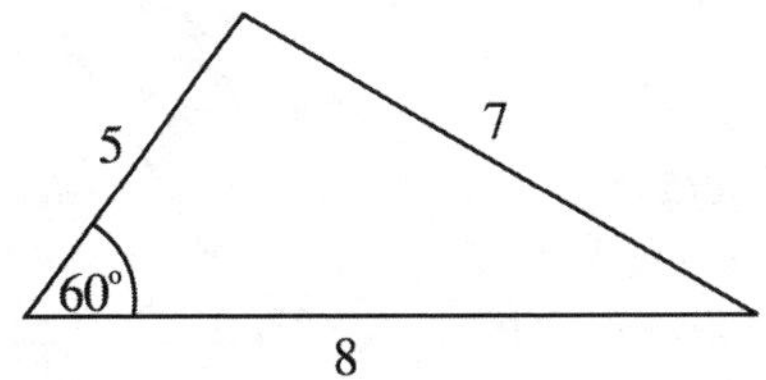

Solution: Area = ½(one side)(another side)(sine of the angle between them)

$= \frac{1}{2}(8)(5)(\sin 60^\circ)$

$= \frac{1}{2}(8)(5)\left(\frac{\sqrt{3}}{2}\right)$

$= 10\sqrt{3}$ square units.

[Note: the length of the third side is irrelevant]

Exercise 15.I

1. Find the areas of these triangles, to the nearest square unit:

 (i)

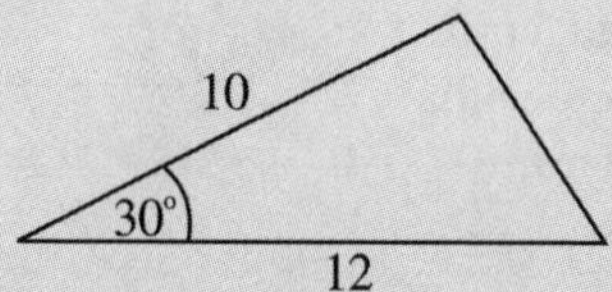

 (ii)

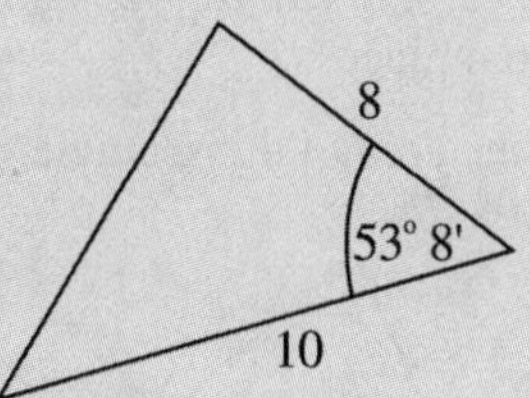

 (iii)

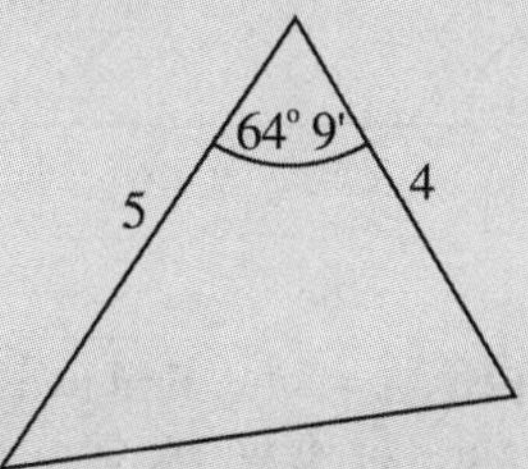

 (iv)

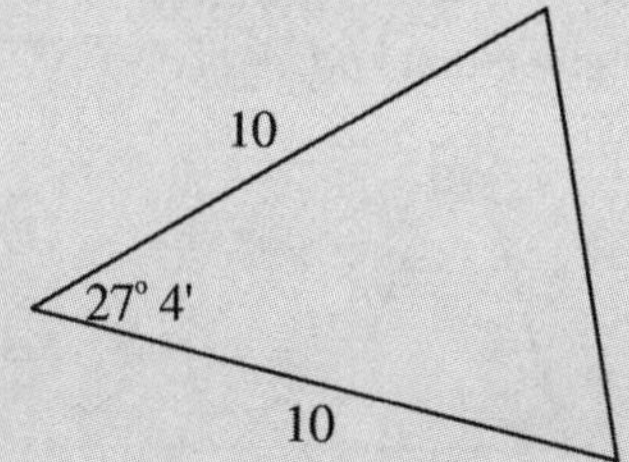

2. If $\cos A = 0.6$, find
 (i) Sine A,
 (ii) area of Δpqr.

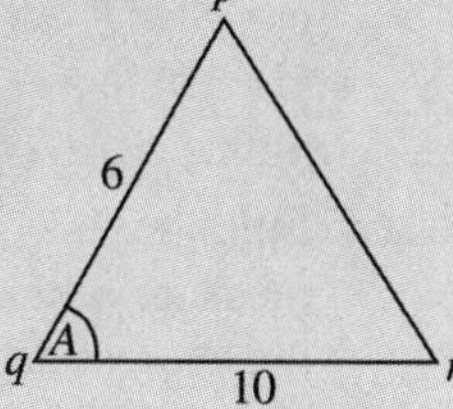

3. (a) If the area of this triangle is 25 cm², find the measure of the acute angle A, to the nearest degree.

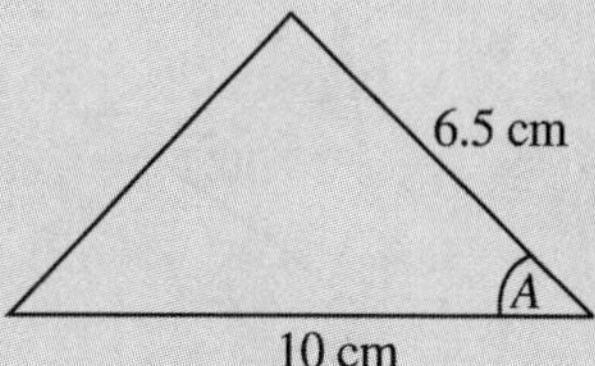

 (b) If the area of Δpqr is 40 cm², find $|pq|$ to the nearest millimetre.

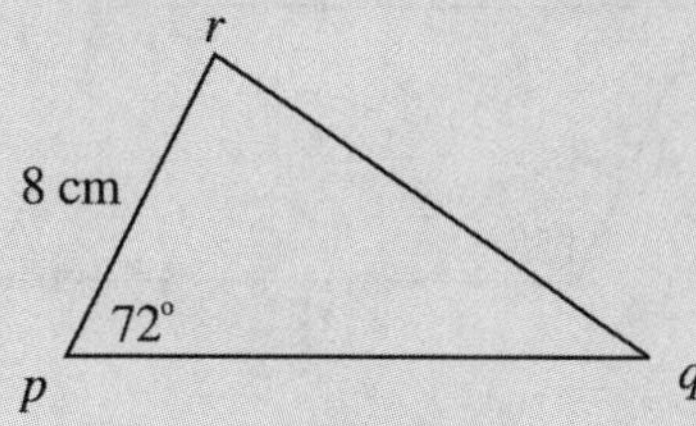

 (c) If the area of this triangle is 14 square units, find the angle C:

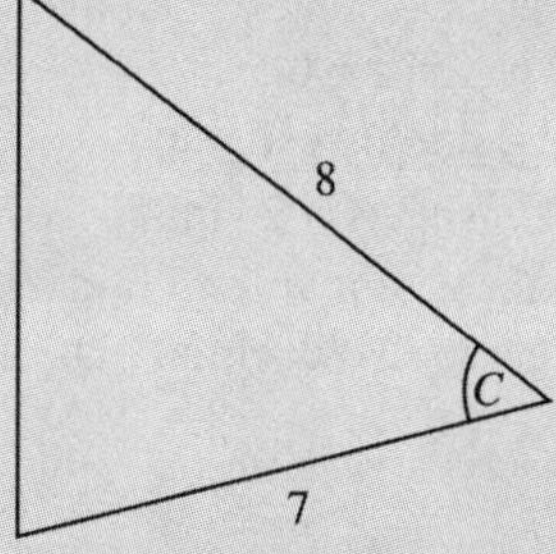

4. (i) Find A to the nearest degree.
 (ii) Find the area of Δxyz.

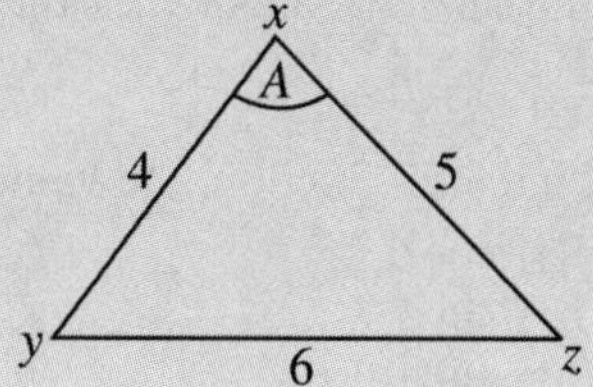

5. The area of this triangular field is 4.2 hectares. Find x to the nearest metre.

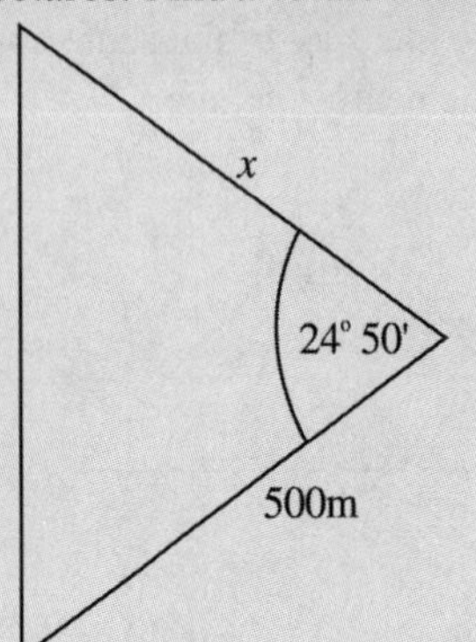

6. Find the area of this parallelogram:

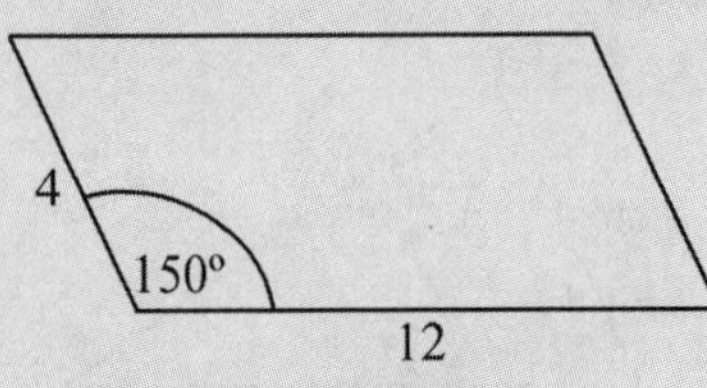

7. xyz is a triangle such that $|xy| = |xz| = 5$ cm and $|\angle xyz| = 40°$
Find, correct to two decimal places,

(i) $|yz|$,

(ii) area Δxyz.

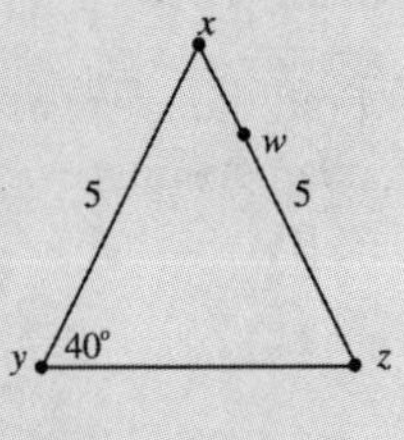

If w is a point on $[xz]$, such that area $\Delta wyz = 8$ cm², find $|wz|$ correct to two decimal places.

8. Find the area of this triangle, given that $\tan A = {}^{24}/_{7}$.

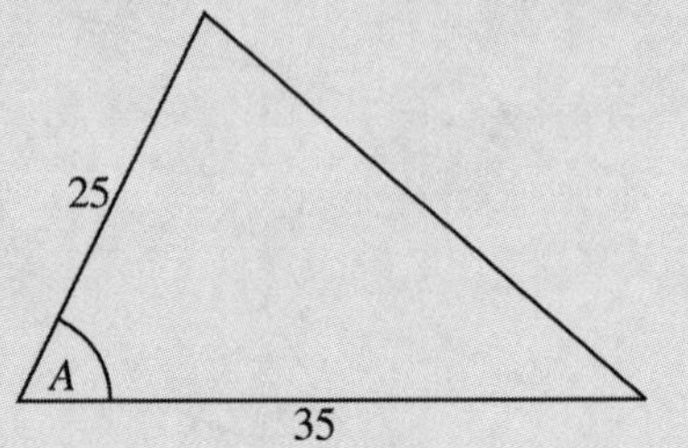

REVISION EXERCISE 15.J

1. (a) A is an acute angle such that

$$\sin A = 0.5$$

Find A and investigate if

$$\sin 2A = 2 \sin A$$

(b) Use the cosine rule to find $|xz|$ correct to two decimal places.

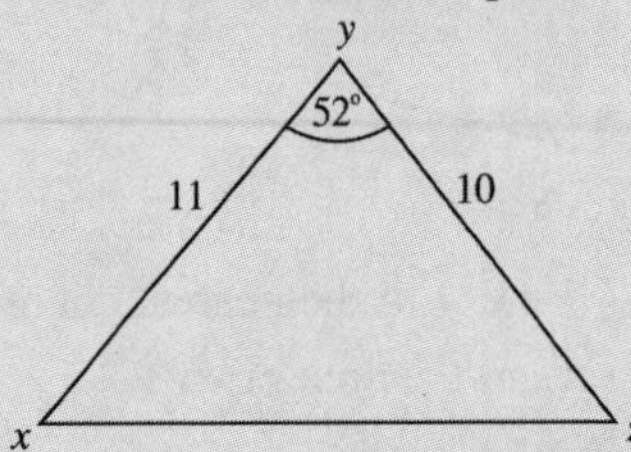

(c) θ is an acute angle such that

$$\tan \theta = \frac{12}{5}$$

Find, as a fraction, the value of

(i) $\cos \theta$,

(ii) $\sin \theta$,

(iii) $\sin 2\theta$.

[HINT: $\sin 2\theta = \sin(\theta + \theta)$]

2. (a) If $\cos A = -\frac{1}{2}$, find two possible values of A, where $0° \leq A \leq 360°$.

(b) Find, correct to one decimal place,

(i) $|bc|$, (ii) $|ad|$,

given that $|bd| = |cd|$.

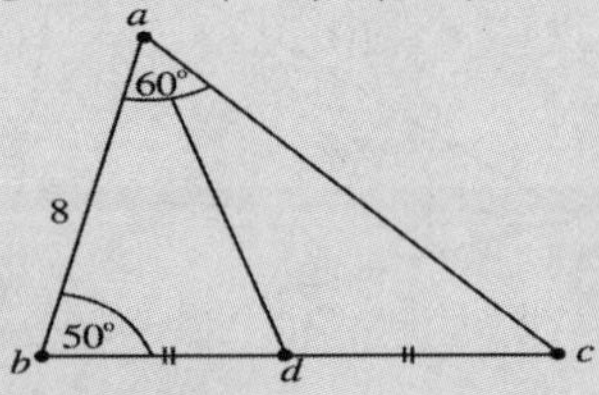

(c) The sides of a triangle are 7 cm, 8 cm and 9 cm in length.

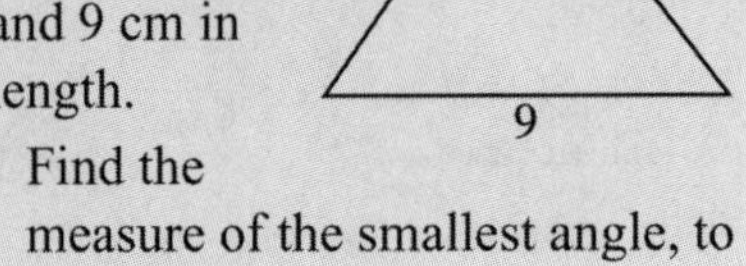

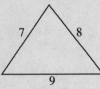

(i) Find the measure of the smallest angle, to the nearest degree,

(ii) Hence find the area of the triangle, correct to one decimal place.

3. (a) If B is an acute angle such that $\tan B = {}^{20}/_{99}$, find the value of $(\sin B + \cos B)$ as a fraction.
   (b) The sides of a triangle have lengths 2, 3, 4. Find the measure of the greatest angle to the nearest ½-degree.
   (c) abc is a triangle, as shown. Find (to the nearest integer)
      (i) $|bd|$,
      (ii) area Δabc.

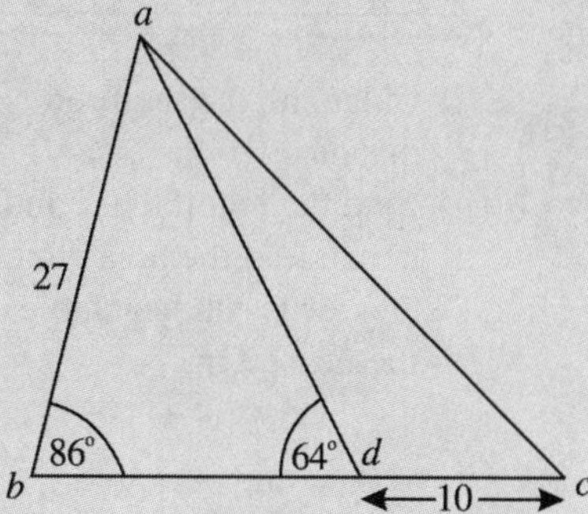

4. (a) If $\tan \theta = 0.6494$, find (to the nearest degree) two possible values of θ, where $0° < \theta < 360°$.
   (b) A and B are acute angles such that $\sin A = {}^{5}/_{13}$ and $\cos B = {}^{3}/_{5}$, find $\sin(A + B)$, giving your answer as a single fraction.
   (c) Find
      (i) $|xz|$ to the nearest unit,
      (ii) $|\angle yzx|$ to the nearest degree.

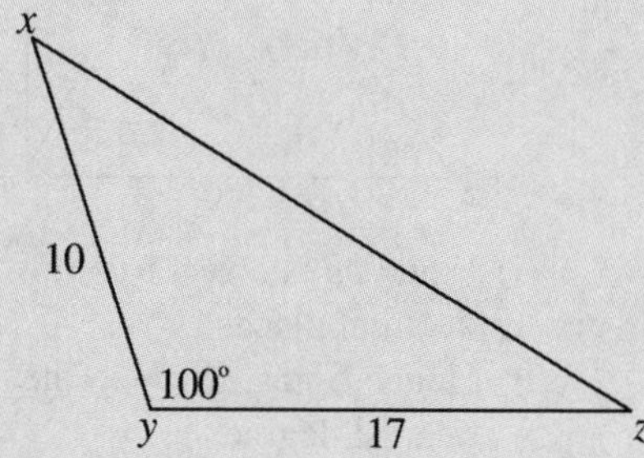

5. (a) Find x to the nearest unit and A to the nearest degree:

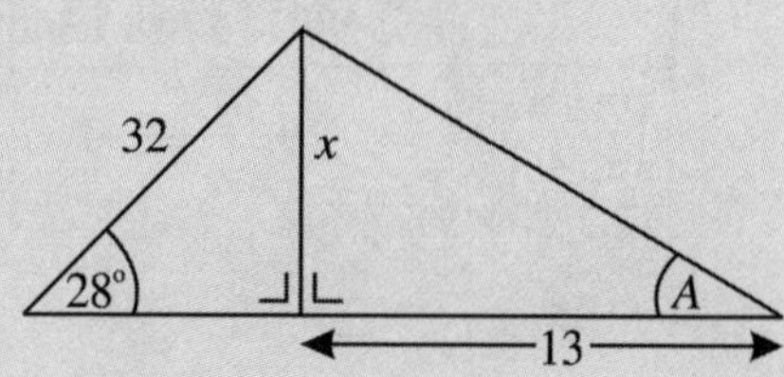

   (b) If A is an acute angle such that $37 \cos A - 35 = 0$, find
      (i) $\sin A$ as a fraction,
      (ii) A to the nearest degree.
   (c) If $\sin \theta = -0.1908$, find (to the nearest degree) two possible values of θ, where $0° < \theta < 360°$.

6. (a) Two of the angles in a triangle are 28° 35′ and 109° 44′. Find the third angle.
   (b) A is an acute angle such that $\sin A = {}^{15}/_{17}$.
   Write these as fractions:
      (i) $\cos A$,
      (ii) $\sin 2A$.
   [HINT: $\sin 2A = \sin(A + A)$]
   (c) Find A, B and b, to the nearest unit:

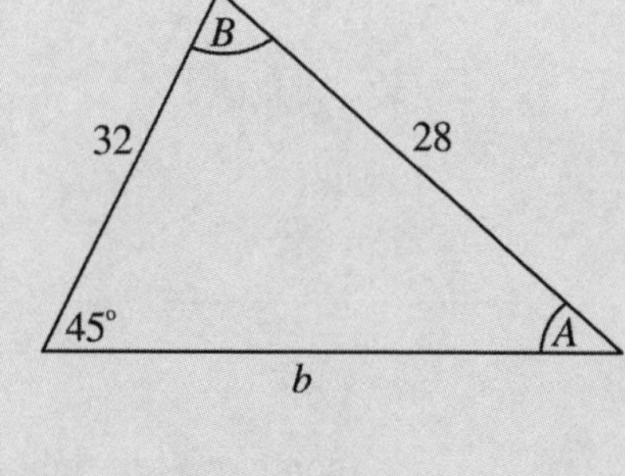

7. (a) Copy and complete this table, without using decimals:

A	60°	90°	270°	300°
$\cos A$				
$\sin A$				
$\tan A$				

(b) The diagram shows the course of a swimming race in the sea. The race begins and ends at p. Calculate the length of the race to the nearest metre.

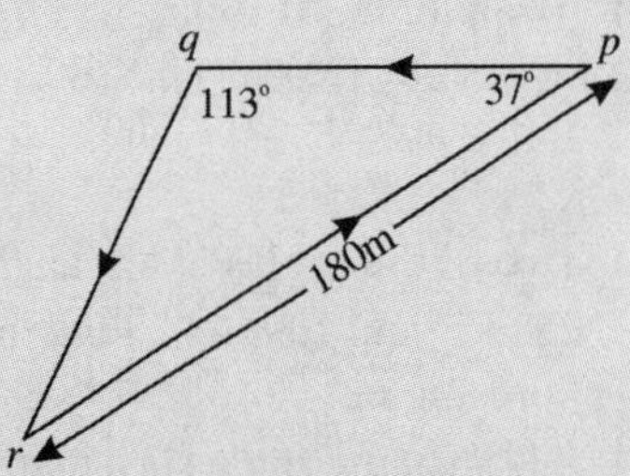

(c) If A is an acute angle such that $\cos A = {}^{45}/_{53}$, write $\sin A$ as a fraction.

8. (a) Find the missing angles A and B in this triangle:

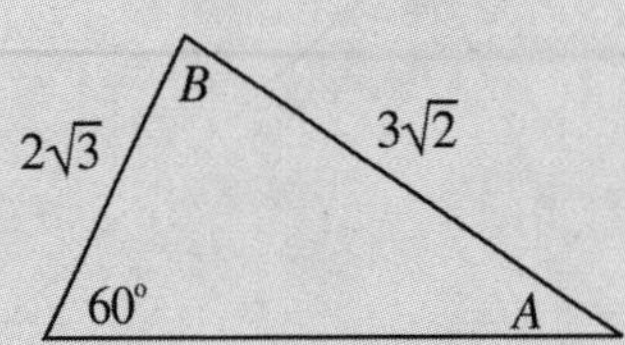

(continued top right →)

(b) A farmer owns a triangular field pqr. She wishes to sow 1140 m² of barley in triangular piece qrx, and vegetables in the rest.

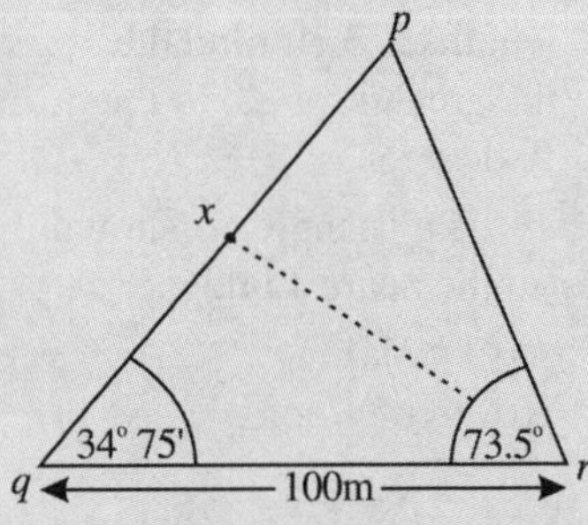

(i) Calculate the required distance $|qx|$.

(ii) Find the length $|pr|$ and hence find the area which will be sown with vegetables, to the nearest m².

9. (a) Given that $\tan C = 3.078$, where $0° < C < 90°$, find C and investigate if $\tan {}^{1}/_{3}\, C = {}^{1}/_{3} \tan C$.

(b) If $\sin B = -\frac{1}{2}$ and $\cos B = \frac{\sqrt{3}}{2}$, find

(i) the measure of B, where $0° \leq B \leq 360°$.

(ii) the value of $\tan B$ in surd form.

(c)

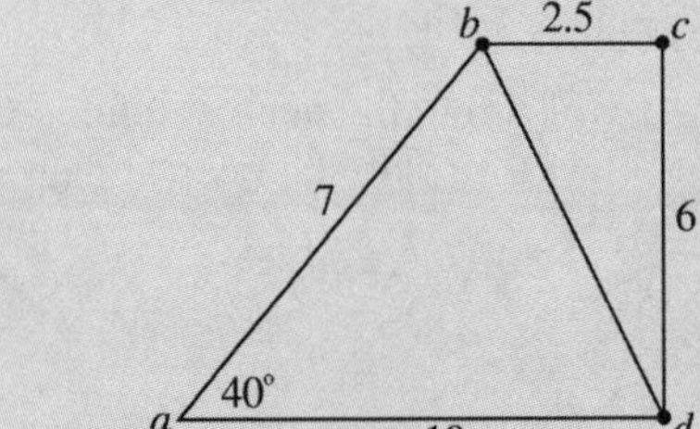

(i) Find $|bd|$ correct to one decimal place.

(ii) Hence find $|\angle bcd|$ to the nearest degree.

10. (a) The radius of this circle is 2.8 cm in length. The arc is of length 6.6 cm. Find the measure of the angle $\angle acb$ subtended by the arc, using $\pi = {}^{22}/_{7}$.

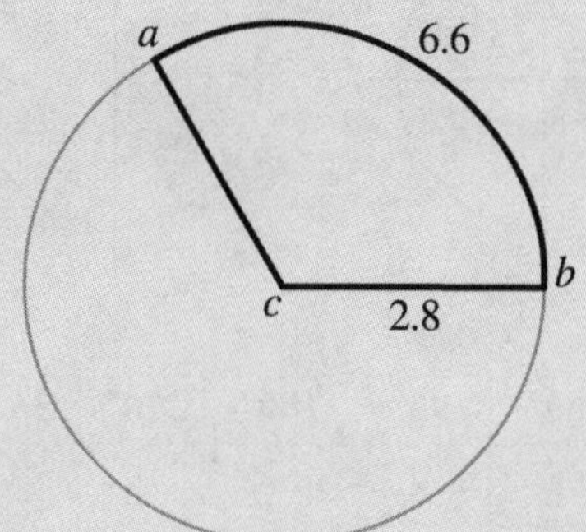

(b)

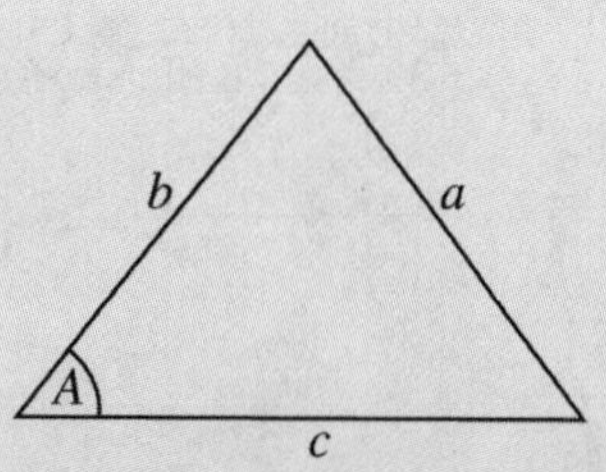

(i) Use the Cosine Formula to deduce that

$$\cos A = \frac{b^2 + c^2 - a^2}{2bc}$$

(ii) If $A = 60°$, prove that

$$a^2 = b^2 + c^2 - bc$$

(c) Write cos 105° in surd form, by writing it as cos(45° + 60°).

1. $\sin A = \dfrac{\text{Opposite}}{\text{Hypotenuse}}$ **S**illy **O**ld **H**arry

$\cos A = \dfrac{\text{Adjacent}}{\text{Hypotenuse}}$ **C**aught **A** **H**erring

$\tan A = \dfrac{\text{Opposite}}{\text{Adjacent}}$ **T**rawling **O**ff **A**merica

2. $\cos A = x$

$\sin A = y$

$\tan A = \dfrac{y}{x} = \dfrac{\text{Sin } A}{\text{Cos } A}$

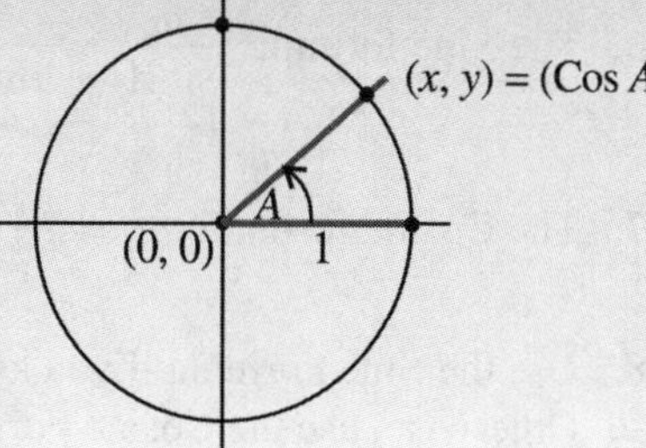

1. $(x, y) =$ (**C**hristian name, **C**osine A, **S**urname, **S**ine A)

(continued over→)

3. This table shows where the various functions have ***positive*** values:

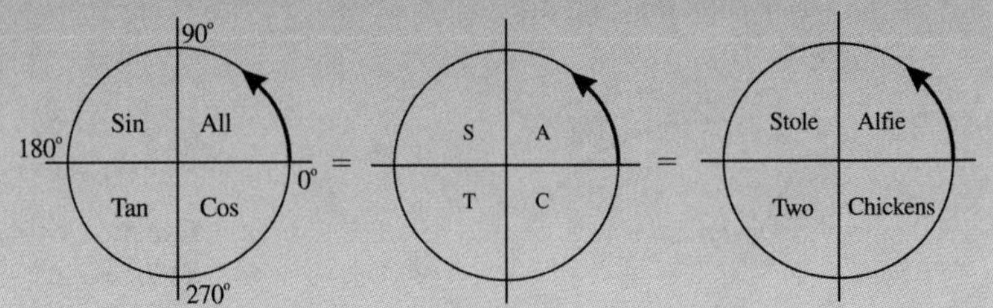

4.

A	0°	30°	45°	60°	90°	180°	270°	360°
cos A	1	$\frac{\sqrt{3}}{2}$	$\frac{1}{\sqrt{2}}$	$\frac{1}{2}$	0	−1	0	1
sin A	0	$\frac{1}{2}$	$\frac{1}{\sqrt{2}}$	$\frac{\sqrt{3}}{2}$	1	0	−1	0
tan A	0	$\frac{1}{\sqrt{3}}$	1	$\sqrt{3}$	—	0	—	0

5. Area $\Delta = \frac{1}{2}ab \sin C$

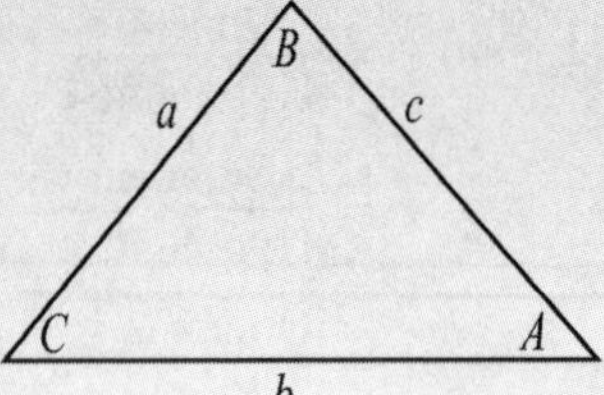

6. The Sine formula: $\dfrac{a}{\sin A} = \dfrac{b}{\sin B} = \dfrac{c}{\sin C}$

7. The Cosine formula: $a^2 = b^2 + c^2 - 2bc \cos A$

8. Use the Sine Formula if you know an angle and the opposite side. Otherwise, use the Cosine Formula.

Chapter 16

Sequences & Series

ARITHMETIC SEQUENCES

A ***sequence*** is a list of numbers. The first number in the list is called ***the first term*** and is denoted T_1 or by the letter ***a***. The second term of the sequence is denoted T_2. The third term is denoted T_3, etc.

Here are some sequences:

1, 3, 5, 7, 9, 11, 13, ...	in which $a = 1$.
10, 20, 30, 40, 50, 60, ...	in which $a = 10$.
44, 42, 40, 38, 36, 34, ...	in which $a = 44$.
3, 6, 12, 24, 48, 96, ...	in which $a = 3$.
$\frac{1}{2}, \frac{1}{3}, \frac{1}{4}, \frac{1}{5}, \frac{1}{6}, \frac{1}{7}, \ldots$	in which $a = ½$.

Of these five sequences, only the first three can be described as ***arithmetic***. In each of these three sequences, the difference between consecutive terms is always the same. This brings us to a formal definition of an ***arithmetic sequence***.

Definition:
An ***arithmetic sequence*** is a sequence of numbers in which the difference between any two consecutive terms is the same.
The ***common difference*** between any two consecutive terms is denoted by the letter ***d***. That is:

$$T_{n+1} - T_n = d.$$

For example, these are all arithmetic sequences:

2, 5, 8, 11, 14, 17, ...	in which $a = 2$ and $d = 3$
4, 11, 18, 25, 32, ...	in which $a = 4$ and $d = 7$
15, 25, 35, 45, 55, ...	in which $a = 15$ and $d = 10$
21, 18, 15, 12, 9, ...	in which $a = 21$ and $d = -3$
5, 4½, 4, 3½, 3, ...	in which $a = 5$ and $d = -½$

Example 1: The nth terms of three sequences are given here. Write down the first four terms of each and say whether or not they are in arithmetic sequence.

(i) $T_n = 2n - 1$ (ii) $T_n = n^2 + 1$ (iii) $T_n = 21 - 3n$

Solution:

(i) Let $n = 1, 2, 3, 4$ in the expression $2n - 1$ to get the first four terms. They are: 1, 3, 5, 7.
This sequence ***is*** arithmetic, since the difference between consecutive terms is a constant (i.e. 2).

(ii) Let $n = 1, 2, 3, 4$ in the expression $n^2 + 1$ to get the first four terms. The first four terms are: 2, 5, 10, 17.
This sequence is ***not*** arithmetic, since the difference between consecutive terms is not a constant.

(iii) Let $n = 1, 2, 3, 4$ in the expression $21 - 3n$ to get the first four terms. They are: 18, 15, 12, 9.
These four terms ***are*** in arithmetic sequence, since the difference between consecutive terms is a constant (i.e. –3).

Example 2: If x, $2x + 1$, $5x - 4$ are the first three terms of an arithmetic sequence. Find the value of x and the fourth term of the sequence.

Solution: Since this sequence is arithmetic, the difference between any two consecutive terms is a constant.

$$\therefore T_2 - T_1 = T_3 - T_2$$
$$\therefore (2x + 1) - x = (5x - 4) - (2x + 1)$$
$$\therefore 2x + 1 - x = 5x - 4 - 2x - 1$$
$$\therefore x + 1 = 3x - 5$$
$$\therefore 6 = 2x$$
$$\therefore x = 3$$

Let $x = 3$ in the sequence $x, 2x + 1, 5x - 4$

Hence the sequence runs 3, 7, 11 (with common difference 4).

The next term will be $11 + 4 = 15$

Exercise 16.A

1. State whether or not the following sequences are ***arithmetic***:
   (i) 2, 4, 6, 8, 10, ...
   (ii) 1, 2, 4, 8, 16, 32, ...
   (iii) 33, 30, 27, 24, 21, ...
   (iv) 1, 4, 9, 16, 25, ...
   (v) $\frac{1}{3}, \frac{1}{4}, \frac{1}{5}, \frac{1}{6}, \frac{1}{7}, \ldots$
   (vi) 2, 2½, 3, 3½, 4, ...
   (vii) 0, ¼, ½, ¾, 1, 1¼, ...
   (viii) –6, –4, –2, 0, 2, ...
   (ix) 1000, 100, 10, 1, ...
   (x) –5, –1, 3, 7, 11, ...

2. In each of these arithmetic sequences, write down the value of a, the value of d and the next two missing terms:
   (i) 2, 6, 10, _, _,
   (ii) 5, 7, 9, 11, _, _,
   (iii) 19, 16, 13, _, _,
   (iv) 100, 90, 80, _, _,
   (v) 13, 20, 27, _, _,
   (vi) –5, –3, –1, _, _,
   (vii) 5½, 6, 6½, 7, _, _,
   (viii) 1, 1¼, 1½, _, _,
   (ix) 72, 61, 50, _, _,
   (x) $\frac{1}{6}, \frac{1}{3}, \frac{1}{2}$, _, _,

3. In each of these arithmetic sequences, write down the value of d (the common difference) and the next three terms:
   (i) 5, 10, _, _, _,
   (ii) 25, 31, _, _, _,
   (iii) 11, 9, _, _, _,
   (iv) 0, 7, _, _, _,
   (v) –7, –4, _, _, _,
   (vi) –11, –9, –7, _, _, _,
   (vii) 15½, 15, 14½, 14, _, _, _,
   (viii) 1, 1¾, 2½, _, _, _,
   (ix) –7, 1, _, _, _,
   (x) $\frac{1}{12}, \frac{1}{6}, \frac{1}{4}$, _, _, _,

4. In each of these arithmetic sequences, write down the value of d (the common difference) and the next three terms:
   (i) –5, –10, _, _, _,
   (ii) 111, 100, _, _, _,
   (iii) 4.4, 6, 7.6, _, _, _,
   (iv) –4, 0, _, _, _,
   (v) –7, 4, _, _, _,
   (vi) –10, –7½, –5, _, _, _,
   (vii) 15½, 14, 12½, _, _, _,
   (viii) 11, 13¾, 16½, _, _, _,
   (ix) –5.4, –1, _, _, _,
   (x) $\frac{1}{10}, \frac{1}{5}, \frac{3}{10}$, _, _, _,

5. The nth term (T_n) of some sequences are given below. Write down the first four terms and state if they are in arithmetic sequence:
   (i) $T_n = 2n + 1$
   (ii) $T_n = 3n - 1$
   (iii) $T_n = n^2 + 3$
   (iv) $T_n = 12 - 2n$
   (v) $T_n = \frac{1}{n}$

6. The nth term (T_n) of some sequences are given below. Write down the first five terms and state if they are in arithmetic sequence:
   (i) $T_n = 4n + 1$
   (ii) $T_n = 13 - n$
   (iii) $T_n = 2n^2$
   (iv) $T_n = 2^n$
   (v) $T_n = \frac{1}{2n-1}$

7. $x + 3, 3x - 1, 4x - 1$ are the first three terms of an arithmetic sequence. Find x.

8. $x + 1, 3x, 2x + 8$ are the first three terms of an arithmetic sequence. Find x.

9. $3x + 2$, 20, $2x + 3$ are the first three terms of an arithmetic sequence.
Find
(i) the value of x,
(ii) the value of d, the common difference,
(iii) the fourth term.

10. $3x - 2$, $2x + 1$, $18 - x$ are the first three terms of an arithmetic sequence.
Find
(i) the value of x,
(ii) the value of d, the common difference,
(iii) the fourth and fifth terms.

11. The nth term of a sequence is given by $T_n = 3n + 1$.
Prove that $T_{n+1} - T_n = 3$

12. The nth term of a sequence is given by $T_n = 5n - 7$.
Prove that $T_{n+1} - T_n =$ a constant.

13. The nth term of a sequence is given by $T_n = 2n + 9$.
Prove that $T_{n+1} - T_n =$ a constant.

THE *n*TH TERM OF AN ARITHMETIC SEQUENCE

Let a = the first term and let d = the common difference of an arithmetic sequence.

$$T_1 = a$$
$$T_2 = a + d$$
$$T_3 = a + 2d$$
$$T_4 = a + 3d$$
$$T_5 = a + 4d$$

In general, $T_n = a + (n - 1)d$

Example 1:

(i) Find the 30th term of this arithmetic sequence: 3, 7, 11, 15, ...

(ii) Find the 42nd term of this arithmetic sequence: 31, 29, 27, 25, ...

Solution:

(i) $a = 3$, $d = 4$ and $n = 30$ (since we want the 30th term).
$\therefore\ T_n = a + (n - 1)d = 3 + (29)(4) = 3 + 116 = 119$

(ii) $a = 31$, $d = -2$ and $n = 42$ (since we want the 42nd term).
$\therefore\ T_n = a + (n - 1)d = 31 + (41)(-2) = 31 - 82 = -51$

Example 2: The fourth term of an arithmetic sequence is 23. The ninth term is 58. Find the first term (a) and the common difference (d).

Solution: $T_4 = 23 \Rightarrow a + (4 - 1)d = 23 \Rightarrow a + 3d = 23$ ... equation I.

$T_9 = 58 \Rightarrow a + (9 - 1)d = 58 \Rightarrow a + 8d = 58$ ... equation II.

Solve the simulataneous equations I and II:

$$\begin{array}{lr} \text{Equation II:} & a + 8d = 58 \\ (-1) \times \text{I:} & \underline{-a - 3d = -23} \\ \text{Add!} & 5d = 35 \end{array}$$

$$\therefore d = 7$$

$$\therefore a + 8(7) = 58 \text{ (from equation I)}$$

$$\therefore a + 56 = 58$$

$$\therefore a = 2$$

Exercise 16.B

1. Find the 21st term of the arithmetic sequence:
   5, 7, 9, 11, ...
2. Find the 16th term of the arithmetic sequence:
   4, 7, 10, 13, ...
3. Find the 31st term of the arithmetic sequence:
   1, 5, 9, 13, ...
4. Find the 41st term of the arithmetic sequence:
   13, 20, 27, 34, ...
5. Find the 11th term of the arithmetic sequence:
   59, 57, 55, ...
6. Find the 17th term of the arithmetic sequence:
   – 12, – 7, – 2, ...
7. Find the 23rd term of the arithmetic sequence:
   43, 40, 37, 34, ...
8. Find the 80th term of the arithmetic sequence:
   11, 22, 33, ...
9. Find the 100th term of the arithmetic sequence:
   –20, –17, –14, ...
10. Find the 44th term of the arithmetic sequence:
    –11, –15, –19, ...
11. Find the nth term of the arithmetic sequence: 3, 5, 7, 9, ...
12. Find the nth term of the arithmetic sequence: 7, 13, 19, 25, ...
13. Find the nth term of the arithmetic sequence: 3, 11, 19, ...
    Which term of this sequence is 155?
14. Find the nth term of the arithmetic sequence: 31, 25, 19, ...
    Which term of this sequence is –5?
15. Find the nth term of the arithmetic sequence: 5, 9, 13, ...
    Which term of this sequence is 145?

16. 116 is the nth term of the arithmetic sequence: 14, 17, 20, ...
Find the value of n.

17. How many terms of the arithmetic sequence 91, 89, 87, ... are positive?

18. How many terms of the arithmetic sequence 101, 94, 87, ... are positive?

19. How many terms of the arithmetic sequence 17, 21, 25, ... are less than 100?

20. How many terms of the arithmetic sequence 123, 138, ... are less than 1000?

21. The 4th term of an arithmetic sequence is equal to 25. The 10th term is 67.
(i) Write down two equations in a (the first term) and d (the common difference).
(ii) Find the values of a and d.

22. The 6th term of an arithmetic sequence is equal to 32. The 11th term is 62.
(i) Write down two equations in a (the first term) and d (the common difference).
(ii) Find the values of a and d.
(iii) Find T_{100}, the 100th term.

23. The fifth term of an arithmetic sequence is 29. The fourteenth term is 110.
Find the first term and the common difference.

24. The 11th term of an arithmetic sequence is 100. The 17th term is 46. Find the first term and the common difference.

25. The first five terms of an arithmetic sequence are: a, 11, b, c, –4.
Find
(i) the first term and the common difference.
(ii) the values of b and c.

26. The 5th term of an arithmetic sequence is equal to 23. The 8th term is five times the first term.
(i) Write down two equations in a (the first term) and d (the common difference).
(ii) Find the values of a and d.

27. The 6th term of an arithmetic sequence is equal to 17. The 7th term is four times the second term.
(i) Write down two equations in a (the first term) and d (the common difference).
(ii) Find the values of a and d.
(iii) Find T_{50}, the 50th term.

28. The 4th term of an arithmetic sequence is 19. The first term is eight times the 6th term.
Find the first term and the common difference.

29. The 11th term of an arithmetic sequence is three times the 3rd term. The 7th term is 12.
Find the first term and the 20th term.

30. The sixth term of an arithmetic sequence is 21. The sum of the 4th and 5th terms is 30.
Find the 1000th term.

THE SUM OF THE FIRST *n* TERMS OF AN ARITHMETIC SERIES.

When we add up the members of a sequence, we call it a series.
There is a formula for finding S_n, the ***sum*** of the first n terms of an arithmetic series:
$a + (a + d) + (a + 2d) + (a + 3d) + ...$ And here it is:

$$S_n = \frac{n}{2}\{2a + (n - 1)d\}$$

Example 1: Find the sum of the first 100 terms of the arithmetic series: 7 + 10 + 13 + ...

Solution:

$$\left.\begin{aligned} a &= 7 \\ d &= 3 \\ n &= 100 \end{aligned}\right\}$$

$$\begin{aligned} S_n &= \frac{n}{2}\{2a + (n-1)d\} \\ &= \frac{100}{2}\{14 + (99)(3)\} \\ &= 50\{14 + 297\} \\ &= 50\{311\} \\ &= 15550 \end{aligned}$$

Example 2: Find the sum of the arithmetic series 11 + 13 + 15 + ... + 51

Solution: We need to know how many terms there are in the series.
Let n = the number of terms. Therefore, the nth term = 51.

$$\left.\begin{aligned} a &= 11 \\ d &= 2 \\ n &= n \end{aligned}\right\}$$

$$\begin{aligned} T_n &= 51 \\ \therefore\ a + (n-1)d &= 51 \\ \therefore\ 11 + (n-1)2 &= 51 \\ \therefore\ 11 + 2n - 2 &= 51 \\ \therefore\ 2n + 9 &= 51 \\ \therefore\ 2n &= 42 \\ \therefore\ n &= 21 \end{aligned}$$

$\therefore$ There are 21 terms

Next, we must find the sum of these 21 terms:

$$\left.\begin{aligned} a &= 11 \\ d &= 2 \\ n &= 21 \end{aligned}\right\}$$

$$\begin{aligned} S_n &= \frac{n}{2}\{2a + (n-1)d\} \\ &= \frac{21}{2}\{22 + (20)(2)\} \\ &= 10.5\{22 + 40\} \\ &= 10.5\{62\} \\ &= 651 \end{aligned}$$

Example 3: The sum of the first eight terms of an arithmetic sequence is 28. The fifth term is 5. Find the values of a, the first term, and of d, the common difference.

Solution:

$$\left.\begin{aligned} a &= a \\ d &= d \\ n &= 8 \end{aligned}\right\} \qquad \begin{aligned} S_8 &= 28 \\ \therefore\ \tfrac{8}{2}\{2a+7d\} &= 28 \\ \therefore\ 4(2a+7d) &= 28 \\ \therefore\ 2a+7d &= 7 \quad \text{...Equation I} \end{aligned}$$

$$\left.\begin{aligned} a &= a \\ d &= d \\ n &= 5 \end{aligned}\right\} \qquad \begin{aligned} T_5 &= 5 \\ \therefore\ a+(n-1)d &= 5 \\ \therefore\ a+4d &= 5 \quad \text{... Equation II} \end{aligned}$$

$$\begin{aligned} \text{Equation I:} \quad & 2a+7d = 7 \\ -2 \times \text{Equation II:} \quad & \underline{-2a-8d = -10} \\ \text{Add!} \quad & -d = -3 \\ \therefore \quad & d = 3 \end{aligned}$$

$$\begin{aligned} \text{But Equation II reads:} \quad & a+4d = 5 \\ \therefore \quad & a+4(3) = 5 \\ \therefore \quad & a+12 = 5 \\ \therefore \quad & a = -7 \end{aligned}$$

Example 4: The sum of the first n terms of an arithmetic series is given by the expression:

$$S_n = n^2 + 5n$$

Find

(i) the sum of the first 10 terms,

(ii) the first term and the common difference.

Solution:

(i) Just put $n = 10$: $\quad S_n = n^2 + 5n$

$$\therefore\ S_{10} = 10^2 + 5(10) = 150$$

(ii) If we let $n = 1$, we get the 'sum of the first one term' (i.e. the first term itself!).

$$S_n = n^2 + 5n$$

$$\therefore\ S_1 = 1^2 + 5(1) = 6$$

$\therefore$ The first term $= 6$

Now, let $n = 2$, to find the sum of the first two terms.

$$S_n = n^2 + 5n$$

$$\therefore \quad S_2 = 2^2 + 5(2) = 14$$

$\therefore$ The sum of the first two terms $= 14$

To find the second term: $\quad T_2 = S_2 - S_1 \quad = 14 - 6 = 8$

Therefore the series is: 6 + 8 + ... and the common difference is 2.

Answer: The first term is 6; the common difference is 2.

In general, $T_n = S_n - S_{n-1}$

Exercise 16.C

1. Find the sum of the first 20 terms of the arithmetic series:
$4 + 7 + 10 + 13 + ...$

2. Find the sum of the first 50 terms of the arithmetic series: $5 + 7 + 9 + ...$

3. Find the sum of the first 12 terms of the arithmetic series:
$3 + 8 + 13 + 18 + ...$

4. Find the sum of the first 10 terms of the arithmetic series:
$14 + 17 + 20 + 23 + ...$

5. Find the sum of the first 21 terms of the arithmetic series:
$15 + 18 + 21 + ...$

6. Find the sum of the first 40 terms of the arithmetic series:
$42 + 37 + 32 + ...$

7. Find the sum of the first 200 terms of the arithmetic series:
$35 + 33 + 31 + ...$

8. Find the sum of the first 51 terms in the arithmetic series:
$-5 + 2 + 9 + ...$

9. Find the sum of the first 80 positive natural numbers:
$1 + 2 + 3 + 4 + ... + 80$

10. Find the sum of the first 30 odd natural numbers:
$1 + 3 + 5 + ... + 59$

11. In the arithmetic series: $70 + 67 + ...$
(i) Find T_{50}, the 50th term.
(ii) Find S_{50}, the sum of the first 50 terms.

12. How many terms are there in the arithmetic series $2 + 4 + 6 + ... + 80$?
Find their sum.

13. How many terms are there in the arithmetic series $3 + 6 + 9 + ... + 99$?
Find their sum.

14. How many terms in the arithmetic series $40 + 37 + 34 + ...$ are positive?
Find their sum.

15. How many multiples of 7 are there between 1 and 100?
Find their sum.
[HINT: The ***multiples*** of seven are: 7, 14, 21, ... etc.]

16. Given the arithmetic series:
$1 + 7 + 13 + 19 + \ldots$
(i) Find the sum of the first ten terms.
(ii) Find the sum of the first twenty terms.
(iii) Find the sum of the ***second*** ten terms.

17. Find the sum of these arithmetic series:
(i) $2 + 5 + 8 + \ldots + 65$.
(ii) $11 + 22 + 33 + \ldots + 319$.
(iii) $88 + 86 + 84 + \ldots + 8$.
(iv) $55 + 51 + \ldots + 11$.
(v) $1\frac{1}{2} + 2\frac{1}{2} + \ldots + 101\frac{1}{2}$.

18. In an arithmetic series, the fourth term is 9.
The sum of the first four terms is 24.
(i) Write down two equations in a (the first term) and d (the common difference).
(ii) Find the values of a and d.

19. In an arithmetic series, the 5th term is 14. The sum of the first ten terms is 155.
(i) Write down two equations in a and d.
(ii) Find the values of a and d.
(iii) Find the sum of the first 20 terms.

20. (i) Show that the sum of the first n terms of the arithmetic series $1 + 3 + 5 + \ldots$ is given by $S_n = n^2$.
(ii) Hence, find S_{30}, the sum of the first 30 terms.
(iii) How many terms need to be added to give a sum of 196?
(iv) Find the least number of terms which must be added to give a total of over 1000.

21. How many terms of the arithmetic series: $3 + 5 + 7 + \ldots$ need to be added in order to get a total of 120?

22. The sum of the first n terms of the arithmetic series $55 + 50 + 45 + \ldots$ is equal to 330. Find two possible values for n.

23. (i) Show that the sum of the first n positive integers $1 + 2 + 3 + \ldots$ is given by

$$S_n = \frac{n(n+1)}{2}$$

(ii) Hence, or otherwise, find the sum of the first 50 positive integers.
(iii) If $1 + 2 + 3 + \ldots + k = 231$, find the value of k.

24. The sum of the first n terms of an arithmetic series is given by

$$S_n = n^2 + 3n$$

(i) Find the values of S_1 and S_2.
(ii) Write down the first term and the common difference.

25. The sum of the first n terms of an arithmetic series is given by

$$S_n = n^2 + n$$

(i) Find the values of S_1, S_2 and S_3.
(ii) Write down the first term and the common difference.
(iii) Find the 31st term.

26. The sum of the first n terms of an arithmetic series is given by

$$S_n = n^2 + 2n$$

Find
(i) S_{10}, the sum to 10 terms,
(ii) S_9, the sum to 9 terms,
(iii) T_{10}, the tenth term.

27. The sum of the first n terms of an arithmetic series is given by

$$S_n = n^2 + 6n$$

Find
(i) S_{10}, the sum to 10 terms,
(ii) S_{11}, the sum to 11 terms,
(iii) T_{11}, the eleventh term.

28. The sum of the first n terms of an arithmetic series is given by $S_n = 2n^2 + n$. Find

(i) the first term,
(ii) the common difference,
(iii) the 10th term.

29. The sum of the first n terms of an arithmetic series is given by

$$S_n = \frac{n(3n+1)}{2}$$

(i) Find the values of S_1, S_2 and S_3.
(ii) Write down the first term and the common difference.
(iii) Find the 20th term.

30. The sum of the first seven terms of an arithmetic series is 147. The fifth term is 27. Find the first term and the common difference.

31. In an arithmetic series, the tenth term is 34 and the sum of the first 10 terms is 205.

(i) Show that the sum of the first n terms is given by $$S_n = \frac{3n^2 + 11n}{2}$$
(ii) Find the sum of the ***second*** ten terms.

32. The sum of the first 9 terms of an arithmetic series is 27. Find the 5th term.

GEOMETRIC SEQUENCES

In some sequences, you ***multiply*** each term by a certain number to get the next term. Such sequences are called ***geometric sequences***. The first term is still denoted by the letter a. The number you multiply by is called the ***common ratio*** and is denoted by the letter r.

In general $r = \dfrac{T_{n+1}}{T_n} = \dfrac{\text{Any term}}{\text{Previous term}}$.

Here are some ***geometric*** sequences:

6, 12, 24, 48, ...	in which $a = 6$ and $r = 2$.
5, 15, 45, 135, ...	in which $a = 5$ and $r = 3$.
10, 5, 2½, 1¼, ...	in which $a = 10$ and $r = ½$.
$\frac{6}{7}, \frac{2}{7}, \frac{2}{21}, \frac{2}{63}, \ldots$	in which $a = \frac{6}{7}$ and $r = \frac{1}{3}$.
3, –6, 12, –24, ...	in which $a = 3$ and $r = -2$.
500, 200, 80, 32, ...	in which $a = 500$ and $r = \frac{200}{500} = 0.4$

In general, the terms of a ***geometric*** sequence are as follows:

$$T_1 = a,\ T_2 = ar,\ T_3 = ar^2,\ T_4 = ar^3,\ \text{etc.}$$

The formula for the nth term is, therefore:

$$T_n = ar^{n-1}$$

Example 1: Find the 11th term of the geometric sequence: 7, 21, 63, ...

Solution:

$$\left.\begin{aligned} a &= 7 \\ r &= 3 \\ n &= 11 \end{aligned}\right\} \qquad \begin{aligned} T_n &= ar^{n-1} \\ \therefore\ T_{11} &= (7)(3)^{10} \\ &= (7)(59049) \quad \text{...powers first} \\ &= 413343 \quad \text{...then multiplication} \end{aligned}$$

Example 2: If $x - 1, x + 1, x + 7$ are in geometric sequence, find the value of x.

Solution: Since these three terms are in ***geometric*** sequence,

$$\begin{aligned} \frac{T_2}{T_1} &= \frac{T_3}{T_2} \\ \therefore\ \frac{x+1}{x-1} &= \frac{x+7}{x+1} \\ \therefore\ (x+1)(x+1) &= (x-1)(x+7) \\ \therefore\ x^2 + 2x + 1 &= x^2 + 6x - 7 \\ \therefore\ 1 + 7 &= 6x - 2x \\ \therefore\ 8 &= 4x \\ \therefore\ x &= 2 \end{aligned}$$

Example 3: In a geometric sequence, the 5th term is 40 and the 8th term is 320. Find the common ratio, r.

Solution:

The 5th term = 40

$$\left.\begin{aligned} a &= a \\ r &= r \\ n &= 5 \end{aligned}\right\} \qquad \begin{aligned} T_5 &= 40 \\ \therefore\ ar^{n-1} &= 40 \\ \therefore\ ar^4 &= 40 \quad \text{... equation I} \end{aligned}$$

The 8th term = 320

$$\left.\begin{aligned} a &= a \\ r &= r \\ n &= 8 \end{aligned}\right\} \qquad \begin{aligned} T_8 &= 320 \\ \therefore\ ar^{n-1} &= 320 \\ \therefore\ ar^7 &= 320 \quad \text{... equation II} \end{aligned}$$

The best thing to do here is to ***divide*** equation II by equation I:

$$\begin{aligned} \therefore\ \frac{ar^7}{ar^4} &= \frac{320}{40} \\ \therefore\ r^3 &= 8 \\ \therefore\ r &= 2 \end{aligned}$$

Example 4: The nth term of a sequence is given by $T_n = 3(2)^n$.

(i) Write down the first four terms.

(ii) Say whether or not these terms are in geometric sequence.

Solution:

(i) $T_1 = 3(2)^1 = 6$

$T_2 = 3(2)^2 = 3(4) = 12$

$T_3 = 3(2)^3 = 3(8) = 24$

$T_4 = 3(2)^4 = 3(16) = 48$

(ii) These terms: 6, 12, 24, 48 ***are*** in geometric sequence, since

$\frac{12}{6} = \frac{24}{12} = \frac{48}{24} = 2.$

Exercise 16.D

1. In each of these geometric sequences, write down the value of r, the common ratio, and fill in the next two terms.

Remember: $r = \frac{\text{Any term}}{\text{Previous term}}$

(i) 1, 2, 4, 8, _ , _ , ...
(ii) 2, 6, 18, _ , _ , ...
(iii) 5, 10, 20, _ , _ , ...
(iv) 1, 3, 9, _ , _ , ...
(v) 7, 14, 28, _ , _ , ...
(vi) 2, 10, 50, _ , _ , ...
(vii) 32, 16, 8, _ , _ , ...
(viii) 80, 40, 20, _ , _ , ...
(ix) 1, 10, _ , _ , ...
(x) $\frac{1}{2}, \frac{1}{4}, \frac{1}{8}$, _ , _ , ...

2. In each of these geometric sequences, write down the value of r and the next term:

(i) 5, 20, _ , ...
(ii) 1, 2, _ , ...
(iii) 1, 1.2, _ , ...
(iv) 100, 80, _ , ...
(v) $\frac{2}{3}, \frac{1}{2}$, _ , ...
(vi) $\frac{3}{8}$, 1, _ , ...
(vii) 2, –2, 2, –2, 2, _ , ...
(viii) 36, 12, _ , ...
(ix) $\frac{1}{6}, \frac{1}{8}$, _ , ...
(x) 0.1, 0.2, _ , ...

3. Find

(i) the 5th term of the geometric sequence: 6, 12, ...,
(ii) the 10th term of the geometric sequence: 7, 14, 28, ...,
(iii) the 7th term of the geometric sequence: 4, 12, 36, ...,
(iv) the 8th term of the geometric sequence: 3, 12, 48, ...,
(v) the 6th term of the geometric sequence: 3, 15, ...,
(vi) the 9th term of the geometric sequence: 1024, 512, 256, ...,
(vii) the 11th term of the geometric sequence: 11, 22, ...,
(viii) the 12th term of the geometric sequence: 1, 2, 4, ...,
(ix) the 4th term of the geometric sequence: 1, 1.2, ...,
(x) the 5th term of the geometric sequence: 1, 1.1, 1.21, ...

4. 2, 4, x, y, are the first four terms of a geometric sequence. Find

(i) the common ratio,
(ii) the values of x and y,
(iii) the 7th term.

5. Find the 15th term of the geometric sequence: 2, 3, ... correct to one decimal place.

6. Find, correct to two decimal places, the 10th term of the geometric sequence : 1, 1.6, ...

7. Find, correct to two decimal places, the 11th term of the geometric sequence : 4, 5, ...

8. Find, correct to three decimal places, the 9th term of the geometric sequence : 500, 400, ...

9. Find, correct to the nearest integer, the 12th term of the geometric sequence : 2, 5, 12½, ...

10. Find, correct to one decimal place, the 8th term of the geometric sequence: 1600, 1200, 900, ...

11. ¾, ½, ... are the first two terms of a geometric sequence. Find
- (i) the common ratio,
- (ii) the 7th term in the form $\frac{m}{n}$ where $m, n \varepsilon N$.

12. Find the nth term of the geometric sequence 5, 10, 20, ...

13. 162, 54, x, y are the first four terms of a geometric sequence. Find
- (i) the common ratio,
- (ii) the values of x and y,
- (iii) an expression for the nth term.

14. If 3, x, y, 24 are the first four terms of a geometric sequence, find
- (i) the values of x and y,
- (ii) the 8th term.

15. 5, x, 45 are the first three terms of a geometric sequence. Find
- (i) the two possible values of x,
- (ii) the 7th term.

16. $x - 3, x - 1, x + 3$ are the first three terms of a geometric sequence. Find
- (i) the value of x,
- (ii) the first term and the common ratio,
- (iii) the 12th term.

17. $x - 7, x - 3, x + 9$ are the first three terms of a geometric sequence. Find
- (i) the value of x,
- (ii) the 9th term.

18. $x - 3, x, 3x + 4$ are the first three terms of a geometric sequence. Find
- (i) the two possible values of x,
- (ii) the first four terms of the two possible sequences.

19. The first term of a geometric sequence is 11 and the fourth term is 88.
Find the common ratio.

20. The second term of a geometric sequence is 6. The fifth term is 162. Find the first term and the common ratio.

21. The third term of a geometric sequence is 50. The sixth term is 6250. Find
- (i) the first term and the common ratio
- (ii) the fifth term.

22. Write down the first four terms of these geometric sequences, given the following nth terms
- (i) $T_n = 3^n$
- (ii) $T_n = 3(2)^n$
- (iii) $T_n = 2(10)^n$
- (iv) $T_n = 5^{n-1}$
- (v) $T_n = 2(3)^{n-1}$

23. $T_1, T_2, T_3, T_4, \ldots$ is a geometric sequence of positive numbers, such that $T_2 = 28$ and $T_4 = 112$. Find the values of T_1 and T_3 and find an expression for the nth term.

24. The nth term of a geometric sequence is given by $T_n = 2^n$.
- (i) Write down the first 5 terms.
- (ii) Write down the common ratio.
- (iii) Is the tenth term greater or less than 1000?

25. The nth term of a geometric sequence is given by $T_n = 16\left(\frac{1}{2}\right)^n$

(i) Write down the first four terms.
(ii) Find the 10th term.
(iii) Write the 19th term in scientific notation, correct to one significant figure.

26. In a geometric sequence, the first term is 3. The sum of the second and third terms is 60.

(i) Find two possible values for the common ratio.
(ii) Write down the first three terms of both possible sequences.

THE SUM OF THE FIRST *n* TERMS OF A GEOMETRIC SERIES

There is a formula for the first n terms of a geometric sequence in which the first term is a and the common ratio is r. Here it is:

$$S_n = \frac{a(1-r^n)}{1-r}$$

Example 1:

(i) Find the sum of the first 11 terms of the geometric series: $4 + 12 + 36 + \ldots$

(ii) Find the sum of the first 8 terms of the geometric series: $20 + 18 + \ldots$ to the nearest whole number

Solution:

(i) $a = 4$, $r = 3$, $n = 11$

$$S_n = \frac{a(1-r^n)}{1-r} = \frac{4(1-3^{11})}{1-3} = \frac{4(-177146)}{-2} = 354292$$

(ii) $a = 20$, $r = \frac{18}{20} = 0.9$, $n = 8$

$$S_n = \frac{a(1-r^n)}{1-r} = \frac{20(1-0.9^8)}{1-0.9} = \frac{20(0.56953)}{0.1} = 114$$

Exercise 16.E

1. Find the sum of the first eight terms of the geometric series 3 + 6 + 12 + ...

2. Find the sum of the first six terms of the geometric series 1 + 5 + 25 + ...

3. Find the sum of the first nine terms of the geometric series 5 + 10 + 20 + ...

4. Find (correct to one decimal place) the sum of the first six terms of the geometric series 20 + 24 + ...

5. Find the sum of the first ten terms of the geometric series 2 + 6 + 18 + ...

6. Find, correct to 4 significant figures, the sum of the first seven terms of the geometric series: $1 + 1.1 + (1.1)^2 + \ldots$

7. Find (to the nearest whole number) the sum of the first twelve terms of the geometric series: 800 + 600 + ...

8. Find the sum of the first 5 terms of the geometric series: $\frac{1}{2} + \frac{1}{6} + \frac{1}{18} + \ldots$ in the form $\frac{m}{n}$ where $m, n \in N$.

9. 7 + 14 + ... are the first two terms of a geometric series. Find
(i) the common ratio,
(ii) the tenth term,
(iii) the sum of the first ten terms.

10. 50 + 40 + ... are the first two terms of a geometric series. Find
(i) the common ratio,
(ii) the third term,
(iii) the sum of the first 14 terms to the nearest integer.

11. ½ + ¼ + ... are the first two terms of a geometric series. Find (as fractions)
(i) the common ratio,
(ii) the 9th term,
(iii) the sum of the first 9 terms.

12. The nth term of a geometric sequence is given by $T_n = 2^n$.
(i) Write down the first four terms.
(ii) Write down the common ratio.
(iii) Find the sum of the first 11 terms.

13. The nth term of a geometric sequence is given by $T_n = \frac{4}{2^{n-1}}$
(i) Write down the first three terms.
(ii) Write down the common ratio.
(iii) Find the sum of the first 6 terms.

14. The first two terms of a geometric series are: 24 + 12 + ...
Find
(i) r, the common ratio,
(ii) T_n, the nth term,
(iii) S_n, the sum to n terms,
(iv) the value of $(T_n + S_n)$ when $n = 12$.

15. The nth term of a geometric sequence is given by $T_n = 12(4)^{n-2}$.
(i) Find T_1, the first term and r, the common ratio.
(ii) Find the sum of the first 13 terms.

16. The first five terms of a geometric series are $a + 12 + c + d + 324 + \ldots$
(i) Find the values of a, c, and d.
(ii) Find the 9th term.
(iii) Find the sum of the first nine terms.

REVISION EXERCISE 16.F

1. (a) Find the 15th term of the arithmetic sequence: 22, 25, ...

(b) Find the 17th term of the geometric sequence 1, 1.2, ... correct to one decimal place.

(c) The first two terms of an arithmetic series are 5 + 7 + ...
Find the sum of the first 11 terms and the sum of the second 11 terms.

2. (a) Find the 20th term and the sum of the first 20 terms of the arithmetic series: –5 + 1 + 7 + ...

(b) $x - 3$, $x + 1$, $4x - 2$ are three consecutive terms in a sequence. Find the value(s) of x if the sequence is

(i) arithmetic,
(ii) geometric.

and write down the first four terms in each case.

3. (a) How many terms are there in the arithmetic series:
4 + 7 + 10 + ... + 106?
Hence, find the sum of this series.

(b) The first two terms of a geometric series are 4 + 3 + ...
Find

(i) the common ratio,
(ii) the third term,
(iii) the sum of the first five terms, correct to one decimal place.

4. (a) Find the sum of the first 40 terms of the arithmetic series:
1.1 + 1.3 + 1.5 + ...

(b) The first two terms of a geometric series are

216 + 54 + ...

Find

(i) the common ratio,
(ii) the sum of the first six terms, correct to two decimal places,
(iii) the sum of the second six terms, correct to two decimal places.

5. (a) Find the 26th term and the sum of the first 26 terms of the arithmetic series 19 + 15 + 11 + ...

(b) 2, 6, 18, ... is a geometric series. Find an expression for

(i) T_n, the nth term,
(ii) S_n, the sum to n terms.

Prove that $2(S_n + 1) = 3T_n$

6. (a) The first two terms of a series are 1 + 2 + ...
Find the sum of the first 11 terms

(i) if the series is arithmetic,
(ii) if the series is geometric.

(b) In an arithmetic sequence, the fifth term is 12 and the fifteenth term is 32. Find

(i) the first term and the common difference,
(ii) the nth term,
(iii) which term of this sequence is 1000.

7. (a) The first two terms of an arithmetic sequence are 6, 0, ... Find the common difference and the 13th term.

(b) The first three terms of a geometric series are ½, 1, 2... Find

(i) the common ratio,
(ii) T_n, the nth term,
(iii) S_6, the sum to six terms.

(c) The sum of the first n terms of an arithmetic series is given by $S_n = n^2 + 7n$. Find the first term and the common difference.

8. (a) How many multiples of 7 are less than 200? Find their sum.
[The multiples of 7 are 7, 14, 21, ...]

(b) The first term of a geometric sequence is 224. The third term is 504. Find the fifth term.

(c) Find the sum of the positive terms of the arithmetic series: 47 + 43 + 39 ...

9. (a) Find, correct to one decimal place, the sum of the first 14 terms of the geometric series: $200 + 120 + 72 + \ldots$

(b) In an arithmetic sequence, the 4th term is 9 and the sum of the first four terms is 24. Find a (the first term) and d (the common difference) and write down the first four terms.

(c) The sum of the first n terms of a geometric series is given by $S_n = 5^n - 1$

(i) Find S_1 and S_2.

(ii) Deduce the values of a, the first term and of r, the common ratio.

10. (a) In an arithmetic series, the fifth term is 14 and the sum of the first 10 terms is 155. Find

(i) a, the first term,

(ii) d, the common difference,

(iii) S_{20}, the sum of the first twenty terms.

(b) The first three terms of a geometric sequence are $1, x + 1, 6x + 1, \ldots$ Find two possible values for x and find the fourth term in each case.

(c) The first three terms of an arithmetic sequence are $\frac{1}{a}, \frac{1}{x}, \frac{1}{b}, \ldots$

Prove that $x = \dfrac{2ab}{a+b}$.

1. Arithmetic sequence: $a, a + d, a + 2d, a + 3d, \ldots$

$$T_n = a + (n-1)d \quad \text{and} \quad S_n = \frac{n}{2}\{2a + (n-1)d\}$$

2. Geometric sequence: $a, ar, ar^2, ar^3, \ldots$

$$T_n = ar^{n-1} \quad \text{and} \quad S_n = \frac{a(1-r^n)}{1-r}$$

3. $T_n = S_n - S_{n-1}$

Chapter 17

Calculus

In the 17th century a giant step was taken in the field of Mathematics. This was the discovery of ***the calculus***. Strangely, this new branch of Mathematics was invented by two men independently in two different countries: Sir Isaac Newton in England and Gottfried Wilhelm Leibnitz in Germany.

Calculus is the study of the rate at which things change: cars that speed up and trains which slow down, comets that move faster as they whizz past the sun, spacecraft that gradually lose mass as they burn up petrol, populations that grow. This invention has revolutionised Mathematics and has enabled mankind to make the huge strides which our world has seen in the last three centuries.

In Mathematics we use ***graphs*** to judge the rate at which things grow. If the graph is increasing, things are on the way up; if the graph is decreasing, things are on the way down.

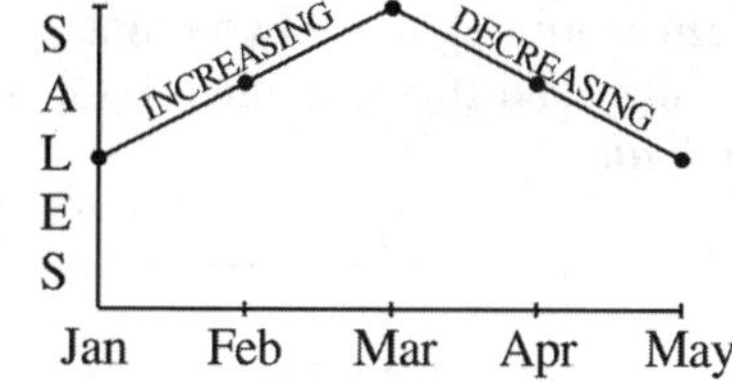

Now, we know that the slope of a line can be got, if we know the co-ordinates of two points on the line (x_1, y_1) and (x_2, y_2).

The slope is given by the formula $\dfrac{y_2 - y_1}{x_2 - x_1}$.

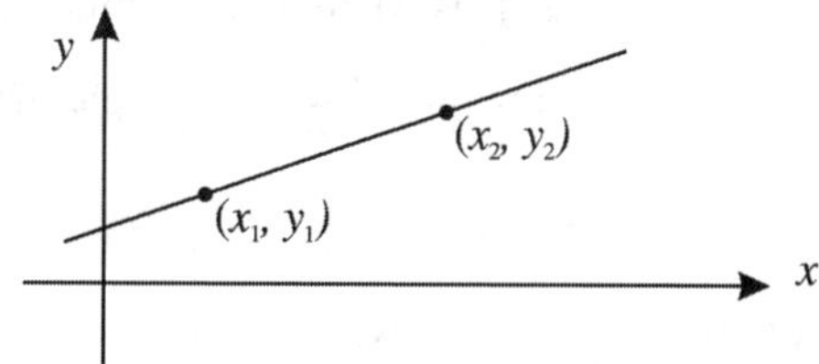

But how can we find the ***slope of a curve***? The trouble about a curve is that the slope at every point is different. But we may ask 'What is the slope of ***this*** curve [say $y = f(x)$] at a particular point [say, $(x, f(x))$]?' Newton's (and Leibnitz's) method was to look at the particular point through an imaginary magnifying glass, enlarged so much that the curve is more or less a straight line.

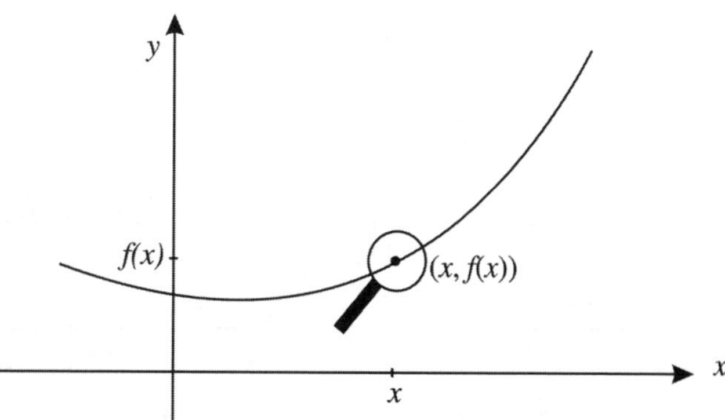

Take $(x, f(x))$ and a nearby point on the curve. Let h = the small distance between the two x-coordinates.
The y-coordinates are, therefore, $f(x)$ and $f(x + h)$.

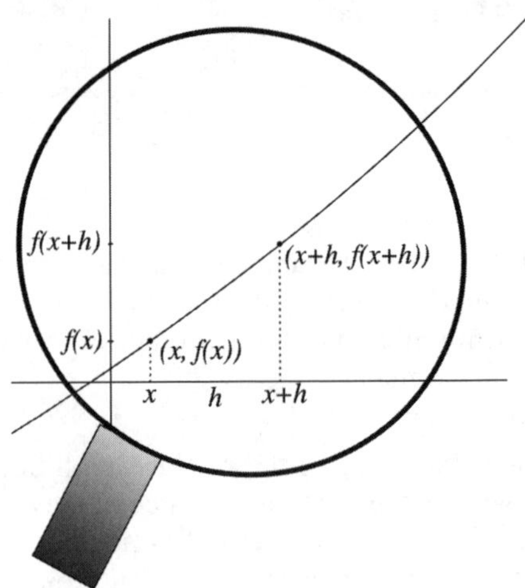

The slope of the line joining these two points $(x, f(x))$ and $(x + h, f(x + h))$ is

$$\frac{y_2 - y_1}{x_2 - x_1} = \frac{f(x+h) - f(x)}{(x+h) - x} = \frac{f(x+h) - f(x)}{h}$$

Now, as we said, this is the slope of the ***line*** joining these points. If we want to get the true slope of the ***curve*** joining these two points, we will have to let h become smaller and smaller (and use a stronger and stronger magnifying glass to see it!). Newton got over this problem by inventing ***the limit***.

He simply said: 'Find $\frac{f(x+h) - f(x)}{h}$ and see what happens to it as h gets smaller and smaller.'

This is written in the following Mathematical way:
$\lim_{h \to 0} \frac{f(x+h) - f(x)}{h}$: 'the limit of $\frac{f(x+h) - f(x)}{h}$ as h approaches zero.'

In this way we can get the ***instantaneous*** rate at which the graph is increasing.

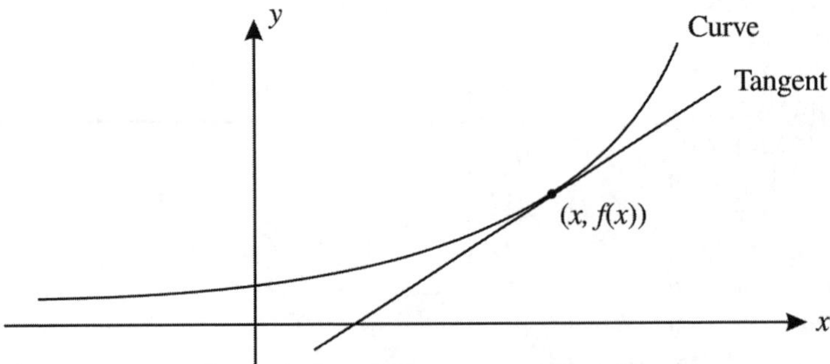

If you carry out this procedure, the task you are performing is called ***differentiating from first principles with respect to x***. Never forget that the resultant outcome is the slope of the curve at a particular point, or, to be more correct, ***the slope of the tangent to the curve at a point***. The slope of the curve at a certain point and the slope of the tangent to the curve at that point are the same, as the diagram shows.

Example 1: Differentiate $f(x) = x^2$ from first principles with respect to x.

Solution:

$$f(x) = x^2$$

$$\therefore f(x+h) = (x+h)^2 = x^2 + 2xh + h^2$$

$$\therefore f(x+h) - f(x) = (x^2 + 2xh + h^2) - x^2 = 2xh + h^2$$

$$\therefore \frac{f(x+h) - f(x)}{h} = \frac{2xh + h^2}{h} = 2x + h$$

$$\therefore \lim_{h \to 0} \frac{f(x+h) - f(x)}{h} = 2x \quad [\text{Letting } h \to 0\ ]$$

This means that the slope of the tangent at any point on the graph of $y = x^2$ is given by 'twice-the-x-coordinate'.

For example, at (2, 4) the slope is $2(2) = 4$

At (1, 1), the slope is $2(1) = 2$

At (0, 0), the slope is $2(0) = 0$

At (–1, 1), the slope is $2(-1) = -2$, etc.

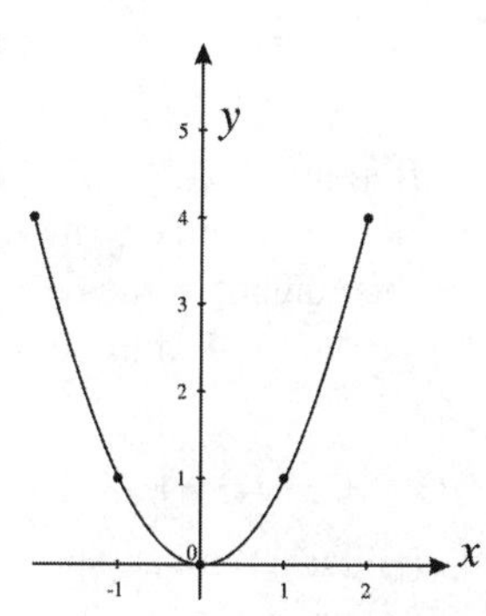

Example 2: Differentiate $3x^2 - 5x + 7$ from first principles. Hence write down the ***slope*** and the ***equation*** of the tangent to the curve $y = 3x^2 - 5x + 7$ at the point (2, 9).

Solution:

$$f(x) = 3x^2 - 5x + 7$$

$$\therefore f(x+h) = 3(x+h)^2 - 5(x+h) + 7 = 3x^2 + 6xh + 3h^2 - 5x - 5h + 7$$

$$\therefore f(x+h) - f(x) = 6xh + 3h^2 - 5h$$

$$\therefore \frac{f(x+h) - f(x)}{h} = \frac{6xh + 3h^2 - 5h}{h} = 6x + 3h - 5$$

$$\therefore \lim_{h \to 0} \frac{f(x+h) - f(x)}{h} = 6x + 3(0) - 5 = 6x - 5$$

This means that the slope of the tangent at any point is given by 'six-times-the-x-coordinate-minus-five'.

The slope at $(2, 9) = 6(2) - 5 = 7$

The equation of this tangent is:

$$y - y_1 = m(x - x_1)$$

$$\Rightarrow y - 9 = 7(x - 2)$$

$$\Rightarrow y - 9 = 7x - 14$$

$$\Rightarrow 7x - y = 5$$

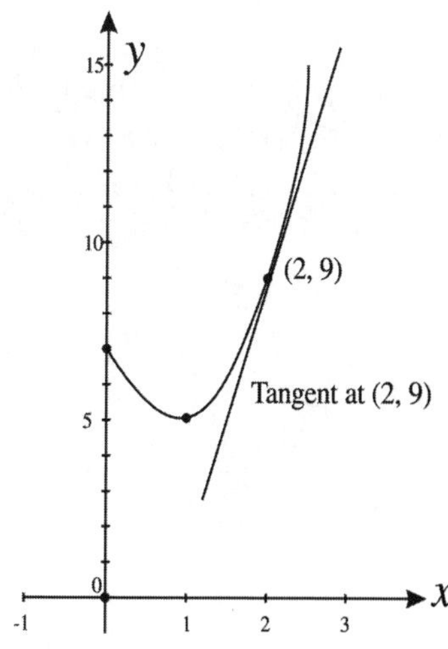

Exercise 17.A

1. Differentiate $x^2 + 2x + 1$ from first principles. Hence write down the slope of the tangent to the curve $y = x^2 + 2x + 1$ at the point (3, 16).

2. Differentiate $x^2 + 3x + 4$ from first principles. Hence write down the slope of the tangent to the curve $y = x^2 + 3x + 4$ at the point (0, 4).

3. Differentiate $x^2 + 7x + 1$ from first principles. Hence write down the slope of the tangent to the curve $y = x^2 + 7x + 1$ at the point where $x = 2$.

4. $f(x) = x^2 - 2x + 11$

(i) Differentiate $f(x)$ from first principles with respect to x.

(ii) Find the slope of the tangent to the curve $y = x^2 - 2x + 11$ at the point (3, 14).

5. (i) Differentiate $3x^2 - 2x + 7$ from first principles.

(ii) Show that (2, 15) is a point on the curve $y = 3x^2 - 2x + 7$

(iii) Find the ***slope*** of the tangent to the curve $y = 3x^2 - 2x + 7$ at the point (2, 15).

6. Differentiate $2x^2 - 10x - 1$ from first principles with respect to x.

7. Differentiate $2x^2 + 2x - 5$ from first principles. Hence write down the slope of the tangent to the curve $y = 2x^2 + 2x - 5$ at the point (1, –1).

8. Differentiate $-x^2$ from first principles. Hence write down the slope of the tangent to the curve $y = -x^2$ at the point (2, –4).

9. Differentiate $1 + 6x - x^2$ from first principles with respect to x.
Hence write down the ***slope*** and the ***equation*** of the tangent to the curve $y = 1 + 6x - x^2$ at the point (2, 9).

10. $f(x) = 1 - 3x^2$

(i) Differentiate $f(x)$ from first principles.

(ii) Find the slope of the tangent to the curve $y = 1 - 3x^2$ at the point (1, –2).

(iii) Find the equation of this tangent.

11. Differentiate $10 - 2x - x^2$ from first principles with respect to x.
Hence find the ***slope*** and the ***equation*** of the tangent to the curve $y = 10 - 2x - x^2$ at the point (1, 7).

12. $f(x) = 7$. Differentiate $f(x)$ from first principles.

NAMES ... AND MORE NAMES

When we differentiate a function $f(x)$, the outcome is called any of the following: 'the slope of the tangent to the curve', 'the gradient', 'the derivative of $f(x)$', 'the differentiation of $f(x)$'. There are three mathematical ways of writing this:

$\frac{dy}{dx}$ or $\frac{df}{dx}$ (the notation of Leibnitz) or $f'(x)$ (the notation of Newton)

DIFFERENTIATING BY RULE

You may be wondering if there is a quick way of differentiating, rather than going through those five arduous steps every time. The answer is: 'There is a quick way: Multiply the power of x by the coefficient and reduce the power by one'.

For example, if $y = 3x^5 + 7x^4 + 2x^3 + 11x^2 + 4x + 9$

then $\frac{dy}{dx} = 15x^4 + 28x^3 + 6x^2 + 22x + 4$

Again, if $y = 5x^2 - 7x + 11$ then $\frac{dy}{dx} = 10x - 7$

x and y are not the only possible variables. For example, if

$s = 9t^2 - 5t + 4$ then $\frac{ds}{dt} = 18t - 5$ (which is called the derivative of s with respect to t).

Finally, if $f(x) = 3 - 2x - 4x^2 - 10x^3$ then $f'(x) = -2 - 8x - 30x^2$

(using Sir Isaac Newton's notation, for a change).

Example 1: Differentiate the following by rule:

(i) $y = 3 - 2x - 5x^2 + x^3$ (ii) $y = 2\sqrt{x}$

Solution:

(i) $y = 3 - 2x - 5x^2 + 1x^3$

$\therefore \frac{dy}{dx} = -2 - 10x + 3x^2$

(ii) $y = 2\sqrt{x} = 2x^{\frac{1}{2}}$

$\therefore \frac{dy}{dx} = 2(\frac{1}{2})x^{-\frac{1}{2}} = 1x^{-\frac{1}{2}} = \frac{1}{\sqrt{x}}$

Exercise 17.B

Differentiate the following by rule:

1. $y = 3x^2 + 5x + 6$
2. $y = 4x^2 + 10x + 2$
3. $y = 5x^2 + 2x + 1$
4. $y = x^2 + 8x + 11$
5. $y = x^2 - 5x + 4$
6. $y = 4x^3 + 5x^2 - 2x + 1$
7. $y = 10x^4 + 2x^3 - 11x^2$
8. $y = x^4 + 20x - 1$
9. $y = 1 - 5x - 2x^2 + x^3$
10. $y = 9x + 4$
11. $y = 1 - 3x$
12. $y = x + 5$
13. $y = x^5 + x^3 + x$
14. $y = 10x^{11} + 11x^{10}$
15. $y = \sqrt{x}$

16. If $f(x) = x^2 + 15x - 6$ find $\frac{df}{dx}$.
17. If $g(x) = 3x^4 - x + 13$ find $\frac{dg}{dx}$.
18. If $A(x) = x^3 - 11x$ find $\frac{dA}{dx}$.
19. If $f(t) = 5t^2 + 50t + 12$ find $\frac{df}{dt}$.
20. If $s = t^3 + 2t^2 - t - 3$ find $\frac{ds}{dt}$.
21. If $A = \pi r^2 + 2\pi r$ find $\frac{dA}{dr}$.
    [Remember that π is a constant]
22. If $s = 2t^2 + t - 9$ find the value of $\frac{ds}{dt}$ when $t = 4$.
23. If $f(x) = x^4 + x - 6$ find $\frac{df}{dx}$ when $x = -1$.
24. $y = 5x^2 - 2x + 1$
    (i) Find $\frac{dy}{dx}$
    (ii) Find the slope of the tangent to the curve $y = 5x^2 - 2x + 1$ at the point (1, 4).
25. $y = x^2 - 12x + 10$
    (i) Find $\frac{dy}{dx}$
    (ii) Find the slope of the tangent to the curve $y = x^2 - 12x + 10$ at the point (3, –17).
    (iii) Find the equation of this tangent.
26. If $y = x^2 - 6x + 4$ show that $\frac{dy}{dx} = 0$ when $x = 3$.
27. If $y = 5x^2 - 20x + 1$ show that $\frac{dy}{dx} = 0$ at (2, –19).
28. $y = x^3 - 6x^2 + 10x + 1$
    (i) Find $\frac{dy}{dx}$
    (ii) Find the slope of the tangent to the curve $y = x^3 - 6x^2 + 10x + 1$ at the point where $x = 2$.
29. $f(x) = 4x^2 - 26x + 49$. Find
    (i) $\frac{df}{dx}$,
    (ii) the slope of the tangent to the curve $y = f(x)$ at (3, 7),
    (iii) the equation of this tangent.
30. Find the equation of the tangent to $y = 3x^2 + 5x + 10$ at (–1, 8).

SEARCHING FOR POINTS WITH SPECIAL SLOPES

Example 1: Find a point on the curve $y = x^2 - 8x + 21$ where the tangent is parallel with the x-axis.

Solution: If the tangent is parallel with the x-axis, then the slope = 0.

$$\therefore \frac{dy}{dx} = 0$$

$$\therefore 2x - 8 = 0$$

$$\therefore x = 4$$

$$\therefore y = x^2 - 8x + 21 = (4^2) - 8(4) + 21 = 5$$

Therefore the point is (4, 5)

Example 2: Find a point on the curve $y = 2x^2 - 7x + 5$ where the tangent makes an angle of 45° with the positive sense of the x-axis.

Solution: If the tangent makes an angle of 45° with the positive sense of the x-axis, then the slope = tan 45° = 1

$$\therefore \frac{dy}{dx} = 1$$

$$\therefore 4x - 7 = 1$$

$$\therefore 4x = 8$$

$$\therefore x = 2$$

$$\therefore y = 2x^2 - 7x + 5 = 2(2)^2 - 7(2) + 5 = -1$$

Therefore, the point is (2, –1).

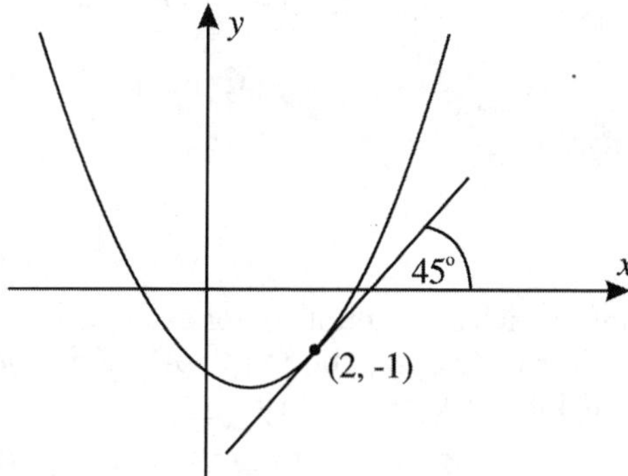

Exercise 17.C

1. Show that the tangent to the curve $y = x^2 - 2x + 5$ at (1, 4) is parallel with the x-axis.

2. Find a point on the curve $y = x^2 - 6x + 11$ where the tangent is parallel with the x-axis.

3. Find a point on the curve $y = 2x^2 - 12x + 25$ where the tangent is parallel with the x-axis.

4. Find a point on the curve $y = x^2 - 10x + 1$ where the slope is equal to 0.

5. Find a point on the curve $y = x^2 - 2x + 11$ where the slope is equal to 6.

6. Find a point on the curve $y = 3x^2 - 11x + 1$ where the tangent makes an angle of 45° with the positive sense of the x-axis.

7. The diagram shows part of the graph of $y = x^2 - x - 2$. Find
   (i) the equation of the tangent T,
   (ii) the coordinates of the point p where T cuts the x-axis.

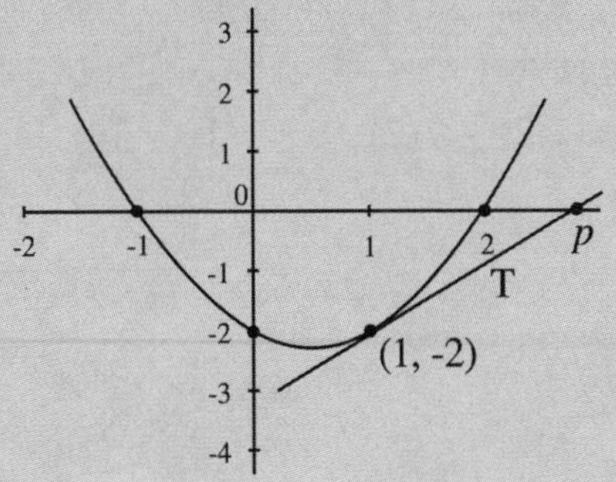

8. Show that the tangents to the curve $y = x^3$ at (2, 8) and at (–2, –8) are parallel.

9. Find ***two*** points on the curve $y = x^3 - 3x - 1$ where the tangents have zero slope.

10. Show that the tangents to $y = 2x^3 - 15x^2 + 30x + 1$ at $x = 1$ and at $x = 4$ are parallel.

11. The diagram shows two tangents to the curve $y = x^2 - 2x - 1$ at the points (2, –1) and (0, –1).
   (i) Find their slopes.
   (ii) Find their equations.
   (iii) Investigate if they are perpendicular.
   (iv) Find their point of intersection.

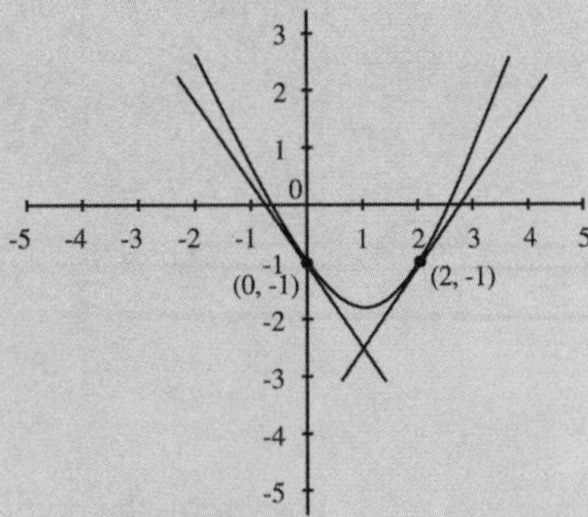

12. Find a point on the curve $y = 2x^2 + 3x + 1$ where the tangent is parallel to the line $3x - y - 5 = 0$.

THE PRODUCT RULE

If you want to differentiate two functions which are multiplied, for example $y = (5x + 7)(2x + 11)$, then you may ***not*** just differentiate each part. Instead, you must apply ***the Product Rule*** which appears on page 42 of the Mathematical Tables. And here it is:

The Product Rule: If $y = uv$ then $\frac{dy}{dx} = u\frac{dv}{dx} + v\frac{du}{dx}$

Example 1: Differentiate $(5x + 7)(2x + 11)$

Solution:

$$y = (5x + 7)(2x + 11)$$

$(5x+7) \to u$, $(2x+11) \to v$

$$\frac{dy}{dx} = u\frac{dv}{dx} + v\frac{du}{dx} = (5x + 7)(2) + (2x + 11)(5)$$

$$= 10x + 14 + 10x + 55 = 20x + 69$$

Example 2: Find the value of the derivative of $(1 - x^2)(x^3 - 2x - 5)$ at the point $(1, 0)$.

Solution:

$$y = (1 - x^2)(x^3 - 2x - 5)$$

$(1-x^2) \to u$, $(x^3-2x-5) \to v$

$$\therefore \frac{dy}{dx} = u\frac{dv}{dx} + v\frac{du}{dx} = (1 - x^2)(3x^2 - 2) + (x^3 - 2x - 5)(-2x)$$

$$= (1 - 1)(3 - 2) + (1 - 2 - 5)(-2) \quad \text{when } x = 1$$

$$= 0(1) + (-6)(-2)$$

$$= 12$$

Exercise 17.D

Differentiate the following products:

1. $(5x + 7)(3x + 1)$
2. $(3x - 1)(7x + 2)$
3. $(x^2 + 1)(5x + 2)$
4. $(4x - 2)(5x + 1)$
5. $(x^2 - 2)(2x + 3)$
6. $y = (x^2 + 2x + 1)(x^2 + 5x + 3)$
   Find the value of $\frac{dy}{dx}$ if $x = 0$.
7. Evaluate the derivative of $(x^2 - 3)(x^2 + 2x - 1)$ at $x = 2$.
8. Evaluate the derivative of $(x^2 - 1)(2x + 1)$ at $x = 3$.
9. If $y = (x^2 + 1)(x^2 - 1)$ find the value of $\frac{dy}{dx}$
   (i) when $x = 0$,
   (ii) when $x = 1$,
   (iii) when $x = -1$.
10. If $y = 2x(3x - 7)$, find $\frac{dy}{dx}$
    (i) by using the ***product rule,***
    (ii) by multiplying out first and then differentiating.
11. (i) If $y = x(x + 1)(x - 1)$, find $\frac{dy}{dx}$,
    (ii) Show that the tangent to this curve at $(1, 0)$ has slope 2.
12. Find the coefficient of x^2 in the derivative of $(3x^2 - 5x + 3)(7x^2 + x - 2)$

THE QUOTIENT RULE

If you are asked to differentiate a quotient, such as $\frac{3x-5}{x^2+1}$, you cannot just differentiate the top and then the bottom.

Instead, you must use the ***Quotient Rule***, which appears on page 42 of the Mathematical Tables. And here it is:

$$\text{If } y = \frac{u}{v} \text{ then } \frac{dy}{dx} = \frac{v\frac{du}{dx} - u\frac{dv}{dx}}{v^2}$$

Example 1: (i) Differentiate $\frac{3x-5}{x^2+1}$.

(ii) Hence find the slope of the tangent to $y = \frac{3x-5}{x^2+1}$ at $(0, -5)$.

Solution: (i)

$$y = \frac{3x-5}{x^2+1} = \frac{u}{v}$$

$$\therefore \frac{dy}{dx} = \frac{v\frac{du}{dx} - u\frac{dv}{dx}}{v^2} = \frac{(x^2+1)(3)-(3x-5)(2x)}{(x^2+1)^2}$$

$$= \frac{(3x^2+3)-(6x^2-10x)}{(x^2+1)^2}$$

$$= \frac{3x^2+3-6x^2+10x}{(x^2+1)^2}$$

$$= \frac{-3x^2+10x+3}{(x^2+1)^2}$$

(ii) $\text{Slope} = \frac{dy}{dx} = \frac{-3x^2+10x+3}{(x^2+1)^2} = \frac{0+0+3}{(0+1)^2} = \frac{3}{1} = 3$ [Letting $x = 0$]

Exercise 17.E

Differentiate the following using the quotient rule:

1. $\frac{3x+5}{2x+1}$
2. $\frac{5x+2}{x+3}$
3. $\frac{3x-2}{4x-1}$
4. $\frac{x}{x^2+1}$
5. $\frac{2x+1}{x^2+2}$
6. $\frac{1}{4x+3}$
7. $\frac{1}{x-1}$
8. $\frac{1}{x}$
9. $\frac{10}{1-x^3}$
10. $\frac{1}{x^2+2x-1}$

11. Find the value of the derivative of $\frac{3x+4}{4x+3}$ when $x = 0$.
12. Find the slope of the tangent to the curve $y = \frac{3x}{x^2-1}$ at $(0, 0)$.
13. Find the value of the derivative of $\frac{5x-1}{x^2+3}$ when $x = 1$.
14. Find the ***slope*** and the ***equation*** of the tangent to the curve $y = \frac{2}{x}$ at the point $(2, 1)$.
15. Tangents are drawn to the curve $y = \frac{3}{x^3}$ at $(1, 3)$ and at $(-1, -3)$. Verify that these tangents are parallel.
16. Let $y = \frac{x^2+5}{x-2}$.

    Find the two values of x for which $\frac{dy}{dx} = 0$
17. Let $f(x) = \frac{-1}{x-1}$ for $x \in R$, $x \neq 1$.
    (i) Find the derivative of $f(x)$.
    (ii) Two tangents to $y = f(x)$ make an angle of 45° with the x-axis. Find the co-ordinates of the points on the curve of $y = f(x)$ at which this occurs.
18. $f(x) = \frac{1}{3-x}$ is defined for all real values of x (except $x = 3$).

    Show that $\frac{dy}{dx} > 0$ for all valid values of x.
19. $y = \frac{x}{1-x^2}$. Find $\frac{dy}{dx}$ and show that $\frac{dy}{dx} > 0$ for all $x \in R$, $x \neq 1, -1$.
20. Use both the product ***and*** quotient rules to evaluate the derivative of

    $\frac{2x-1}{x+1}(3x+4)$ when $x = 0$.

THE CHAIN RULE

If you are asked to differentiate a function, which is itself raised to a power of n, for example, $(x^2 + 3x + 1)^4$, then you must use ***the Chain Rule***. And here it is:

$$\text{If } y = [f(x)]^n \text{ then } \frac{dy}{dx} = n[f(x)]^{n-1} f'(x)$$

So, if $y = (x^2 + 3x + 1)^4$ then $\frac{dy}{dx} = 4(x^2 + 3x + 1)^3(2x + 3)$

Example 1: Find the slope of the tangent to the curve $y = (x^2 - x - 5)^3$ when $x = 3$.

Solution:

$$y = (x^2 - x - 5)^3$$

$$\therefore \frac{dy}{dx} = 3(x^2 - x - 5)^2(2x - 1)$$

$$= 3(9 - 3 - 5)^2(6 - 1) \quad [\text{When } x = 3]$$

$$= 3(1)(5)$$

$$= 15$$

Exercise 17.F

Differentiate the following using the chain rule:

1. $(3x + 1)^5$
2. $(x^2 + 7)^4$
3. $(8x + 3)^3$
4. $(x^3 + 2)^2$
5. $(x^2 + x - 4)^7$
6. $(x^2 - 1)^{20}$
7. $(2x + 3)^{10}$
8. $(x^3 + 2x^2 - x + 1)^2$
9. $(x^2 + 7x - 6)^8$
10. $(x^5 + 1)^9$

11. Evaluate the derivative of $(2x + 1)^7$ when $x = 0$.
12. Evaluate the derivative of $(x^3 + 1)^2$ when $x = 1$.
13. Evaluate the derivative of $(3x - 1)^3$ when $x = 2$.
14. $y = (x^3 - 25)^4$. Find the value of $\frac{dy}{dx}$ when $x = 3$.
15. If $y = (x^3 - 5)^3$, show that $\frac{dy}{dx} \geq 0$ for all real values of x.
16. Find the slope of the tangent to the curve $y = (3x^2 - x - 3)^5$ at $(1, -1)$.
17. Find the ***slope*** and ***equation*** of the tangent to the curve $y = (2x - 1)^{100}$ at the point $(1, 1)$.
18. Differentiate
    (i) $\frac{x - 1}{x + 1}$
    (ii) $\left(\frac{x - 1}{x + 1}\right)^3$
19. Differentiate
    (i) $\frac{x^2}{x + 4}$
    (ii) $\left(\frac{x^2}{x + 4}\right)^2$
20. Differentiate
    (i) $\frac{1}{x} + x$
    (ii) $\left(\frac{1}{x} + x\right)^4$
    (iii) $\sqrt{\frac{1}{x} + x}$

TURNING POINTS

If you are cycling up and down over hilly ground, your bicycle will be in a horizontal position on two occasions: at the top of a hill and at the bottom of a valley.

On a graph, the top of a hill is called a ***local maximum point*** and the bottom of a valley is called a ***local minimum point***. If a point is either a local maximum or a local minimum, we call it a ***turning point***.

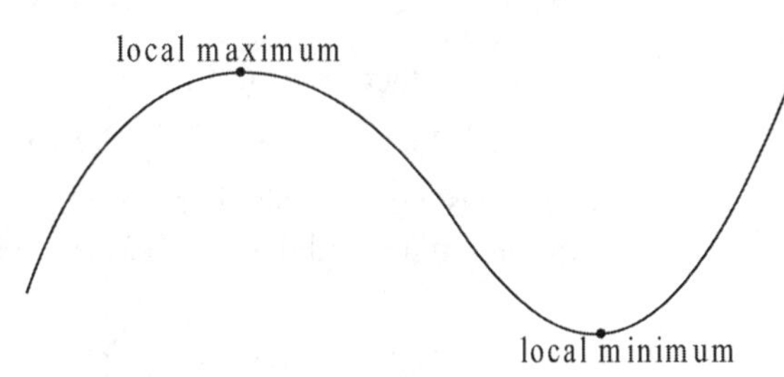

What distinguishes all turning points is this: they are points where the slope is zero. Therefore we find them by solving the equation $\frac{dy}{dx} = 0$.

Example 1: Find a local minimum point on the curve $y = x^2 - 4x + 11$

Solution:

$$y = x^2 - 4x + 11$$

$$\therefore \frac{dy}{dx} = 0 \Rightarrow 2x - 4 = 0 \Rightarrow 2x = 4 \Rightarrow x = 2$$

$$\therefore y = (2)^2 - 4(2) + 11 = 4 - 8 + 11 = 7$$

$$\therefore \text{The local minimum point} = (2, 7)$$

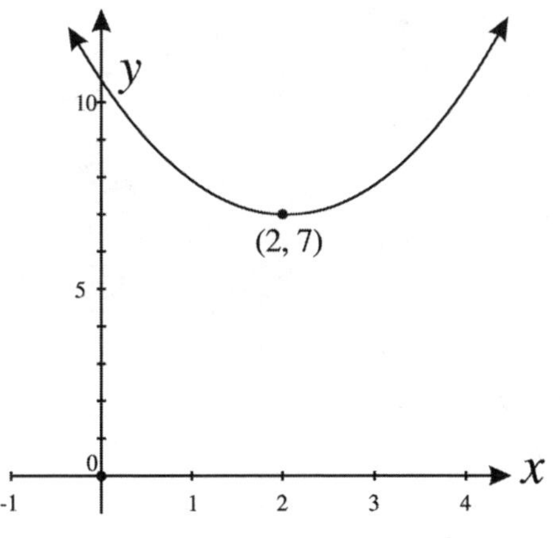

Example 2: Find the two turning points of the curve $y = x^3 - 3x^2 - 9x + 15$ and determine which is a local minimum and which is a local maximum. Hence draw a rough sketch of the graph, showing these features.

Solution:

$$y = x^3 - 3x^2 - 9x + 15$$

$$\therefore \frac{dy}{dx} = 0 \Rightarrow 3x^2 - 6x - 9 = 0$$

$$\therefore x^2 - 2x - 3 = 0$$

$$\therefore (x+1)(x-3) = 0$$

$$\therefore x = -1 \text{ or } 3$$

If $x = -1$ then $y = (-1)^3 - 3(-1)^2 - 9(-1) + 15 = 20 \ : \ (-1, 20)$

If $x = 3$ then $y = 3^3 - 3(3)^2 - 9(3) + 15 = -12 \ : \ (3, -12)$

Since 20 is a greater number than –12, we can conclude that (–1, 20) is the local maximum and that (3, –12) is the local minimum.

Here is a rough sketch of the graph:

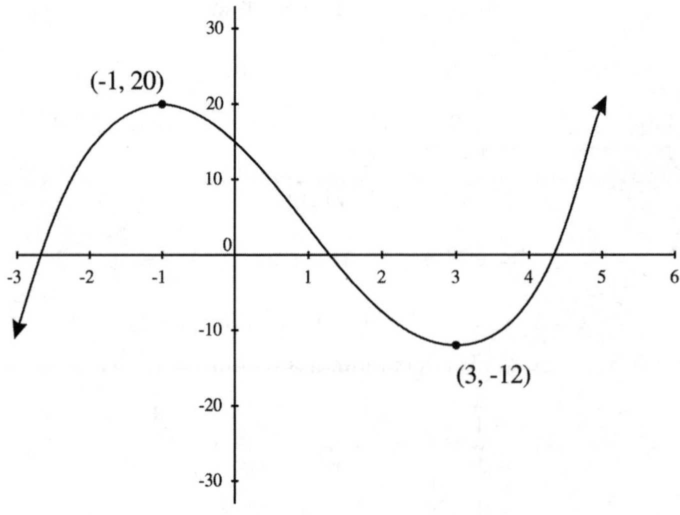

Exercise 17.G

1. Find a minimum point on the curve $y = x^2 - 4x + 10$.

2. Find a minimum point on the curve $y = x^2 - 6x + 17$.

3. Find a minimum point on the curve $y = x^2 - 2x + 4$.

4. Find a maximum point on the curve $y = 1 + 8x - x^2$.

5. Find a maximum point on the curve $y = 3 + 10x - x^2$.

6. Find a minimum point on the curve $y = 3x^2 - 12x + 1$.

7. $f(x) = 2x^2 - 20x + 75$ is a function. Find the minimum value of $f(x)$.

8. $f(x) = 3 - 2x - x^2$ is a function. Find the maximum value of $f(x)$.

9. $f(x) = x^2 + bx + c$ is a function such that $f(1) = 2$ and $f(5) = 10$.
   (i) Find the values of b and c.
   (ii) Find a minimum point on the curve $y = f(x)$.
   (iii) Draw a rough sketch of the curve $y = f(x)$.

10. $f(x) = 1 - 4x - x^2$ is a function.
    (i) Find a maximum point on the curve $y = f(x)$
    (ii) Draw a rough sketch of the curve $y = f(x)$.
    (iii) Investigate if the tangents at $(-3, 4)$ and at $(-1, 4)$ are perpendicular.

11. Find a maximum and a minimum point on the curve $y = x^3 - 12x$.

12. Find a maximum and a minimum point on the curve $y = 2x^3 - 3x^2 - 12x - 4$.

13. Find a local maximum and minimum point on the curve $y = x^3 - 3x + 1$.

14. Find a local maximum and minimum point on the curve $y = 2x^3 - 3x^2 - 36x + 10$.

15. Find a local maximum and minimum point on the curve $y = 10 + 15x + 6x^2 - x^3$.

16. Find a local maximum and minimum point on the curve $y = (x + 1)^2(2 - x)$.

17. $f(x) = ax^3 + bx$ is a function such that $f(1) = -26$ and $f(2) = -46$.
    (i) Find the values of a and b.
    (ii) Find a local maximum and a local minimum point on the curve $y = f(x)$.

18. Let $A = xy$ and let $3x - y = 24$.
    (i) Write y in terms of x.
    (ii) Write A in terms of x.
    (iii) Find the minimum value of A.

19. $f(x) = ax^3 + bx^2$ is a function such that $f(1) = -2$ and $f(4) = 64$.
    (i) Find the values of a and b.
    (ii) Find the values of x for which $f'(x) = 0$.
    (iii) Find the co-ordinates of points p and q on the curve $y = f(x)$ at which the tangents are perpendicular to the line $x + 8y = 0$.

20. Let $f(x) = 3x^3 - 6x^2 - 5x + 11$.
    (i) Find the values of x for which $f'(x) = 0$.
    (ii) Determine the slope and equation of the tangent to $y = f(x)$ at $(2, 1)$.
    (iii) Find the equation of a parallel tangent.

RATES OF CHANGE

We have seen how if $y = f(x)$, then $\frac{dy}{dx}$ measures the rate at which y is changing with respect to x. If $\frac{dy}{dx}$ is positive, then y is on the increase; if $\frac{dy}{dx}$ is negative, then y is on the decrease.

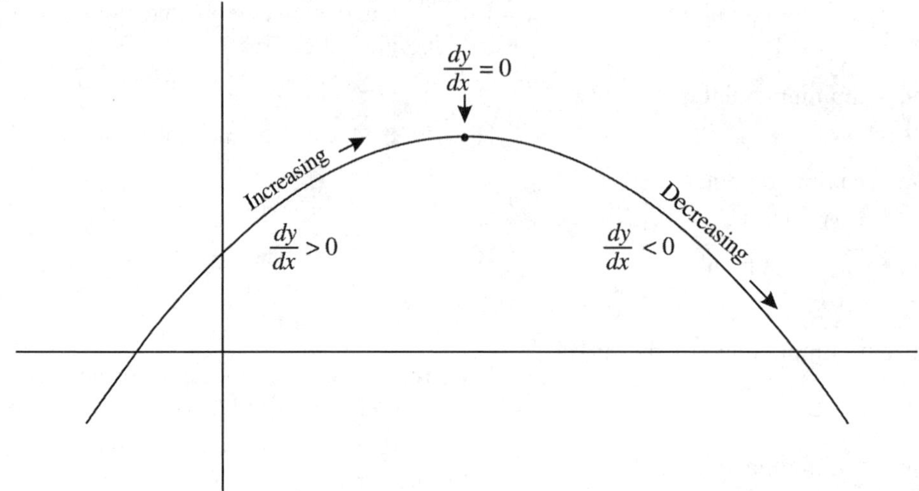

Similarly, if $h(t)$ is a function which gives us the height of a football above the ground, then $\frac{dh}{dt}$ measures the rate at which the height is changing, as time goes by.

If $\frac{dh}{dt}$ is positive, then the ball is rising.

If $\frac{dh}{dt}$ is negative, then the ball is falling.

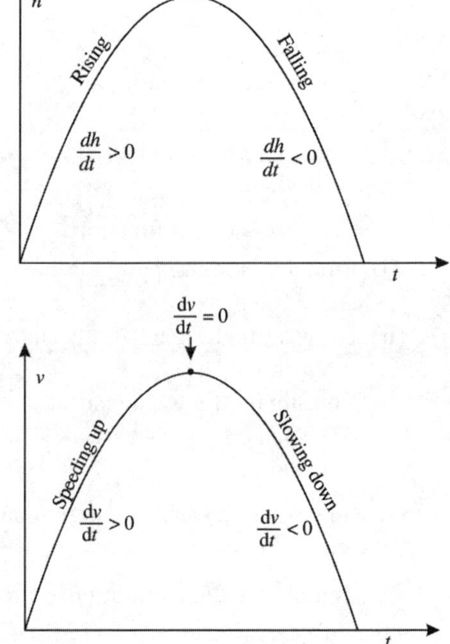

If $v(t)$ is a function which gives us the velocity of a car at time t, then $\frac{dv}{dt}$ is the rate at which the velocity is changing.

The English word for this is ***acceleration***.

If $\frac{dv}{dt}$ is positive, then the car is speeding up.

If $\frac{dv}{dt}$ is negative, then the car is slowing down.

Finally, let $s(t)$ be a function which gives us the distance s of a person from a point p at any time t. $\frac{ds}{dt}$ is the rate at which this distance changes. If $\frac{ds}{dt}$ is positive, the person is moving away from p and the distance is increasing.

If $\frac{ds}{dt}$ is negative, then the person is moving towards p and the distance is decreasing.
The technical term for $\frac{ds}{dt}$ is ***speed*** (or ***velocity***) and is measured in m/s.

Summary

We use the letter s for distance, or displacement - not for speed.

$\frac{ds}{dt}$ = speed (or velocity) = v and $\frac{dv}{dt}$ = acceleration a.

In general, $\frac{dw}{dz}$ = the rate of change of w with respect to z.

Example 1: A tennis ball is hit straight up into the air. The height h after t seconds is given by $h(t) = 1 + 30t - 5t^2$.

(i) Find the height of the ball after 2 seconds.
(ii) Find the rate at which the ball is rising after 2 seconds.
(iii) Find the time at which the ball reaches its maximum height.
(iv) Find the maximum height reached.

Solution

(i) $h(2) = 1 + 30(2) - 5(2)^2 = 1 + 60 - 20 = 41$ metres.

(ii) $\frac{dh}{dt} = 30 - 10t$ = the rate at which the ball is rising.
At $t = 2$, this rate $= 30 - 10(2) = 30 - 20 = 10$ m/s.

(iii) Maximum height $\Rightarrow \frac{dh}{dt} = 0$

$$\Rightarrow 30 - 10t = 0$$
$$\Rightarrow 30 = 10t$$
$$\Rightarrow t = 3$$

(iv) The height at $t = 3$ is given by $h(t) = 1 + 30t - 5t^2$

$$= 1 + 30(3) - 5(3)^2$$
$$= 1 + 90 - 45 = 46 \text{ metres}$$

Example 2: The distance s (in metres) of a car from a point p after t seconds is given by

$$s = 3t^2$$

(i) Calculate the speed of the car after t seconds.
(ii) Calculate the speed of the car after 4 seconds.
(iii) Find the constant acceleration a of the car.

Solution:

(i) Speed $= v = \frac{ds}{dt} = 6t$.
(ii) At $t = 4$, $v = 6(4) = 24$ m/s.
(iii) $a = \frac{dv}{dt} = 6$ m/s^2.

Exercise 17.H

1. For what values of x is the graph of $y = x^2 - 14x + 1$ increasing?

2. For what values of x is the graph of $y = x^2 - 9x + 1$ decreasing?

3. A car accelerates in a straight line so that its distance s (in metres) from its starting point p after t seconds is given by $s = t^2$. Find
 (i) its distance from p after 2 seconds,
 (ii) its distance from p after 3 seconds,
 (iii) the speed of the car, in terms of t,
 (iv) the speed of the car after 4 seconds.

4. A cyclist accelerates in a straight line so that its distance s (in metres) from its starting point p after t seconds is given by $s = \frac{1}{2}t^2$. Find
 (i) its distance from p after 4 seconds,
 (ii) its distance from p after 5 seconds,
 (iii) the distance travelled during the fifth second (from $t = 4$ until $t = 5$)
 (iv) the speed of the car, in terms of t,
 (v) the speed of the car after 7 seconds.

5. A ball is thrown straight up into the air. The height h after t seconds is given by $h(t) = 40t - 5t^2$
 (i) Find the height of the ball after 1 second.
 (ii) Find the height of the ball after 2 seconds.
 (iii) Find the speed at which the ball is rising after t seconds.
 (iv) Find the speed at which the ball is rising after 3 seconds.
 (v) Find the time at which the ball reaches its maximum height.
 (vi) Find the maximum height reached.

6. A car passes a point p and applies its brakes. The car's distance, s, from p at any subsequent time t is given by $s = 20t - 2t^2$ where s is measured in metres and t in seconds.
Find
 (i) the distance of the car from p after 4 seconds,
 (ii) the car's speed at any time t,
 (iii) the speed of the car at $t = 4$,
 (iv) the car's speed as it passed through p,
 (v) the time at which the car comes to rest,
 (vi) the distance of the car from p when it stops.

7. The volume V of a certain gas is given by $V = \frac{600}{P}$, where P is the pressure.
 (i) Find the rate of change of V with respect to P.
 (ii) Calculate this rate of change when $P = 20$.

8. Show that the graph of $y = x^3 + 1$ never decreases.

9. Show that the graph of $y = \frac{x+1}{x-1}$ is decreasing for all values of x, where $x \neq 1$.

10. The force of attraction F between two particles is given by the formula

$$F = \frac{1000}{r^2}$$

where r is the distance between them.
 (i) Find the rate of change of F with respect to r.
 (ii) Evaluate this rate of change when $r = 10$.

11. As soon as it touches down, an aeroplane applies its brakes. The distance, s, which the plane has travelled along the runway at any subsequent time t is given by

$s = 200t - 4t^2$

where s is measured in metres and t in seconds.

Find

(i) the distance travelled after 10 seconds,
(ii) the plane's speed at any time t,
(iii) the speed of the plane at $t = 10$,
(iv) the planes's speed as it touched down,
(v) the time at which the plane comes to rest,
(vi) the distance which the plane has travelled along the runway when it stops,
(vii) the constant deceleration of the plane.

12. A particle moves in a straight line so that its distance s, from a point o at any subsequent time t is given by

$s = t^3 - 2t^2 + t$

where s is measured in metres and t in seconds.

Find

(i) the distance of the particle from o after 2 seconds,
(ii) the particle's speed after 2 seconds,
(iii) the acceleration of the particle after 2 seconds,
(iv) the times at which the particle is at rest,
(v) the time when the acceleration is zero.

13. A particle moves in a straight line so that its distance s, from a point o at any subsequent time t is given by

$$s = \frac{144t}{t+1}$$

where s is measured in metres and t in seconds and $t > 0$.

Find

(i) the distance of the particle from o after 2 seconds,
(ii) the distance of the particle from o after 3 seconds,
(iii) the distance travelled between $t = 2$ and $t = 3$,
(iv) the particle's speed after t seconds,
(v) the particle's speed after 2 seconds
(vi) the time when the speed of the particle is 4 m/s
(vii) the times at which the particle's speed is less than 1 m/s.

14. The velocity v (in m/s) of a particle moving in a straight line at time t seconds (where $t > 0$) is given by

$v = t(t-2)^2 + 3$.

Calculate

(i) the velocity of the particle at $t = 5$ and at $t = 7$,
(ii) the acceleration in terms of t,
(iii) the times at which the acceleration is zero.

REVISION EXERCISE 17.I

1. (a) Differentiate x^2 from first principles with respect to x.

(b) Differentiate the following with respect to x:

(i) $2x + 1$

(ii) $(2x + 1)(3x + 2)$

(iii) $(2x + 1)^3$

(c) Find the slope and the equation of the tangent to the curve $y = x^3 - 5x - 1$ at the point $(1, -5)$.

2. (a) Let $f(x) = x^2 - 5x + 3$, for $x \varepsilon R$. Find $f'(x)$, the derivative of $f(x)$. For what value of x is $f'(x) = 0$?

(b) Find the derivative of $\dfrac{2x-2}{3x+7}$ and then find its value when $x = -1$.

(c) A ball is thrown straight up into the air. The height h after t seconds is given by $h = 25t - 5t^2$.

(i) Find the height of the ball after 1 second.

(ii) Find the speed at which the ball is rising after t seconds.

(iii) Find the speed at which the ball is rising after 1.5 seconds.

(iv) Find the time at which the ball reaches its maximum height and calculate that height.

3. (a) Differentiate $x^2 + 4x - 7$ from first principles with respect to x.

(b) Differentiate the following:

(i) $5x^3 + 11$,

(ii) $(5x^3 + 11)(1 - x^2)$,

(iii) $(5x^3 + 11)^4$.

(c) Let $y = x^3 - x - 6$. Show that the tangents at the points $(-2, -12)$ and at $(2, 0)$ are parallel.

4. (a) Let $f(x) = 2x^2 - 12x + 1$, for $x \varepsilon R$. Find $f'(x)$, the derivative of $f(x)$. For what values of x is $f(x)$ a decreasing function?

(b) Let $y = \dfrac{12x}{x+3}$. Find $\dfrac{dy}{dx}$ and find two values of x for which $\dfrac{dy}{dx} = 1$.

(c) A ball is dropped from a height of 100 metres. Its height h above the ground after t seconds is given by $h = 100 - 4t^2$.

(i) Find the height of the ball after 2 seconds.

(ii) Find the speed at which the ball is falling after t seconds.

(iii) Find the speed at which the ball is falling after 3.5 seconds.

(iv) Find the time which the ball takes to fall to the ground.

5. (a) Differentiate $1 - x^2$ from first principles with respect to x.

(b) Differentiate the following:

(i) $1 + 5x - x^2 - 2x^3$,

(ii) $\dfrac{2x-1}{1-x^2}$,

(iii) $(1 - x^2)^5$

(c) Find a local maximum and a local minimum point of the curve $y = 2x^3 - 24x + 10$.

6. (a) Let $s = t^2 - t - 11$.
For what value(s) of t is
(i) $s = 9$,
(ii) $\frac{ds}{dt} = 9$?

(b) Find the derivative of
(i) $x^2 - \frac{1}{x^2}$,
(ii) $\left(x^2 - \frac{1}{x^2}\right)^4$
where $x \neq 0$.

(c) A cyclist travels in a straight line so that her distance s from a point p after t seconds is given by
$s = \frac{3t^2}{2}$.
Calculate
(i) her speed at $t = 4$,
(ii) the distance travelled between $t = 5$ and $t = 7$,
(iii) her acceleration.

7. (a) Differentiate $5x - 6$ from first principles with respect to x.

(b) Given that $f(x) = \frac{x-2}{x+2}$, prove that $f(x)$ is an increasing function for all $x \in R$, $x \neq -2$.

(c) Find the minimum point on the curve $y = (x - 3)(x + 1)$.

8. (a) Let $f(x) = (1 - 4x)^8$.
Find $f'(x)$, the derivative of $f(x)$, and find its value when $x = ½$.

(b) If $y = \frac{x^2 - 5}{3x + 7}$, find $\frac{dy}{dx}$ and the values of x for which $\frac{dy}{dx} = 0$.

(c) The volume V of a spherical balloon of radius r is given by $V = \frac{4}{3}\pi r^3$. Find (in terms of π)
(i) the rate of change of V with respect to r,
(ii) this rate of change when $r = 5$.

9. (a) Differentiate the following with respect to x:
(i) $1 - x - x^2 - x^3$,
(ii) $(1 - x - x^2 - x^3)^2$,
(iii) $\sqrt{1 - x - x^2 - x^3}$.

(b) Find the derivative of $\left(1 - \frac{1}{x}\right)^3$ and find its value when $x = -1$.

(c) The points on a curve are determined by the equation $y = x^2(3 - x)$. Find
(i) the points on the curve at which $\frac{dy}{dx} = 0$.,
(ii) the slope of the tangent T at the point p(–1, 4),
(iii) another point q at which the tangent is parallel to T.

Draw the graph of $y = x^2(3 - x)$, in the domain $-1 \leq x \leq 3, x \in R$.

10. (a) Differentiate $1 + 6x - 5x^2$ from first principles with respect to x.

(b) A body moves in a straight line so that its distance, s metres from a fixed point o after a time t seconds is given by $s = 11 + 100t - 3t^3$, where $t > 0$. Find
(i) its speed after t seconds,
(ii) its speed after 2½ seconds,
(iii) the time at which the body is at rest,
(iv) the deceleration after 3 seconds.

(c) Let $f(x) = \frac{ax + b}{x^2 - 4}$ be a function defined for all $x \in R$, $x \neq -2, 2$.
If $f(0) = -1.25$ and if $f(-2.5) = 0$, find
(i) the values of a and b,
(ii) the values of x for which $f'(x) = 0$.

1. $\dfrac{df}{dx} = \lim_{h \to 0} \dfrac{f(x+h) - f(x)}{h}$ = the slope of the tangent to the curve $y = f(x)$.

2. The derivative of ax^n is nax^{n-1}.

3. The ***product rule***: If $y = uv$, then $\dfrac{dy}{dx} = u\dfrac{dv}{dx} + v\dfrac{du}{dx}$.

4. The ***quotient rule***: If $y = \dfrac{u}{v}$ then $\dfrac{dy}{dx} = \dfrac{v\dfrac{du}{dx} - u\dfrac{dv}{dx}}{v^2}$.

5. The ***chain rule***: If $y = [f(x)]^n$ then $\dfrac{dy}{dx} = n[f(x)]^{n-1} f'(x)$.

6. Local maximum points and local minimum points are points at which $\dfrac{dy}{dx} = 0$.

7. $\dfrac{dw}{dz}$ = the rate of change of w with respect to z.

8. If s = distance, then $\dfrac{ds}{dt}$ = speed (or velocity) = v and $\dfrac{dv}{dt}$ = acceleration.

Chapter 18

Option 1: Linear Programming

THE POSITIVE AND NEGATIVE SIDES OF A LINE

Take the line $2x + 3y - 6 = 0$. To draw this line, we find any two points which satisfy the equation.
For example: (3, 0) and (0, 2).

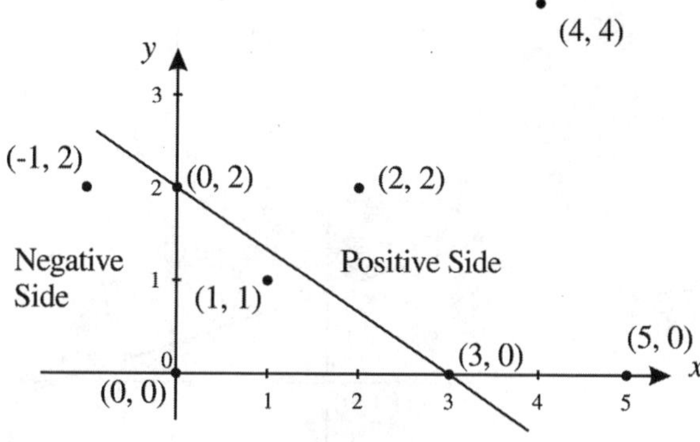

On one side of this line, you will find points which satisfy the inequality $\mathbf{2x + 3y - 6 < 0}$. This side is called the ***negative*** side of the line. In this case, points such as (0, 0), (1, 1) and (−1, 2) are on the negative side of the given line (the South-West side). All of these points satisfy the inequality $2x + 3y - 6 < 0$. This should be verified by the student. The area occupied by these points is often referred to as a ***half-plane***.

On the other side of this line, you will find points which satisfy the inequality $\mathbf{2x + 3y - 6 > 0}$. This side is called the ***positive*** side of the line.
In this case, points such as (4, 4), (5, 0) and (2, 2) are on the positive side of the given line (the North-East side). All of these points satisfy the inequality $2x + 3y - 6 > 0$. Again, this should be verified by the student.

To graph a linear inequality, of the form $ax + by + c \geq 0$ or $ax + by + c \leq 0$, follow these three steps:

1. FIND TWO POINTS ON THE LINE ax + by + c = 0 AND DRAW IT.
2. TEST A POINT ON ONE SIDE OF THE LINE TO SEE IF IT SATISFIES THE INEQUALITY.
3. IF THE TEST-POINT WORKS, SHADE IN THAT SIDE OF THE LINE. IF THE TEST-POINT DOESN'T WORK, SHADE IN THE OTHER SIDE OF THE LINE.

Example 1: Show on the x-y plane the set of points (x, y) which satisfy $x - 3y - 6 \geq 0$.

Solution:

***Step 1*:** Draw the line $x - 3y - 6 = 0$. Two points on it are $(6, 0)$ and $(0, -2)$.

Step 2*:** Test $(0, 0)$ to see if it satisfies the inequality $x - 3y - 6 \geq 0$. $(0) - 3(0) - 6 \geq 0$? No, this is ***not true.

Step 3*:** Shade in the side which does ***not contain $(0, 0)$.

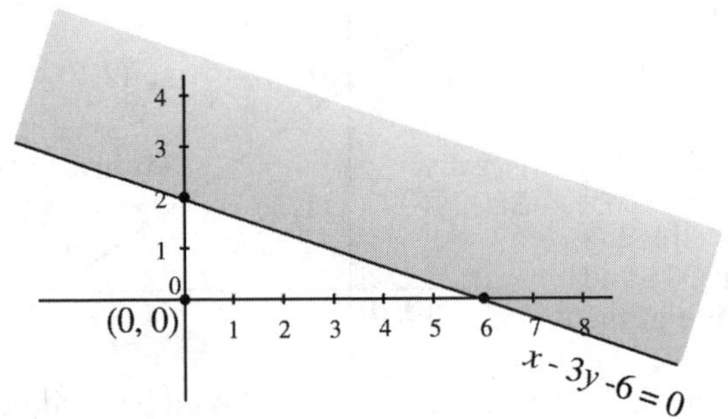

Example 2: Shade in the half-plane of points which satisfy $x \leq 3$.

Solution:

***Step 1*:** Draw the line $x = 3$. Two points on it are $(3, 0)$ and $(3, 2)$.

Step 2*:** Test $(0, 0)$ to see if it satisfies the inequality $x \leq 3$. $0 \leq 3$? Yes, this ***is true.

Step 3*:** Shade in the side which ***does contain $(0, 0)$.

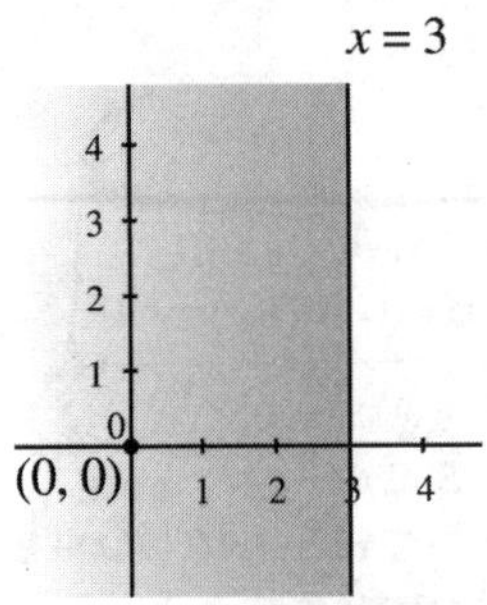

Exercise 18.A

1. In separate diagrams, shade in the set of points (x, y) which satisfy these inequalities:
   (i) $x+y \leq 4$
   (ii) $2x+y \geq 6$
   (iii) $x+3y \leq 12$
   (iv) $2x+5y \geq 10$
   (v) $x-y \leq 3$
   (vi) $x-2y \geq 8$
   (vii) $4x-y+8 \leq 0$
   (viii) $x-3y+6 \geq 0$
   (ix) $2x+7y-14 \leq 0$
   (x) $3x+y-15 \geq 0$

2. In separate diagrams, shade in the half-planes which satisfy these inequalities:
   (i) $x+4y \leq 4$
   (ii) $2x-y \geq 12$
   (iii) $x+y-3 \leq 0$
   (iv) $12x+5y \geq 30$
   (v) $x-y \leq 0$
   (vi) $x \geq 8$
   (vii) $y \leq 4$
   (viii) $y \geq 3$
   (ix) $2x \leq 5$
   (x) $2y-11 \geq 0$

3. In separate diagrams, shade in the set of points (x, y) which satisfy these inequalities:
   (i) $x \leq 4$
   (ii) $2x+y-5 \geq 0$
   (iii) $y \leq 1$
   (iv) $x \geq 7$
   (v) $x+2y \leq 0$
   (vi) $3x-2y \geq 0$
   (vii) $4x \leq 5$
   (viii) $x \geq 4y$
   (ix) $x \geq 0$
   (x) $y \geq 0$

4. In separate diagrams, shade in the half-planes which satisfy these inequalities:
   (i) $y \leq 5$
   (ii) $x-2y-5 \geq 0$
   (iii) $x \leq 6$
   (iv) $2x \geq 7$
   (v) $x+2y \leq 10$
   (vi) $3x-y \geq 6$
   (vii) $2x \leq 11$
   (viii) $x \geq 3y$
   (ix) $2x+9 \leq 0$
   (x) $2y+3 \leq 0$

FINDING THE INEQUALITY

Example 1: Write down the inequality which is satisfied by the points in the shaded region.

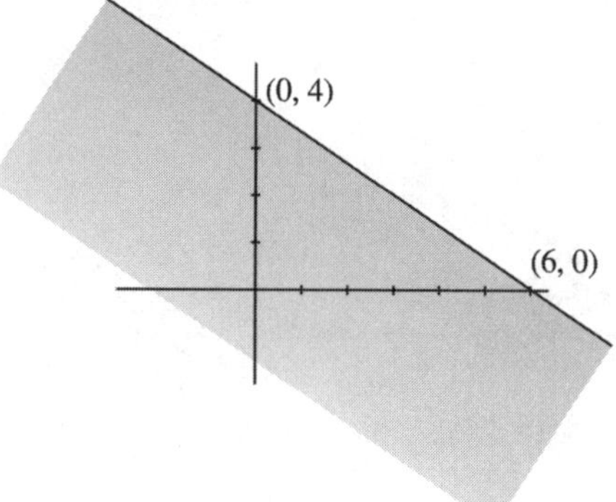

Solution: The ***line*** which passes through the points (6, 0) and (0, 4) has slope given by

$$m = \frac{y_2 - y_1}{x_2 - x_1} = \frac{4-0}{0-6} = \frac{4}{-6} = -\frac{2}{3}.$$

Therefore, its equation is

$$y - y_1 = m(x - x_1)$$

$$\Rightarrow y - 0 = -\frac{2}{3}(x - 6)$$

$$\Rightarrow 3y = -2x + 12$$

$$\Rightarrow 2x + 3y - 12 = 0$$

The ***inequality*** which we are looking for must be either $2x + 3y - 12 \geq 0$ or $2x + 3y - 12 \leq 0$. But which one? We will have to test a point from the shaded region to find out. Let's test the point (0, 0) to see if it satisfies $2x + 3y - 12 \geq 0$.

$2(0) + 3(0) - 12 \geq 0 \Rightarrow -12 \geq 0$, which is ***not*** true.

Therefore, the inequality which we are looking for must be the other one: $2x + 3y - 12 \leq 0$.

Exercise 18.B

In each case, find the inequality which defines the shaded region:

1.

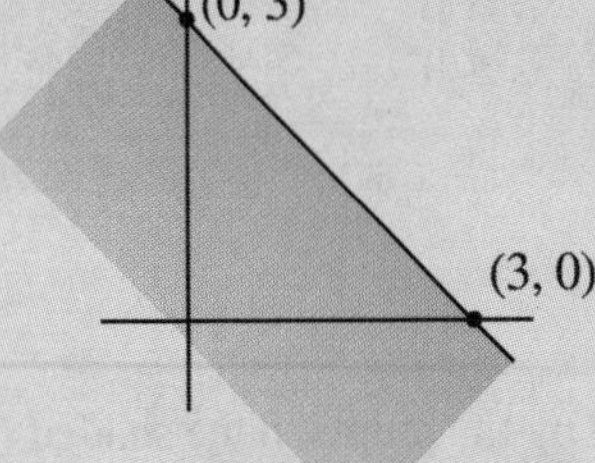

2.

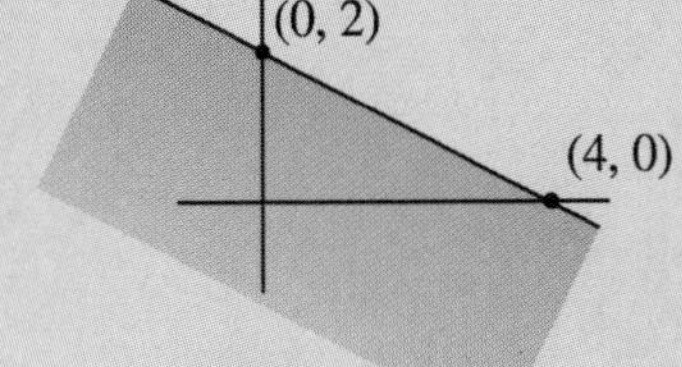

3.

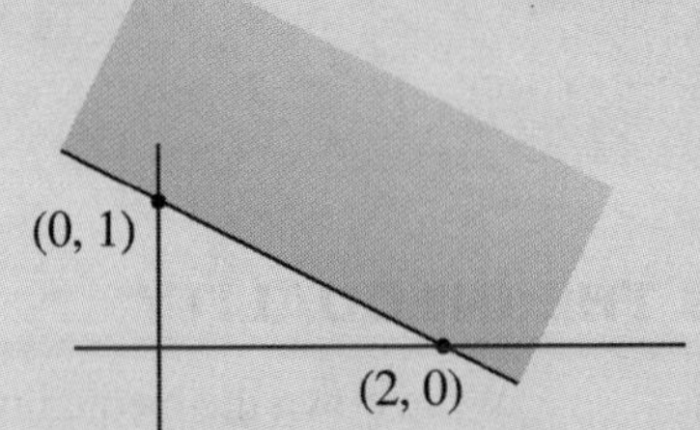

4.

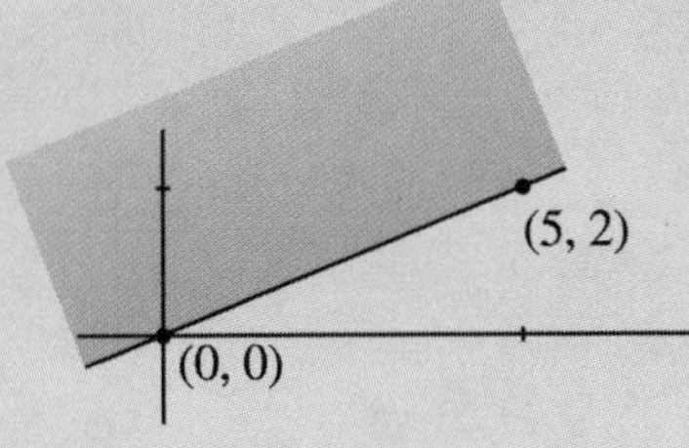

5.

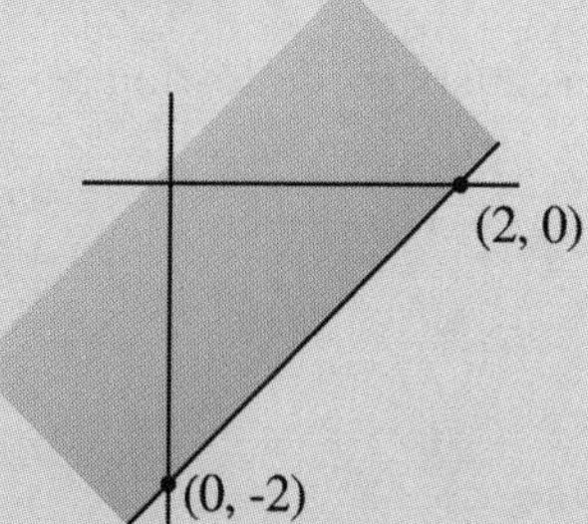

9.

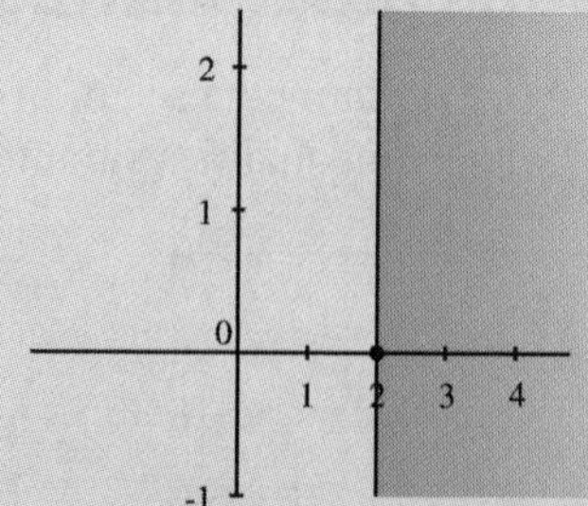

6.

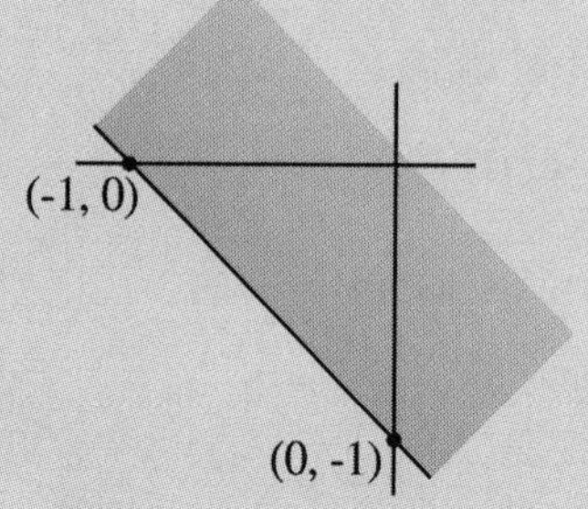

10.

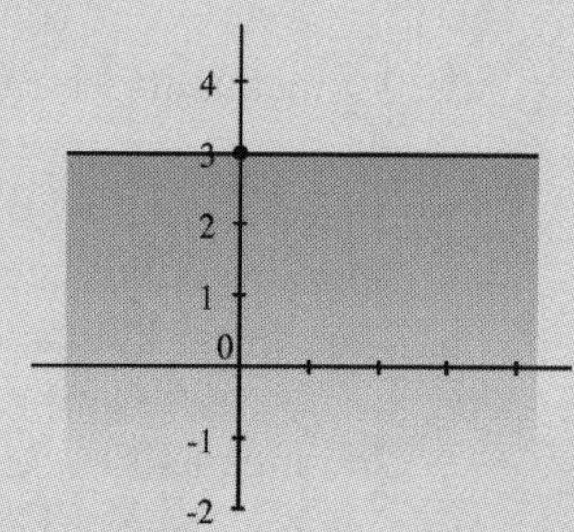

7.

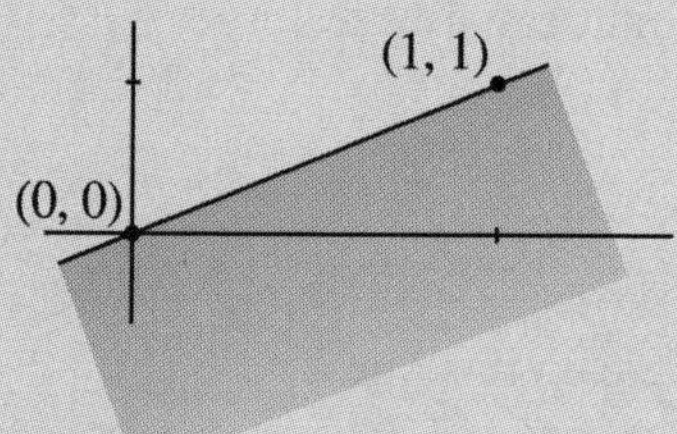

11.

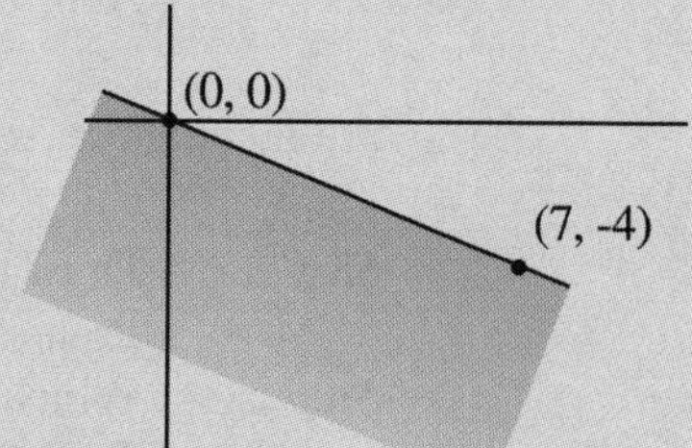

8.

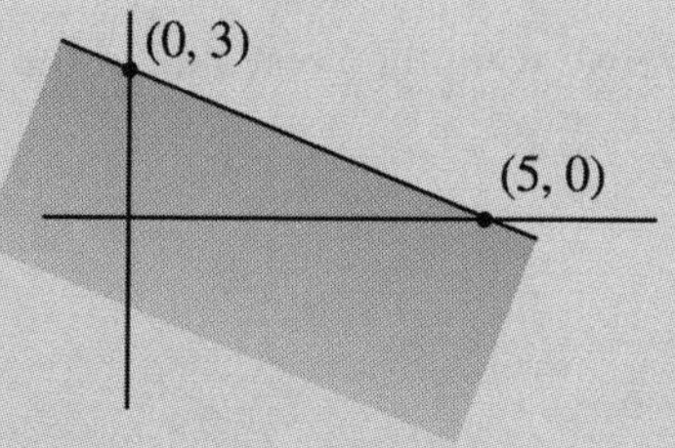

12.

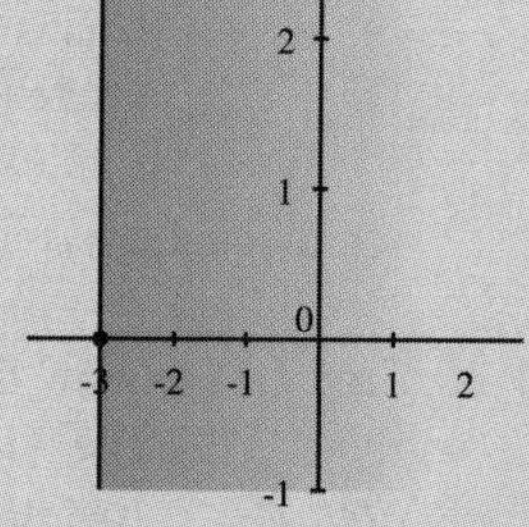

SIMULTANEOUS INEQUALITIES

Example 1: (i) Show the set, S, of points (x, y) which satisfy the following inequalities simultaneously:

$$x \geq 0$$
$$y \geq 2$$
$$2x + y \leq 8$$
$$x + y \leq 6$$

(ii) Find the maximum value of $7x + 4y$, where $(x, y) \in S$.

Solution: (i) 1st inequality: $x \geq 0$:

Step 1: Draw the line $x = 0$ (the y-axis).
Step 2: Which side?
Points to the East of the y-axis satisfy $x \geq 0$.

2nd inequality: $y \geq 2$:

Step 1: Draw the line $y = 2$.
Step 2: Which side?
Above the line $y = 2$, points satisfy $y \geq 2$.

3rd inequality: $2x + y \leq 8$:

Step 1: Draw the line $2x + y = 8$.
Points (0, 8) and (4, 0) are on this line.
Step 2: Which side?
Test (0, 0) in the expression

$$2x + y \leq 8$$
$$\Rightarrow 2(0) + 0 \leq 8$$
$$\Rightarrow 0 \leq 8$$

This is true. Therefore we want the West side of the line, where (0, 0) lies.

4th inequality: $x + y \leq 6$:

Step 1: Draw the line $x + y = 6$.
The points (0, 6) and (6, 0) are on this line.
Step 2: Test (0, 0) in

$$x + y \leq 6$$
$$\Rightarrow 0 + 0 \leq 6$$

This is true. So the side we want is that side of $x + y = 6$ which contains (0, 0).

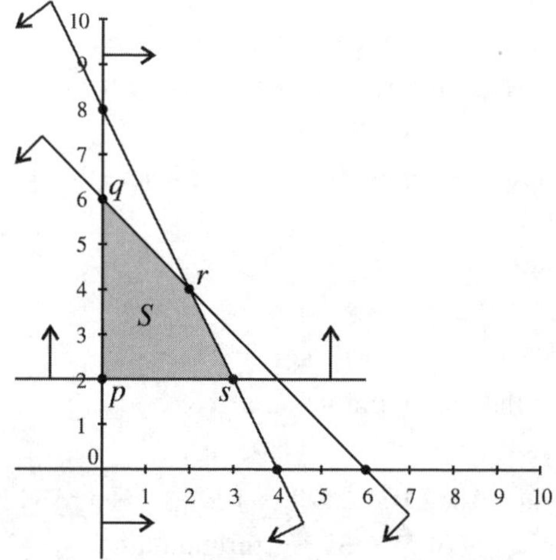

(ii) Any LINEAR expression (i.e. any expression of the form $ax + by + c$) will have its maximum value (or minimum value) at a VERTEX of the region.

We find the vertices of the set S by solving 'simultaneous equations'.

p is where $x = 0$ and $y = 2$ intersect. $\therefore\ p = (0, 2)$.

q is where $x = 0$ and $x + y = 6$ intersect $\therefore\ q = (0, 6)$.

r is where $2x + y = 8$ and $x + y = 6$ intersect.

$$\begin{aligned} 2x + y &= 8 \\ x + y &= 6 \end{aligned}$$

SUBTRACT $x \quad = 2$ and hence $y = 4$.

$\therefore\ r = (2, 4)$.

s is where $y = 2$ and $2x + y = 8$ intersect.

$y = 2 \Rightarrow 2x + 2 = 8 \Rightarrow 2x = 6 \Rightarrow x = 3$

$\therefore\ s = (3, 2)$.

Here is a table to find which of the points p, q, r, s have the maximum value for $7x + 4y$:

POINT	$7x + 4y$	VALUE
$p(0, 2)$	$0 + 8$	8
$q(0, 6)$	$0 + 24$	24
$r(2, 4)$	$14 + 16$	30
$s(3, 2)$	$21 + 8$	29

$\therefore$ The maximum value is 30 which is achieved at the point $r(2, 4)$

Exercise 18.C

1. Shade in the set of points which simultaneously satisfy $x \geq 0, y \geq 0, x + y \leq 6$.
At what point of this region does $2x + y$ achieve its maximum value?

2. Indicate by the letter A the region of the plane where the points (x, y) satisfy
$x \geq 0, y \geq 0, 2x + y \leq 10$.
What is the minimum value of $x - y$ in A?

3. Show the set of points $E = \{(x, y) | x \geq y, y \geq 0, x + y \leq 5\}$.
If (x, y) is in E, find the maximum value of $x + 2y$.

4. Show the set $S = \{(x, y) | x \geq 0, y \geq 0, x + y \leq 6, 2x + y \leq 8\}$
Find the maximum value of $5x + 3y + 1$ throughout S.

5. (i) Using the same axes and the same scales and taking $x, y \in R$, graph the following inequalities:

$P_1 : y \geq 0$

$P_2 : 9x + 5y \geq 1800$

$P_3 : 4x + 5y \leq 1000$

(ii) Indicate the set of points $A = P_1 \cap P_2 \cap P_3$.

(iii) Calculate the co-ordinates of the vertex common to P_2 and P_3.

(iv) Calculate the value of $100x + 75y$ for each vertex of A.

6. $E = \{(x, y) | x - y \geq 2, x + 2y \leq 5, y \geq 0, x \in R, y \in R\}$.

(i) Shade in the region E on graph paper.

(ii) What is the maximum value of $10x + 11y$ over E?

7. (a) On the same set of axes show the half-planes:

$A = \{(x, y) | y - x \leq 1\}$

$B = \{(x, y) | x + y \leq 7\}$

$C = \{(x, y) | x \geq 0\}$

$D = \{(x, y) | y \geq 0\}$.

(b) Indicate the set $S = A \cap B \cap C \cap D$.

(c) If $(x, y) \in S$, find the maximum value of:

(i) $3x + 4y$,

(ii) $3x - 4y$.

8. In the diagram, the line L has equation $4x + 3y = 12$. Write down the equations of the three inequalities which determine the triangular shaded region on the diagram.

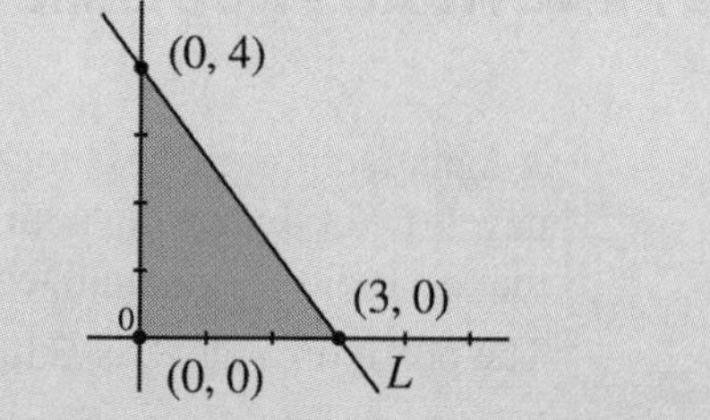

9. In the diagram, the line L has equation $x + 3y = 12$ and the line M has equation $x - y = 0$. Write down the equations of the three inequalities which determine the triangular shaded region on the diagram.

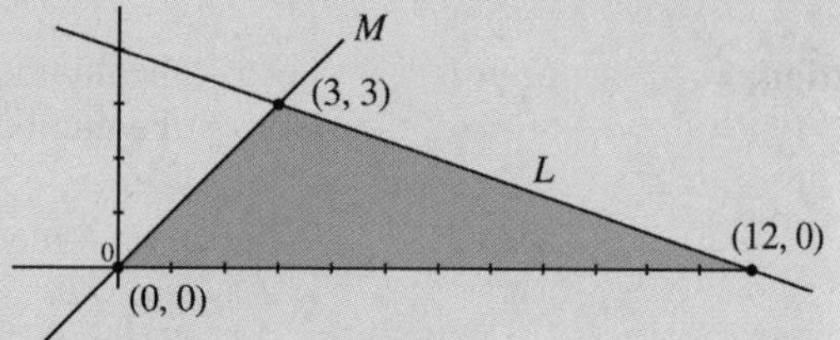

10. (i) Find the equations of the three lines L, M, N in the diagram.
(ii) Write down the three inequalities which determine the shaded region.

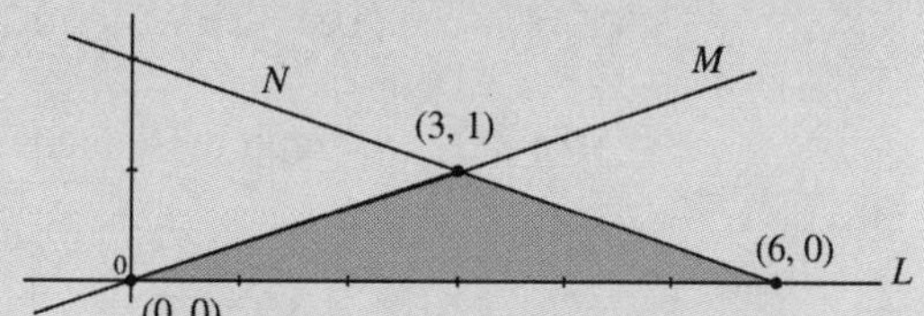

11. (i) Find the equations of the three lines L, M, N in the diagram.
(ii) Write down the three inequalities which determine the shaded region.
(iii) Find the maximum value of $3x + 2y$ in the shaded region.

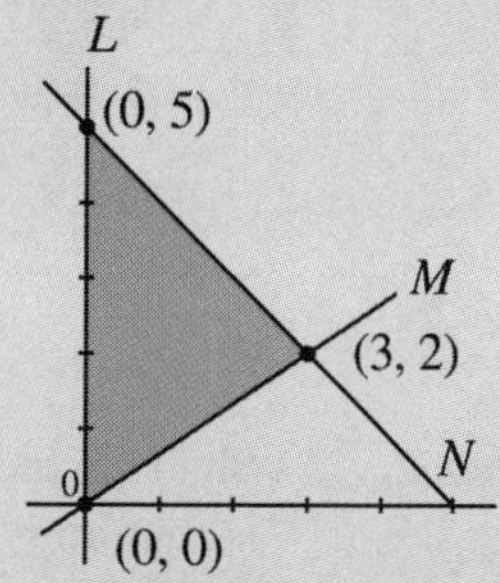

12. (i) Find the equations of the lines L and M in the diagram.
(ii) Write down the four inequalities which determine the shaded region.
(iii) Find the minimum value of $(x + 3y)$ in the shaded region.

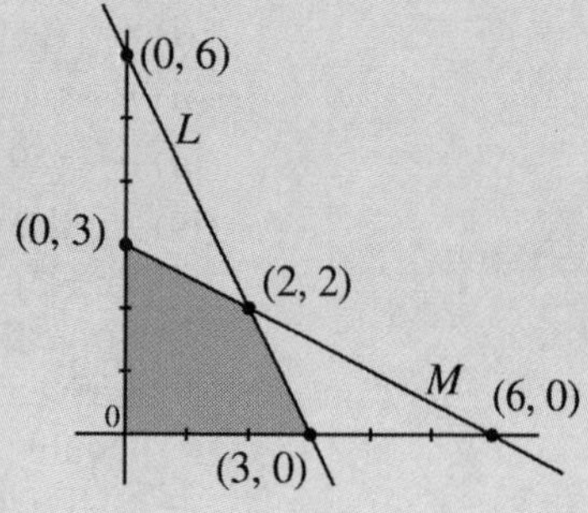

SOLVING PRACTICAL PROBLEMS WITH LINEAR PROGRAMMING

Example 1: A manufacturer makes clocks and radios. He can make at most 50 items a day. It takes 4 working hours to make a clock and 6 working hours to make a radio. The manufacturer has 240 working hours available per day.

The profit on a clock is €30 and on a radio is €40.

Find the maximum profit.

Solution:

***Step 1*:** Let x = the number of clocks which are made per day.
Let y = the number of radios which are made per day.

***Step 2*:** Write down 4 inequalities:

1.	$x \geq 0$	(You can't make less than zero clocks!)
2.	$y \geq 0$	(Have you ever seen –2 radios?!)
3.	$x + y \leq 50$	(50 items, at most, are made)
4.	$4x + 6y \leq 240$	(240 man-hours, at most, are available)
i.e.	$2x + 3y \leq 120$	(dividing by 2)

***Step 3*:** Graph these inequalities on the x-plane, as before.

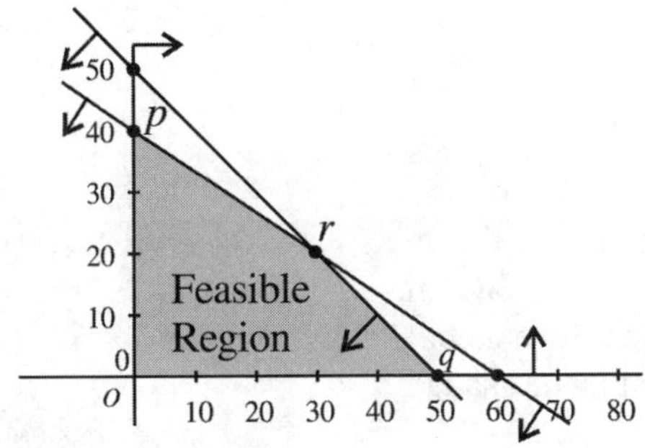

***Step 4*:** Shade in the feasible region, the set of points which satisfy all inequalities above.

***Step 5*:** Find the vertices.

(i) $o = (0, 0)$

(ii) $p = (0, 40)$

(iii) $q = (50, 0)$

(iv) r = the point of intersection of $x + y = 50$ and $2x + 3y = 120$

Solve these 'simultaneous equations' to find r.

Leave the 2nd equation:	$2x + 3y = 120$
Double the 1st equation:	$\underline{2x + 2y = 100}$
SUBTRACT!	$y = 20$

But $x + y = 50$.
$\therefore\ x = 30$
$\therefore\ r = (30, 20)$

***Step 6*:** The manufacturer makes a profit of €30 on each clock and €40 on each radio, so this profit on x clocks and y radios amounts to € $30x + 40y$. We have to find the maximum possible value of $30x + 40y$ throughout the feasible region.

VERTICES	$30x + 40y$	PROFIT
(0, 0)	0 + 0	0
(0, 40)	0 + 1600	1600
(30, 20)	900 + 800	1700
(50, 0)	1500 + 0	1500

***Step 7*:** Answer the question!!
The maximum profit is €1700 per day.

Exercise 18.D

1. A woman farmer has 5 hectares in which to grow either grain or vegetables. To sow a hectare of grain costs €1200 while to sow a hectare of vegetables costs €600. She has €3600 available. If she sows x hectares of grain and y hectares of vegetables, write down two inequalities in x and y. Graph these inequalities. Profit on a hectare of grain is €800 while profit on a hectare of vegetables is €500.
How should she sow the 5 hectares in order to maximise her profits?

2. A factory can make jeans or trousers. Each pair of jeans takes 3 working hours to make, trousers take 2 working hours. There are 90 working hours available per day.
Each pair of jeans costs €10 to produce, each pair of trousers €15 to produce. There is a budget of €600 per day available.
Let x = the number of jeans produced and y = the number of trousers produced each day.
Write down two inequalities in x and y and graph them.
A pair of jeans yields a profit of €8; and pair of trousers €6. How many of each should the factory produce in order to maximise profits?

3. A man buys a house with 9 rooms. He can convert them into offices or flats.
To convert a room into an office costs €3000, while to convert a room into a flat costs €6000. He has €36 000 available. If he creates x offices and y flats, write down two inequalities and graph them.
Rent on an office will be €300 per week, while rent for a flat will be €400 per week.
How many offices and how many flats should he create in order to get the maximum amount of rent per week?

4. A builder can build 3-bedroomed or 5-bedroomed houses. A 3-bedroomed house occupies an area of 400 m^2. A 5-bedroomed house occupies an area of 500 m^2. He has 20 000 m^2 of land available. To build a 3-bedroomed house costs €48 000; to build a 5-bedroomed house costs €90 000. He has €2 880 000 available.
If he builds x 3-bedroomed houses and y 5-bedroomed houses, write down 2 inequalities in x and y and graph them.
He can sell the 3-bedroomed houses for €62 000 each and 5-bedroomed houses for €110 000 each.
Calculate the PROFIT on each type of house.
How many of each type should he make in order to maximise his profits?

5. A holiday campsite caters for caravans and tents. Each caravan accommodates 8 people and each tent accommodates 5 people. If there are x caravans and y tents on the site and if the site facilties cannot accommodate more than 400 people, write down an inequality to express this information.
Each caravan is allotted an area of 60 m^2 and each tent is allotted 50 m^2. The total area available for caravans and tents is 3600 m^2. Write down an inequality to express this information.
Graph the set showing the possible numbers of caravans and tents on the site.
If there were only caravans on the site, what is the maximum number of caravans which could be catered for?
The charges on the site are €30 per caravan and €20 per tent.
How many caravans and how many tents should be on the site to give maximum income?
Indicate on your graph the region where the income would be less than €600.

6. A man is told by his nutritionist that he must supplement his diet with at least 20 mg of vitamin A and 12 mg of vitamin B per day. He can take either red or green tablets. Each red tablet contains 2 mg of vitamin A and 1 mg of vitamin B. Each green tablet contains 4 mg of vitamin A and 3 mg of vitamin B.
(i) If he were to take green tablets only, what is the least number which he would need to take per day?
(ii) If red tablets cost 12 cent each and green ones cost 27 cent each, how many of each should he take in order to minimise his costs?
(iii) In a sale, red tablets are reduced to 11 cent and green tablets to 21 cent. How many of each would minimise the cost?

7. A manufacturer makes radios and CD players. This table shows the manufacturing time, the manufacturing cost and the profit made on each item.

	RADIO	CD PLAYER
TIME (in working hours)	4	6
COST (in €)	30	70
PROFIT (in €)	36	60

The manufacturer has 240 working hours and capital of €2100 available per week. What is the maximum weekly profit?

8. A ship has space for, at most, 200 containers which are of two types: refrigerated and unrefrigerated. Each refrigerated container carries a load of 3 tonnes and each unrefrigerated container carries a load of 8 tonnes. The maximum load the ship can carry is 1200 tonnes. Freight charges on each refrigerated container are €100 and on each unrefrigerated container €80.

Graph the set showing the possible numbers of each type of container that the ship can carry.

If operating costs on each journey amount to €14 000, indicate by the letter K that region of your graph where the ship is not operating at a loss.

Calculate the maximum profit if a ready supply of each container is available.

REVISION EXERCISE 18.E

1.

$$A = \{(x, y) | y \geq 0\}$$
$$B = \{(x, y) | x \geq 0\}$$
$$C = \{(x, y) | x + y \leq 5\}$$
$$D = \{(x, y) | x + 2y \leq 6\}$$

(i) Indicate on the x-y plane the set of points $E = A \cap B \cap C \cap D$.

(ii) At what point of E does $2x - 3y$ achieve its minimum value?

2. (i) Using the same scales and axes and taking $x, y \in R$, graph each of the following half-planes:

$$A = \{(x, y) | y \geq 0\}$$
$$B = \{(x, y) | 3x + 4y \geq 120\}$$
$$C = \{(x, y) | 2x + y \leq 60\}$$

(ii) Indicate the set of points $D = A \cap B \cap C$.

(iii) Calculate the co-ordinates of vertices of D (it is not sufficient to read these co-ordinates from your graph).

(iv) Find the couple $(x, y) \in D$ for which $100x + 40y$ is a maximum.

3. (a) Illustrate the half-plane: $\{(x, y) \mid 2x + y \geq 0\}$ on graph paper.

(b) A farmer has 8 hectares for either tillage or pasture. Each hectare of tillage requires 2 hours of his time per day, each hectare of pasture requires 1 hour per day. He can work for up to 10 hours per day.
He makes a profit of €800 per annum on each hectare of tillage and €300 on each hectare of pasture. How should he use his land in order to make maximum profit?

4. (a) Write down the equation of the line L in the diagram.
Write down the inequality which determines the shaded region.

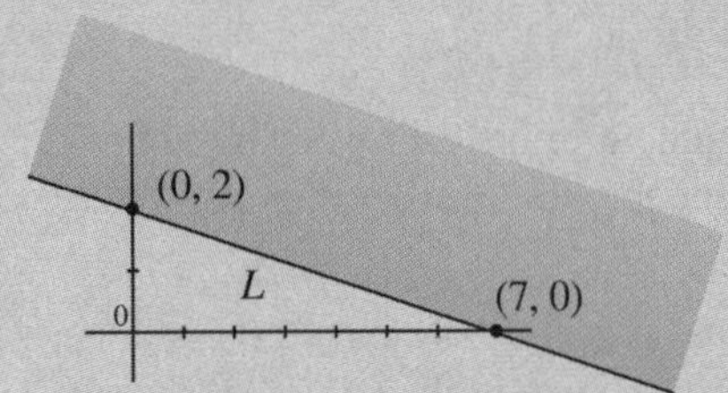

(b) A manufacturer has a ready market for components of two types: type A and type B.
The maximum machine time available for their manufacture is 9 hours.
The maximum energy available is 180 units.
The following table shows the time and energy requirement for each type of component.

COMPONENT	Type A	Type B
Minutes per component	12	10
Energy units per component	3	4

If the profit on each type A component is €7 and on each type B component is €9, calculate the number of components of each type which should be made in order to have a maximum profit.

5. (a) L is the line $y = 6$. M is the line $x + y = 8$.
Write down the four inequalities which determine the shaded region.

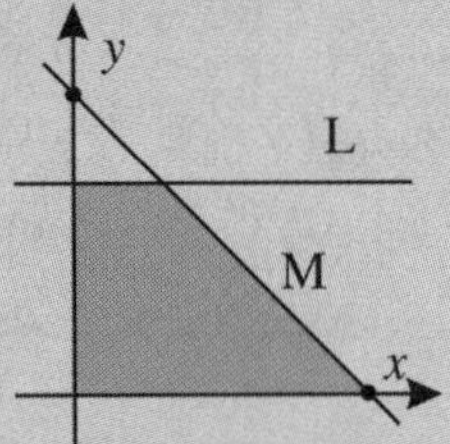

(b) A tour operator has to bring 60 tourists from the airport to their hotel. She may hire taxis, which carry 3 persons each, or minibuses which carry 12 passengers each. The hire firm insists that she uses at least as many taxis as minibuses.
Hire for a taxi will be €30, for a minibus €80. How many of each should the tour operator use in order to minimise her costs?

6. (a) Write down the equation of the line L in the diagram. Write down the inequality which determines the shaded region.

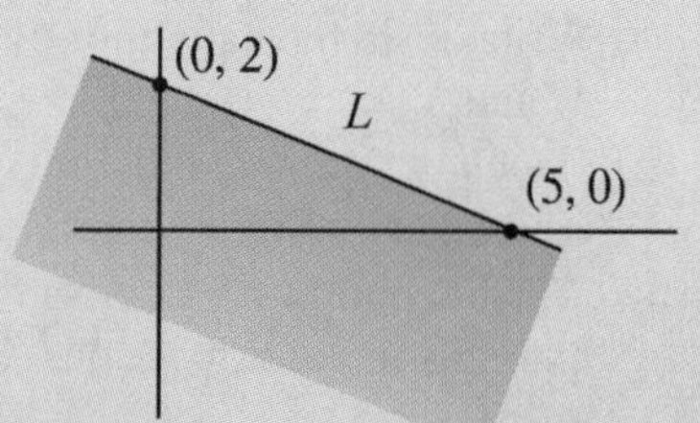

(b) A manufacturer produces two products P and Q. The time in hours required for the CUTTING and FINISHING of each unit produced is shown in the table.

	P	*Q*
Cutting hours per unit	6	6
Finishing hours per unit	3	6

There are, at most, 180 hours available for cutting and at most 150 hours for finishing. Assume that a profit of €50 is made on the sales of each unit of P and a profit of €10 on the sale of each unit of Q and that there is a ready sale for both products.

(i) Graph the set of all possible sales of P and Q.

(ii) Graph the set of all possible sales of P and Q that yields a profit of €700 and say what is the sale for P alone that would yield this profit.

(iii) Find the sales of P and Q that yield maximum profit.

7. (a) L is the line $x + y = 6$. M is the line $x - y = 0$. Write down the three inequalities which determine the shaded region.

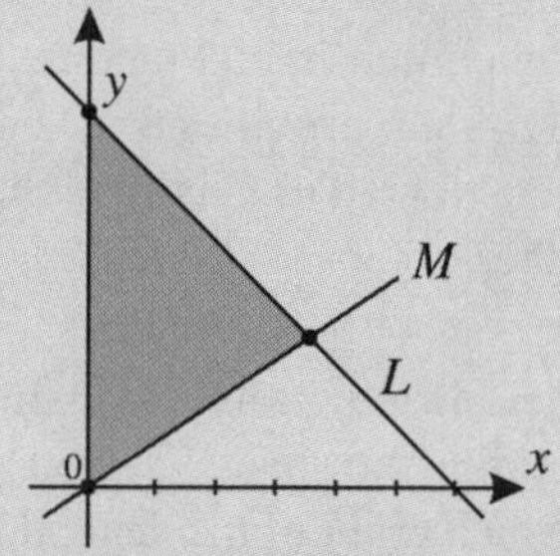

(b) A car hire firm supplies small and large cars. The firm must have at least twice as many small cars as large cars. The average daily cost of maintaining a small car is €15 and of maintaining a large car is €45. The total average daily costs must not exceed €225.
Graph the set showing the possible numbers of each type of car which the firm can have.
If the daily hire charges are €45 for a small car and €60 for a large car, write down an expression for the daily ***profit*** and indicate by the letter K that region where the daily profit is greater than €225.
Also calculate the maximum daily profit that could be made.

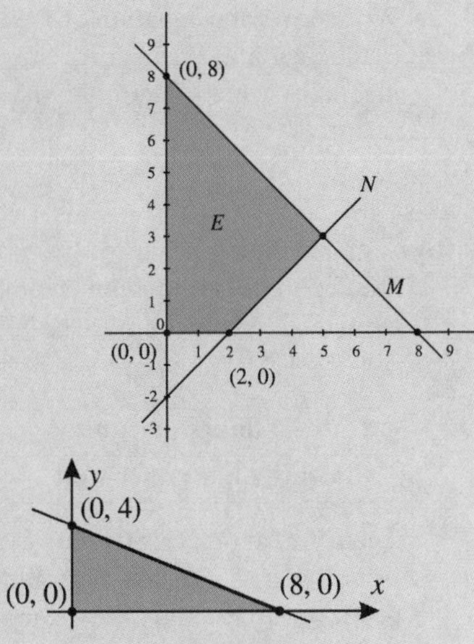

8. (a) (i) Write down the equations of the lines M and N.

(ii) Hence write down the 4 inequalities which determine the region E.

(iii) At what point of E does $4x + 3y$ attain its maximum value?

(b) List the six couples which satisfy $x + y \leq 4$, where $x, y \in N_0$.
[Hint: $N_0 = \{1, 2, 3, 4, ...\}$]

9. (a) Write down the three inequalities which determine the shaded region.

(b) A property developer wants to construct a business centre consisting of shops and offices. The floor space for each shop is 50m² and for each office is 20m². The total floor space must not exceed 700m².
Each shop takes 4 working days to complete and each office 3 days to complete. There are 84 working days available, at most.

(i) If the developer constructs x shops and y offices, write down two inequalities in x and y and illustrate these on graph paper.

(ii) If the rental charge is €300 per month for a shop and €220 for an office, how many of each should be constructed in order to maximise rental income? Find this maximum rental income.

(iii) If each shop provides 8 jobs and each office 3 jobs, how many of each should be constructed to maximise the total number of jobs. Find, also, this maximum number of jobs.

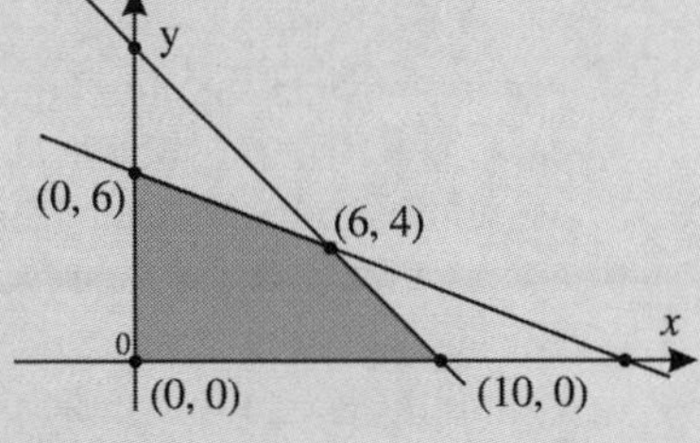

10. (a) (i) Write down the four inequalities which determine the shaded region.

(ii) At which point of the shaded region does $(x - 2y)$ attain its minimum value?

(b) A woman is told by her nutritionist that she must take at least 30 milligrams of vitamin C and 18 milligrams of vitamin E per day. She can take either orange or blue tablets. Each orange tablet contains 3 milligrams of vitamin C and 3 milligrams of vitamin E. Each blue tablet contains 5 milligrams of vitamin C and 1 of vitamin E.
The woman consumes x orange tablets and y blue tablets per day.

(i) Write down two inequalities in x and y and illustrate them on graph paper.

(ii) If an orange tablet costs 7 cent and a blue tablet costs 10 cent, what is the minimum possible cost to the woman per day?

1. To graph a linear inequality, of the form $ax + by + c \geq 0$ or $ax + by + c \leq 0$, follow these steps:
   1. Find two points on the line $ax + by + c = 0$ and draw it.
   2. Test a point on one side of the line to see if it satisfies the inequality.
   3. If the test-point works, shade in that side of the line. If the test-point doesn't work, shade in the other side of the line.

2. To solve a linear programming problem, follow these steps:
   1. Let x and y represent appropriate variables.
   2. Write down two inequalities in x and y.
   3. Graph these inequalities.
   4. Shade in the ***feasible region*** where the points satisfy both inequalities.
   5. Find the vertices by solving 'simultaneous equations'.
   6. Draw up a table and find which vertex yields the desired maximum (or minimum) value.
   7. Answer the question precisely!

Chapter 19

Option 2: Further Sequences and Series and the Binomial Theorem

In Chapter 16, four formulae were established:

(a) For Arithmetic Sequences: $a, a + d, a + 2d, a + 3d, \ldots$

(i) the nth term, $T_n = a + (n - 1)d$

(ii) the sum of the first n terms, $S_n = \frac{n}{2}\{2a + (n - 1)d\}$

(b) For Geometric Sequences: $a, ar, ar^2\ ar^3, \ldots$

(i) the nth term, $T_n = ar^{n-1}$

(ii) the sum of the first n terms, $S_n = \dfrac{a(1 - r^n)}{1 - r}$

In this chapter we will put these formulae to practical use!

Example 1: A girl puts 25 cent into a new account. The next week she puts in 35 cent, and the next week 45 cent. She continues in this way for 52 weeks.

(i) How much will she put into her account in the 52nd week?

(ii) How much will she then have in her account altogether?

Solution:

(i) The amounts going into the account could be listed in this way: 25, 35, 45, 55, ...

This is an **ARITHMETIC** sequence, since 10 is being ADDED each time.

We want to find the 52nd term in this sequence:

$$\left.\begin{aligned} a &= 25 \\ d &= 10 \\ n &= 52 \end{aligned}\right\} \quad \begin{aligned} T_n &= a + (n - 1)d \\ &= 25 + (51)(10) \\ &= 535 \\ &= €5.35 \text{ : The answer.} \end{aligned}$$

(ii) In this part we want to find the sum of the first 52 terms:
$25 + 35 + 45 + 55 + \ldots + 535$

$$\left.\begin{aligned} a &= 25 \\ d &= 10 \\ n &= 52 \end{aligned}\right\} \quad \begin{aligned} S_n &= \frac{n}{2}\{2a + (n-1)d\} \\ &= 26\{50 + (51)(10)\} \\ &= 26\{560\} \\ &= 14560 \\ &= €145.60 : \text{The answer} \end{aligned}$$

Example 2: The population of a town decreases by 5% per annum. If the present population is 16 000, what will the population be in 10 years' time?

Solution: Each year, the population will be 95% of the previous year's population, i.e. this year's population = 0.95 x last year's population.

Hence, after 1 year it will be 16 000 x 0.95 = 15 200
after 2 years it will be 15 200 x 0.95 = 14 440
after 3 years it will be 14 440 x 0.95 = 13 718 etc.

This list 15200, 14440, 13718, ... is a GEOMETRIC sequence since we are MULTIPLYING by 0.95 each time.
We want to find the 10th term of this sequence:

$$\left.\begin{aligned} a &= 15200 \\ r &= 0.95 \\ n &= 10 \end{aligned}\right\} \quad \begin{aligned} T_n &= ar^{n-1} \\ &= 15200(0.95)^9 \\ &= 15200(0.63025) \\ &= 9579.8 \\ &= 9580 \text{ to the nearest whole person!} \end{aligned}$$

Example 3: A couple invest €200 EVERY year for twenty years. If the rate of compound interest is 6% per annum, how much will they have in their account at the end of the 20th year?

Solutions: The first €200 which they invest will be in the bank, earning interest, for 20 years. In accordance with the compound interest formula,

it will be worth .... $€200(1.06)^{20}$

The second €200 will amount to .... $€200(1.06)^{19}$

The third €200 will amount to .... $€200(1.06)^{18}$

⋮ ⋮

The 19th €200 will amount to .... $€200(1.06)^{2}$

The last €200 will amount to .... $€200(1.06)^{1}$

In their account will be the sum of all these amounts, which is (reading from the BOTTOM up):

$$200(1.06) + 200(1.06)^2 + 200(1.06)^3 + \ldots + 200(1.06)^{20}$$

This is the SUM of the first 20 terms of a GEOMETRIC series.

$$\left.\begin{aligned} a &= 200(1.06) = 212 \\ r &= 1.06 \\ n &= 20 \end{aligned}\right\} \quad \begin{aligned} S_n &= \frac{a(1-r^n)}{1-r} \\ &= \frac{212(1-1.06^{20})}{1-1.06} \\ &= \frac{212(1-3.207135)}{(-0.06)} \\ &= \frac{212(-2.207135)}{(-0.06)} \\ &= \frac{-467.9127}{-0.06} \\ &= €7798.55 : \textit{Answer} \end{aligned}$$

Exercise 19.A

1. A boy's pocket money starts at 20 cent and goes up each week by 5 cent.

(i) Write out in a sequence the pocket-money which he receives in the first five weeks.
(ii) Is this sequence ARITHMETIC or GEOMETRIC?
(iii) How much pocket money will he get in the 30th week?
(iv) If he saves all his pocket money for 30 weeks, how much will he save altogether?

2. A barrel and 8 pebbles are placed in a straight line, at equal intervals of 10 metres. A competitor has to start at the barrel, run to the first pebble, bring it back to the barrel and put it in. Then the competitor runs to the next pebble, brings it back and puts it into the barrel, etc.

(i) Write in a sequence the distances (from the barrel back to the barrel) which the competitor runs each time.
(ii) Is this sequence ARITHMETIC or GEOMETRIC?
(iii) How far does the competitor run altogether?

3. A tennis-ball is hit 16 metres straight up into the air from ground level. Each time that it bounces, it reaches 0.75 of the height of the previous bounce.

(i) Write in a sequence the heights reached on the first 4 occasions.
(ii) Is this sequence ARITHMETIC or GEOMETRIC?
(iii) How high (to the nearest centimetre) will the ball reach on its 10th 'flight'?
(iv) How far (to the nearest metre) will the ball have travelled when it lands from its 10th 'flight'? (Remember to include the distance travelled down as well as up!)

4. Every year Sylvester has a birthday cake with the number of candles equal to his age (which, of course, he blows out.) How many candles will he have blown out, up to and including his 21st birthday?

5. A woman trains for a 20 km race. She starts by running 2 km on the first day. The next day she runs 2.5 km. The next day she runs 3 km. This goes on until the day before the race, when she runs 19.5 km. On the day of the race itself she runs 20 km.

(i) Write in a sequence the number of kilometres which she runs each day for the first week.
(ii) Is this sequence ARITHMETIC or GEOMETRIC?
(iii) How far will she have run altogether over the 37 days of running?

6. A boy got 60% in his first year Maths exam. After that, he improved each year, so that his mark every year is 1.1 times that of the year before.
What mark (to the nearest percent) will he get in sixth year?

7. A couple decide to invest €100 at 5% compound interest per annum ***each*** year for 4 years.

(i) How much will the first €100 have amounted to after 4 years?
(ii) How much will they have altogether in their account after 4 years?

8. A couple invest €360 each year for 6 years in an investment institution, to save for their children's education. The institution pays 6% per annum in compound interest. How much will they have altogether in their account after 6 years, to the nearest euro?

9. A pianist wants to prepare for a forthcoming exam. She practises for 30 minutes on the first day, 35 minutes the next day, 40 minutes the next, etc.

(i) For how long will she practise on the 11th day?
(ii) How many minutes of practice will she have done over these 11 days?

10. A colony of bacteria doubles in number every hour.

(i) Starting from a single bacterium, how many bacteria will there be after 24 hours?
(ii) How many bacteria would amount to 921 600 after 12 hours?

11. After winning the lottery, a man has €625 000 altogether. He spends 0.2 of this money. Each year, he spends 0.2 of the money which he has left.

(i) Write out in a sequence the amounts which he spends each year over the first 4 years.
(ii) Is this sequence ARITHMETIC or GEOMETRIC?
(iii) How much will be spent in the 9th year?
(iv) How much will he have left after 9 years?

12. A colony of rabbits increases in number by 20% every three months. If you start with 10 rabbits, how many will you have
(i) after 2 years,
(ii) after 5 years?

13. A company invests €5000 at the beginning of ***each*** year for three consecutive years. Each investment earns 10% compound interest per annum.
(i) Find the value of the ***first*** investment at the end of the third year.
(ii) Find the total value of all three investments at the end of the third year.
(iii) If the company continues to invest €5000 each year for 12 consecutive years, what will the total of the 12 investments be worth at the end of 12 years, to the nearest ten euro?

14. A student invests €50 each year in an account which yields 8% compound interest per annum. Find the total amount in the student's account at the end of six years.

15. A person invested €200 at the beginning of each year for 15 years. Each investment earned 4% per annum compound interest. Find the total value of the investments at the end of the fifteenth year, to the nearest hundred euro.

16. A life assurance company invested €x in bonds at the beginning of each year for five years. Each investment earned 20% per annum compound interest. The total value of the five investments at the end of the fifth year was €1 785 984.
Find the value of x.

17. The population of the world increases by 2% per annum. In the year 2000 the population is 8 billion. Write down the population of the world (in billions, correct to three significant figures) in these years:
(i) 2002 (ii) 2010 (iii) 2020 (iv) 2050

18. An investment company invested €x in stocks and shares at the beginning of each year for ten years. Each investment earned 10% per annum compound interest. The total value of the ten investments at the end of the tenth year was (to the nearest euro) €70 125.
Find the value of x, to the nearest euro.

THE SUM TO INFINITY OF A GEOMETRIC SERIES

Suppose that you get a huge cake for your birthday. You eat $^1/_2$ of it on the first day, $^1/_4$ of it the next day, $^1/_8$ of it the next, and so on. If you go on like this forever, how much of the cake will you eat?

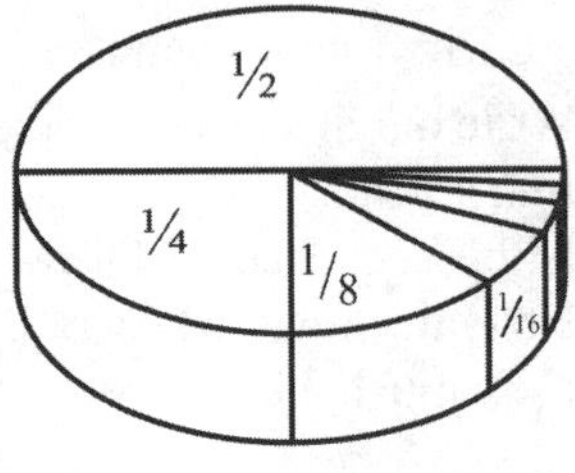

What we are asking is this:

'If you add up $^1/_2 + ^1/_4 + ^1/_8$ ... ad infinitum, what number do you get closer and closer to?'

We call this the SUM TO INFINITY of the series $^1/_2 + ^1/_4 + ^1/_8$ ...

It is written S_∞. (The Mathematical symbol ∞ means infinity.)

TO PROVE THAT $S_\infty = \frac{a}{1-r}$

Take any number between –1 and +1, say 0.8. When such a number is raised to higher and higher powers, the answers get closer and closer to zero.

For example:

$$0.8^2 = 0.64$$
$$0.8^5 = 0.32768$$
$$0.8^{10} = 0.107374$$
$$0.8^{100} = 0.0000000002037$$

So, if $-1 < r < 1$, then as n gets bigger and bigger, r^n tends towards 0.

We write: 'As $n \to \infty$, $r^n \to 0$' or '$\lim\limits_{n \to \infty} r^n = 0$' if $-1 < r < 1$.

Now, the sum of n terms of a geometric series is $\frac{a(1-r^n)}{1-r}$.

But, if $-1 < r < 1$, then as $n \to \infty$, $r^n \to 0$

$$\therefore\ S_\infty = \frac{a(1-0)}{1-r} = \frac{a}{1-r}$$

In the cake series, $a = \frac{1}{2}$ and $r = \frac{1}{2}$

$$\therefore\ \text{the sum to infinity} = S_\infty = \frac{a}{1-r} = \frac{\frac{1}{2}}{1-\frac{1}{2}} = \frac{\frac{1}{2}}{\frac{1}{2}} = 1.$$

So, you will get nearer and nearer to having eaten just one cake, even if you were to live forever!

RECURRING DECIMALS

Decimals which recur (repeat) can be written in a special way.

For example

$$^1/_3 = 0.33333... = 0.\dot{3}$$
$$^1/_6 = 0.166666... = 0.1\dot{6}$$

If a block of numbers repeats, put a dot over the first and the last digits of the recurring block.

For example:

$$^7/_{11} = 0.363636... = 0.\dot{3}\dot{6}$$
$$^{11}/_{999} = 0.011011011... = 0.\dot{0}1\dot{1}$$

Example 1:

(i) Show that the recurring decimal $0.\dot{7} = 0.7777777...$ can be written as the sum to infinity of a geometric series.

(ii) Hence write $0.\dot{7}$ as a fraction.

(iii) Write $3.\dot{7}$ as a fraction also.

Solution:

(i) $0.77777... = \frac{7}{10} + \frac{7}{100} + \frac{7}{1000} + ...$

$= S_\infty$ of a geometric series, $a = \frac{7}{10}$ and $r = \frac{1}{10}$

(ii) $S_\infty = \frac{a}{1-r}$

$= \frac{\frac{7}{10}}{1 - \frac{1}{10}}$

$= \frac{7}{10-1}$ (multiplying above and below by 10)

$= \frac{7}{9}$

(Check on a calculator: $7 \div 9 = 0.7777777...$ Correct!)

(iii) $3.\dot{7} = 3 + \frac{7}{9} = \frac{27+7}{9} = \frac{34}{9}$

(Check on a calculator: $34 \div 9 = 3.777777...$ Correct!)

Exercise 19.B

1. Find the sum to infinity of the following geometric series:

(i) $\frac{1}{4} + \frac{1}{12} + \frac{1}{36} + ...$

(ii) $1 + \frac{1}{2} + \frac{1}{4} + ...$

(iii) $80 + 60 + 45 + ...$

(iv) $90 + 30 + 10 + ...$

(v) $\frac{1}{2} + \frac{1}{10} + \frac{1}{50} + ...$

(vi) $1 - \frac{1}{2} + \frac{1}{4} - ...$

(vii) $\frac{2}{3} - \frac{1}{6} + \frac{1}{24} - ...$

(viii) $1 + (0.9) + (0.9)^2 + ...$

(ix) $1000 + 100 + 10 ...$

(x) $(0.2) - (0.2)^2 + (0.2)^3 - ...$

2. (i) Show that $0.\dot{1}$ (= 0.1111111...) can be written as the sum to infinity of a geometric series.

(ii) Hence write $0.\dot{1}$ as a fraction of integers.

(iii) Deduce that $3.\dot{1} = {}^{28}/_{9}$.

3. (a) Show that $0.\dot{6}$ can be written as the sum to infinity of a geometric series and hence write $0.\dot{6}$ as ${}^{a}/_{b}$ where $a, b \in Z$.

(b) Use the same method to write these as fractions:

(i) $0.\dot{8}$

(ii) $0.0\dot{6}$

(iii) $0.\dot{2}$

(iv) $0.0\dot{9}$

4. $16 + 8 + 4 + ...$ are the first three terms of a geometric series.

(i) Find the sum of the first 7 terms.

(ii) Find the sum to infinity.

5. What is the difference between the sum of the first 5 terms and the sum of all the terms of the infinite geometric series

$1 + \frac{1}{5} + \frac{1}{25} + ...?$

6. The first term of a geometric series is 2. The sum to infinity is 3. Find the common ratio.

7. The third term of a geometric series is 2. The sum to infinity is equal to twice the first term. If a is the first term and r the common ratio,

(i) write down two equations in a and r,
(ii) find the values of a and r.

8. The 2nd term of a geometric series is 54. The 5th term is 2.

(i) Write down 2 equations in a (the first term) and r (the common ratio).
(ii) Find the values of a and r.
(iii) Find the sum to infinity of the series.

9. Show that $0.\dot{2}\dot{1}$ (= 0.212121212121 ...) can be written as

$$\frac{21}{100} + \frac{21}{10\,000} + \frac{21}{1\,000\,000} + \ldots$$

Hence write $0.\dot{2}\dot{1}$ as a fraction of natural numbers.

10. (i) By writing $0.2\dot{1}$ (= 0.2111111 ...) as $\frac{2}{10} + \left(\frac{1}{100} + \frac{1}{1000} + \frac{1}{10\,000} + \ldots\right)$ write $0.2\dot{1}$ as a fraction.

(ii) Deduce that $1.2\dot{1} = \frac{109}{90}$

11. A woman puts €175 into a piggy-bank one year. Every year after that, she puts in 0.8 of what she put in the piggy-bank the year before.

(i) Write, in a sequence, the amounts which she puts in over the first three years. Is this sequence geometric or arithmetic?
(ii) Find, showing the formula used, her total savings over the first eight years.
(iii) If she were to go on forever, what figure would her savings approach, as time went by?

12. A rubber ball is thrown straight up in the air from ground level, a distance of 20 metres. After each bounce, it reaches a height which is equal to half of the height reached on the previous occasion.

(i) Write, in a sequence, the DISTANCE travelled on each of the first four 'flights' (which includes the journey down as well as up).
(ii) Write down the value of a (the first term) and of r (the common ratio) for this sequence.
(iii) Find the total distance travelled over the first 7 'flights'.
(iv) Find the total distance travelled by the ball as it continues to bounce ad infinitum.

13. $1 + (2x - 1) + (2x - 1)^2 + (2x - 1)^3 + ...$ is an infinite geometric series, where x is a positive real number.

(i) Write down the common ratio, in terms of x.
(ii) Write, in terms of x, the sum to infinity.
(iii) Find the value of the sum to infinity if $x = {}^1/_3$.
(iv) If the sum to infinity is 1, find x.
(v) For what values of x does the sum to infinity exist?

14. Use an infinite geometric series to write $0.0\dot{3}$ as ${}^a/_b$, where $a,\ b \in N$. Hence write these as fractions:

(i) $0.1\dot{3}$
(ii) $4.1\dot{3}$
(iii) $0.\dot{3} - 0.0\dot{3}$

15. Use infinite geometric series to write these as fractions:

(i) $0.0\dot{2}$
(ii) $0.\dot{2}\dot{7}$
(iii) $0.2\dot{7}$
(iv) $2.\dot{3}$
(v) $0.015\dot{3}$

THE BINOMIAL THEOREM

Let us imagine that you are asked to multiply out (or '***expand***') $(1 + x)^4$. There are two approaches you could take. You could multiply $(1 + x)$ by itself four times, which would be rather arduous. Or you could use the ***Binomial Theorem*** which will give you the answer more-or-less instantly. And here it is.

The Binomial Theorem:

$$(1 + x)^n = \binom{n}{0} + \binom{n}{1}x + \binom{n}{2}x^2 + \binom{n}{3}x^3 + \ldots + \binom{n}{n}x^n$$

[The definition of $\binom{n}{r}$ appears on page 184]

For example:

$$(1 + x)^4 = \binom{4}{0} + \binom{4}{1}x + \binom{4}{2}x^2 + \binom{4}{3}x^3 + \binom{4}{4}x^4$$
$$= 1 + 4x + 6x^2 + 4x^3 + x^4$$

This expression is called the ***binomial expansion*** of $(1 + x)^4$.

Example 2: Expand $(1+x)^5$ and hence write $(1+\sqrt{3})^5$ in the form $p+q\sqrt{3}$.

Solution:

$$(1+x)^5 = \binom{5}{0}+\binom{5}{1}x+\binom{5}{2}x^2+\binom{5}{3}x^3+\binom{5}{4}x^4+\binom{5}{5}x^5$$
$$= 1+5x+10x^2+10x^3+5x^4+x^5$$

We will now replace every x with $\sqrt{3}$.

$$\therefore\ (1+\sqrt{3})^5 = 1+5\sqrt{3}+10\sqrt{3}^2+10\sqrt{3}^3+5\sqrt{3}^4+\sqrt{3}^5$$
$$= 1+5\sqrt{3}+10(3)+10(3\sqrt{3})+5(9)+9\sqrt{3}$$
$$= 1+5\sqrt{3}+30+30\sqrt{3}+45+9\sqrt{3}$$
$$= 76+44\sqrt{3}$$

If you are asked to expand $(1-x)^n$, you use the negative form of the binomial theorem, which is the same as the original, except that every second term is negative:

$$(1-x)^n = \binom{n}{0}-\binom{n}{1}x+\binom{n}{2}x^2-\binom{n}{3}x^3+\binom{n}{4}x^4-\ldots$$

Example 3: Show that $(1+x)^3-(1-x)^3 = 6x+2x^3$

Solution:

$$(1+x)^3 = \binom{3}{0}+\binom{3}{1}x+\binom{3}{2}x^2+\binom{3}{3}x^3 = 1+3x+3x^2+x^3$$
$$(1-x)^3 = \binom{3}{0}-\binom{3}{1}x+\binom{3}{2}x^2-\binom{3}{3}x^3 = 1-3x+3x^2-x^3$$
$$\therefore\ (1+x)^3-(1-x)^3 = (1+3x+3x^2+x^3)-(1-3x+3x^2-x^3)$$
$$= 1+3x+3x^2+x^3-1+3x-3x^2+x^3$$
$$= 6x+2x^3$$

Exercise 19.C

1. Expand $(1+x)^6$.

2. Expand $(1+x)^7$.

3. Write out the binomial expansion of $(1+x)^2$.

4. Write out the binomial expansion of $(1-x)^4$.

5. Write out the binomial expansion of $(1-x)^5$.

6. (i) Expand $(1+x)^5$.
   (ii) Deduce that $(1+\sqrt{2})^5 = 41+29\sqrt{2}$.

7. (i) Expand $(1+x)^3$.
   (ii) Deduce that $(1+\sqrt{7})^3 = 22+10\sqrt{7}$.

8. (i) Expand $(1+x)^4$.
   (ii) Deduce that $(1+\sqrt{2})^4 = 17+12\sqrt{2}$.

9. Use the binomial theorem to show that $(1+x)^2+(1-x)^2 = 2+2x^2$.

10. (i) Use the binomial theorem to prove that $(1+x)^4+(1-x)^4 = 2(1+6x^2+x^4)$.
    (ii) Deduce that $(1+\sqrt{2})^4+(1-\sqrt{2})^4 = 34$.

11. Expand (in ascending powers of x): $(1+x)^5$. Use the expansion to write $(1+\sqrt{10})^5$ in the form $a+b\sqrt{10}$.
    Also, prove that $(1+x)^5-(1-x)^5 = 10x+20x^3+2x^5$.

12. (i) Show that $(1+x)^7-(1-x)^7 = 2x(7+35x^2+21x^4+x^6)$.
    (ii) Deduce that $(1+\sqrt{3})^7-(1-\sqrt{3})^7 = 656\sqrt{3}$.

13. Expand $(1+x)^6$ and, by letting $x=0.01$ on both sides, show that $(1.01)^6 > 1.061$

14. Expand $(1-x)^3$ and verify your answer by letting $x=2$ on both sides.

15. Use the binomial theorem to show that $(1-2\sqrt{5})^4 = 521-168\sqrt{5}$.

16. Write out the first three terms in ascending powers of x of the binomial expansion of $(1+x)^7$.
    Deduce that $(1.02)^7 > 1.148$

REVISION EXERCISE 19.D

1. (a) A girl puts 50 cent into her bank account one week, then 55 cent the next, then 60 cent the next, and so on, in an arithmetic sequence.

(i) How much will she put in the bank account in the 30th week?

(ii) How much will she have put in altogether over the first 30 weeks?

(b) Find the sum to infinity of the geometric series:

$3 + \frac{3}{2} + \frac{3}{4} + \ldots$

(c) (i) Expand $(1 + x)^4$.

(ii) Deduce that

$(1 + \sqrt{3})^4 = 28 + 16\sqrt{3}$.

2. (a) Find the sum to infinity of the infinite geometric series:

$\frac{2}{10} + \frac{2}{100} + \frac{2}{1000} + \ldots$ and deduce that $5.\dot{2} = \frac{47}{9}$.

(b) Use the binomial theorem to prove that

$(1 + x)^3 + (1 - x)^3 = 2 + 6x^2$.

(c) A colony of bacteria double in number every hour. A colony contains 30 bacteria. How many bacteria will the colony contain after 13 hours?

3. (a) The first two terms of an infinite geometric series are

$\frac{5}{6} + \frac{2}{3} + \ldots$.

Find (as fractions):

(i) the common ratio,

(ii) the next term,

(iii) the sum to infinity of the series.

(b) A couple invest €250 in a building society ***each year*** for five successive years. The investments earn 6% compound interest per annum.

(i) How much will the first investment be worth after 5 years?

(ii) How much will they have in the account altogether after 5 years?

(c) Use the binomial theorem to show that $(1 + x)^2 - (1 - x)^2 = 4x$.

4. (a) Write $0.\dot{8}$ as an infinite geometric series and deduce that

$0.\dot{8} = \frac{8}{9}$ and that $2.\dot{8} = \frac{26}{9}$.

(b) Use the binomial theorem to prove that $(1 + x)^6 - (1 - x)^6$

$= 4x(3 + 10x^2 + 3x^4)$.

Deduce that

$(1 + \sqrt{2})^6 - (1 - \sqrt{2})^6 = 140\sqrt{2}$.

(c) A grandmother gives her grandson €2 for every year of his life, as a birthday present. (e.g. she gives him €14 on his seventh birthday). How much will she have given to him altogether by his 21st birthday?

5. (a) A basket and 12 stones are placed in a straight line, each 7 metres apart. A competitor has to run from the basket to each stone in turn and to bring them back, one by one, to the basket. How far does the competitor have to run altogether?

(b) Find the sum to infinity of the geometric series

$$\frac{6}{7}+\left(\frac{6}{7}\right)^2+\left(\frac{6}{7}\right)^3+\ldots$$

(c) (i) Expand $(1-x)^7$.

(ii) Deduce that

$$(1-\sqrt{2})^7 = 239-169\sqrt{2}.$$

6. (a) Write $0.\dot{1}$ as an infinite geometric series, and hence write $0.\dot{1}$ as a fraction. Hence write the following as fractions:

(i) $0.0\dot{1}$

(ii) $11.\dot{1}$

(b) (i) €2000 is invested at 7% compound interest per annum. What will it amount to after 10 years?

(ii) If €2000 is invested ***each year*** for ten years, what will the total amount be in the account at the end of ten years?

7. (a) $a+b+800+640+e+\ldots$ are the first five terms of an infinite geometric series.

(i) Find r, the common ratio.

(ii) Find the values of a, b and e.

(iii) Find the sum of the first 16 terms, to the nearest integer.

(iv) Find the sum to infinity of the entire series.

(b) A couple invest €400 in a building society ***each year*** for twenty successive years. The investments earn 4½% compound interest per annum.

(i) How much (to the nearest euro) will they have in the account altogether after 20 years?

(ii) If the couple wanted to end up with €40 000 at the end of the twenty years, how much (to the nearest euro) should they have invested each year?

8. (a) A man discovers that he is eating 5 kg of sugar per week. He decides to cut down by 10% per week. So, he eats 5 kg the first week, 4.5 kg the next week, 4.05 the next week, etc.

(i) If he wants to buy enough sugar ***now*** to last him the first 13 weeks, how many 1 kilogram bags should he buy?

(ii) If he wants to buy enough to last him his life-time, no matter how long he lives, how many bags should he buy?

(b) Use the binomial theorem to show that

$$(1+2\sqrt{x})^7+(1-2\sqrt{x})^7$$
$$= 2(1+84x+560x^2+448x^3).$$

9. (a) The second term of an infinite geometric series is 2. The sum to infinity is 9. Find two possible values for r, the common ratio, and the corresponding first term in each case.

(b) (i) Show that $0.1\dot{8} = 0.181818\ldots$ can be written as an infinite geometric series:

$$\frac{18}{100} + \frac{18}{10\,000} + \ldots$$

and hence write $0.\dot{1}\dot{8}$ as a fraction of natural numbers.

(ii) By writing $0.1\dot{8}$ $(= 0.188888\ldots)$ in the form $\frac{1}{10} + \left(\frac{8}{100} + \frac{8}{1000} + \frac{8}{10\,000} + \ldots\right)$, write $0.1\dot{8}$ as a fraction.

(iii) Write as a single fraction: $0.1\dot{8} - 0.\dot{1}\dot{8}$

(c) (i) Expand $(1 - x)^3$.

(ii) Deduce that $(1 - 3\sqrt{3})^3 = 82 - 90\sqrt{3}$.

10. (a) Use the binomial theorem to prove that $(1 + x)^4 - (1 - x)^4 = 8x(1 + x^2)$.
Deduce that $(1 + \sqrt{2})^4 - (1 - \sqrt{2})^4 = 24\sqrt{2}$.

(b) A couple invest €x in a post-office account ***each year*** for six successive years. The investments earn 4% compound interest per annum. If the total amount at the end of six years is €10 000, find x to the nearest integer.

(c) $1 + (4x - 1) + (4x - 1)^2 + (4x - 1)^3 + \ldots$ is an infinite geometric series, where x is a positive real number.

(i) Write down (in terms of x) the common ratio.

(ii) Write down, in terms of x, an expression for the sum to infinity.

(iii) Find the value of the sum to infinity if $x = {}^1/_3$.

(iv) For what value of x is the sum to infinity equal to ${}^5/_6$?

(v) For what values of x does the sum to infinity exist?

1. For an arithmetic series:
$T_n = a + (n - 1)d$ and $S_n = \frac{n}{2}\{2a + (n - 1)d\}$

2. For a geometric series: $T_n = ar^{n-1}$ and $S_n = \frac{a(1 - r^n)}{1 - r}$ and the sum to infinity of the series is $S_\infty = \frac{a}{1 - r}$ where $-1 < r < 1$.

3. The binomial theorem:
$(1 + x)^n = \binom{n}{0} + \binom{n}{1}x + \binom{n}{2}x^2 + \binom{n}{3}x^3 + \ldots + \binom{n}{n}x^n$ and
$(1 - x)^n = \binom{n}{0} - \binom{n}{1}x + \binom{n}{2}x^2 - \binom{n}{3}x^3 + \binom{n}{4}x^4 - \ldots$

Chapter 20

Option 3: Vectors

Here is a ship being pulled by two tug-boats. The more northerly one is pulling with greater force than the other. In what direction will the ship go?

We will resolve this problem by means of ***vectors***.

The forces are represented by ***vectors***. Vectors are line segments with arrow tips at the end. They are denoted by letters with arrows on top (e.g. $\vec{b}$). The arrow tip shows the direction of the vector; the length of the vector represents its size, or magnitude.

So, we see that the more northerly vector, $\vec{a}$, is longer than the other because it represents a greater force than the other.

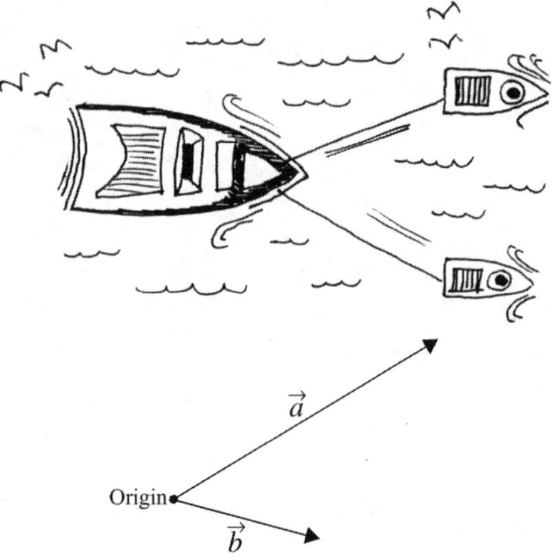

To find out where the ship will go, we have to add $\vec{a}$ and $\vec{b}$, to get $\vec{a} + \vec{b}$. We do this by the 'parallelogram method'.

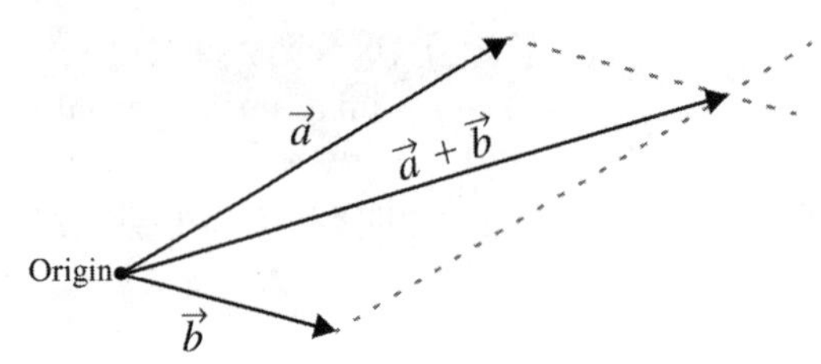

Step 1: Draw a line through the tip of $\vec{a}$, parallel to $\vec{b}$.
Draw a line through the tip of $\vec{b}$, parallel to $\vec{a}$.

Step 2: Find the point where these two lines intersect.

Step 3: Join the ship (at the origin o) to the point of intersection and show an arrow tip.

Step 4: Label this vector $\vec{a} + \vec{b}$.

The ship will travel in the direction of $\vec{a} + \vec{b}$.

If $\vec{x}$ is a vector then $2\vec{x}$ is a vector twice as long, in the same direction. Similarily, $3\vec{x}$ is a vector in the same direction as $\vec{x}$ but three times as long. $-\vec{x}$ is a vector, the same length as $\vec{x}$, but in the OPPOSITE direction. $-2\vec{x}$ is twice as long as $\vec{x}$, but in the opposite direction.

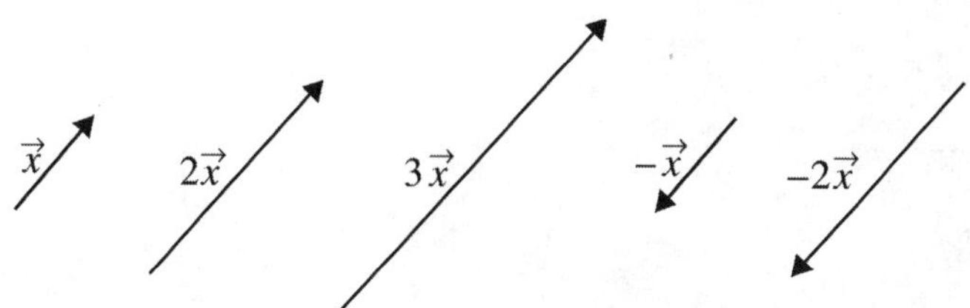

$\vec{x}$ is a vector. In the five examples, above, $\vec{x}$ has been multiplied by the real numbers 1, 2, 3, –1 and –2. In this context, real numbers are often called ***scalars*** (as opposed to vectors).

Example 1: Show the vector $2\vec{a} + \vec{b}$.

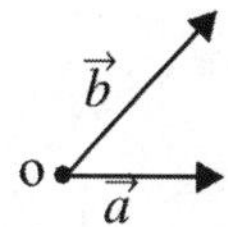

Solution:

1. Get $2\vec{a}$ by doubling $\vec{a}$.
2. Add $2\vec{a}$ and $\vec{b}$ by the parallelogram method.
3. Label your answer $2\vec{a} + \vec{b}$.

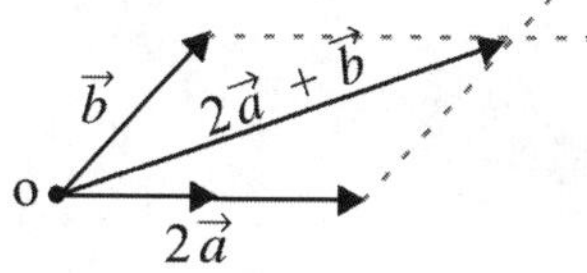

Example 2: Show $3\vec{x} - ½\vec{y}$.

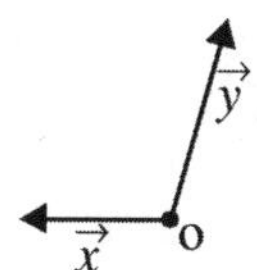

Solution:

1. Get $3\vec{x}$ by trebling $\vec{x}$.
2. Get $-½\vec{y}$ by halving $\vec{y}$'s length and changing its direction.
3. Add $3\vec{x}$ and $-½\vec{y}$ by the parallelogram method.
4. Label the answer .

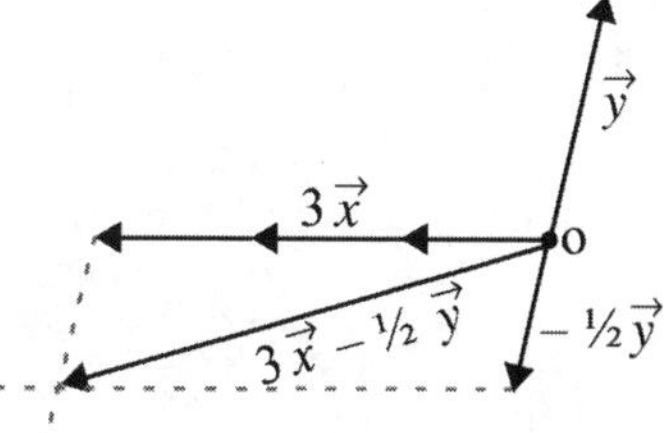

Exercise 20.A

1. Show $\vec{a} + \vec{b}$.

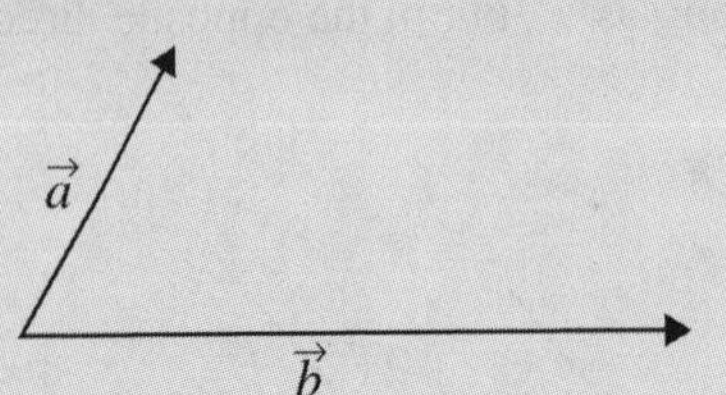

6. Show $\vec{x} + ½\vec{y}$.

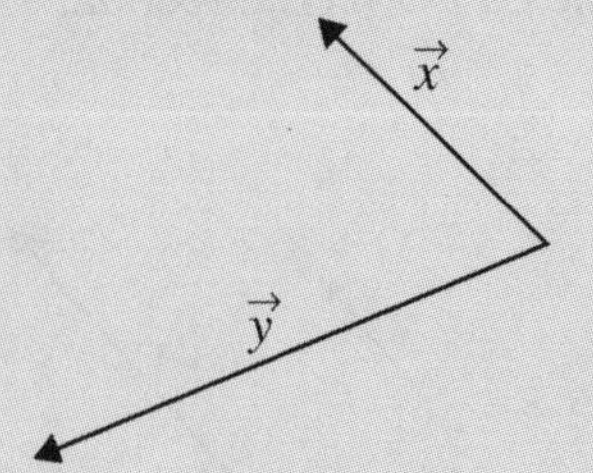

2. Show $\vec{x} - \vec{y}$.

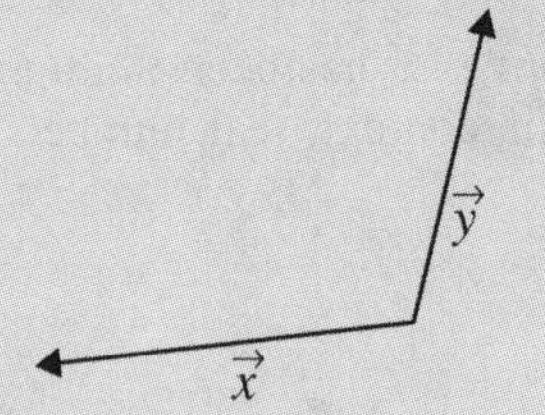

7. Construct $3\vec{x} + ½\vec{y}$.

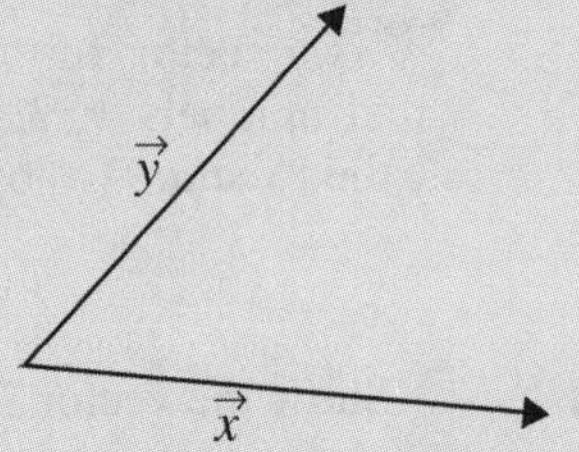

3. Show $\vec{p} + \vec{s}$.

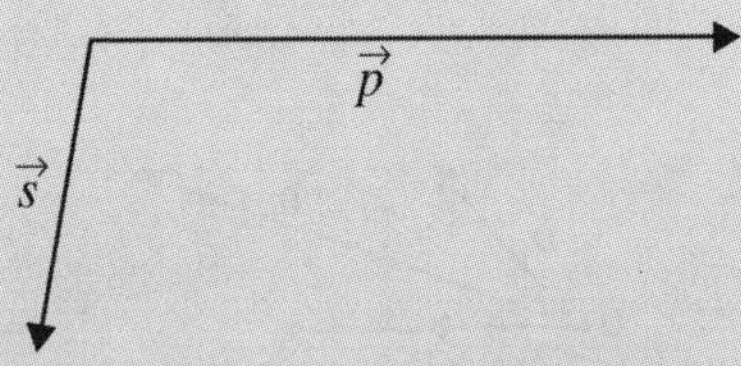

8. Show $2\vec{a} + ½\vec{b}$.

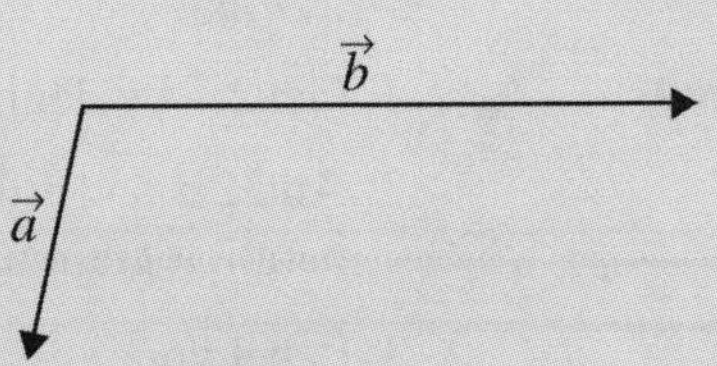

4. Construct $\vec{k} - \vec{t}$.

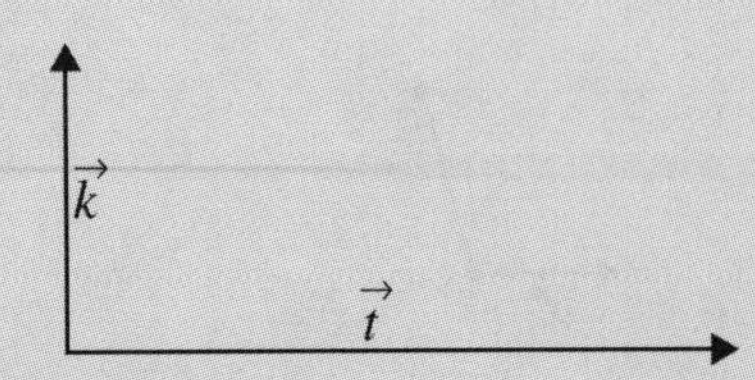

9. Construct $\vec{x} - \vec{y}$.

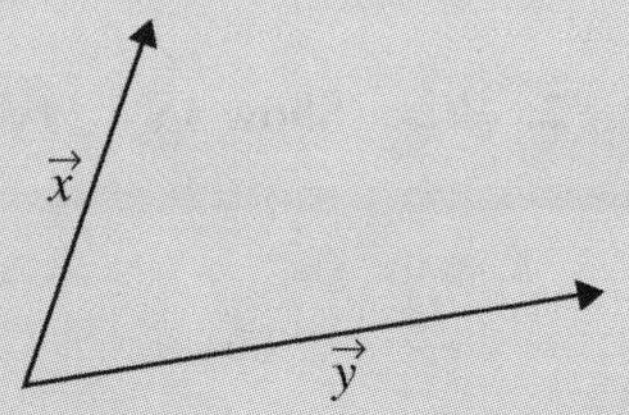

5. Construct $2\vec{a} + \vec{b}$.

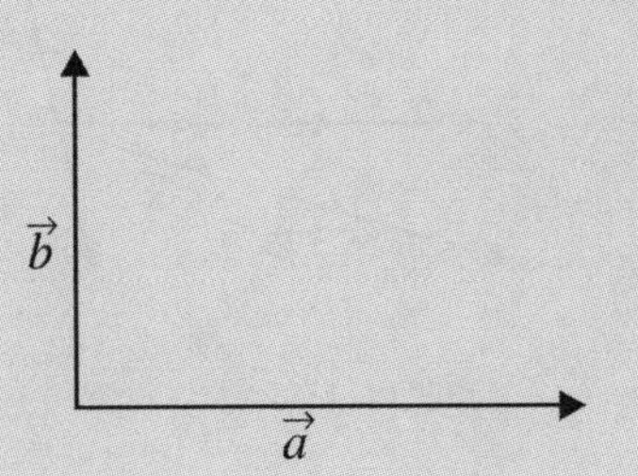

10. Show the vector $2\vec{b} - ½\vec{a}$.

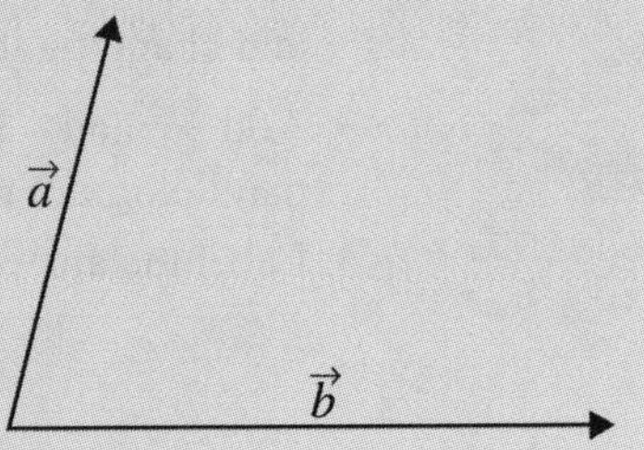

11. Show the vector $\vec{x} - 3\vec{y}$.

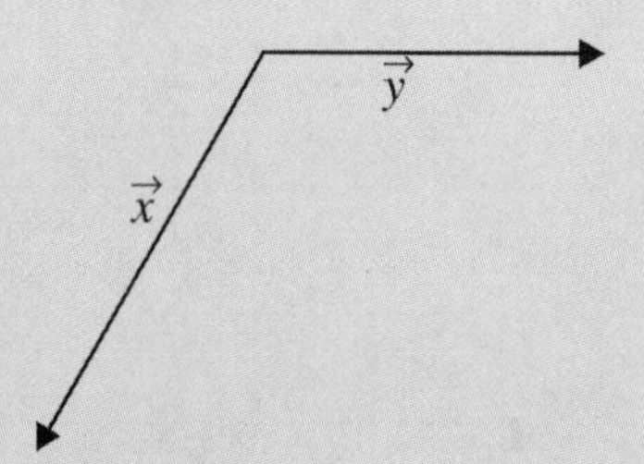

12. Construct the vector $\vec{y} - \vec{x}$.

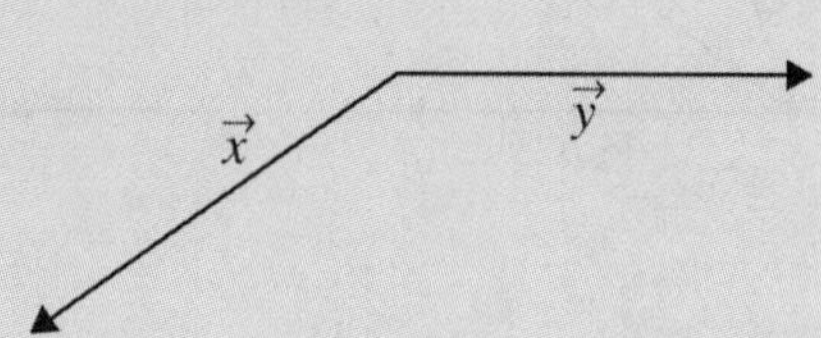

13. On separate diagrams show the vectors

(i) $2\vec{x} - \vec{y}$

(ii) $2\vec{y} - \vec{x}$

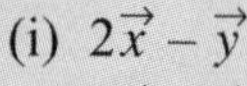

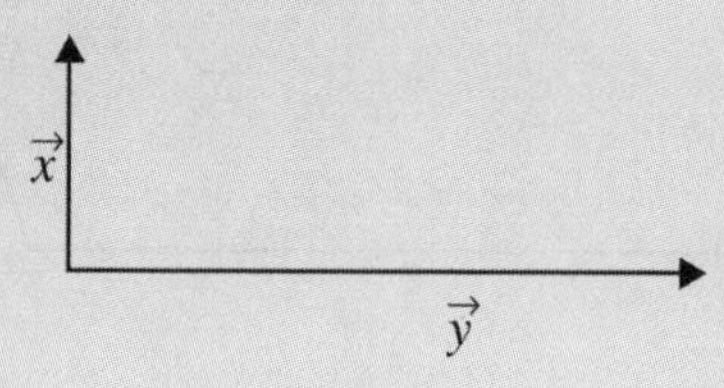

14. Show on separate diagrams:

(i) $\frac{1}{2}\vec{a} - \vec{b}$

(ii) $\vec{a} - \frac{1}{2}\vec{b}$

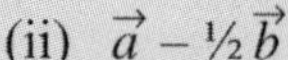

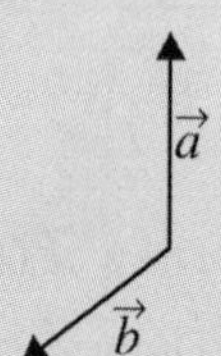

15. Show on the same diagram:

(i) $3\vec{a} - \vec{b}$

(ii) $\vec{b} - 3\vec{a}$

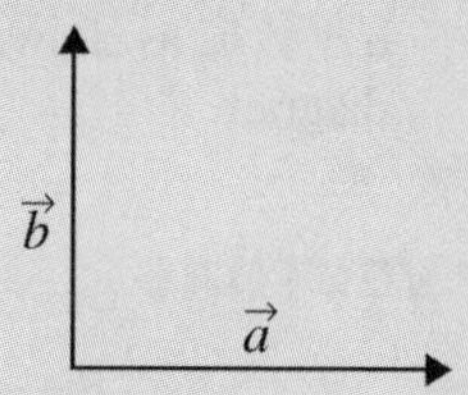

16. Using separate diagrams, show:

(i) $(\vec{a} + \vec{b}) + \vec{c}$

(ii) $\vec{a} + (\vec{b} + \vec{c})$

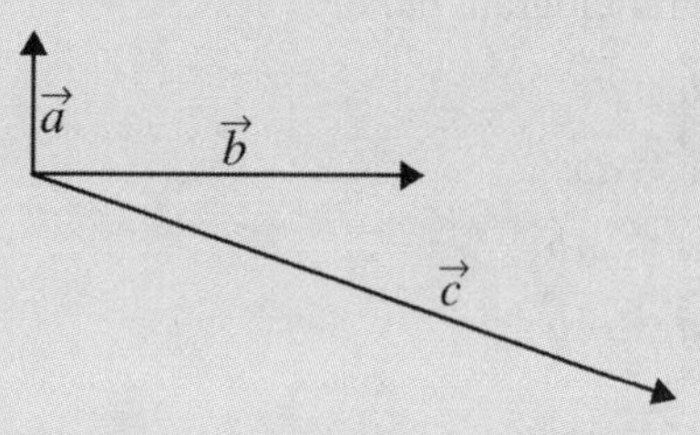

Is $(\vec{a} + \vec{b}) + \vec{c} = \vec{a} + (\vec{b} + \vec{c})$?

POINTS

The vector going from the point a to the point b is called $\overrightarrow{ab}$. Similarly, $\overrightarrow{bc}$ runs from b to c. But the vector going from the origin, o, to the point a can be called $\overrightarrow{oa}$ or just $\vec{a}$. Similarly, the vector from o to c can be called $\overrightarrow{oc}$ or simply $\vec{c}$.

Since $\overrightarrow{ab}$ and $\overrightarrow{ba}$ have the same length (or magnitude) but have opposite directions, it is clear that

$$\overrightarrow{ab} = -\overrightarrow{ba}$$

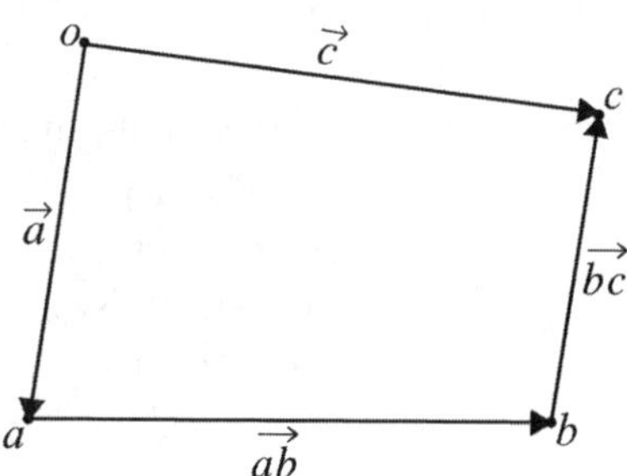

Example 1: Find the point k if $\vec{k} = \vec{a} + \frac{1}{2}\vec{b}$.

a•

o• •b

Solution:

1. Draw $\vec{a}$ (from o to a).
2. Draw $\vec{b}$ (from o to b).
3. Add $\vec{a} + \frac{1}{2}\vec{b}$, as before.
4. Since $\vec{a} + \frac{1}{2}\vec{b} = \vec{k} = \overrightarrow{ok}$, k must be at the tip of $\vec{a} + \frac{1}{2}\vec{b}$, as shown in the diagram.

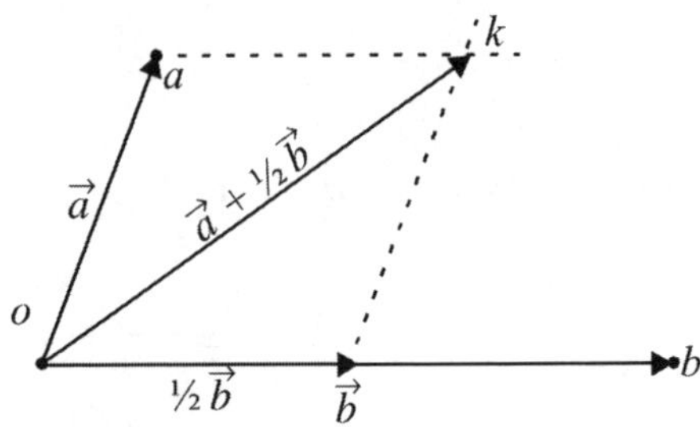

EQUALITY OF VECTORS

Any two vectors which have the ***SAME MAGNITUDE*** and the ***SAME DIRECTION*** are equal.

In the parallelogram *oabc*,

$\overrightarrow{ab} = \overrightarrow{dc}$

$\overrightarrow{bc} = \overrightarrow{ad}$

$\overrightarrow{cd} = -\overrightarrow{ab}$

$\overrightarrow{ad} = -\overrightarrow{cb}$

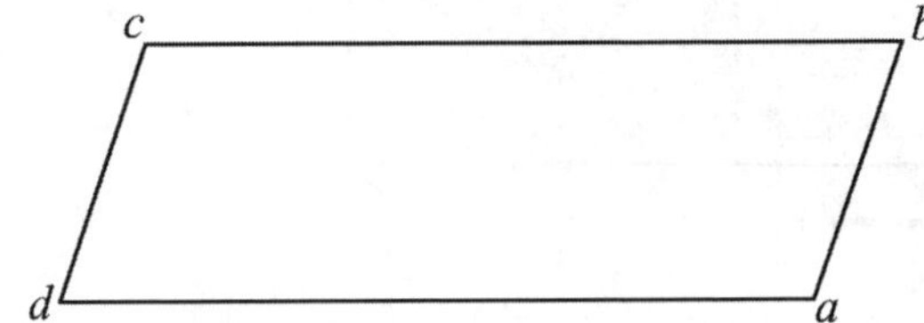

Example 2: Add $\vec{x} + \vec{y}$

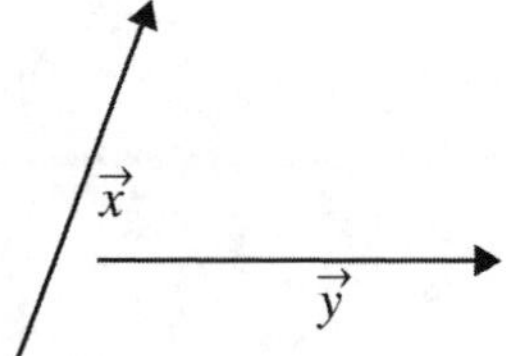

Solution: Slide $\vec{y}$ along so that $\vec{x}$ and $\vec{y}$ emerge from the same point. Now, add them, as before.

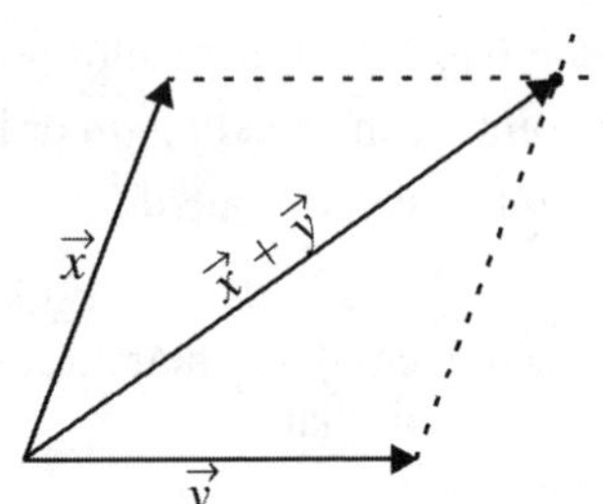

Exercise 20.B

1. $wxyz$ is a rectangle. Write down another vector equal to:

   (i) $\overrightarrow{wz}$

   (ii) $\overrightarrow{zy}$

   (iii) $\overrightarrow{xw}$

   (iv) $\overrightarrow{yz}$

   Is $\overrightarrow{wy} = \overrightarrow{xz}$? Give a reason.

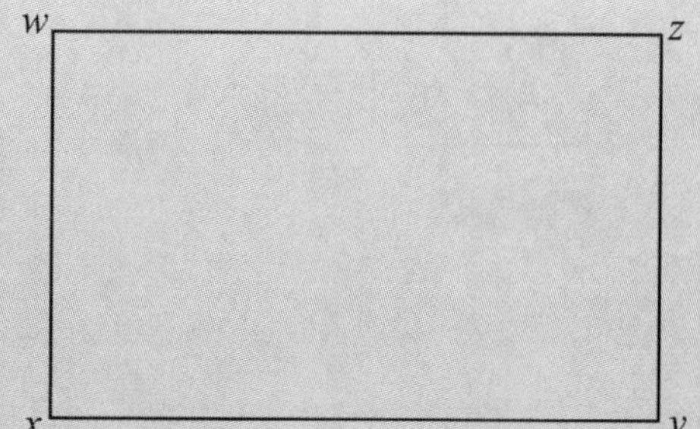

2. $ocba$ is a parallelogram, where o is the origin, m is the midpoint of $[oa]$. State whether the following are true or false:

   (i) $\overrightarrow{ab} = \vec{c}$

   (ii) $\overrightarrow{mc} = \overrightarrow{ab}$

   (iii) $\vec{a} = 2\vec{m}$

   (iv) $\vec{b} = \overrightarrow{ac}$

   (v) $\overrightarrow{mb} = \overrightarrow{mc}$

   (vi) $\overrightarrow{bc} = -\vec{a}$

   (vii) $\overrightarrow{ba} = -\vec{c}$

   (viii) $\overrightarrow{cb} = 2\vec{m}$

   (ix) $\overrightarrow{am} = \vec{m}$

   (x) $\overrightarrow{ca} = 2\overrightarrow{cm}$

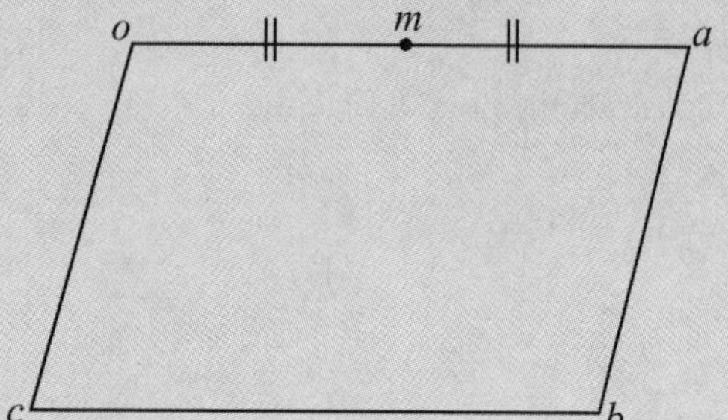

3. $oabcde$ is a regular hexagon, where o is the origin. Write down a vector equal to:

   (i) $\overrightarrow{ac}$

   (ii) $\overrightarrow{ed}$

   (iii) $\vec{a}$

   (iv) $\overrightarrow{bd}$

   (v) $\overrightarrow{ec}$

   (vi) $-\overrightarrow{bd}$

   (vii) $\vec{e}$

   (viii) $2\vec{a}$

   (ix) $2\vec{e}$

   (x) $-2\overrightarrow{bc}$

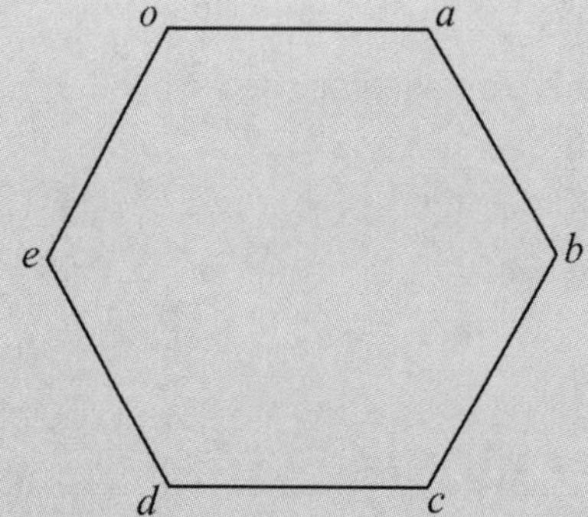

4. Copy this diagram and show the vector $\vec{a} + \vec{b}$.

a •

b •

o •

5. Copy this diagram and construct the vector $\vec{p} + \vec{q}$.

p •

q • o •

6. Construct the point k such that $\overrightarrow{oa} + \overrightarrow{ob} = \overrightarrow{ok}$.

a •

o • b •

7. Show the point t if $\vec{t} = 2\vec{a} + \vec{b}$.

b •

a • o •

8. Copy this diagram twice and show the vectors:

(i) $\vec{p} + \vec{q}$

(ii) $\vec{p} - \vec{q}$

q •

o • p •

9. Copy the diagram and show points k_1 and k_2 such that $\overrightarrow{ok_1} = \frac{1}{2}\overrightarrow{oa} + \overrightarrow{ob}$ and $\overrightarrow{ok_2} = \overrightarrow{oa} - \frac{1}{2}\overrightarrow{ob}$.

b •

a •

o •

10. Construct $\vec{x} + \vec{y}$ in each case:

(i)

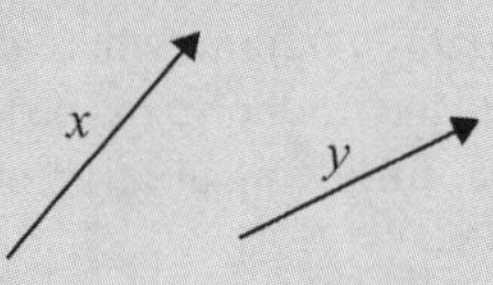

(ii)

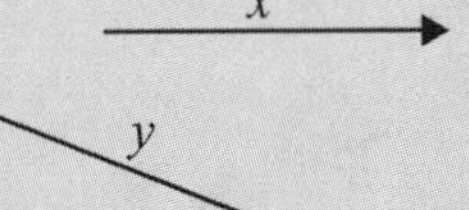

(iii)

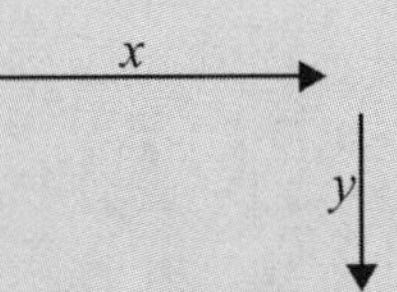

11. abc is an equilateral triangle.

(i) Construct the point p such that $\overrightarrow{cp} = \overrightarrow{ca} + \overrightarrow{cb}$.

(ii) Write down a vector equal to $\overrightarrow{ap}$.

(iii) Write down a vector equal to $-\overrightarrow{bp}$.

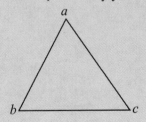

(iv) Is $\overrightarrow{ab} = \overrightarrow{pc}$? Justify your answer.

a

b c

THE TRIANGLE LAW

$\overrightarrow{ab} + \overrightarrow{bc} = \overrightarrow{ac}$, for any triangle abc.

You could look on $\overrightarrow{ab}$ as a journey from a to b and $\overrightarrow{bc}$ as a journey from b to c.

$\overrightarrow{ac} + \overrightarrow{bc}$ = a journey from a to b followed by b to c.
= a long journey from a to c.
$= \overrightarrow{ac}$

THE NULL VECTOR

$\vec{0}$, the number zero with an arrow on top, is called the ***null vector.*** It represents any vector with magnitude zero.

Example 1: $oacb$ is a parallelogram. k, m, t are midpoints of $[oa]$, $[ac]$, $[bc]$ respectively.

Write these as one vector:

(i) $\overrightarrow{bc} + \overrightarrow{ca}$

(ii) $\overrightarrow{ka} + 2\overrightarrow{am}$

(iii) $\vec{a} + \vec{b}$

(iv) $\overrightarrow{ct} - \overrightarrow{kt}$

(v) $\frac{1}{2}\overrightarrow{bc} + \overrightarrow{ca}$

(vi) $\overrightarrow{am} - \overrightarrow{mc}$

(vii) $\overrightarrow{ka} + \overrightarrow{ma}$

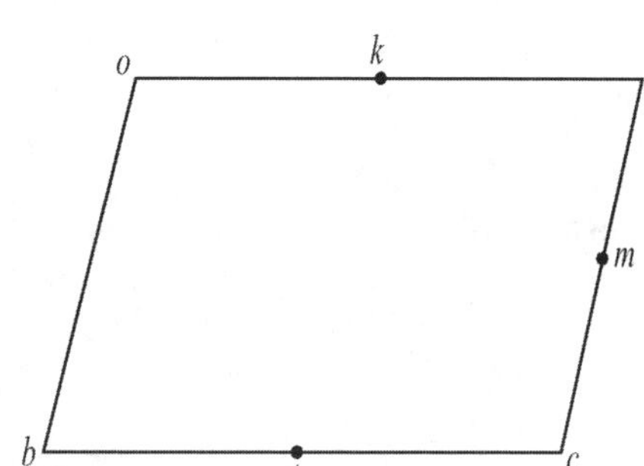

Solution:

(i) $\overrightarrow{bc} + \overrightarrow{ca} = \overrightarrow{ba}$ (by the triangle law)

(ii) $\overrightarrow{ka} + 2\overrightarrow{am} = \overrightarrow{ka} + \overrightarrow{ac}$ (since $2\overrightarrow{am} = \overrightarrow{ac}$)
$= \overrightarrow{kc}$ (triangle law)

(iii) $\vec{a} + \vec{b} = \overrightarrow{oa} + \overrightarrow{ob}$
$= \overrightarrow{oa} + \overrightarrow{ac}$ ($\overrightarrow{ob}$ and $\overrightarrow{ac}$ have same length and direction).
$= \overrightarrow{oc}$ or just $\vec{c}$ (triangle law)

(iv) $\vec{ct} - \vec{kt} = \vec{ct} + \vec{tk}$ (since $-\vec{kt} = +\vec{tk}$)

$= \vec{ck}$ (triangle law)

(v) $\frac{1}{2}\vec{bc} + \vec{ca} = \vec{bt} + \vec{ca}$

$= \vec{bt} + \vec{tk}$ ($\vec{ca}$ and $\vec{tk}$ are equal)

$= \vec{bk}$ (triangle law)

(vi) $\vec{am} - \vec{mc} = \vec{am} + \vec{cm}$

$= \vec{am} + \vec{ma}$

$= \vec{aa}$ (but a journey from a to a has no length)

$= \vec{0}$ (the null vector)

(vii) $\vec{ka} + \vec{ma} = \vec{ka} + \vec{ap}$, where p is as shown below.

$= \vec{kp}$ (triangle law)

$= \vec{tm}$ (since $\vec{tm} = \vec{kp}$)

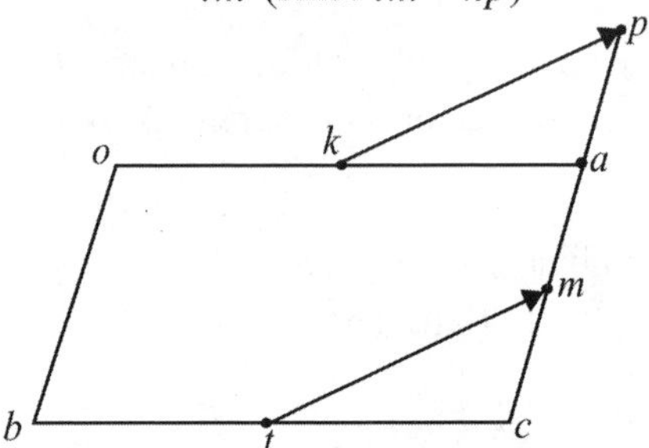

Exercise 20.C

1. $abcd$ is a parallelogram, m and n are midpoints of $[ad]$ and $[bc]$.
   Write as one vector:
   (i) $\vec{ab} + \vec{bn}$
   (ii) $\vec{dc} + \vec{cb}$
   (iii) $\vec{dc} + \vec{dm}$
   (iv) $\vec{ab} + 2\vec{am}$
   (v) $\vec{dc} - \vec{bc}$
   (vi) $\vec{ab} - \vec{ma}$
   (vii) $2\vec{dm} - \vec{ab}$
   (viii) $\vec{mn} + \vec{ba}$

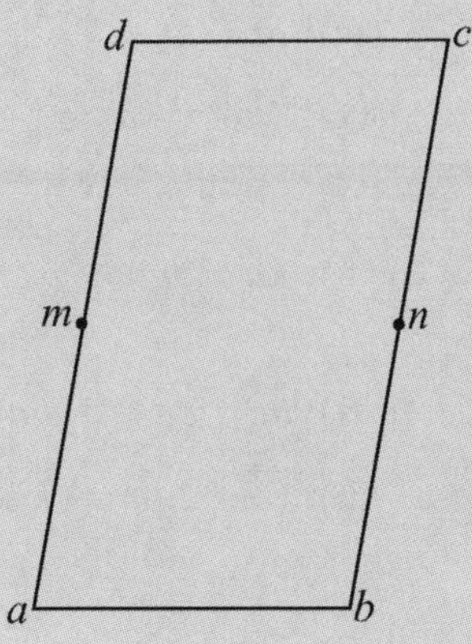

2. *oabcde* is a regular hexagon, with *o* as the origin. Write these as one vector:

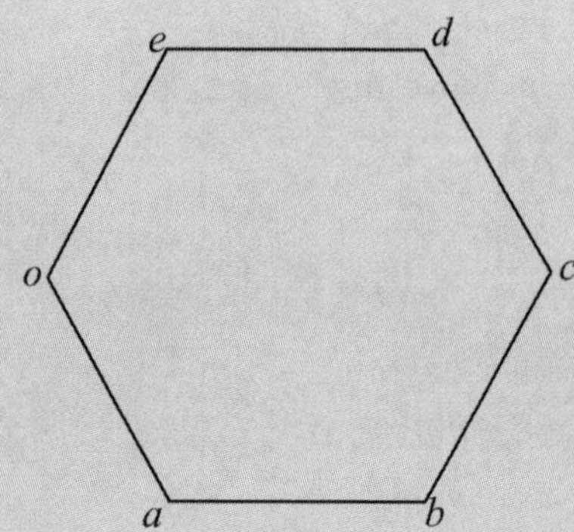

(i) $\overrightarrow{ed} + \overrightarrow{dc}$

(ii) $\vec{e} + \overrightarrow{ab}$

(iii) $\vec{a} + 2\vec{e}$

(iv) $\frac{1}{2}\overrightarrow{ad} + \overrightarrow{ab}$

(v) $\overrightarrow{ae} - \overrightarrow{de}$

(vi) $\vec{e} + \vec{b}$

(vii) $\overrightarrow{ed} - \overrightarrow{ab}$

(viii) $\vec{c} - \vec{e}$

3. *abc* is a triangle. *m* and *n* are midpoints of [*bc*] and [*ac*] respectively. *g* divides both [*bn*] and [*am*] in the ratio 2 : 1. Write as one vector:

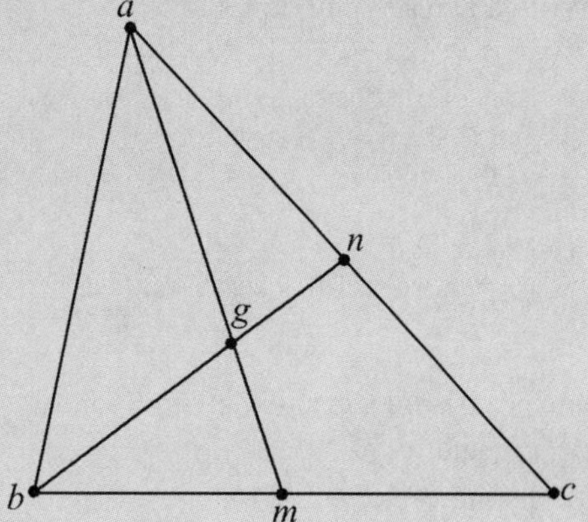

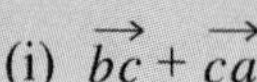

(i) $\overrightarrow{bc} + \overrightarrow{ca}$

(ii) $\overrightarrow{ab} + \frac{1}{2}\overrightarrow{bc}$

(iii) $\overrightarrow{bm} + \frac{1}{3}\overrightarrow{ma}$

(iv) $\overrightarrow{ba} + \frac{2}{3}\overrightarrow{am} + \overrightarrow{gn}$

(v) $\frac{1}{2}\overrightarrow{ac} - \frac{1}{3}\overrightarrow{bn}$

(vi) $\overrightarrow{bc} - \frac{1}{2}\overrightarrow{ac} + \frac{1}{3}\overrightarrow{nb}$

4. *opqr* is a parallelogram, with *o* as origin.

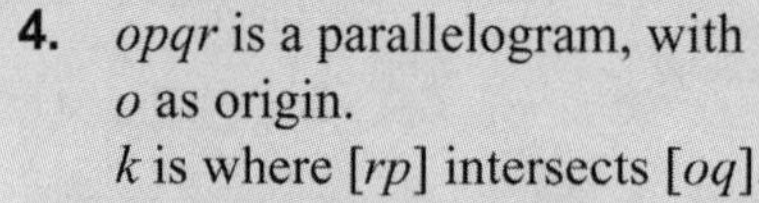

k is where [*rp*] intersects [*oq*].

Write down one vector equal to:

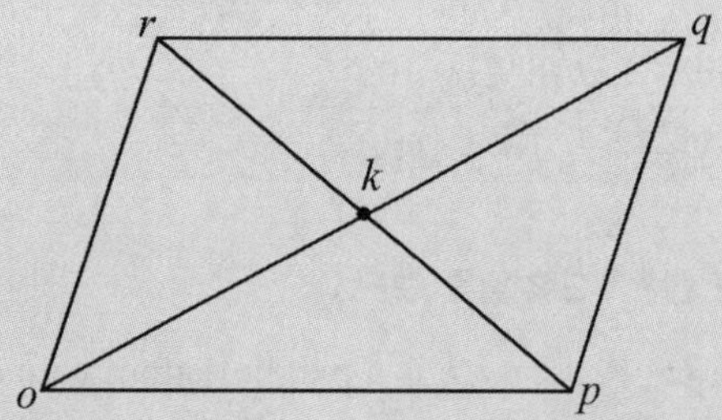

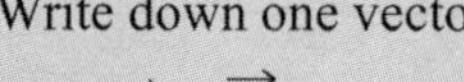

(i) $\vec{r} + \overrightarrow{rk}$

(ii) $\vec{p} + \vec{r}$

(iii) $2\vec{k} - \vec{p}$

(iv) $\vec{q} - \vec{p}$

(v) $\overrightarrow{pk} + \overrightarrow{rq}$

5. *amcd* is a parallelogram. $\overrightarrow{am} = \overrightarrow{mb}$.
[*db*] intersects [*mc*] in *k*.
Write as one vector:

(i) $\overrightarrow{am} + \frac{1}{2}\overrightarrow{mc}$
(ii) $\overrightarrow{am} + \overrightarrow{ad}$
(iii) $\overrightarrow{am} + \frac{1}{2}\overrightarrow{ad}$
(iv) $2\overrightarrow{mk} + \overrightarrow{ma}$
(v) $\overrightarrow{cd} - \overrightarrow{bm}$
(vi) $\overrightarrow{dc} - \overrightarrow{md}$

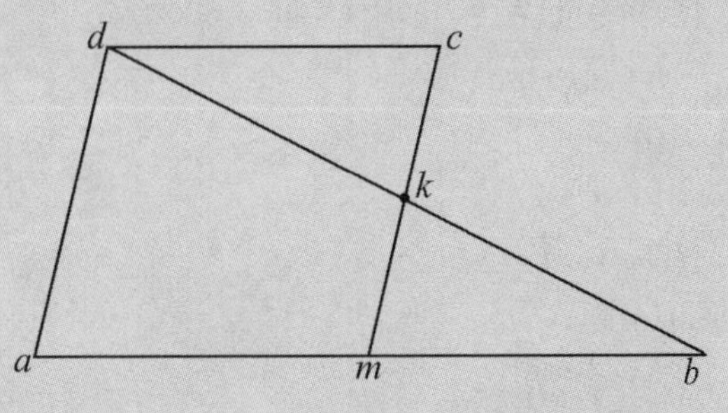

6. *oab* is a triangle with *o* as origin.
$|bd| : |do| = 3 : 2 = |be| : |ea|$
Write down a vector equal to:

(i) 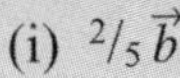 $\frac{2}{5}\vec{b}$
(ii) $\vec{a} + \overrightarrow{ab}$
(iii) $\vec{b} + \frac{3}{5}\overrightarrow{ba}$
(iv) $\vec{d} + \frac{3}{5}\vec{a}$
(v) $\vec{b} - \vec{a}$

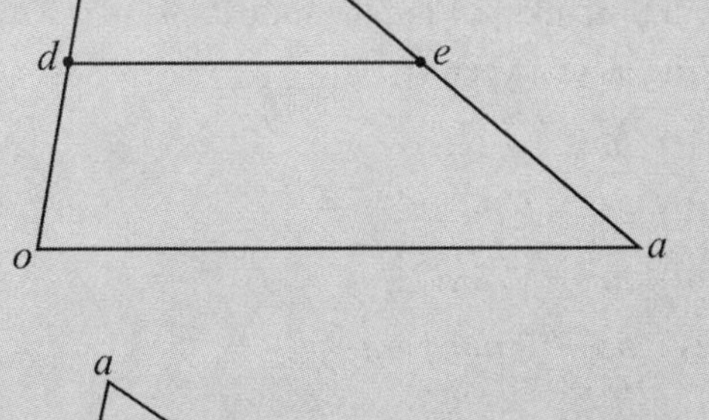

7. *abc* is a triangle, *m* and *n* are midpoints of [*ab*] and [*ac*].
Write one vector equal to:

(i) $\overrightarrow{am} + \overrightarrow{mn}$
(ii) $2\overrightarrow{an}$
(iii) $\frac{1}{2}\overrightarrow{ab} + \frac{1}{2}\overrightarrow{bc}$
(iv) $\overrightarrow{bc} - \frac{1}{2}\overrightarrow{ac} - \overrightarrow{mn}$

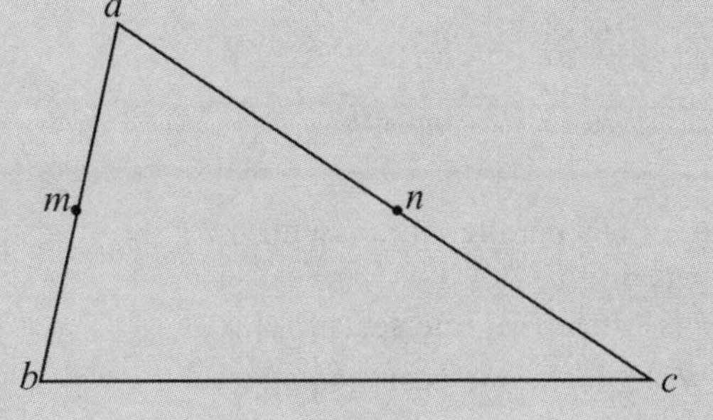

WRITE IN TERMS OF ...

Example 1: *oacb* is a parallelogram with *o* as origin.
$|am| = |mc|$. $|op| : |pb| = 2 : 1$
Write in terms of $\vec{a}$ and $\vec{b}$:

(i) 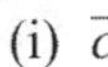 $\vec{c}$
(ii) $\vec{m}$
(iii) $\overrightarrow{cp}$
(iv) $\overrightarrow{ab}$

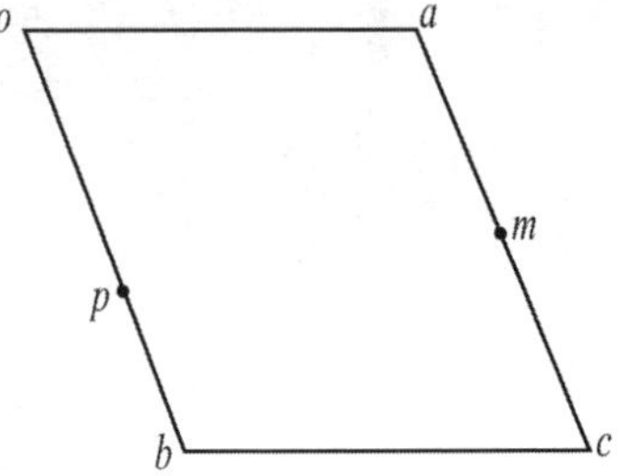

Solution:

Step 1:

Show the vectors $\vec{a}$ $(= \overrightarrow{oa})$ and $\vec{b}$ $(= \overrightarrow{ob})$

Step 2:

Divide $[ob]$ into 3 equal pieces.

Step 3:

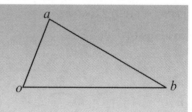

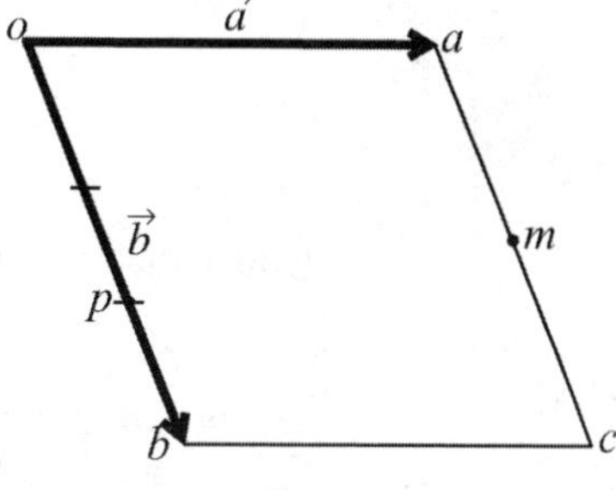

(i) $\vec{c} = \overrightarrow{oc}$ (by definition)

$= \overrightarrow{oa} + \overrightarrow{ac}$ (triangle law)

$= \vec{a} + \vec{b}$ (since $\vec{b} = \overrightarrow{ac}$)

(ii) $\vec{m} = \overrightarrow{om}$ (by definition)

$= \overrightarrow{oa} + \overrightarrow{am}$ (triangle law)

$= \vec{a} + \frac{1}{2}\vec{b}$ (since $\overrightarrow{am} = \frac{1}{2}\vec{b}$)

(iii) $\overrightarrow{cp} = \overrightarrow{cb} + \overrightarrow{bp}$ (triangle law)

$= -\vec{a} - \frac{1}{3}\vec{b}$

(iv) $\overrightarrow{ab} = \overrightarrow{ao} + \overrightarrow{ob}$

$= -\overrightarrow{oa} + \overrightarrow{ob}$

$= -\vec{a} + \vec{b}$

$= \vec{b} - \vec{a}$

TWO IMPORTANT LAWS

Law 1: $\overrightarrow{ab} = \vec{b} - \vec{a}$

Proof: $\overrightarrow{ab} = \overrightarrow{ao} + \overrightarrow{ob}$

$= -\overrightarrow{oa} + \overrightarrow{ob}$

$= -\vec{a} + \vec{b}$

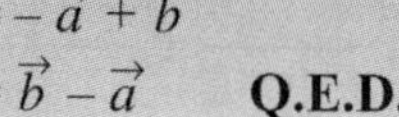

$= \vec{b} - \vec{a}$ **Q.E.D.**

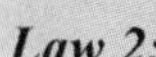

Law 2: If m is the midpoint of $[ab]$, then

$\vec{m} = \frac{1}{2}\vec{a} + \frac{1}{2}\vec{b}$

Proof: Let the origin o be anywhere.

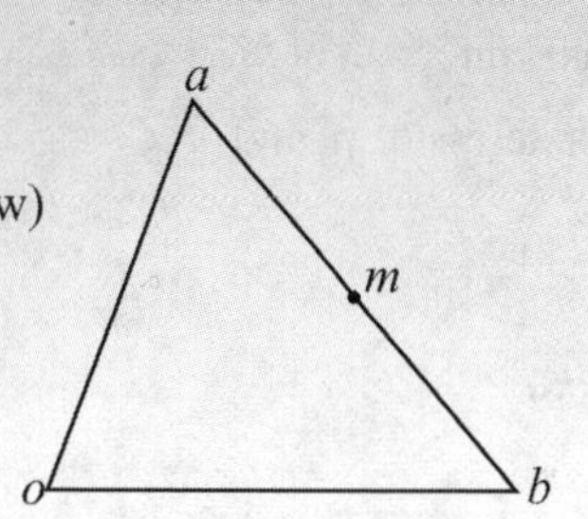

$\vec{m} = \overrightarrow{om}$

$= \overrightarrow{oa} + \overrightarrow{am}$ (triangle law)

$= \overrightarrow{oa} + \frac{1}{2}\overrightarrow{ab}$

$= \vec{a} + \frac{1}{2}(\vec{b} - \vec{a})$ (law 1)

$= \vec{a} + \frac{1}{2}\vec{b} - \frac{1}{2}\vec{a}$

$= \frac{1}{2}\vec{a} + \frac{1}{2}\vec{b}$ **Q.E.D.**

Example 2: *opqr* is a parallelogram.
m is the midpoint of [*pq*].
oq intersects *rp* at *k*.
Write in terms of $\vec{p}$ and $\vec{q}$

(i) $\vec{m}$

(ii) $\vec{k}$

(iii) $\vec{km}$

Deduce that the line *km* is parallel with *op*.

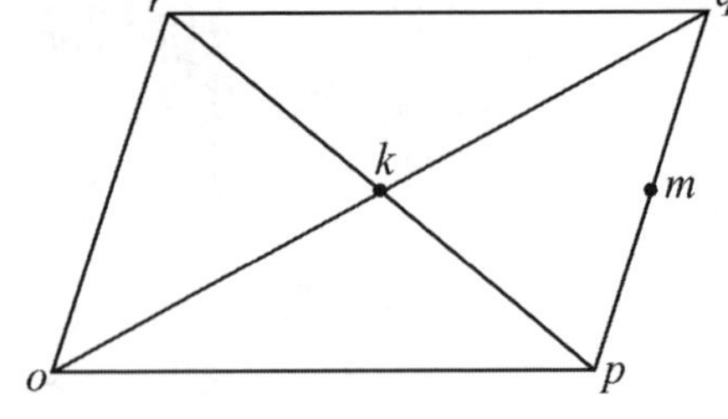

Solution:

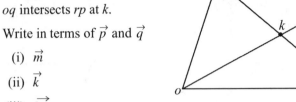

(i) $\vec{m}$ = midpoint of [*pq*]

$\therefore \vec{m} = ½\vec{p} + ½\vec{q}$

(ii) $\vec{k} = ½\vec{q}$

(iii) $\vec{km} = \vec{m} - \vec{k} = (½\vec{p} + ½\vec{q}) - ½\vec{q}$
$= ½\vec{p}$

Since $\vec{km} = ½\vec{p}$, *km* must be parallel with *op*.

Exercise 20.D

1. *oxyz* is a rectangle. *m*, *n* are midpoints of [*xy*] and [*yz*] respectively.

Write in terms of $\vec{x}$ and $\vec{z}$:

(i) $\vec{y}$

(ii) $\vec{m}$

(iii) $\vec{n}$

(iv) $\vec{xz}$

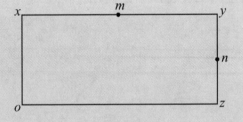

2. *opqr* is a parallelogram, whose diagonals intersect at *m*.

Write in terms of $\vec{p}$ and $\vec{r}$:

(i) $\vec{q}$

(ii) $\vec{m}$

(iii) $\vec{mq}$

(iv) $\vec{pr}$

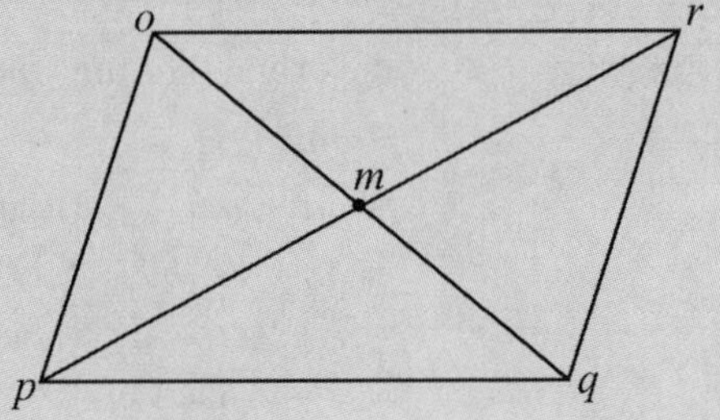

3. In the diagram, $|ok| : |ka| = 1 : 3$

$|ot| : |tb| = 2 : 1$

$|am| : |mb| = 1 : 1$

Write in terms of $\vec{a}$ and $\vec{b}$:

(i) $\vec{m}$

(ii) $\vec{k}$

(iii) $\vec{t}$

(iv) $\overrightarrow{km}$

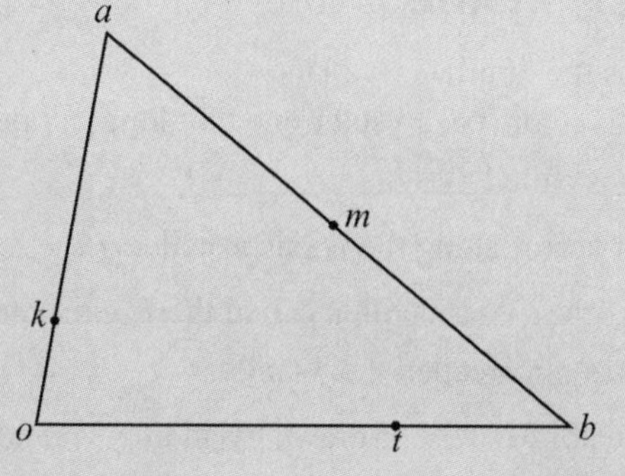

4. abc is a triangle.
x, y and z are the midpoints of $[ab]$, $[ac]$ and $[bc]$ respectively.

Write these in terms of $\vec{a}$, $\vec{b}$ and $\vec{c}$:

(i) $\vec{x}$

(ii) $\vec{y}$

(iii) $\vec{z}$

Deduce that $\vec{x} + \vec{y} + \vec{z} = \vec{a} + \vec{b} + \vec{c}$.

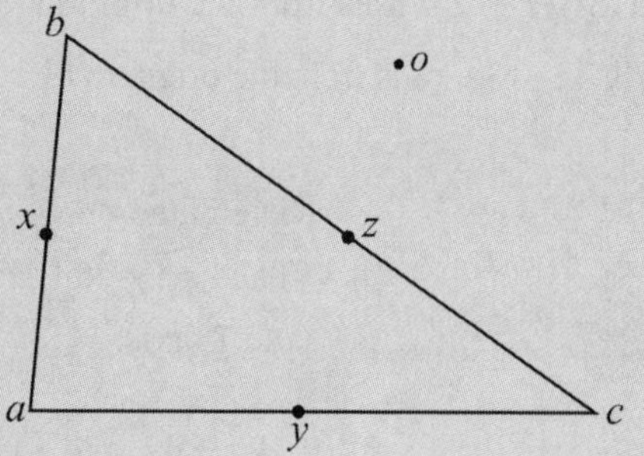

5. s and t are midpoints of $[ac]$ and $[bc]$.

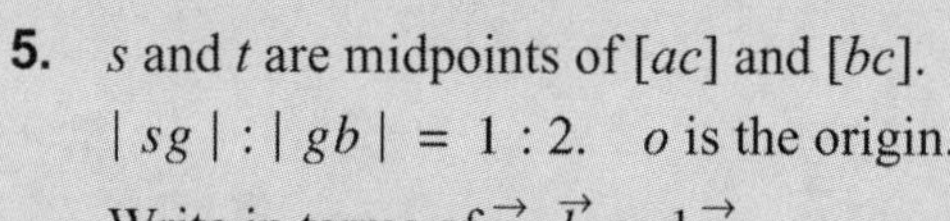

$|sg| : |gb| = 1 : 2$. o is the origin.

Write in terms of $\vec{a}$, $\vec{b}$ and $\vec{c}$:

(i) $\vec{s}$

(ii) $\overrightarrow{sb}$

(iii) $\overrightarrow{sg}$

(iv) $\vec{g}$

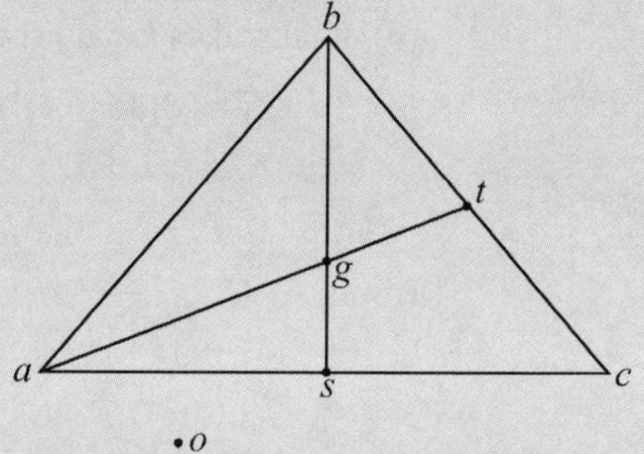

6. $oabc$ is a parallelogram, o is the origin.

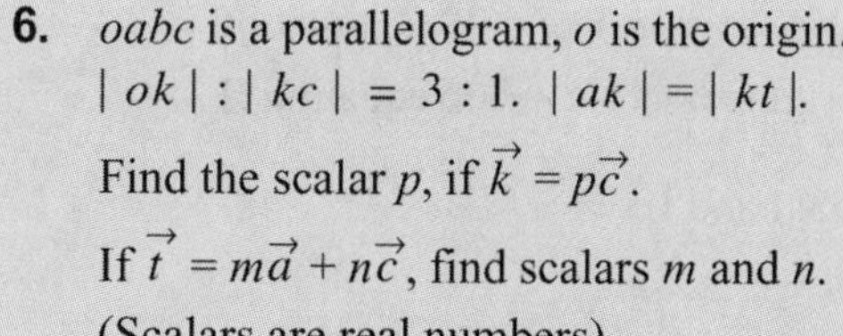

$|ok| : |kc| = 3 : 1$. $|ak| = |kt|$.

Find the scalar p, if $\vec{k} = p\vec{c}$.

If $\vec{t} = m\vec{a} + n\vec{c}$, find scalars m and n.
(Scalars are real numbers).

7. In the diagram, $|px| : |xq| = 4 : 1$.

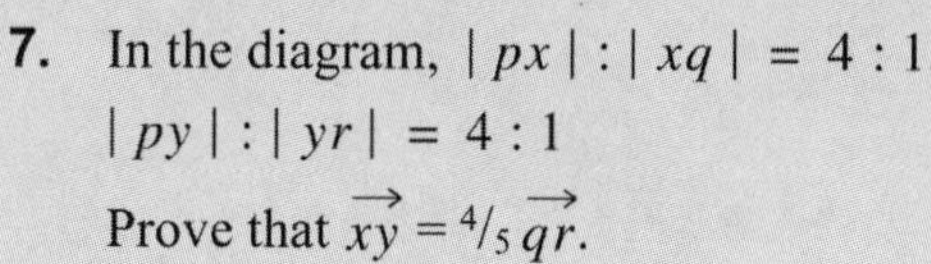

$|py| : |yr| = 4 : 1$

Prove that $\overrightarrow{xy} = {}^4/_5\,\overrightarrow{qr}$.

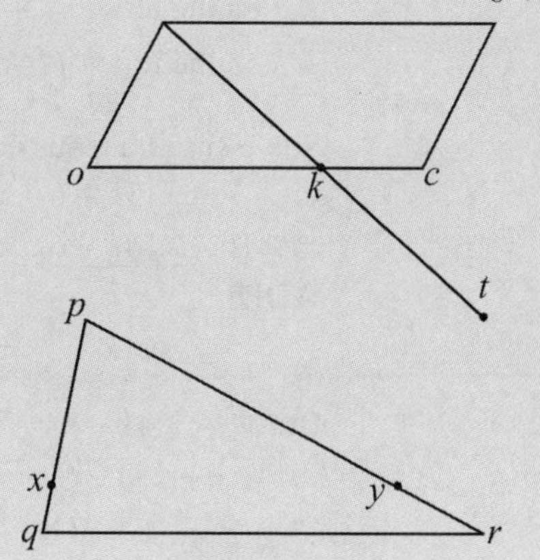

THE *i-j* PLANE

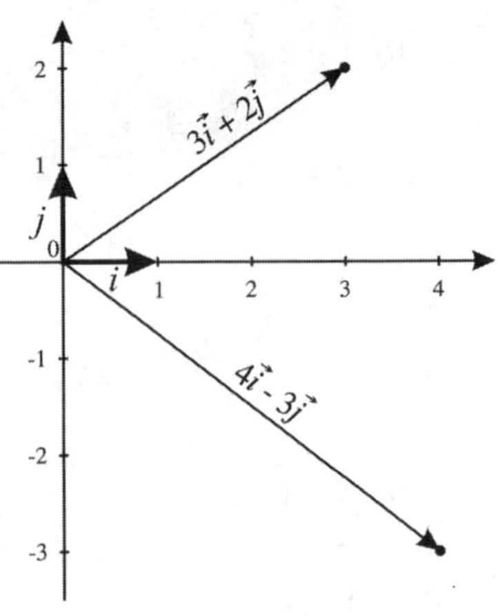

Here is the familiar x-y plane.
A unit vector (i.e. a vector one unit long) along the x-axis is called $\vec{i}$.

A unit vector along the y-axis is called $\vec{j}$.

Hence, the x-axis is often called the $\vec{i}$-axis and the y-axis is often called the $\vec{j}$-axis.

The vector $3\vec{i}+2\vec{j}$ is drawn by adding $3\vec{i}$ and $2\vec{j}$ by the parallelogram method.

The vector $3\vec{i}+2\vec{j}$ runs from the origin to (3, 2).

Similarly $4\vec{i}-3\vec{j}$ runs from the origin to (4, –3) as shown.

The plane on which these vectors appear is called the $\vec{i}$-$\vec{j}$ plane. The horizontal axis is called the $\vec{i}$-axis. The vertical axis is called the $\vec{j}$-axis.

Example 1: Let $\vec{u}=3\vec{i}+4\vec{j}$ and $\vec{v}=6\vec{i}-\vec{j}$.

(i) Write $3\vec{u}-2\vec{v}$ in terms of $\vec{i}$ and $\vec{j}$.
(ii) Find scalars k and t such that $k\vec{u}+t\vec{v}=39\vec{i}+7\vec{j}$.

Solution:

(i)
$$\begin{aligned}3\vec{u}-2\vec{v} &= 3(3\vec{i}+4\vec{j})-2(6\vec{i}-\vec{j})\\ &= 9\vec{i}+12\vec{j}-12\vec{i}+2\vec{j}\\ &= -3\vec{i}+14\vec{j}\end{aligned}$$

(ii)
$$\begin{aligned}k\vec{u}+t\vec{v} &= 39\vec{i}+7\vec{j}\\ \Rightarrow k(3\vec{i}+4\vec{j})+t(6\vec{i}-\vec{j}) &= 39\vec{i}+7\vec{j}\\ \Rightarrow 3k\vec{i}+4k\vec{j}+6t\vec{i}-t\vec{j} &= 39\vec{i}+7\vec{j}\\ \Rightarrow (3k+6t)\vec{i}+(4k-t)\vec{j} &= 39\vec{i}+7\vec{j}\end{aligned}$$

$\vec{i}$'s on the left = $\vec{i}$'s on the right $\Rightarrow 3k+6t=39$ ... equation I
$\vec{j}$'s on the left = $\vec{j}$'s on the right $\Rightarrow 4k-t=7$ ... equation II

Solve simultaneous equations I and II:

I	$3k+6t$	$=39$
$6\times$ II	$24k-6t$	$=42$
ADD!	$27k$	$=81$
$\therefore$	k	$=3$

But	$4k-t$	$=7$
$\therefore$	$4(3)-t$	$=7$
$\therefore$	t	$=5$
Answer:	$k=3, t=5$	

Exercise 20.E

1. Show these vectors in the $\vec{i}$-$\vec{j}$ plane.

(i) $4\vec{i}+3\vec{j}$
(ii) $3\vec{i}-3\vec{j}$
(iii) $-3\vec{i}+\vec{j}$
(iv) $-2\vec{i}-4\vec{j}$
(v) $-4\vec{j}$
(vi) $3\vec{i}$

2. Show these vectors in the $\vec{i}$-$\vec{j}$ plane.

(i) $4\vec{i}$
(ii) $-3\vec{j}$
(iii) $4\vec{i}-3\vec{j}$
(iv) $-4\vec{i}+3\vec{j}$

3. $\vec{x}=2\vec{i}+\vec{j}$, and $\vec{y}=3\vec{i}-2\vec{j}$.

Write these in terms of $\vec{i}$ and $\vec{j}$:

(i) $4\vec{x}+\vec{y}$
(ii) $\vec{x}+\vec{y}$
(iii) $\vec{x}-\vec{y}$

Show that $2\vec{x}+\vec{y}$ is along the $\vec{i}$-axis.

4. If $\vec{a}=3\vec{i}+\vec{j}$ and $\vec{b}=\vec{i}-7\vec{j}$, write in terms of $\vec{i}$ and $\vec{j}$.

(i) $\vec{a}+\vec{b}$
(ii) $\vec{a}-3\vec{b}$
(iii) $\overrightarrow{ab}$

5. Solve these equations (for a and b):

(i) $(a\vec{j}+b\vec{j})+(3\vec{i}+2\vec{j})=7\vec{i}+5\vec{j}$
(ii) $(3\vec{i}+\vec{j})+(a\vec{i}+b\vec{j})=10\vec{i}-\vec{j}$
(iii) $(a\vec{i}+7\vec{j})=(4\vec{i}+3\vec{j})-(5\vec{i}-b\vec{j})$
(iv) $(3\vec{i}+4\vec{j})-(a\vec{i}-b\vec{j})=-3\vec{j}$
(v) $a\vec{i}-b\vec{j}+b\vec{i}+a\vec{j}=7\vec{i}-\vec{j}$

6. $\vec{a}=3\vec{i}+2\vec{j}$ and $\vec{b}=4\vec{i}-\vec{j}$.
Find scalars l and k such that $l\vec{a}+k\vec{b}=2\vec{i}+5\vec{j}$.

7. $\vec{p}=2\vec{i}+\vec{j}$ and $\vec{q}=4\vec{i}-7\vec{j}$.

(i) Write $(\vec{p}+\vec{q})$ in terms of $\vec{i}$ and $\vec{j}$.
(ii) If $t(\vec{p}+\vec{q})=3\vec{i}+(k+1)\vec{j}$, find the value of t and k.

8. $\vec{x}=3\vec{i}-\vec{j}$ and $\vec{y}=9\vec{i}+4\vec{j}$.

(i) Show that $-3\vec{x}+\vec{y}$ is along the $\vec{j}$-axis.
(ii) If $k\vec{x}+\vec{y}$ is along the $\vec{i}$-axis, find the value of $k \in R$.

9. $\vec{o}=0\vec{i}+0\vec{j}$, $\vec{a}=3\vec{i}+\vec{j}$, $\vec{b}=-\vec{i}+7\vec{j}$.

Find (in terms of $\vec{i}$ and $\vec{j}$):

(i) $\vec{p}$, where *oapb* forms a parallelogram,
(ii) $\vec{m}$ where m is the midpoint of $[ab]$.

10. $\vec{u}=7(\vec{i}-\vec{j})$ and $\overrightarrow{uv}=3\vec{i}+4\vec{j}$.
Write $\vec{v}$ in terms of $\vec{i}$ and $\vec{j}$.

11. $\vec{m}=5\vec{i}-6\vec{j}$, $\vec{n}=-10\vec{i}+2\vec{j}$.

(i) Find $\overrightarrow{mn}$ in terms of $\vec{i}$ and $\vec{j}$.
(ii) If $\vec{m}+½\overrightarrow{mt}=\vec{n}$, find $\vec{t}$ in terms of $\vec{i}$ and $\vec{j}$.

Modulus:

The ***modulus*** (or ***length*** or ***magnitude***) of a vector is defined by

$$|a\vec{i} + b\vec{j}| = \sqrt{a^2 + b^2}$$

For example, the modulus of $3\vec{i} + 2\vec{j}$ is given by
$|3\vec{i} + 2\vec{j}| = \sqrt{3^2 + 2^2} = \sqrt{9 + 4} = \sqrt{13} = 3.606$
This means that the vector $3\vec{i} + 2\vec{j}$ is 3.606 units long.

Example 1: $\vec{p} = -2\vec{i} + 3\vec{j}$. $\vec{q} = -6\vec{i} + 6\vec{j}$.
Find $|\vec{p}|$, $|\vec{q}|$ and $|\vec{pq}|$.
Verify that $|\vec{pq}| < |\vec{p}| + |\vec{q}|$.

Solution: $|\vec{p}| = |-2\vec{i} + 3\vec{j}| = \sqrt{(-2)^2 + 3^2} = \sqrt{4+9} = \sqrt{13} = 3.606$

$|\vec{q}| = |-6\vec{i} + 6\vec{j}| = \sqrt{(-6)^2 + 6^2} = \sqrt{36+36} = \sqrt{72} = 8.485$

$\vec{pq} = \vec{q} - \vec{p} = (-6\vec{i} + 6\vec{j}) - (-2\vec{i} + 3\vec{j})$

$= -6\vec{i} + 6\vec{j} + 2\vec{i} - 3\vec{j} = -4\vec{i} + 3\vec{j}$

$\therefore\ |\vec{pq}| = |-4\vec{i} + 3\vec{j}| = \sqrt{(-4)^2 + 3^2} = \sqrt{16+9} = \sqrt{25} = 5$

$|\vec{pq}| = 5$ but $|\vec{p}| + |\vec{q}| = 3.606 + 8.485 = 12.091$

$\therefore\ |\vec{pq}| < |\vec{p}| + |\vec{q}|$ **Q.E.D.**

Exercise 20.F

1. Find, in surd form where necessary, the ***modulus*** of these vectors:

(i) $4\vec{i} + 6\vec{j}$
(ii) $2\vec{i} - \vec{j}$
(iii) $5\vec{i} + 3\vec{j}$
(iv) $8\vec{i} - 2\vec{j}$
(v) $-\vec{i} - \vec{j}$
(vi) $4\vec{j}$
(vii) $6\vec{j}$
(viii) $\vec{i} - \vec{j}$
(ix) $12\vec{i} - 5\vec{j}$
(x) $-3\vec{i} - \vec{j}$

2. Show that = $|7\vec{i} + 4\vec{j}| = |8\vec{i} + \vec{j}|$.

3. Investigate if $|7\vec{i} - \vec{j}| = |5(\vec{i} - \vec{j})|$.

4. If $|11\vec{i} + 2\vec{j}| = |k\vec{i} + 5\vec{j}|$,
find 2 possible values of $k \in R$.

5. If $|t\vec{i} + 24\vec{j}| = |15\vec{i} - 20\vec{j}|$,
find 2 possible values of $t \in R$.

6. $\vec{a} = 4\vec{i} + \vec{j}$ and $\vec{b} = 7\vec{i} + 5\vec{j}$.

(i) Write $\overrightarrow{ab}$ in terms $\vec{i}$ of and $\vec{j}$.

(ii) Evaluate $|\overrightarrow{ab}|$.

7. If $\vec{p} = 2(\vec{i} - \vec{j})$ and $\vec{q} = -2(2\vec{i} + 5\vec{j})$, evaluate $|\overrightarrow{pq}|$.

8. $\vec{x} = 2\vec{i} + \vec{j}$ and $\vec{y} = \vec{i} + 3\vec{j}$.

(i) Find $|\vec{x}|$, $|\vec{y}|$ and $|\vec{x} + \vec{y}|$.

(ii) Show that $|\vec{x} + \vec{y}| < |\vec{x}| + |\vec{y}|$.

9. If $\vec{x} = -8\vec{i} + 6\vec{j}$, prove that $|\vec{x}| + |9\vec{j}| > |\vec{x} + 9\vec{j}|$

10. $\vec{a} = 2(3\vec{i} - \vec{j})$ and $\vec{b} = -4\vec{i} + 3\vec{j}$.

Write in terms of $\vec{i}$ and $\vec{j}$:

(i) $\vec{a} + \vec{b}$

(ii) $\vec{a} - \vec{b}$

(iii) $\overrightarrow{ab}$

Show that $|\vec{a} + \vec{b}| < |\vec{a}| + |\vec{b}|$.

11. $\vec{p} = 5\vec{i} - 2\vec{j}$ and $\vec{q} = 4\vec{i} - \vec{j}$.

(i) Prove that $|\vec{p} + \vec{q}| < |\vec{p}| + |\vec{q}|$.

(ii) Prove that $|\overrightarrow{qp}| > |\vec{p}| - |\vec{q}|$.

(iii) Find scalars k and t such that $\vec{p} + k\vec{q} = t\vec{i}$.

(iv) Investigate if $|k\vec{q}| = k|\vec{q}|$.

DOT PRODUCT

Any two vectors may be multiplied in an operation called the ***dot product*** (sometimes called the ***scalar product***). It is defined in the following way:

Note:

$$(a\vec{i} + b\vec{j}).(c\vec{i} + d\vec{j}) = ac + bd$$

For example: $(3\vec{i} + 5\vec{j}).(7\vec{i} + 2\vec{j}) = (3)(7) + (5)(2) = 21 + 10 = 31$

And $(2\vec{i} - 4\vec{j}).(6\vec{i} + \vec{j}) = (2)(6) + (-4)(1) = 12 - 4 = 8$

And $(5\vec{i} - \vec{j}).(7\vec{j}) = (5\vec{i} - 1\vec{j}).(0\vec{i} + 7\vec{j}) = (5)(0) + (-1)(7) = 0 - 7 = -7$

Exercise 20.G

1. Evaluate the following dot products:
   (i) $(2\vec{i}+6\vec{j}).(3\vec{i}+5\vec{j})$
   (ii) $(7\vec{i}+2\vec{j}).(8\vec{i}+3\vec{j})$
   (iii) $(5\vec{i}+8\vec{j}).(2\vec{i}+5\vec{j})$
   (iv) $(3\vec{i}+7\vec{j}).(4\vec{i}-2\vec{j})$
   (v) $(3\vec{i}+\vec{j}).(10\vec{i}+6\vec{j})$
   (vi) $(\vec{i}+6\vec{j}).(11\vec{i}-3\vec{j})$
   (vii) $(\vec{i}-\vec{j}).(2\vec{i}+2\vec{j})$
   (viii) $(12\vec{i}-\vec{j}).(3\vec{i}-2\vec{j})$
   (ix) $4\vec{i}.(2\vec{i}+6\vec{j})$
   (x) $(2\vec{i}-6\vec{j}).7\vec{j}$

2. If $\vec{x}=6\vec{i}-5\vec{j}$, $\vec{y}=4\vec{i}+3\vec{j}$, $\vec{z}=2\vec{i}+\vec{j}$, evaluate:
   (i) $\vec{x}.\vec{y}$
   (ii) $\vec{x}.\vec{z}$
   (iii) $\vec{x}.(\vec{y}+\vec{z})$
   Investigate if
   $\vec{x}.\vec{y}+\vec{x}.\vec{z}=\vec{x}.(\vec{y}+\vec{z})$

3. $\vec{a}=3\vec{i}-5\vec{j}$, $\vec{b}=\vec{i}+\vec{j}$, $\vec{c}=2\vec{i}+6\vec{j}$.
   Evaluate:
   (i) $\vec{a}.\vec{b}$
   (ii) $\vec{a}.\vec{c}$
   (iii) $\vec{a}.(\vec{b}-\vec{c})$
   Investigate if
   $\vec{a}.(\vec{b}-\vec{c})=\vec{a}.\vec{b}-\vec{a}.\vec{c}$

4. $\vec{p}=4\vec{i}-2\vec{j}$, $\vec{q}=\vec{i}+2\vec{j}$, $\vec{r}=5\vec{i}$, $\vec{s}=2\vec{i}+4\vec{j}$
   Show that:
   (i) $\vec{p}.\vec{q}=0$
   (ii) $\vec{p}.\vec{r}>\vec{q}.\vec{r}$
   (iii) $\vec{p}.(\vec{q}+\vec{r})=\vec{p}.\vec{q}+\vec{p}.\vec{r}$
   (iv) $\vec{p}.(\vec{q}-\vec{s})=\vec{p}.\vec{q}-\vec{p}.\vec{s}$
   (v) $\vec{q}.\vec{s}=|\vec{q}|\,|\vec{s}|$
   (vi) $\vec{q}.\vec{s}=\vec{s}.\vec{q}$

5. $\vec{p}=4\vec{i}+5\vec{j}$, $\vec{q}=2\vec{i}+k\vec{j}$.
   Find the value of $k\in R$ if
   (i) $\vec{p}.\vec{q}=48$
   (ii) $\vec{p}.\vec{q}=0$
   (iii) $\vec{p}.\vec{q}=\vec{p}.\vec{p}$

6. $\vec{p}=4\vec{i}-6\vec{j}$ and $\vec{q}=k\vec{i}-\vec{j}$.
   Find the value of k if:
   (i) $\vec{p}.\vec{q}=18$
   (ii) $\vec{p}.\vec{q}=0$
   (iii) $\vec{p}.\vec{q}=-2$

7. $\vec{p}=2\vec{i}-\vec{j}$ and $\vec{q}=10\vec{i}+7\vec{j}$.
   (i) Write $\vec{pq}$ in terms of $\vec{i}$ and $\vec{j}$.
   (ii) Evaluate $\vec{p}.\vec{pq}$
   (iii) Evaluate $\vec{q}.\vec{pq}$

8. $\vec{p}=2\vec{i}-3\vec{j}$ and $\vec{q}=6\vec{i}+\vec{j}$.
   (i) Write $\vec{pq}$ in terms of $\vec{i}$ and $\vec{j}$.
   (ii) Evaluate $\vec{p}.\vec{pq}$
   (iii) Show that $\vec{p}.\vec{pq}=\vec{p}.\vec{q}-|\vec{p}|^2$

9. $\vec{p}=\vec{i}-8\vec{j}$ and $\vec{q}=3\vec{i}+2\vec{j}$.
   (i) Write $\vec{pq}$ in terms of $\vec{i}$ and $\vec{j}$.
   (ii) Evaluate $\vec{q}.\vec{pq}$
   (iii) Show that $|\vec{q}|^2-\vec{q}.\vec{pq}=\vec{p}.\vec{q}$

10. $\vec{a}=30\vec{i}+5\vec{j}$ and $\vec{b}=5\vec{i}+k\vec{j}$.
    Find the value of k if $\vec{a}.\vec{ab}=0$.

DOT PRODUCT AND ANGLE

Two important properties which connect dot product and angle are given here:

1. $\vec{x}.\vec{y} = 0$ if and only if $\vec{x} \perp \vec{y}$.
2. The angle A between two vectors $\vec{x}$ and $\vec{y}$ is given by the formula:

$$\cos A = \frac{\vec{x}.\vec{y}}{|\vec{x}||\vec{y}|}$$

Example 1: $\vec{p} = 6\vec{i} - 8\vec{j}$; $\vec{q} = 4\vec{i} + 3\vec{j}$ and $\vec{r} = 10\vec{i} + \vec{j}$

(i) Show that $\vec{p} \perp \vec{q}$.

(ii) Find the angle between $\vec{q}$ and $\vec{r}$ to the nearest degree.

Solution:

(i) $\vec{p}\,.\,\vec{q} = (6\vec{i} - 8\vec{j})\,.\,(4\vec{i} + 3\vec{j}) = (6)(4) + (-8)(3) = 24 - 24 = 0$

$\therefore \ \vec{p} \perp \vec{q}$

(ii) $\cos A = \dfrac{\vec{q}.\vec{r}}{|\vec{q}||\vec{r}|} = \dfrac{(4\vec{i} + 3\vec{j})\,.\,(10\vec{i} + \vec{j})}{|4\vec{i} + 3\vec{j}||10\vec{i} + \vec{j}|} = \dfrac{43}{5\sqrt{101}} = 0.855$

$\therefore \ A = 31^\circ$ to the nearest degree.

Exercise 20.H

1. Prove that $2\vec{i} + 3\vec{j} \perp 6\vec{i} - 4\vec{j}$.

2. $\vec{a} = 5\vec{i} - 2\vec{j}$ and $\vec{b} = 6\vec{i} + 15\vec{j}$
Investigate if $\vec{a} \perp \vec{b}$.

3. $\vec{a} = 9\vec{i} - 6\vec{j}$ and $\vec{b} = 2\vec{i} + 3\vec{j}$
Verify that $\vec{a} \perp \vec{b}$.

4. $\vec{a} = 5\vec{i} - 17\vec{j}$ and $\vec{b} = 10\vec{i} + 3\vec{j}$
Investigate if $\vec{a} \perp \vec{b}$.

5. $\vec{a} = 6\vec{i} - 4\vec{j}$ and $\vec{b} = 6\vec{i} + k\vec{j}$
Find the value of k if $\vec{a} \perp \vec{b}$.

6. $\vec{p} = 5\vec{i} + 5\vec{j}$ and $\vec{q} = 7\vec{i} + \vec{j}$.
Investigate if $(\vec{p} + \vec{q}) \perp (\vec{p} - \vec{q})$.

7. $\vec{p} = \vec{i} + \vec{j}$ and $\vec{q} = 5\vec{i} + \vec{j}$.
Investigate if $(\vec{p} + \vec{q}) \perp (\vec{p} - \vec{q})$.

8. $\vec{p} = 8\vec{i} + \vec{j}$ and $\vec{q} = 4\vec{i} + k\vec{j}$.
Write $\overrightarrow{pq}$ in terms of $k, \vec{i}$ and $\vec{j}$.
If $\overrightarrow{pq} \perp \vec{p}$, find the value of k.

9. $\vec{p} = 8\vec{i} + 6\vec{j}$ and $\vec{q} = 2\vec{i} - {}^{8}\!/_{3}\,\vec{j}$.
Verify the following:
(i) $\vec{p} \perp \vec{q}$
(ii) $\vec{p}\,.\,\vec{p} = |\vec{p}|^2$
(iii) $\vec{p}\,.\,\vec{q} = |\vec{p}|^2 + \vec{p}\,.\,\overrightarrow{pq}$

10. Use the formula $\cos A = \dfrac{\vec{x}.\vec{y}}{|\vec{x}||\vec{y}|}$ to find the angle between these pairs of vectors (to the nearest degree):
(i) $3\vec{i} + 4\vec{j}$ and $4\vec{i} + 3\vec{j}$
(ii) $5\vec{i} + 12\vec{j}$ and $12\vec{i} + 5\vec{j}$
(iii) $7\vec{i} + \vec{j}$ and $\vec{i} - \vec{j}$
(iv) $8\vec{i} - \vec{j}$ and $-7\vec{i} + 4\vec{j}$
(v) $-4\vec{i} + 2\vec{j}$ and $6\vec{i} + 12\vec{j}$

THE PERPENDICULAR VECTOR $\vec{r}^{\perp}$

Let $\vec{r}$ be any vector. If you swing $\vec{r}$ through 90° in an anti-clockwise direction about the origin, then the new vector is called $\vec{r}^{\perp}$.

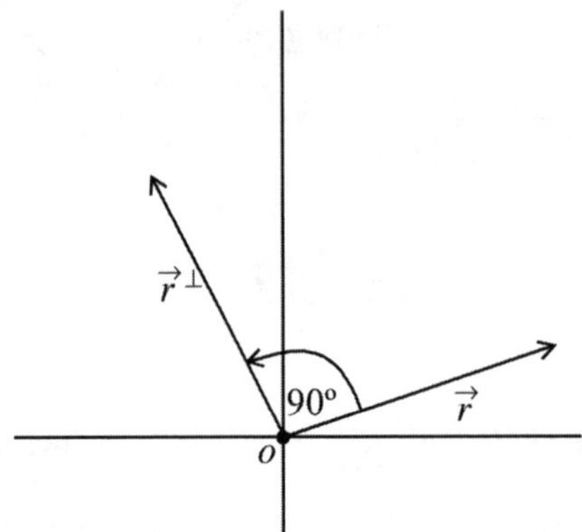

In general if $\vec{r} = x\vec{i} + y\vec{j}$, then $\vec{r}^{\perp} = -y\vec{i} + x\vec{j}$

For example if $\vec{r} = 8\vec{i} + 3\vec{j}$, then $\vec{r}^{\perp} = -3\vec{i} + 8\vec{j}$

And if $\vec{p} = 7\vec{i} - 6\vec{j}$, then $\vec{p}^{\perp} = 6\vec{i} + 7\vec{j}$

Finally, if $\vec{q} = -5\vec{i} + 13\vec{j}$, then $\vec{q}^{\perp} = -13\vec{i} - 5\vec{j}$

Example 1: Let $\vec{r} = 4\vec{i} + 3\vec{j}$ and let $\vec{p} = 6\vec{i} - 2\vec{j}$

(i) Write $\vec{r}^{\perp}$ and $\vec{p}^{\perp}$ in terms of $\vec{i}$ and $\vec{j}$

(ii) Investigate if $(\vec{r}^{\perp} + \vec{p}^{\perp}) = (\vec{r} + \vec{p})^{\perp}$

Solution:

(i) $\vec{r}^{\perp} = -3\vec{i} + 4\vec{j}$ and $\vec{p}^{\perp} = 2\vec{i} + 6\vec{j}$

(ii) The Left hand side: $\vec{r}^{\perp} + \vec{p}^{\perp} = -3\vec{i} + 4\vec{j} + 2\vec{i} + 6\vec{j} = -\vec{i} + 10\vec{j}$

The Right hand side: $\vec{r} + \vec{p} = 4\vec{i} + 3\vec{j} + 6\vec{i} - 2\vec{j} = 10\vec{i} + \vec{j}$

$\therefore (\vec{r} + \vec{p})^{\perp} = -\vec{i} + 10\vec{j}$

$\therefore (\vec{r}^{\perp} + \vec{p}^{\perp}) = (\vec{r} + \vec{p})^{\perp}$

Exercise 20.I

1. In each case write down the perpendicular vector, $\vec{r}^{\perp}$:

(i) $\vec{r} = 4\vec{i} + 7\vec{j}$
(ii) $\vec{r} = 9\vec{i} + 3\vec{j}$
(iii) $\vec{r} = 10\vec{i} + 9\vec{j}$
(iv) $\vec{r} = \vec{i} + 8\vec{j}$
(v) $\vec{r} = 5\vec{i} + \vec{j}$
(vi) $\vec{r} = 4\vec{i} - 6\vec{j}$
(vii) $\vec{r} = 6\vec{i} - 5\vec{j}$
(viii) $\vec{r} = -5\vec{i} + 3\vec{j}$
(ix) $\vec{r} = -\vec{i} + 7\vec{j}$
(x) $\vec{r} = -7\vec{i} - 6\vec{j}$

2. $\vec{r} = 7\vec{i} + 2\vec{j}$ and $\vec{p} = \vec{i} + 3\vec{j}$.

(i) Write $\vec{r}^{\perp}$ and $\vec{p}^{\perp}$ in terms of $\vec{i}$ and $\vec{j}$.
(ii) Verify that $\vec{r} \,.\, \vec{r}^{\perp} = 0$.
(iii) Verify that $\vec{p}^{\perp} \,.\, \vec{p} = 0$.

3. $\vec{r} = 5\vec{i} + 2\vec{j}$ and $\vec{p} = 2\vec{i} + \vec{j}$.

(i) Write $\vec{r}^{\perp}$ and $\vec{p}^{\perp}$ in terms of $\vec{i}$ and $\vec{j}$.
(ii) Investigate if
$(\vec{r}^{\perp} + \vec{p}^{\perp}) = (\vec{r} + \vec{p})^{\perp}$.

4. Let $\vec{x} = 7\vec{i} + 4\vec{j}$ and $\vec{y} = 4\vec{i} - 2\vec{j}$.

(i) Write $\vec{x}^{\perp}$ and $\vec{y}^{\perp}$ in terms of $\vec{i}$ and $\vec{j}$.
(ii) Investigate if
$$(\vec{x}^{\perp} - \vec{y}^{\perp}) = (\vec{x} - \vec{y})^{\perp}$$
(iii) Investigate if
$$\overrightarrow{xy} \,.\, (\vec{x}^{\perp} - \vec{y}^{\perp}) = 0$$

5. Let $\vec{x} = \vec{i} + 9\vec{j}$ and $\vec{y} = \vec{i} - 2\vec{j}$.

(i) Write $(\vec{x}^{\perp} + \vec{y}^{\perp})$ and $(\vec{x}^{\perp} - \vec{y}^{\perp})$ in terms of $\vec{i}$ and $\vec{j}$.
(ii) Investigate if
$(\vec{x}^{\perp} + \vec{y}^{\perp}) \,.\, (\vec{x}^{\perp} - \vec{y}^{\perp}) = 0$

6. Let $\vec{x} = 2\vec{i} + 4\vec{j}$.

(i) Write $\vec{x}^{\perp}$ in terms of $\vec{i}$ and $\vec{j}$.
(ii) Show that $(\vec{x}^{\perp})^{\perp} = -\vec{x}$.
(iii) Verify that $|\vec{x}^{\perp}| = |\vec{x}|$.

REVISION EXERCISE 20.J

1. (a) Copy the diagram and construct the vectors:

(i) $\vec{x} + \vec{y}$

(ii) $\vec{x} - \vec{y}$

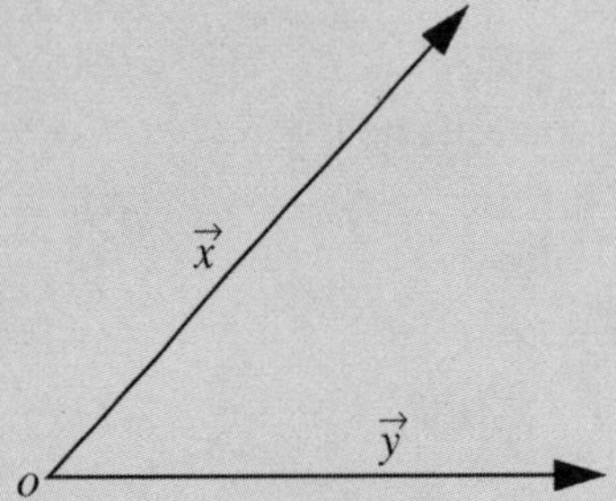

(b) *oabc* is a square. *m* is the midpoint of [*ab*]. Express in terms of $\vec{a}$ and $\vec{c}$

(i) $\vec{b}$

(ii) $\vec{m}$

(iii) $\overrightarrow{mc}$

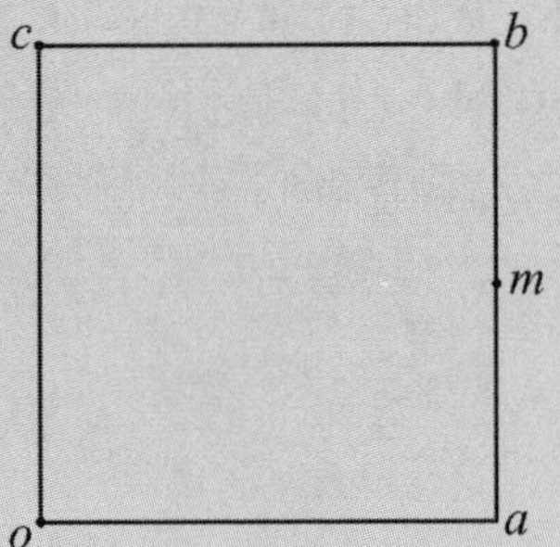

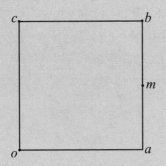

(c) Let $\vec{x} = 3\vec{i} + 2\vec{j}$ and $\vec{y} = 6\vec{i} - 2\vec{j}$.

(i) Express $\overrightarrow{xy}$ in terms of $\vec{i}$ and $\vec{j}$.

(ii) Calculate $|\overrightarrow{xy}|$.

(iii) Evaluate $\vec{x} \,.\, \vec{y}$

(iv) Write $(\vec{x}^{\perp} - \vec{y}^{\perp})$ in terms of $\vec{i}$ and $\vec{j}$.

2. (a) Copy the diagram and construct the vectors $\vec{a}$ and $\vec{c}$ such that

(i) $\vec{a} = 2\vec{x}$

(ii) $\vec{c} = -\vec{y}$

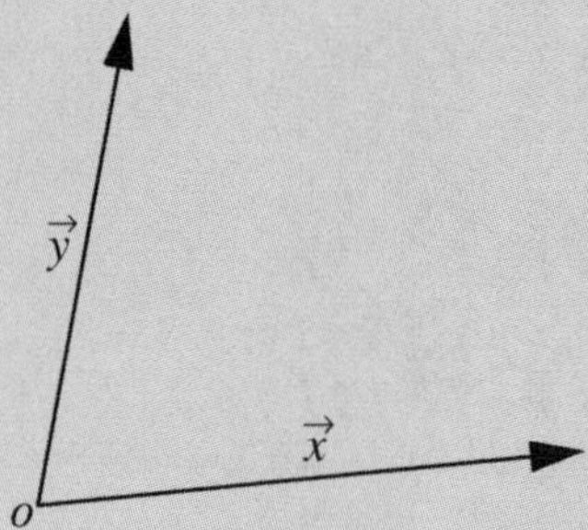

(b) Let $\vec{x} = 5\vec{i} + \vec{j}$ and $\vec{y} = \vec{i} - 4\vec{j}$.

(i) Express $(\vec{x} + \vec{y})$ in terms of $\vec{i}$ and $\vec{j}$.

(ii) Calculate $|\vec{x} + \vec{y}|$.

(iii) Evaluate $\vec{x} \,.\, \vec{y}$

(iv) Write $(\vec{x}^{\perp} + \vec{y}^{\perp})$ in terms of $\vec{i}$ and $\vec{j}$.

(v) Investigate if

$$(\vec{x}^{\perp} + \vec{y}^{\perp}) = (\vec{x} + \vec{y})^{\perp}$$

(c) *oab* is a triangle. *m* is the midpoint of [*ob*]. $|mg| = ½|ga|$.
Express in terms of $\vec{a}$ and $\vec{b}$:

(i) $\vec{m}$

(ii) $\overrightarrow{ma}$

(iii) $\overrightarrow{mg}$

(iv) $\vec{g}$

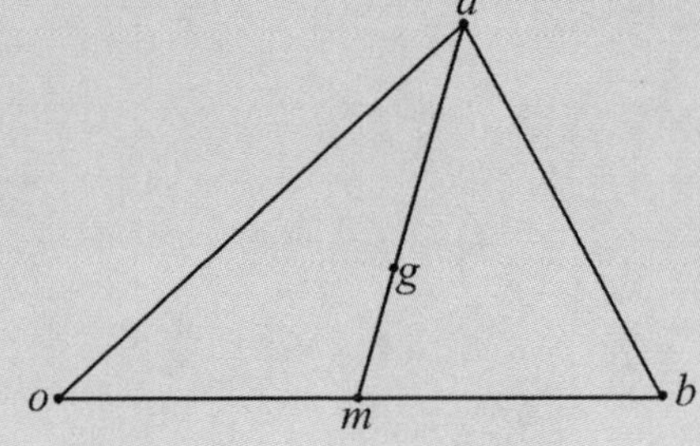

3. (a) Copy the diagram and construct the vectors

(i) $\vec{x} + 2\vec{y}$

(ii) $2\vec{x} - \vec{y}$

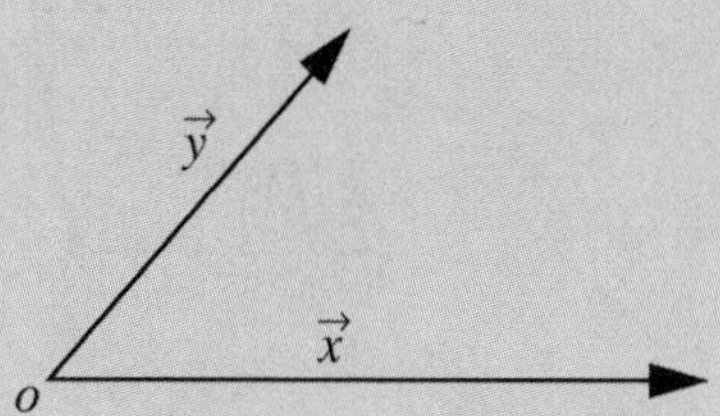

(b) $oabc$ is a rectangle. m is the midpoint of $[bc]$. Express in terms of $\vec{a}$ and $\vec{c}$

(i) $\vec{b}$

(ii) $\vec{m}$

(iii) $\overrightarrow{am}$

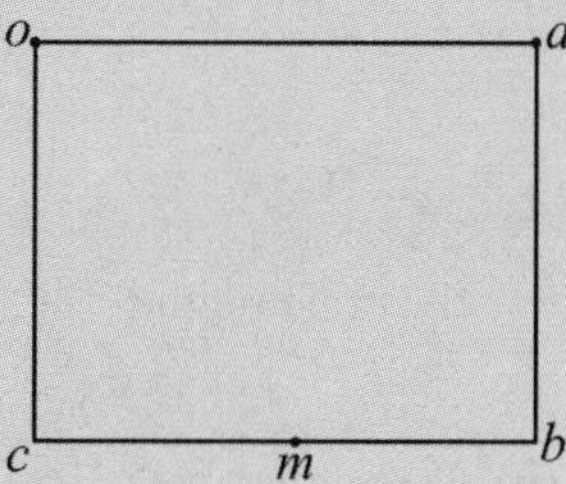

(c) Let $\vec{x} = \vec{i} + 4\vec{j}$ and $\vec{y} = 5\vec{i} + 2\vec{j}$.

(i) Illustrate on the $\vec{i}$ - $\vec{j}$ plane:

$\vec{x}$, $\vec{y}$ and $\vec{x} + \vec{y}$

(ii) Calculate $|\vec{x} + \vec{y}|$.

(iii) Verify that

$|\vec{x} + \vec{y}| < |\vec{x}| + |\vec{y}|$

(iv) Evaluate $\vec{x} \cdot \vec{y}$

(v) $\vec{x}^{\perp} + \vec{z}^{\perp} = \vec{y}^{\perp}$

Find $\vec{z}$ in terms of of $\vec{i}$ and $\vec{j}$.

4. (a) Copy the diagram twice and construct the points k_1 and k_2 such that:

(i) $\overrightarrow{k_1} = \vec{p} + ½\vec{q}$

(ii) $\overrightarrow{k_2} = \vec{p} - ½\vec{q}$

•q

o•

•p

(b) $oabc$ is a rectangle. m is the midpoint of $[ab]$.

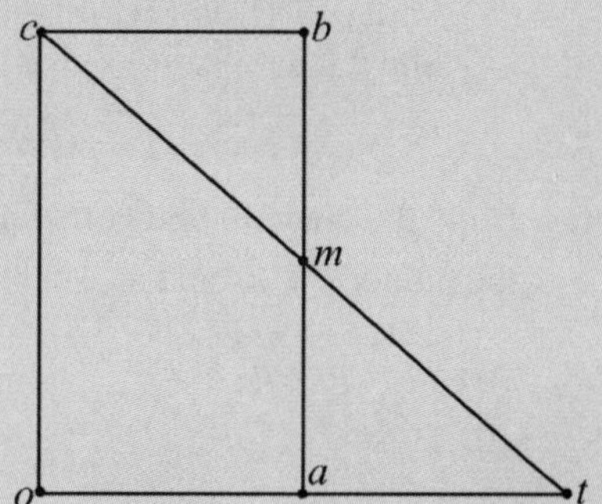

Express in terms of $\vec{a}$ and $\vec{c}$:

(i) $\vec{t}$

(ii) $\vec{m}$

(iii) $\overrightarrow{mt}$

(iv) $\overrightarrow{ct}$

If $\vec{a} = 4\vec{i}$ and $\vec{c} = 6\vec{j}$, calculate $|\overrightarrow{ct}|$ and evaluate $\vec{a} \cdot \vec{m}$

5. (a) Copy the diagram and construct the vectors:

(i) $\vec{x} + \vec{y}$

(ii) $\frac{1}{2}\vec{x} - \vec{y}$

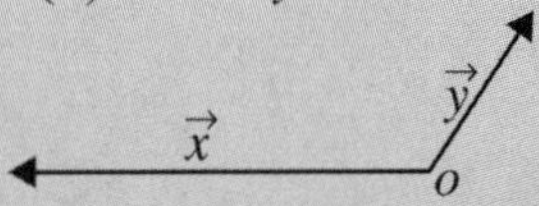

(b) Let $\vec{a} = 2\vec{i} + 3\vec{j}$, $\vec{b} = 7\vec{i} - \vec{j}$ and $\vec{c} = 4\vec{i} - 2\vec{j}$.

(i) Illustrate these three vectors on the $\vec{i} - \vec{j}$ plane.

(ii) Write $\vec{a} + \vec{b}$ in terms of $\vec{i}$ and $\vec{j}$.

(iii) Write $\vec{cb}$ in terms of $\vec{i}$ and $\vec{j}$.

(iv) Verify that $|\vec{cb}| > |\vec{b}| - |\vec{c}|$.

(v) Show that

$$\vec{a} \cdot \vec{b} = \vec{a} \cdot \vec{c} + \vec{a} \cdot \vec{cb}$$

6. (a) Copy the diagram and construct the points k_1, k_2 and k_3 such that

(i) $\vec{k_1} = \vec{p} + \vec{q}$

(ii) $\vec{k_2} = \vec{p} - \vec{q}$

(iii) $\vec{k_3} = \frac{1}{2}(\vec{p} - \vec{q})$

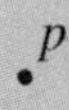

•o

•q

(b) Let $\vec{x} = 3\vec{i} - 5\vec{j}$.

(i) Illustrate on the $\vec{i} - \vec{j}$ plane:

$\vec{x}$ and $\vec{x}^{\perp}$

(ii) Calculate $|\vec{x} + \vec{x}^{\perp}|$.

(iii) Verify that $|\vec{x} + \vec{x}^{\perp}| < 2|\vec{x}|$.

(iv) Verify that $\vec{x} \cdot \vec{x}^{\perp} = 0$.

(v) Find the values of the scalars m and n if

$$m\vec{x} + n\vec{x}^{\perp} = 2(2\vec{i} - 9\vec{j})$$

7. (a) $oabc$ is a parallelogram.

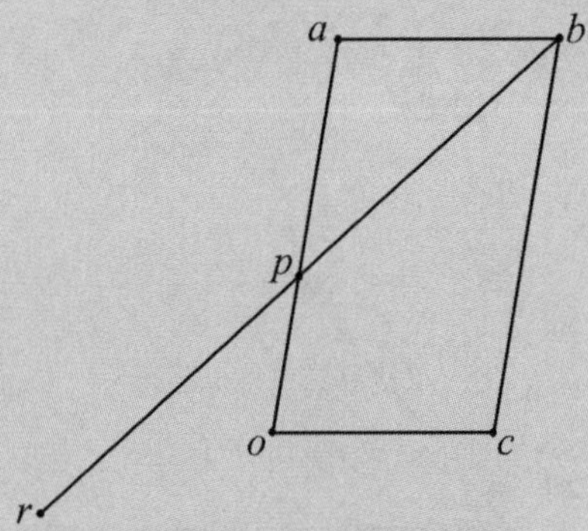

p is a point on $[oa]$ such that $|op| : |pa| = 2 : 3$

r is a point such that $\vec{bp} = \vec{pr}$

Express in terms of $\vec{a}$ and $\vec{c}$:

(i) $\vec{b}$

(ii) $\vec{p}$

(iii) $\vec{bp}$

(iv) $\vec{r}$

(b) Let $\vec{x} = 5\vec{i} + 7\vec{j}$ and $\vec{y} = 3\vec{i} - \vec{j}$.

(i) Illustrate on the $\vec{i} - \vec{j}$ plane:

$\vec{x}$, $\vec{y}$ and $\vec{x} + \vec{y}$

(ii) Calculate $|\vec{x} + \vec{y}|$.

(iii) Find the values of the scalars m and t if

$$m(\vec{x} + \vec{y}) = 16\vec{i} + (t + 2)\vec{j}$$

(iv) Investigate if

$$\vec{x} \perp \vec{y}$$

8. (a) Copy the diagram and construct the point k such that $\overrightarrow{ok} = \overrightarrow{ob} + \tfrac{1}{2}\overrightarrow{oc}$

$b\bullet$ $\bullet c$

$o\bullet$

(b) Let $\vec{x} = 3\vec{i} + 4\vec{j}$ and $\vec{y} = 5\vec{i} + 12\vec{j}$.

(i) Express in terms of $\vec{i}$ and $\vec{j}$:

$(\vec{x} + \vec{y})$ and $\vec{x}^{\perp}$ and $\vec{y}^{\perp}$

(ii) Verify that $|\vec{x} + \vec{y}| < |\vec{x}| + |\vec{y}|$

(iii) Evaluate $\vec{x} \cdot \vec{y}$

(iv) Investigate if $\vec{x} \cdot \vec{y} = |\vec{x}||\vec{y}|$

(v) Investigate if $\vec{x}^{\perp} \cdot \vec{y}^{\perp} = \vec{x} \cdot \vec{y}$

9. (a) xyz is an equilateral triangle.

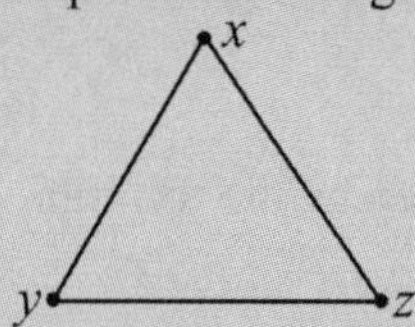

(i) Copy the diagram and construct $(\overrightarrow{xy} + \overrightarrow{zx})$

(ii) Write down a single vector equal to $(\overrightarrow{xy} + \overrightarrow{zx})$

(iii) Construct the point t such that $\overrightarrow{xy} + \tfrac{1}{2}\,\overrightarrow{yz} = \overrightarrow{zt}$

(b) Let $\vec{r} = 2\vec{i} - 5\vec{j}$ and $\vec{s} = -6\vec{i} + \vec{j}$.
Let $\vec{p} = \vec{r} + \vec{s}$ and $\vec{q} = \vec{r} - \vec{s}$.

(i) Express $\vec{p}$ and $\vec{q}$ in terms of $\vec{i}$ and $\vec{j}$.

(ii) Illustrate on the $\vec{i}$ - $\vec{j}$ plane:

$\vec{r}, \vec{s}, \vec{p}$ and $\vec{q}$

(iii) Verify that $|\vec{p}\vec{q}| < |\vec{p}| + |\vec{q}|$.

(iv) The angle θ between $\vec{p}$ and $\vec{q}$ is given by the formula

$$\cos\theta = \frac{\vec{p} \cdot \vec{q}}{|\vec{p}||\vec{q}|}$$

Calculate θ to the nearest degree.

10. (a) $oabcde$ is a regular hexagon, with o as the origin.

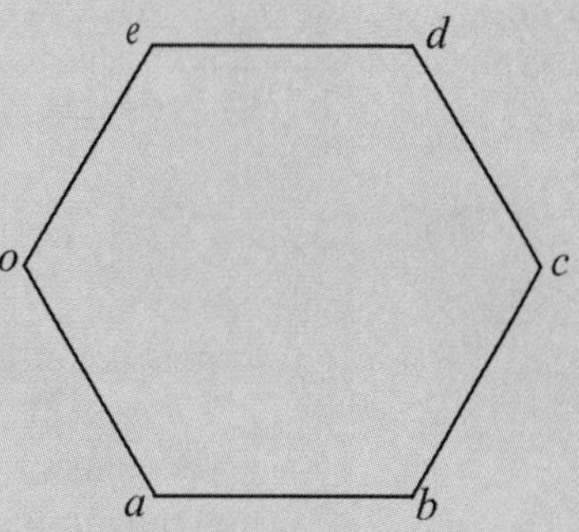

Write down a single vector equal to:

(i) $\overrightarrow{ab} + \overrightarrow{bc}$

(ii) $2\vec{a}$

(iii) $\overrightarrow{cd} - \overrightarrow{ed}$

(iv) $\vec{a} + \vec{e}$

(v) $-\tfrac{1}{2}\vec{c}$

(b) Let $\vec{x} = 3\vec{i} + 4\vec{j}$ and
$\vec{y} = 12\vec{i} - 9\vec{j}$ and
$\vec{z} = 4\vec{i} + 3\vec{j}$.

(i) Evaluate $\vec{x} \cdot \vec{y}$ and hence verify that $\vec{x} \perp \vec{y}$.

(ii) Investigate if

$\vec{x} \cdot \vec{z} = |\vec{x}||\vec{z}|$

(iii) The angle θ between $\vec{x}$ and $\vec{z}$ is given by the formula

$$\cos\theta = \frac{\vec{x} \cdot \vec{z}}{|\vec{x}||\vec{z}|}$$

Calculate θ to the nearest degree.

(iv) Investigate if

$(\vec{x}^{\perp} + \vec{y}^{\perp} + \vec{z}^{\perp}) = (\vec{x} + \vec{y} + \vec{z})^{\perp}$

1. $\vec{ab} = -\vec{ba}$

2. The triangle law: $\vec{ab} + \vec{bc} = \vec{ac}$

3. $\vec{ab} = \vec{b} - \vec{a}$

4. If m is the midpoint of $[ab]$, then $\vec{m} = \frac{1}{2}\vec{a} + \frac{1}{2}\vec{b}$

5. Two vectors are equal if, and only if, they have the same direction and magnitude.

6. The ***modulus*** of the vector $a\vec{i} + b\vec{j}$ is $|a\vec{i} + b\vec{j}| = \sqrt{a^2 + b^2}$

7. ***Dot product*** (or ***scalar product***): $(a\vec{i} + b\vec{j}) . (c\vec{i} + d\vec{j}) = ac + bd$

8. $\vec{x} . \vec{y} = 0$ if and only if $\vec{x} \perp \vec{y}$

9. The angle θ between $\vec{p}$ and $\vec{q}$ is given by the formula
$$\cos\theta = \frac{\vec{p}.\vec{q}}{|\vec{p}||\vec{q}|}$$

10. If $\vec{r} = x\vec{i} + y\vec{j}$, then $\vec{r}^{\perp} = -y\vec{i} + x\vec{j}$

Chapter 21

Option 4: Further Theorems

Here are two things you must know before starting the first theorem:

1. If the two sides of a triangle are equal in length, then the two opposite angles are equal in measure (i.e. the number of degrees in both is equal). We call such triangles ISOSCELES.

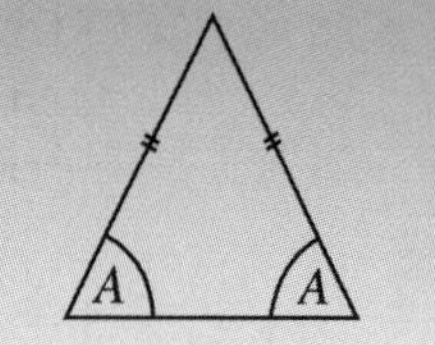

2. Given a triangle, the exterior angle is equal to the sum of the two opposite interior angles, i.e. $X = B + C$.

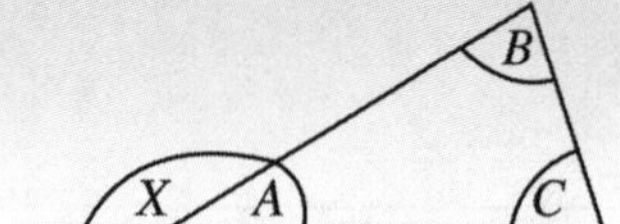

THEOREM A: The degree-measure of an angle subtended at the centre of a circle by a chord is equal to twice the degree-measure of any angle subtended by the chord at a point of the arc of the circle which is on the same side of the chordal line as is the centre.

Given: A circle with centre c.
An angle $<acb$ at the centre.
An angle $<akb$ at the circle, standing on the same arc.

To prove: $| <acb | = 2| <akb |$

Construction: Join $[kc]$ and ***produce*** to x.
(i.e. extend to x)

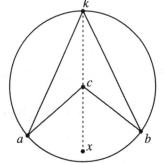

Proof: $| ca | = | ck |$ (both are radii of the circle)

$\therefore \Delta ack$ is an ***isosceles*** triangle

$\therefore | <cak | = | <cka |$ (by No. 1, above)

Now $|\angle acx| = |\angle cka| + |\angle cak|$ (Exterior angle = Sum of opposite interior angles)

But $|\angle cak| = |\angle cka|$

$\therefore |\angle acx| = 2|\angle cka|$

Similarly, $|\angle bcx| = 2|\angle ckb|$ (Same arguments again)

Adding the above two results gives

$|\angle acx| + |\angle bcx| = 2[|\angle cka| + |\angle ckb|]$

$\therefore |\angle acb| = 2|\angle akb|$ **Q.E.D.**

The converse of the above theorem is also true.

Deduction 1: The angles which are subtended by a chord of the circle at points of the circle which are on one side of the chordal line have equal degree-measures.

Proof:

$|\angle axb| = \frac{1}{2}|\angle acb|$ (theorem)

$|\angle ayb| = \frac{1}{2}|\angle acb|$ (theorem)

$\therefore |\angle axb| = |\angle ayb|$

$\therefore$ Any two angles at the circle standing on the same arc are equal in measure. **Q.E.D.**

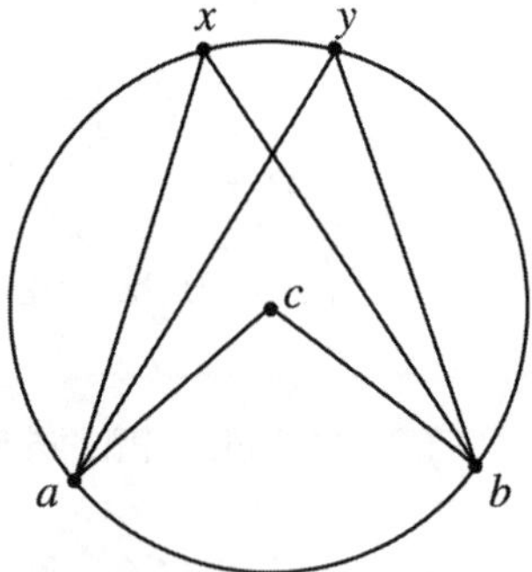

Deduction 2: An angle standing on a diameter is a right angle (90°).

Proof:

$|\angle acb| = 180°$ (straight angle)

But $|\angle akb| = \frac{1}{2}|\angle acb|$ (theorem)

$\therefore |\angle akb| = 90°$ **Q.E.D.**

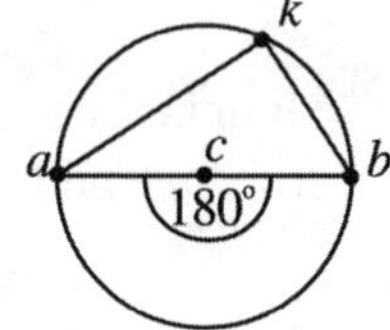

Deduction 3: The sum of opposite angles in a cyclic quadrilateral is 180°.

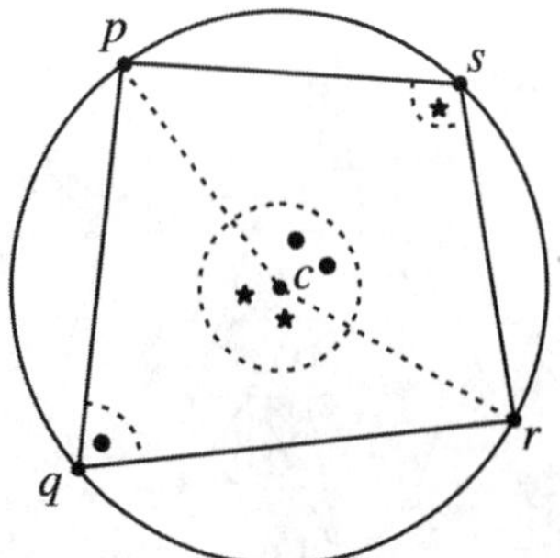

> A cyclic quadrilateral is ANY four-sided figure inset in a circle.

Proof:

$| <psr | = \frac{1}{2}| <pcr |$ (by the theorem)

$| <rqp | = \frac{1}{2}| <rcp |$ (by the theorem)

Add these two to get

$| <psr | + | <rqp | = \frac{1}{2}[| <pcr | + | <rcp |]$

But $[| <pcr | + | <rcp |] = 1$ full turn $= 360°$

$\therefore | <psr | + | <rqp | = \frac{1}{2}(360°) = 180°$ **Q.E.D.**

Example 1:

Here is a circle, centre c.

$| <cak | = 25°$

$| <acb | = 140°$

Find $| <cbk |$.

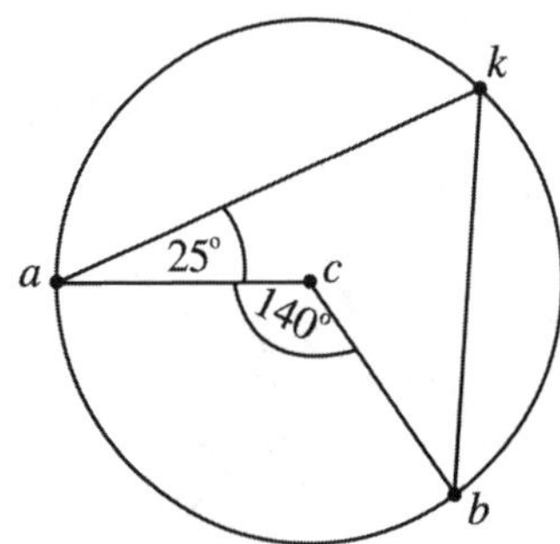

Solution:

$| <akb | = \frac{1}{2}| <acb |$ (theorem)

$\therefore | <akb | = 70°$

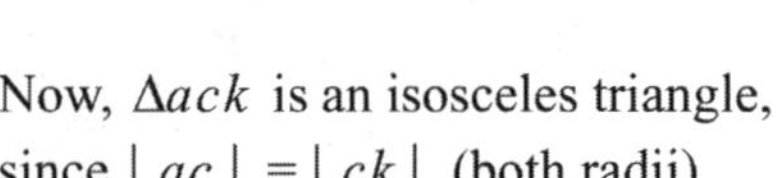
Now, Δack is an isosceles triangle, since $| ac | = | ck |$ (both radii)

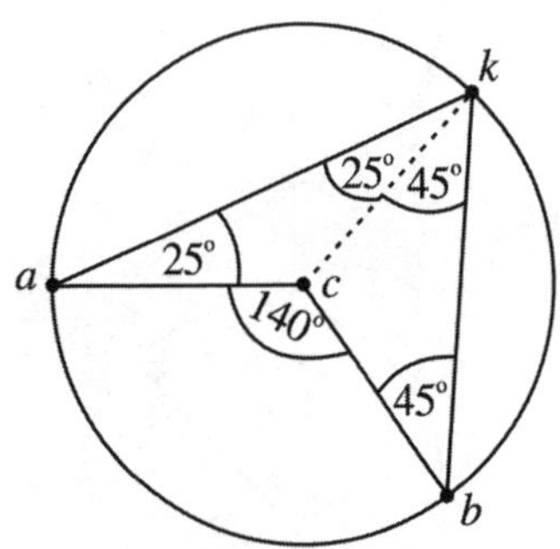

$\therefore | <akc | = 25°$

$\therefore | <bkc | = 70° - 25° = 45°$

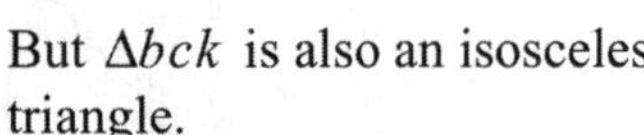
But Δbck is also an isosceles triangle.

$\therefore | <cbk | = 45°$

Exercise 21.A

1. Find the value of x in each case: (c = centre)

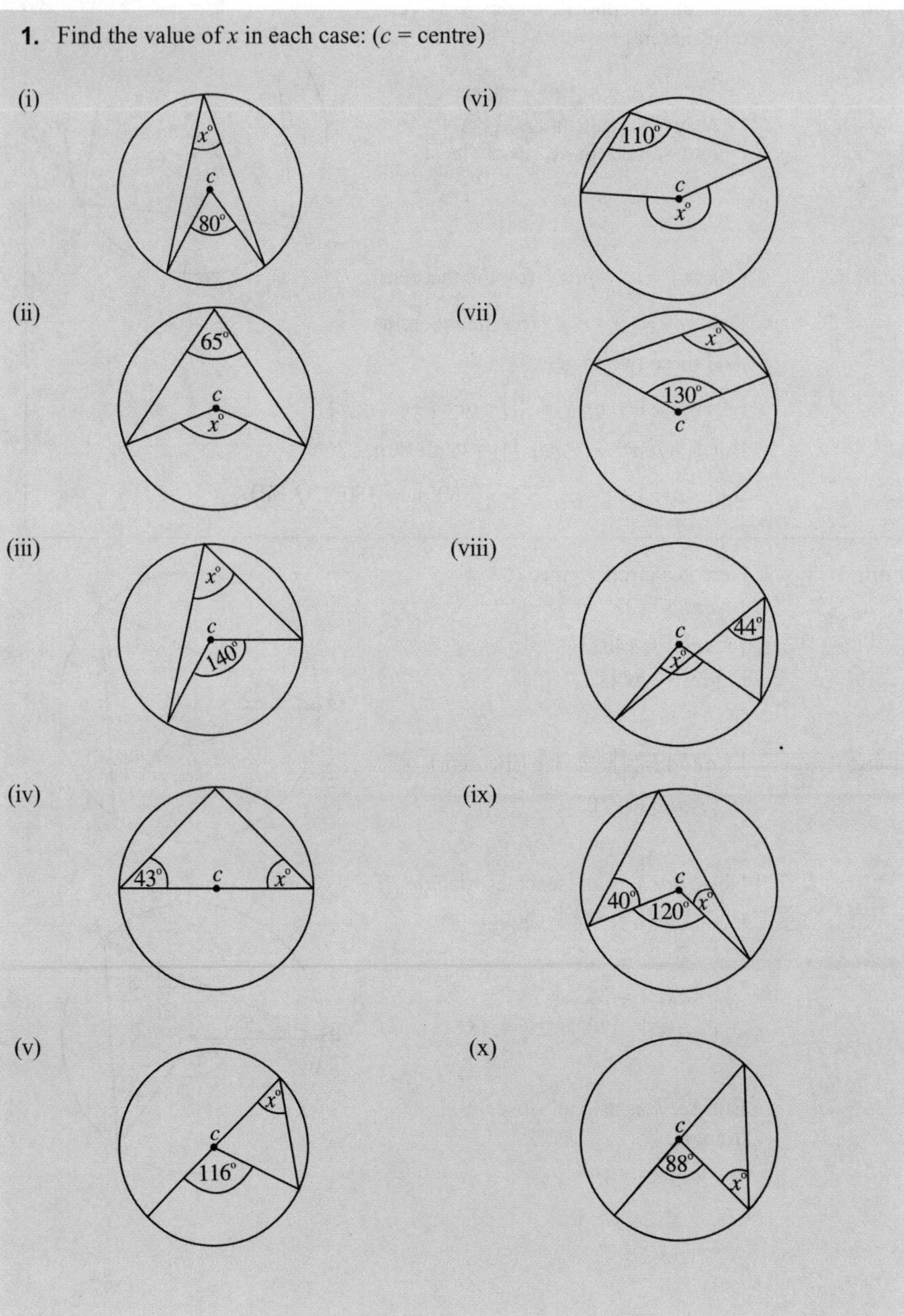

2. Find the value of x and y in each case:

(i)

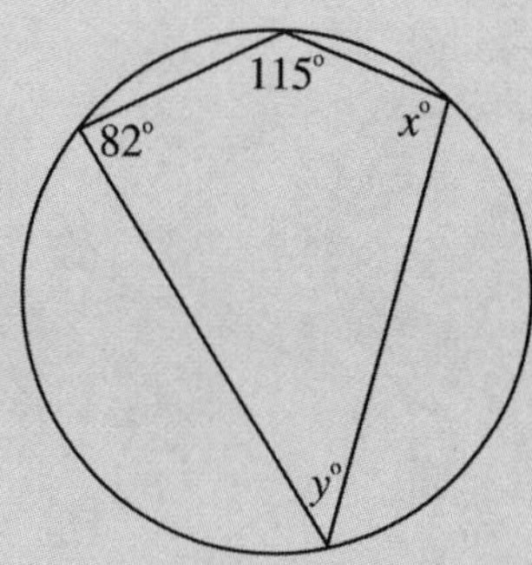

(iii)

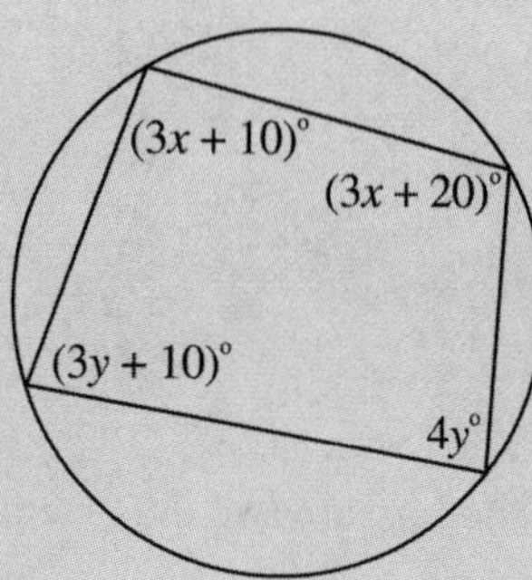

(ii)

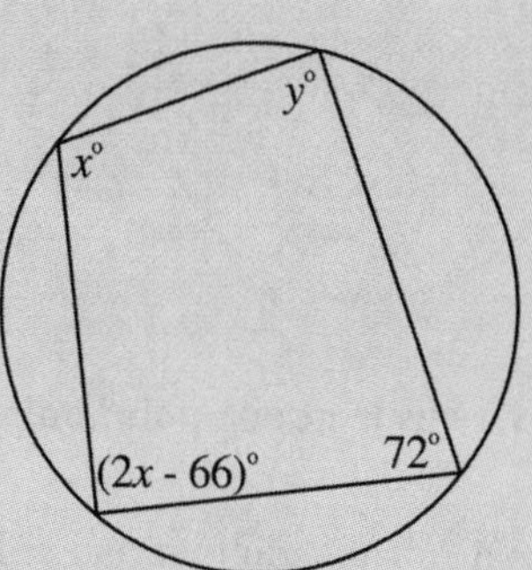

(iv)

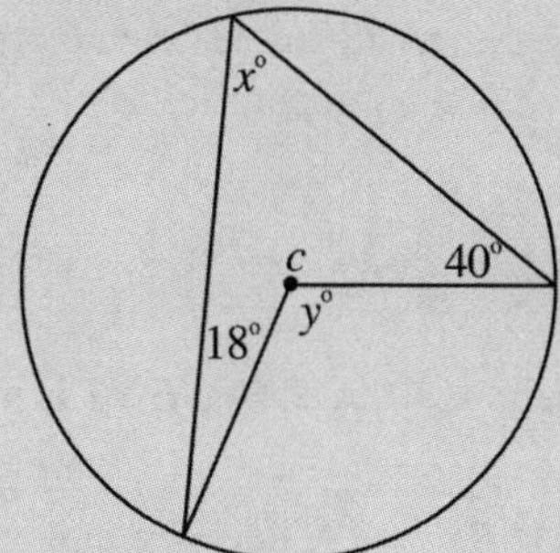

3. $pqrs$ are points of a circle, centre c.
Name an angle equal in measure to

(i) $2|\angle rps|$,
(ii) $|\angle qsp|$,
(iii) a right angle.

If $|pq| = |pr|$ and $|\angle qsr| = 36°$, calculate $|\angle prs|$.

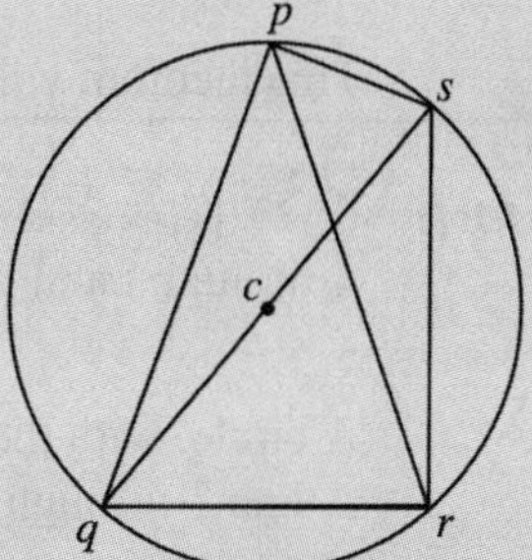

4. r is a point of a circle, centre c.
$|\angle cpq| = 40°$.
Calculate

(i) $|\angle pcq|$,
(ii) $|\angle prq|$.

If $|\angle pcr| = 200°$, see diagram, find $|\angle crp|$.

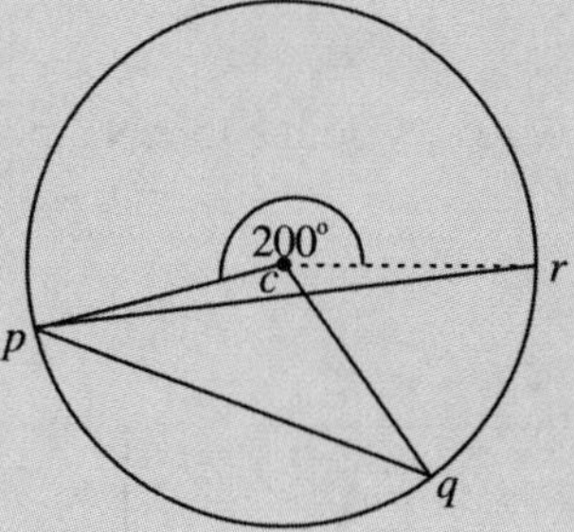

5. Noting that the sum of all four angles in any quadrilateral is 360°, find the value of $|\angle bdc|$ in each case:

(i)

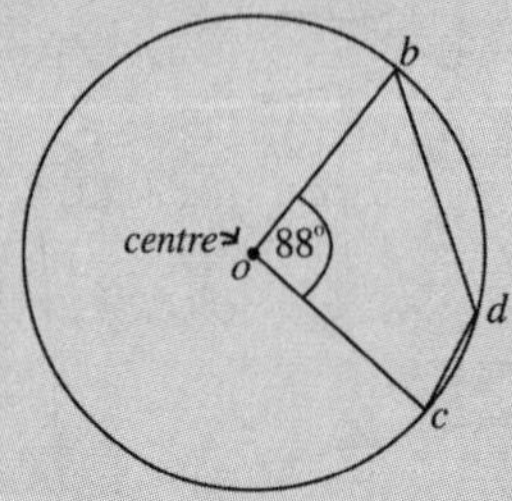

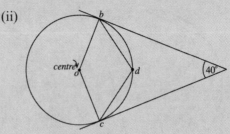

(ii)

6. $[ab]$ and $[qp]$ are two diameters of a circle.

Prove that $|\angle qab| = |\angle qpb|$.

Using alternate angles, or otherwise, prove that aq is parallel to pb.

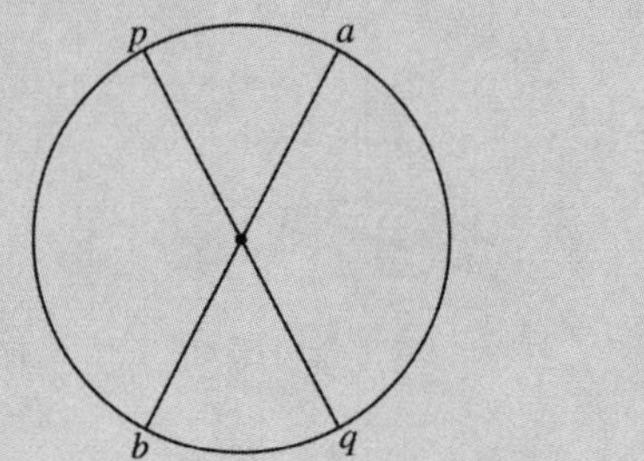

Definition: **A *TANGENT* is a line which touches a circle at one point only.**

THEOREM B: A line is a tangent to a circle at a point t of the circle if and only if it passes through t and is perpendicular to the line through t and the centre.

This theorem will be divided into two parts, proven separately.

THEOREM B1: If a line passes through t on a circle and is perpendicular to the line through t and the centre, then it is a tangent to the circle.

Given: A circle, with the centre c, containing a point t.
A line T through t, such that $ct \perp T$.

To prove: T is a tangent to the circle.

Construction: Join c to ANY point p on T.

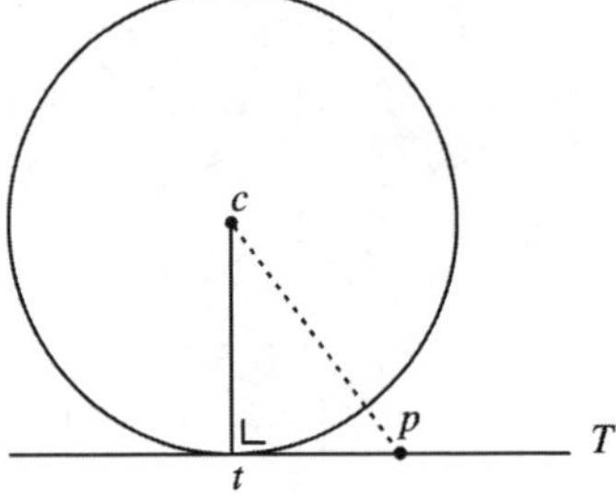

Proof:

$|<ctp| = 90^\circ$.

$\therefore |<cpt| < |<ctp|$ (because three angles in any triangle add up to 180°, and so $|<cpt| < 90^\circ$)

$\therefore |cp| > |ct|$ (Theorem 9)

$\therefore$ p is outside the circle.

$\therefore$ EVERY point on T (except for t) is outside the circle.

$\therefore$ T touches the circle at one point only.

$\therefore$ T is a tangent to the circle. **Q.E.D.**

THEOREM B2: If T is a tangent to a circle at the point t, then T is perpendicular to the line through t and the centre of the circle.

Given: A circle, with the centre c, containing a point t. A tangent T to the circle at t.

To prove: That the line through t, perpendicular to T contains the point c.

Construction: Let x be any point on T outside the circle. Draw the line L through t, perperdicular to T. L intersects the circle at q.

Proof: Suppose that c is NOT on L. Join q to c and produce to p on the circle.

Now, $[pq]$ is a diameter.

$\therefore |<ptq| = 90^\circ$.

But, $|<xtq| = 90^\circ$.

$\therefore |<xtp| = 180^\circ$ (a straight angle)

$\therefore$ p is on the tangent T

$\therefore$ T cuts the circle at t and p, which is a contradiction as T is a tangent.

$\therefore$ The original assumption is wrong.

$\therefore$ c is on L. **Q.E.D.**

Example 1: c is the centre of the circle.
Find the angles:

(i) $|<xty|$

(ii) $|<txy|$

(iii) $|<xyt|$

(see diagram)

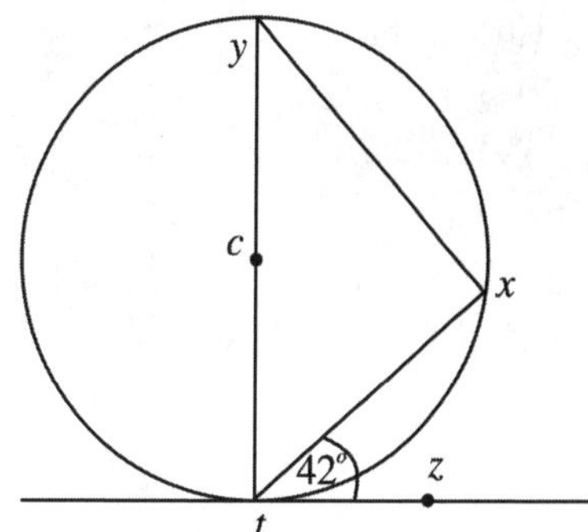

Solution:

(i) $|{<}zty| = 90^\circ$. (Theorem B)

$\therefore |{<}xty| = 90^\circ - 42^\circ = 48^\circ$

(ii) $|{<}txy| = 90^\circ$ (standing on a diameter: Theorem A, Deduction 2)

(iii) The sum of the angles in a triangle = 180°

$\therefore |{<}xyt| = 180^\circ - 90^\circ - 48^\circ = 42^\circ$

Exercise 21.B

1. Given that $|{<}xtz| = 57^\circ$, and that c is the centre of the circle, find

(i) $|{<}xty|$
(ii) $|{<}txy|$
(iii) $|{<}xyt|$
(see diagram)

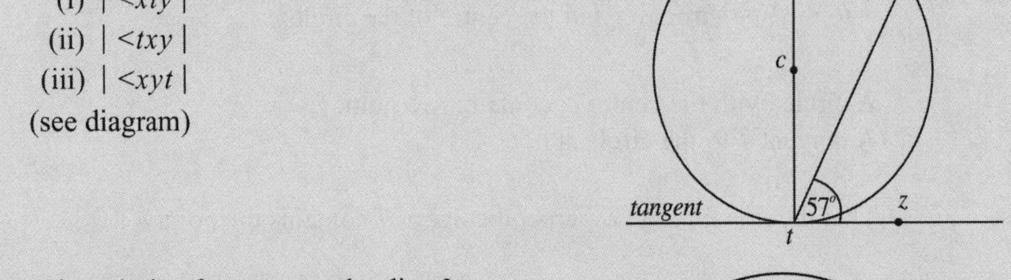

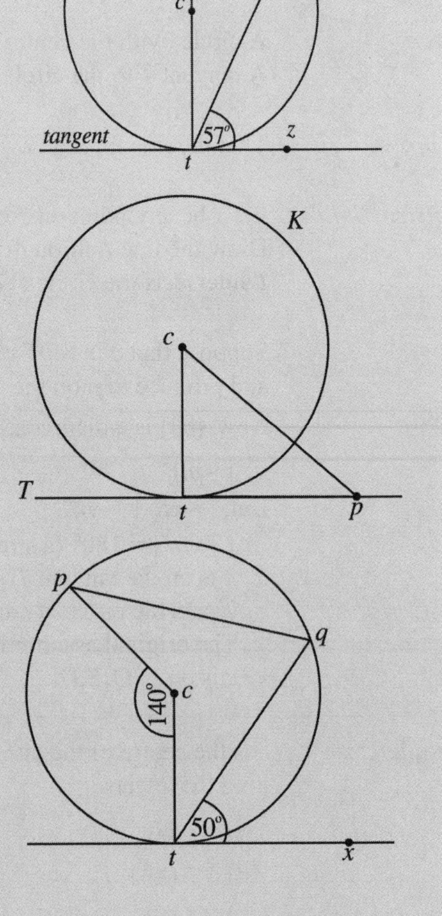

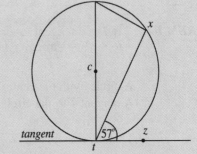

2. K is a circle of centre c and radius 3.
T is a tangent to K at t.
p is a point on the tangent T such that $|pt| = 4$.
Find $|cp|$.

3. c is the centre of the circle and xt is a tangent (see diagram).
$|{<}xtq| = 50^\circ$. $|{<}pct| = 140^\circ$.
Write down the values of

(i) $|{<}ctx|$
(ii) $|{<}ctq|$
(iii) $|{<}pqt|$
(iv) $|{<}cqt|$
(v) $|{<}cqp|$
(vi) $|{<}qpc|$

4. c is the centre of the circle and zt is a tangent.

Let $|\angle xtz| = A$

(see diagram)

Prove that $|\angle xqt| = A$

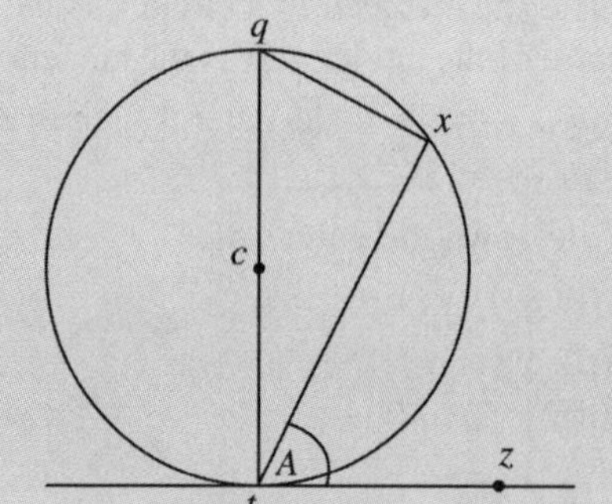

5. (a) Two tangents pt and px are drawn to a circle from a point p outside the circle.

Prove that $|pt| = |px|$

(HINT: Let r = radius and let $|pc| = y$. Use Pythagoras' Theorem on Δptc and on Δpxc).

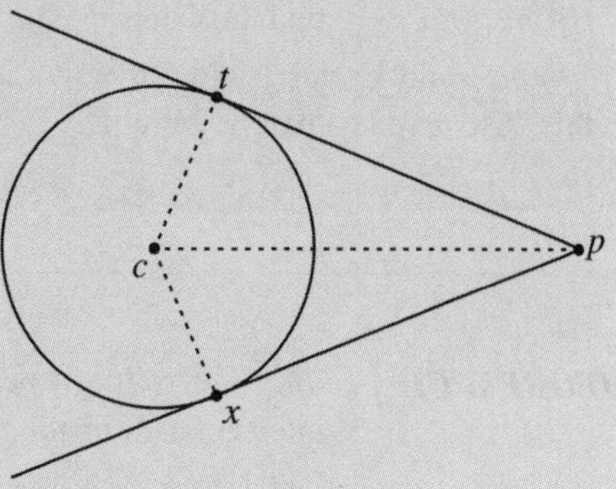

(b) In the diagram below, c is the centre of the circle. px and pt are both tangents to the circle.

Given that $|\angle xtp| = 55°$ and that $|\angle xbp| = 40°$, write down the values of:

(i) $|\angle txp|$

(ii) $|\angle xpt|$

(iii) $|\angle xpb|$

(iv) $|\angle pxb|$

(v) $|\angle pxc|$

(vi) $|\angle txc|$

Hence prove that Δacx is equilateral.

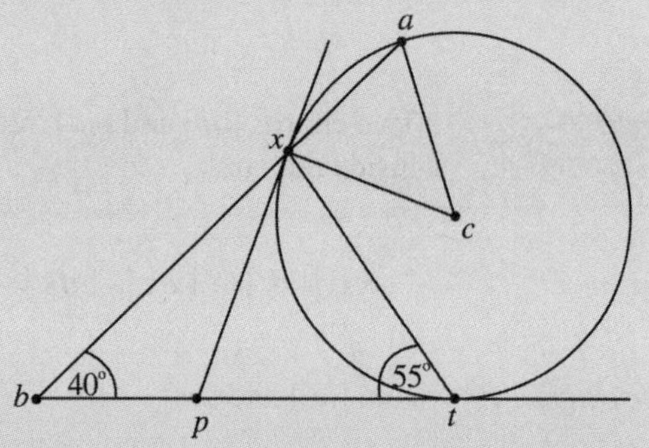

6. The diagram shows a circle, with centre c and radius of length r.

t is a point on the circle.

pt is a tangent to the circle such that $|pc| = 13$ and $|pt| = 12$.

Find r and hence find $|pk|$ (as in the diagram).

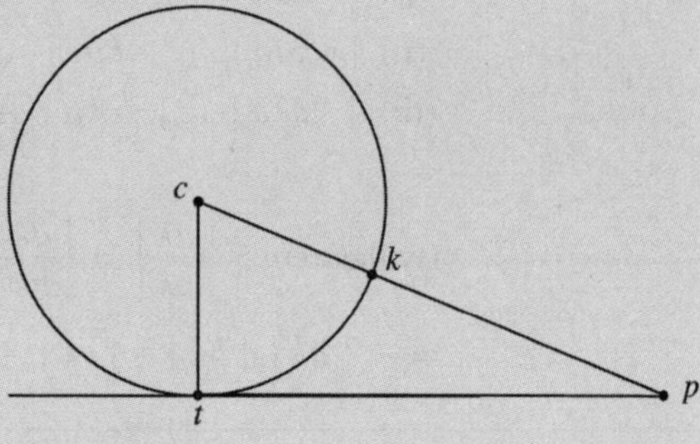

7. $[pq]$ is the diameter of a circle. c is the centre of the circle. qx is the tangent at q. $prsq$ is a cyclic quadrilateral such that $|\angle prs| = 120°$.

Write down the values of:

(i) $|\angle pqs|$
(ii) $|\angle sqx|$
(iii) $|\angle qsp|$
(iv) $|\angle spq|$

Show that Δqcs is equilateral.

If $|pr| = |rs|$, find the value of $|\angle rps|$ and $|\angle rpc|$ and prove that in this case $prsc$ is a parallelogram.

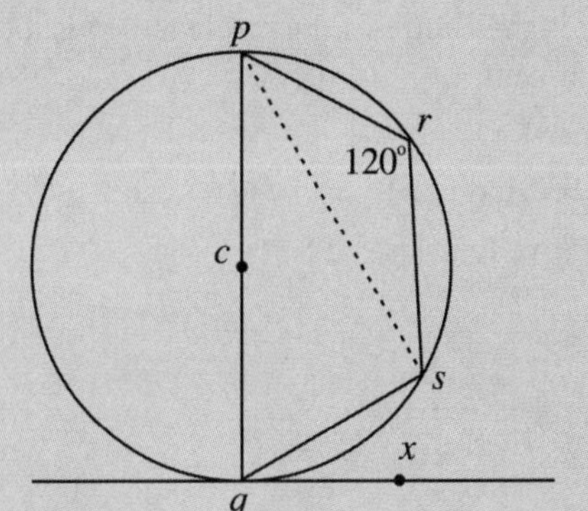

THEOREM C1: $[ab]$ and $[cd]$ are two chords of a circle. If the lines ab and cd intersect at k, inside the circle, then

$|ak|\ |bk| = |ck|\ |dk|$

Given: Two chords $[ab]$ and $[cd]$ intersecting at k inside the circle.

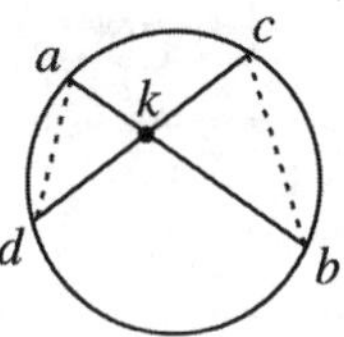

To prove: $|ak|\ |bk| = |ck|\ |dk|$

Construction: Join $[ad]$ and $[bc]$.

Proof: Δadk and Δbck are equiangular because

(i) $|\angle kad| = |\angle kcb|$ (standing on the same arc)
(ii) $|\angle kda| = |\angle kbc|$ (standing on the same arc)
(iii) $|\angle akd| = |\angle ckb|$ (vertically opposite angles)

By theorem 5, $\dfrac{|ak|}{|ck|} = \dfrac{|dk|}{|bk|}$

$\Rightarrow\ |ak|\ |bk| = |ck|\ |dk|$ **Q.E.D.**

The converse of this theorem is also true:
If $|ak|\,|bk| = |ck|\,|dk|$ then $[ab]$ and $[cd]$ are chords of a circle.

Example 1: Find x in the diagram.

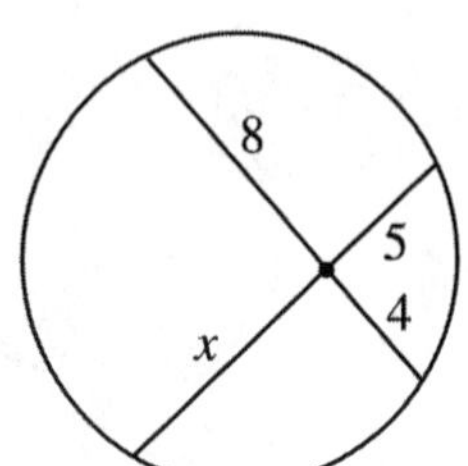

Solution:

$$(5)(x) = (4)(8)$$
$$\therefore\ 5x = 32$$
$$\therefore\ x = 6.4$$

Example 2: In the diagram $|ak| : |kb| = 3 : 1$
$|ck| = 8;\ |dk| = 6.$
Find $|ab|$.

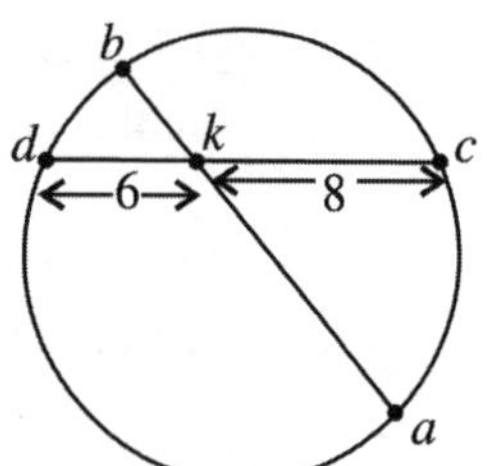

Solution: Let $|bk| = x \quad \therefore |ak| = 3x$

$|ak|\,|bk| = |ck|\,|dk|$ (Theorem)

$$\Rightarrow\quad (3x)(x) = (8)(6)$$
$$\Rightarrow\quad 3x^2 = 48$$
$$\Rightarrow\quad x^2 = 16$$
$$\Rightarrow\quad x = 4$$

$\therefore |ab| = 3x + x = 4x = 4(4) = 16$: ***Answer***

THEOREM C2: $[ab]$ and $[cd]$ are two chords of a circle. If the lines ab and cd intersect at k, outside the circle, then
$|ak|\,|bk| = |ck|\,|dk|$

Given: Two chords $[ab]$ and $[cd]$ intersecting at k, outside the circle.

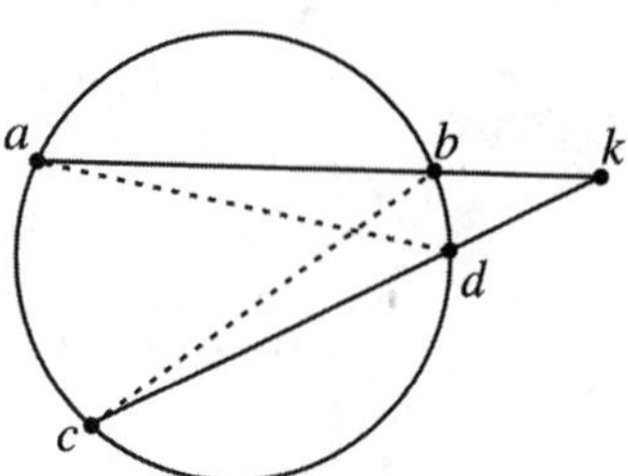

To prove: $|ak|\,|bk| = |ck|\,|dk|$

Construction: Join $[ad]$ and $[bc]$.

Proof: Δbck and Δadk are equiangular because

(i) $| <bck | = | <kad |$ (standing on the same arc)

(ii) $| <bkc | = | <akd |$ (common angle to both triangles)

(iii) $| <cbk | = | <adk |$ (remaining angle out of 180°)

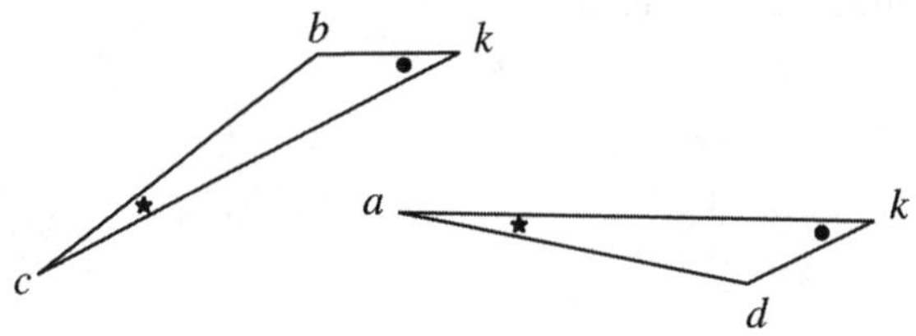

By theorem 5, $\dfrac{|bk|}{|dk|} = \dfrac{|ck|}{|ak|}$

$\Rightarrow \quad |ak|\,|bk| = |ck|\,|dk|$ **Q.E.D.**

1. Again, the converse of this theorem is true:
   If $|ak|\,|bk| = |ck|\,|dk|$ then [*ab*] and [*cd*] are chords of a circle.

2. When you use Theorem C2, it reads
   (Outside bit) x (Whole line) = (Outside bit) x (Whole line)

Example 1: In the diagram find the value of x.

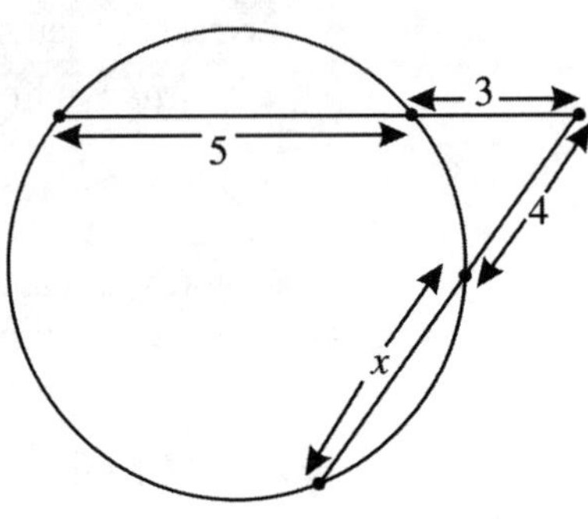

Solution: (Outside bit) x (Whole line) = (Outside bit) x (Whole line)

$\Rightarrow \quad (3)(3+5) = (4)(4+x)$

$\Rightarrow \quad (3)(8) = (4)(4+x)$

$\Rightarrow \quad 24 = 16 + 4x$

$\Rightarrow \quad 2 = x$

Answer : $x = 2$

THEOREM C3: If $[ab]$ is a chord of a circle, $p \in ab$ and pt is a tangent to the circle at the point t, then

$$|pa|\,|pb| = |pt|^2$$

Given: A circle and a point p outside it. A tangent from p touching the circle at t, and a line from p intersecting the circle at a and b.

To prove: $|pa|\,|pb| = |pt|^2$

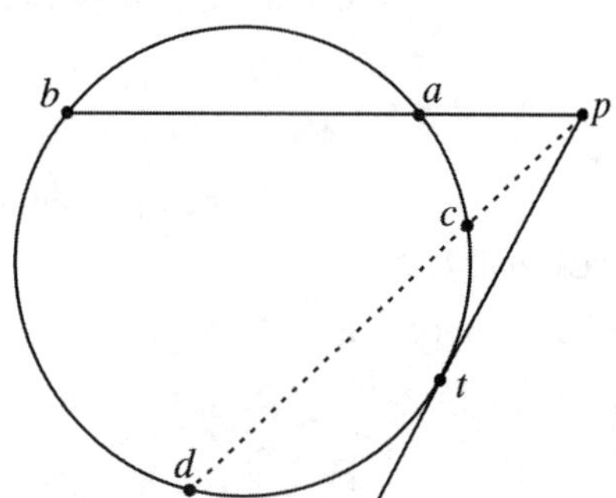

Construction: Draw another line from p intersecting the circle at c and d.

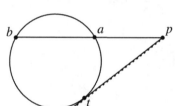

Proof: From Theorem C2,

$|pa|\,|pb| = |pc|\,|pd|$

Let c and d move around until they meet at t so that $c = d = t$.

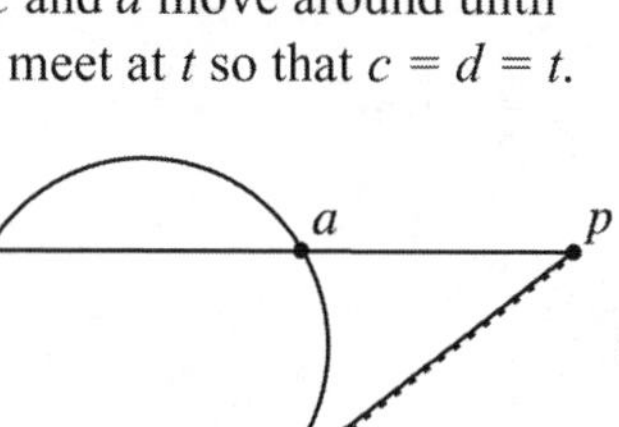

In this case $|pa|\,|pb| = |pt|\,|pt|$

$\Rightarrow \quad |pa|\,|pb| = |pt|^2$ **Q.E.D.**

Example 1: In the diagram, find x.

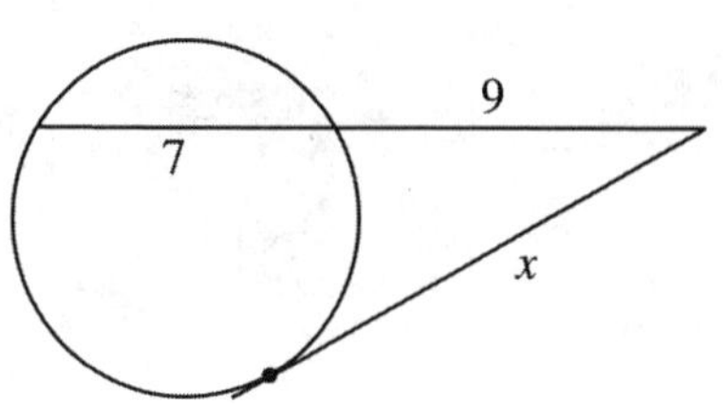

Solution: From the theorem,

$\Rightarrow \quad (9)(9+7) = x^2$

$\Rightarrow \quad 144 = x^2$

$\Rightarrow \quad x = 12$: ***Answer***

Example 2: In the diagram, prove that p is the midpoint of $[kt]$.

Solution: Take the large circle. By theorem C3,

$$|pa|\,|pb| = |pk|^2$$

Now, take the small circle. By theorem C3,

$$|pa|\,|pb| = |pt|^2$$

Combining these two results gives

$$|pk|^2 = |pt|^2$$

$$\Rightarrow |pk| = |pt|$$

$\Rightarrow p$ is the midpoint of $[kt]$. **Q.E.D.**

Exercise 21.C

Find the value of x in each case.

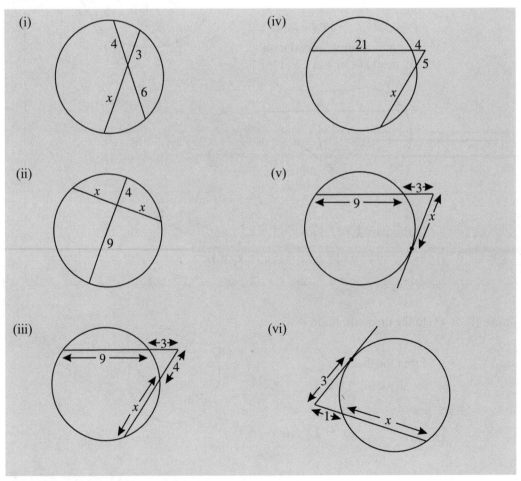

(i)

(ii)

(iii)

(iv)

(v)

(vi)

(vii)

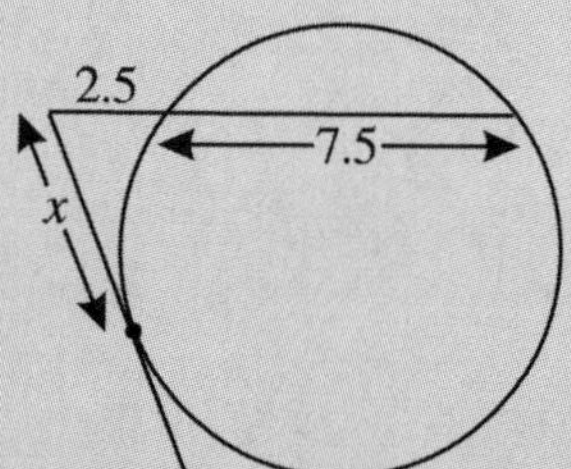

(ix)

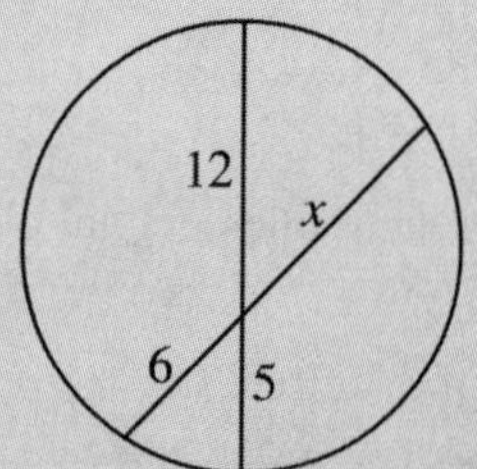

(viii)

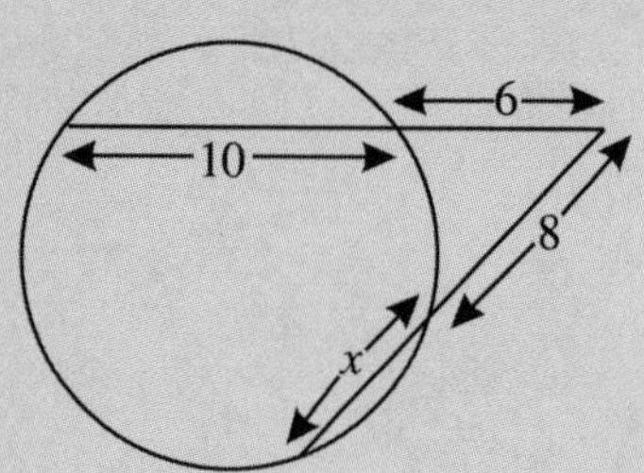

(x)

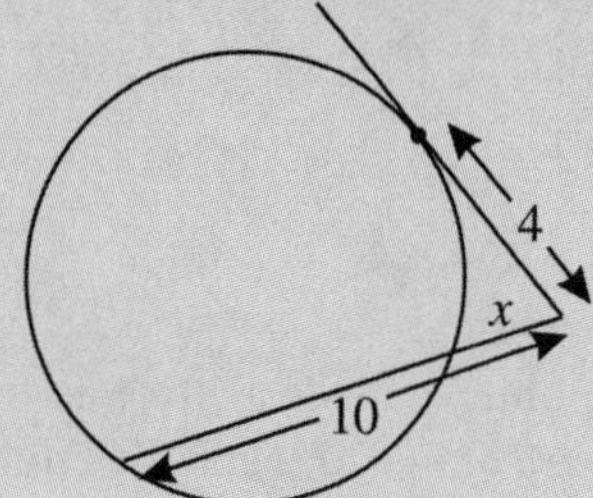

2. In the diagram $|dk| = 8$ and $|ck| = 1$
$|ak| : |bk| = 2 : 1$
Find $|ab|$.

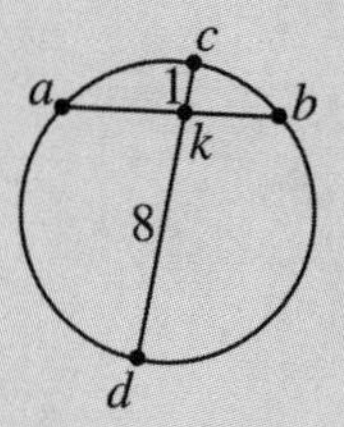

3. c is the centre of the circle.
$|ac| = |cb| = |bt|$
$|qt| = 6$, $|pq| = 2$.
Find the radius of the circle.

a c b t 2 6 q p

4. In the diagram, b is the midpoint of $[ak]$.
$|cd| = 5$
$|dk| = 4$
Find $|ab|$ in surd form.

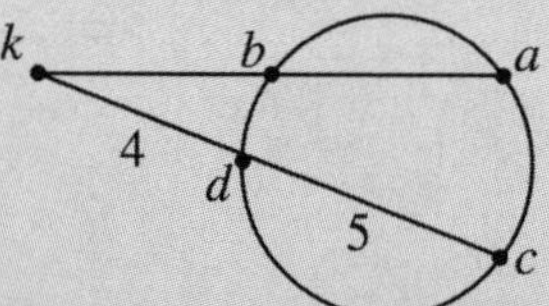

5. In the diagram $|ab| : |bc| = 2 : 1$.
If $|ct| = 4\sqrt{3}$, find $|ab|$.

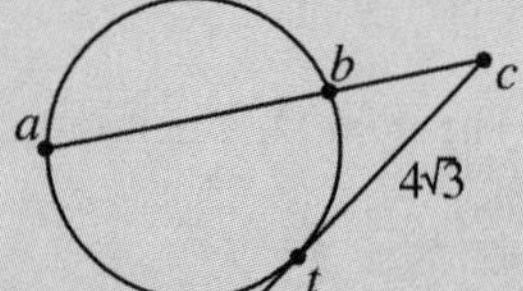

6. In the diagram, $|ab| : |bp| = 3 : 1$.
If $|pt| = 4$, find $|ab|$.

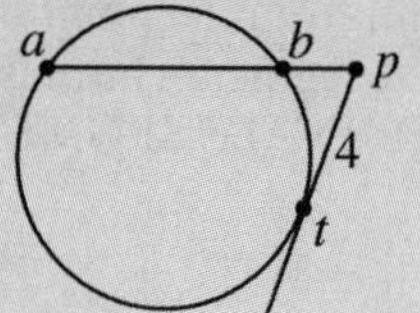

7. In the diagram,

$|ab| = 5, |kt| = 4.$

Find $|ka|$ correct to one decimal place.

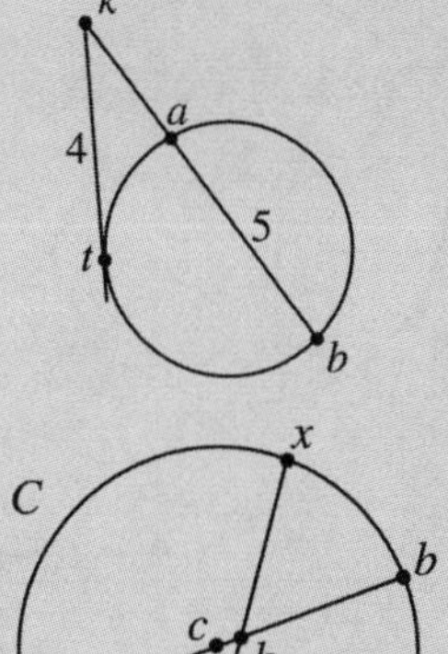

8. c is the centre of the circle C.

$|ak| = 6; |xk| = 4.8; |ky| = 5.$

Find

(i) $|kb|$

(ii) $|ab|$

(iii) $|ac|$

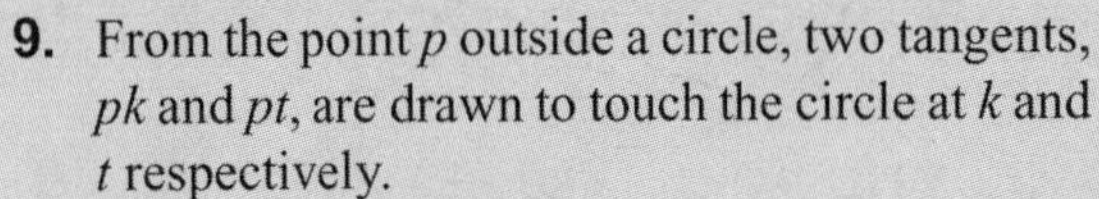

9. From the point p outside a circle, two tangents, pk and pt, are drawn to touch the circle at k and t respectively.

Prove that $|pk| = |pt|$.

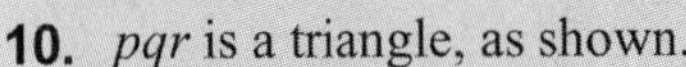

10. pqr is a triangle, as shown.

Prove that

$|px|^2 = |pt|^2$

Hence, prove that

$|pr| + |rq| > |pq|$

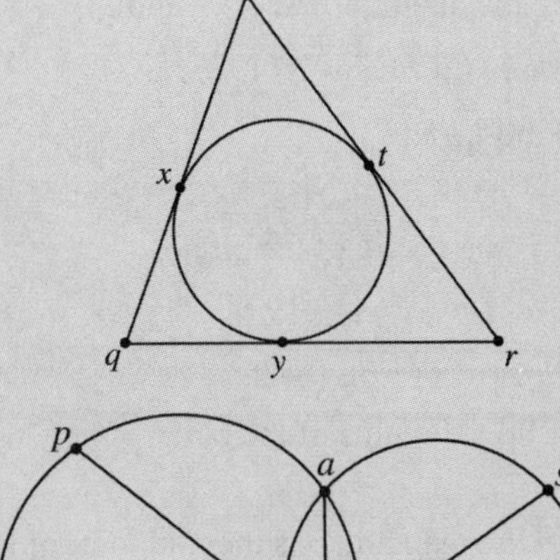

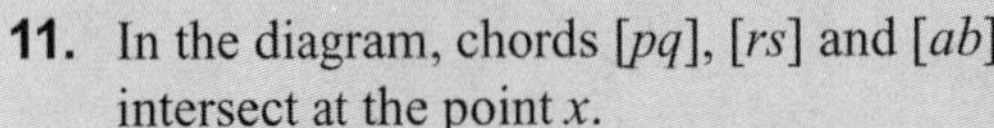

11. In the diagram, chords $[pq]$, $[rs]$ and $[ab]$ intersect at the point x.

Prove:

$|px|\ |xq| = |sx|\ |xr|$

Prove:

$|\angle qpr| = |\angle qsr|$

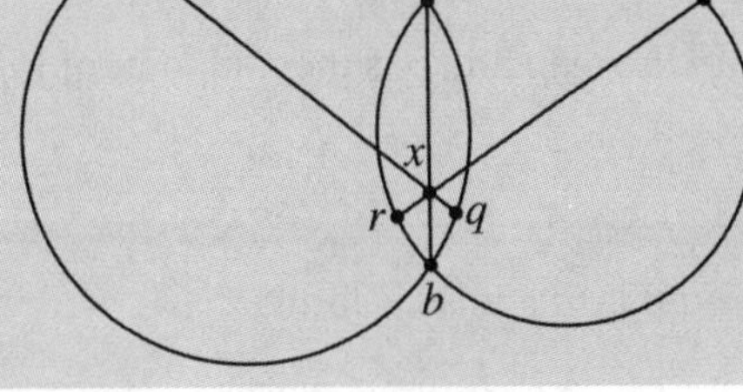

Before looking at Theorem D, it is important to know what an 'alternate segment' is.

A chord cuts a circle into two SEGMENTS. Looking at the diagram from the point of view of the point k, the shaded segment (furthest from k) is known as 'the ALTERNATE SEGMENT'.

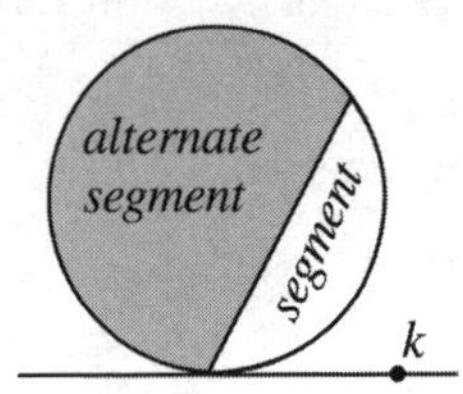

THEOREM D: An angle between a tangent ak and a chord $[ab]$ of a circle has degree-measure equal to that of any angle in the alternate segment.

Given: A circle, with chord $[ab]$ and a tangent ak.
An angle $<acb$ in the alternate segment to k.

To prove: $|<kab| = |<acb|$, i.e. that $X = V$.

Construction: Draw the diameter $[ad]$. Join $[db]$.

Proof:

$$|<kad| = 90° \quad \text{(Theorem B)}$$
$$\therefore\ X + Y = 90°$$
$$\therefore\ X = 90° - Y \quad \text{... result I}$$

Now $|<abd| = 90°$ (Standing on a diameter)

$$\therefore\ W + Y = 90° \quad \text{(Since } W + Y + Z = 180°\text{)}$$
$$\therefore\ W = 90° - Y \quad \text{... result II}$$

Combining results I and II leads to the conclusion that

$$X = W \quad \text{... result III}$$

Now $<acb$ and $<adb$ are both standing on the same arc, and hence they are equal,

$$\text{i.e. } V = W \quad \text{... result IV}$$

Combining results III and IV gives $X = V$ Q.E.D.

Example 1: Find $|<acb|$.

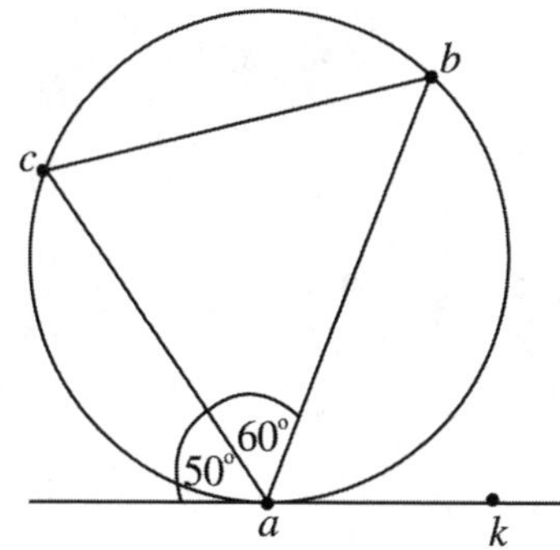

Solution: $|<bak| = 180° - 60° - 50° = 70°$ (Straight angle = 180°)

$\therefore\ |<acb| = 70°$ (By Theorem D)

Exercise 21.D

1. State, giving a reason, the values of:

(i) $|\angle acb|$
(ii) $|\angle cak|$

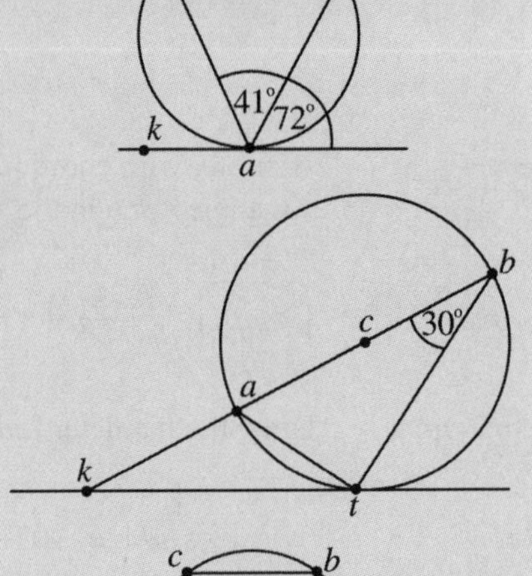

2. In the diagram c is the centre of the circle.

(a) Write down the values of:

(i) $|\angle atk|$
(ii) $|\angle bta|$

(b) Hence deduce that Δkat is isosceles.

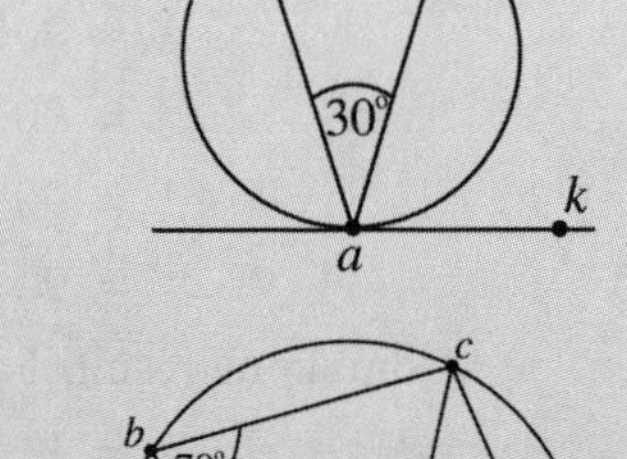

3. Given that $|ab| = |ac|$, find:

(i) $|\angle abc|$
(ii) $|\angle bca|$
(iii) $|\angle bak|$

Deduce that bc is parallel to ak.

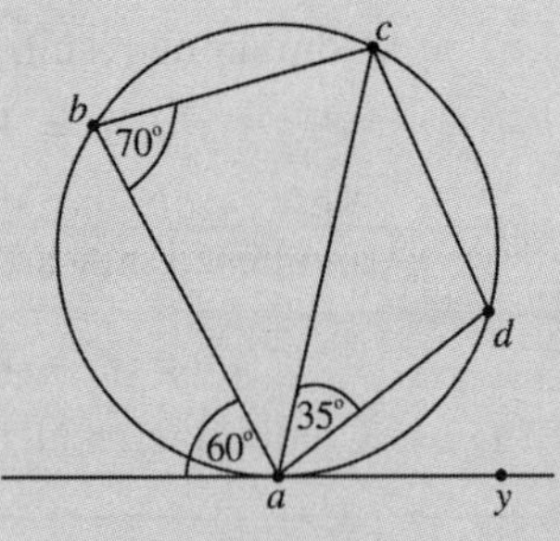

4. $abcd$ is a cyclic quadrilateral. State, with reasons, the values of:

(i) $|\angle bca|$
(ii) $|\angle cda|$
(iii) $|\angle day|$

Hence, deduce that $|dc| = |ad|$.

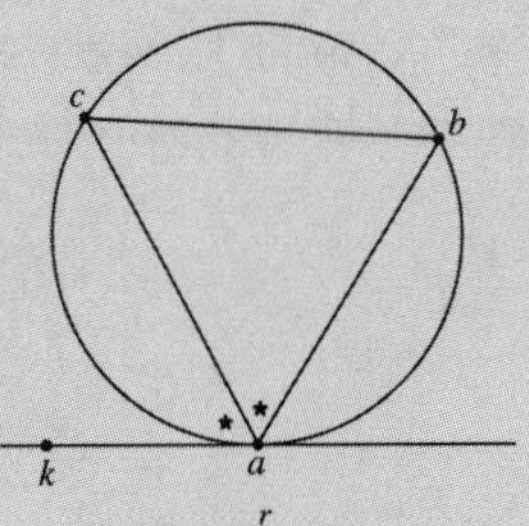

5. In the diagram, $[ac]$ is the bisector of $|\angle kab|$.
Prove that $|ac| = |cb|$.

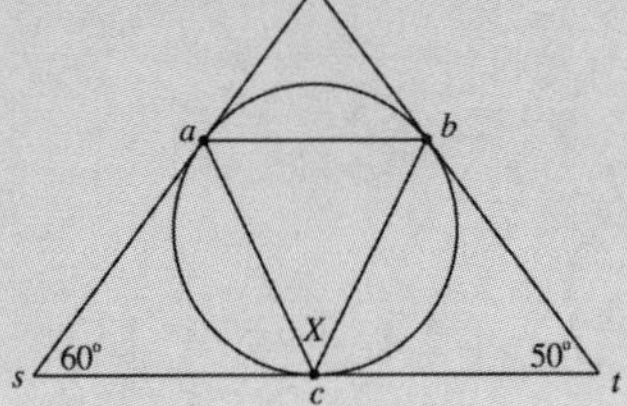

6. In the diagram let $|\angle acb| = X$.
Write down the value of $|\angle arb|$.
Say why $|\angle rab| = X$.
Name a third angle equal to X.
Hence find the value of X.

REVISION EXERCISE 21.E

1. (a) Prove that the degree-measure of an angle subtended at the centre of a circle by a chord is equal to twice the degree-measure of any angle subtended by the chord at a point of the arc of the circle which is on the same side of the chordal line as is the centre.

(b) Deduce that the angles which are subtended by a chord of the circle at points of the circle which are on one side of the chordal line have equal degree-measures.

(c) Prove, in each case, that $|\angle xab| = |\angle bca|$

(i)

(ii)

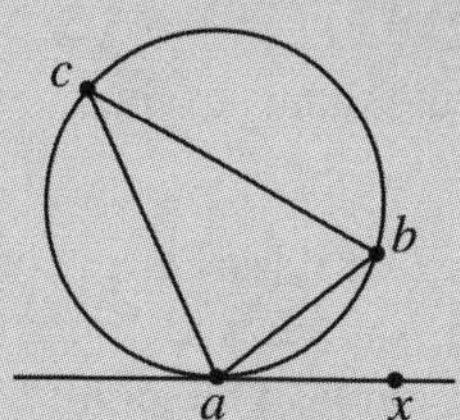

2. (a) Prove that if a line passes through t on a circle and is perpendicular to the line through t and the centre, then it is a tangent to the circle.

(b) In the diagram, $ct \perp at$, where c = centre. Given that $|\angle tbk| = 40°$, find

(i) $|\angle tck|$

(ii) $|\angle kta|$

3. (a) Prove that if T is a tangent to a circle at the point t, then T is perpendicular to the line through t and the centre of the circle.

(b) K is a circle of radius r, and centre c. m is the midpoint of $[cp]$. A tangent is drawn to the circle from p. It touches the circle at t. Find $|pt|$ in terms of r.

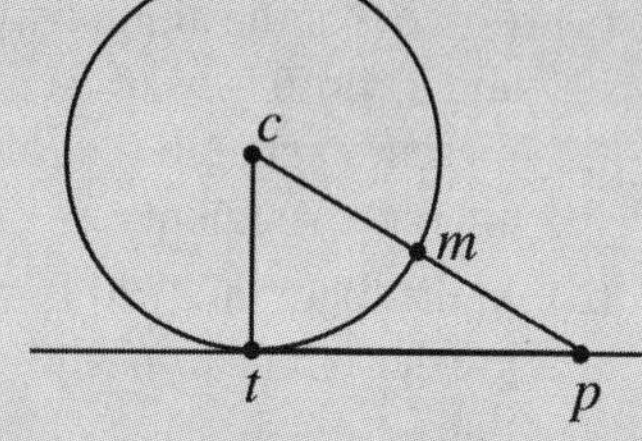

4. (a) Prove that if $[ab]$ and $[cd]$ are two chords of a circle, which intersect at k inside the circle, then $|ak|\,|bk| = |ck|\,|dk|$

(b) In the diagram,

$|ak| = 4$

$|bk| = 5$

$|cd| = 10$

$|ck| > |dk|$

Let $|ck| = x$.

Write down an equation in x and hence find the true value of x, correct to one decimal place.

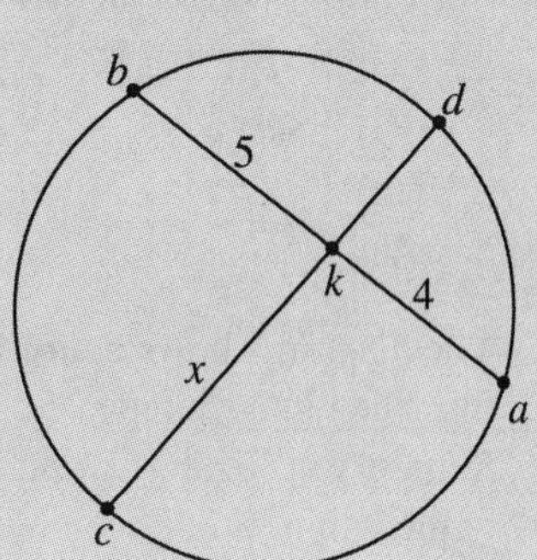

5. (a) $[ab]$ and $[cd]$ are chords of a circle. ab and dc intersect at k, outside the circle. Prove that
$|ak|\,|bk| = |ck|\,|dk|$

(b) In the diagram, c is the centre of the circle.
$|ac| = |cb| = |bp|$
$|py| = 8$; $|xy| = 5.5$
Find the radius of the circle.

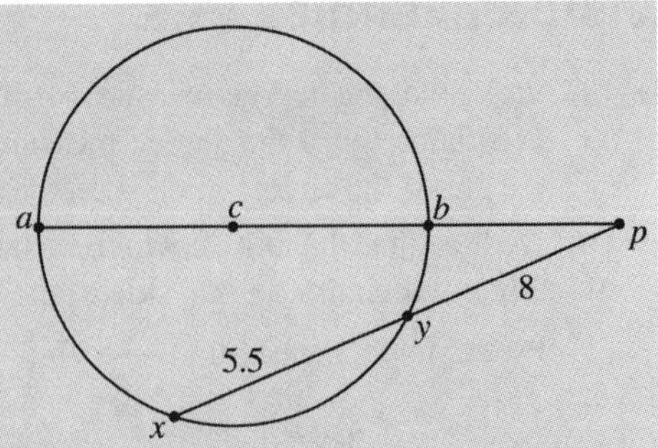

6. (a) Prove that if $[ab]$ is a chord of a circle, $k \in ab$ and kt is a tangent to the circle at the point t, then
$|ak|\,.\,|kb| = |kt|^2$

(b) c is the centre of the circle, which has radius 5.
m is the midpoint of $[ab]$.
$|mc| = 4$, $|bp| = 2$.
Find $|am|$ and $|ab|$.
If pt is a tangent to the circle at t, find $|pt|$.

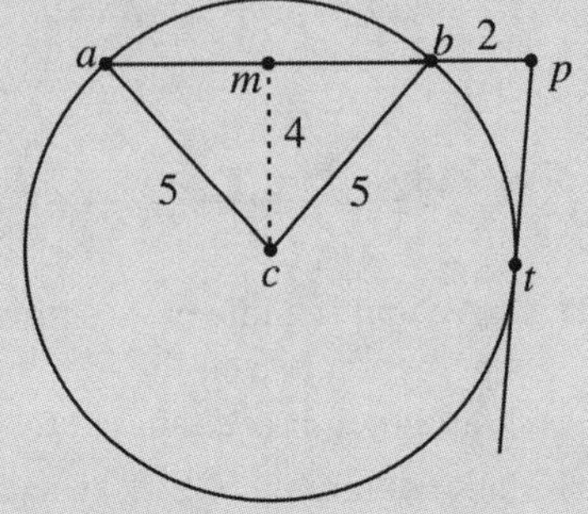

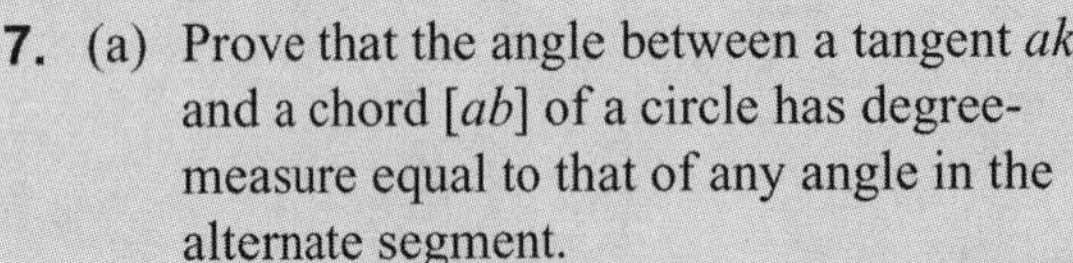

7. (a) Prove that the angle between a tangent ak and a chord $[ab]$ of a circle has degree-measure equal to that of any angle in the alternate segment.

(b) In the diagram, $[ab]$ is a diameter of the greater circle. abw and xyz are straight lines.
$|\angle wbx| = 65°$
Find, giving reasons:
(i) $|\angle byx|$
(ii) $|\angle ayz|$
(iii) $|\angle abz|$

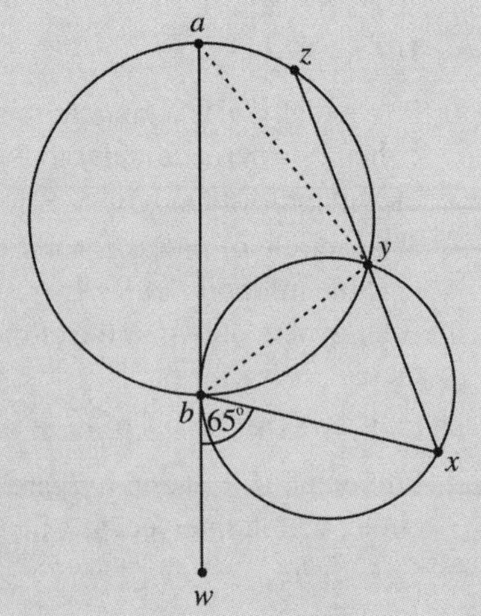

8. The diagram shows a circle inscribed in a triangle abc.
State why $|\angle ars| = X$ and name a third angle which is equal to X.
Prove that $X = ½(P + Q)$.

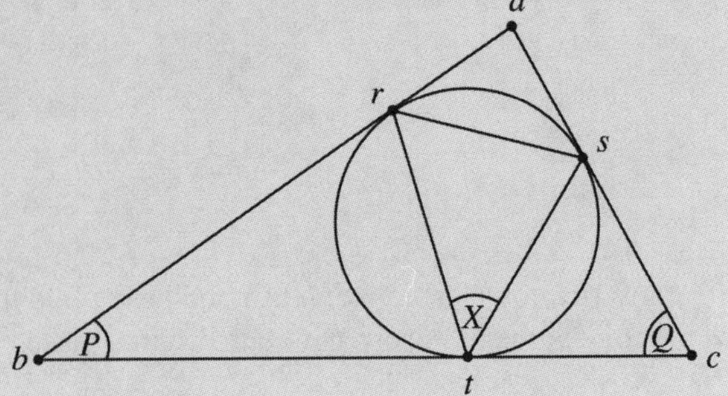

Theorem A: The degree-measure of an angle subtended at the centre of a circle by a chord is equal to twice the degree-measure of any angle subtended by the chord at a point of the arc of the circle which is on the same side of the chordal line as is the centre.

Corollary: The angles which are subtended by a chord of the circle at points of the circle which are on one side of the chordal line have equal degree-measures.

Theorem B: A line is a tangent to a circle at a point t of the circle if and only if it passes through t and is perpendicular to the line through t and the centre.

Theorem C: If $[ab]$ and $[cd]$ are chords of a circle and the lines ab and cd meet at the point k, then
$|ak|\,|bk| = |ck|\,|dk|$

If $[ab]$ is a chord of a circle, $k \in ab$ and kt is a tangent to the circle at the point t, then
$|ak|\,|bk| = |kt|^2$

Theorem D: An angle between a tangent ak and a chord $[ab]$ of a circle has degree-measure equal to that of any angle in the alternate segment.

Chapter 22

Preparing for the Exams

This chapter provides the following information to assist you in preparing for the two Leaving Certificate Mathematics Exams:

- The Papers
- Revision Tips
- The Marking Scheme and the Exams
- Check-list for the Exams
- Common Pitfalls
- Revision Timetable

THE PAPERS

Here is a list of what turns up on each paper:

PAPER 1

You must do six of the following seven questions:

1. Arithmetic: Ratio; Money; Compound interest; Tax; Scientific notation; Percentage error.
2. Equations: Simultaneous equations; Linear equations and inequalities; Quadratic equations; Equations with indices; Equations with algebraic fractions; Substitution.
3. Equations & functions: Manipulating formulae; Cubic equations; Functions.
4. Complex numbers: Adding, subtracting, multiplying and dividing complex numbers; Modulus; Conjugate; Argand diagrams; Complex equations.
5. Sequences & series: Arithmetic sequences: $t_n = a + (n-1)d$,

   $S_n = \frac{n}{2}\{2a + (n-1)d\}$ and geometric sequences $t_n = ar^{n-1}$, $S_n = \frac{a(1-r^n)}{1-r}$.
6. Functions and graphs: Periodic graphs; Linear graphs; Quadratic graphs; Cubic graphs; Graphs with asymptotes; Differentiation gives the slope of the tangent to a graph.
7. Calculus: Differentiation from first principles; Product, quotient and chain rules; Displacement, speed and acceleration.
8. Differentiation; Maximum and minimum points are where the derivative is zero.

PAPER 2

You must answer five questions from section A and one from section B:

Section A (Five of these)

1. Length; Area; Volume; Triangles; Parallelograms; Circles; Cylinders; Cones and spheres; Simpson's rule.
2. Co-ordinate geometry: The line; Distance between two points; Slope; Midpoint; Area of a triangle; Equation of a line; Intersection of lines.
3. The circle: Centre; Radius and equation of a circle: $x^2 + y^2 = r^2$ and $(x-h)^2 + (y-k)^2 = r^2$; Intersection of a line and a circle; Equation of tangent to a circle.
4. Theorems and enlargements: Ten theorems; Enlargements and reductions of scale factor k.
5. Trigonometry: Sine cosine and tan of angles; The four quadrants (Alfie stole two chickens); Sectors and arcs of circles; The sine and cosine rules for solving non-right-angled triangles; Area of triangle as $\frac{1}{2}ab\sin C$.
6. Probability: Counting; Arranging; Choosing; Probability.
7. Statistics: Mean, median and mode; Frequency tables; Mid-interval values; Weighted mean; Histograms; Cumulative frequency curves (ogives); The four quartiles; Standard deviation.

Section B (One of these)

8. Further theorems: Four further theorems and their consequences.
9. Further sequences and series and the binomial theorem; Applications of the sequence formulae; Sum to infinity of a geometric series: $S_\infty = \frac{a}{1-r}$; Binomial theorem for $(1+x)^n$ and $(1-x)^n$ for $2 \le n \le 7$.
10. Vectors: Addition of vectors; Equality of vectors; The $\vec{i}$ -$\vec{j}$ plane; Modulus; Dot product; The perpendicular vector $\vec{r}^{\perp}$.
11. Positive and negative side of a line; Graphing $ax + by + c \le 0$ and $ax + by + c \ge 0$; Solving problems.

REVISION TIPS

10 TIPS TO HELP YOU REVISE WELL

1. Start your revision as early as possible. If you start when there are 18 weeks to go, you can revise one chapter per week. If you haven't time to do all the questions, do the even-numbered questions.
2. The nature of the questions varies little from year to year, and so this makes Mathematics an easy subject to revise. Do the revision exercise at the end of each chapter in this book. If you can do these, you are ready for the exam. If you want to practise some more, do questions from past papers.
3. When you are stuck and don't know how to solve a problem, make a note of it and ask somebody: one of the family, your teacher or a top student in your school.
4. Avoid **reading**. Instead, try to spend most of your revision time **writing**. The exams are written exams, so you prepare by writing out solutions to maths problems. The more you practise, the better you get.
5. Become familiar with the Mathematical Tables. Where is the formula for the area of a parallelogram, for the volume of a sphere, for the number of kilograms in a tonne, for Simpson's rule, for the product and quotient rules, for Sin(A + B) and cos (A + B) and for the sine and cosine rules?
6. When you work, it is best to work in short bursts of say 45 minutes, followed by a break for five or ten minutes.
7. Work at an uncluttered desk in a quiet, undisturbed place. Turn off your mobile, let others answer the door, don't have music or a TV on within hearing distance; too many inputs can overload your brain and you will not retain as much information as you should.
8. Don't panic. Try to be systematic, organised and consistent. You can get there little by little. As the Chinese proverb says: the longest journey starts with a single step. If you feel really lost, ask for help.
9. Remember, nobody expects you to be another Albert Einstein. Revision is to make sure that you get at least the grade that you deserve – and to make the most of what you **do** know.
10. Avoid last minute revision on the evening before the exams themselves. Relax and get a bit of fresh air. Have a good night's sleep. You want your brain to be in good working order in the morning – don't you?

THE MARKING SCHEME AND THE EXAMS

1. There are two papers to sit. Each gives a maximum of 300 marks. Your total mark is, therefore, out of **600 marks**.

2. The corrector gives you 600 marks to start with. If you make a mistake or leave out a part of a question, you will **lose** marks.

3. If you make a numerical mistake, this is called a **slip** and you lose 1 mark out of 600. For example, if you write $3 - 7 = 4$, you lose 1 mark. If you write $\cos 90^\circ = 1$, you lose 1 mark. If you write $5 \div 2 = 0.4$, you lose 1 mark.

4. If you make a more serious mistake, this is called a **blunder** and you lose 3 marks (out of 600). For example, if you write: $(a^3)^2 = a^5$, you will lose 3 marks for breaking the Laws of Indices. If you are calculating $3x^2$ when $x = 5$ and you write $3x^2 = 3 \times 5^2 = 15^2 = 225$, you will lose 3 marks for breaking the BIRDMAS code. If you write that $\sin A = \frac{adjacent}{hypotenuse}$, you will lose 3 marks for writing the wrong formula.

5. If, as a result of making a mistake, you get all the rest of the question wrong, this **doesn't matter**. So long as your methods are right from there on, you will not be penalised again.

6. Using the **right method** is more important than getting the right answer.

7. **You must show all your work.** Suppose that you are doing a 20-mark part of a question. If you write down just the answer and it is wrong, you will get no marks. But if you show your work and make one slip, so that your answer is wrong, you will get 19 marks out of 20.

8. **Never do roughwork** in a Maths exam (and especially don't do roughwork on some other page). All work that you do is important and should be shown on the page.

9. When taking readings from a graph, **show how you get your answers**, by putting horizontal and vertical lines onto your graph. It may make the graph look messy, but it shows the examiner that you know what you are doing, which is what counts for marks.

10. After each step with a calculator, write the result on your answer book. Don't do a whole series of calculations on the calculator, and then write only the answer. Also, you are supposed to write EC in the margin when you use a calculator.

11. Give reasons for your answers, if possible. For example: '*abc* is an isosceles triangle because $|ab| = |bc|$'.

12. Avoid Tippex. Why not just cross out a mistake and get on with it? Waiting for Tippex to dry can be a waste of time.

13. Try to write reasonably neatly and work down the page in a logical order. Avoid having all kinds of calculations all over the page in an unordered fashion.

14. When you have completed a part of a question, shade in (with a highlighter pen) that part of the question on your exam paper. Check to see that you have answered precisely what you were asked. Students often leave out little bits of a question.

15. Did you know that if you do any correct step in a question, then you will get one third of the marks for that question? This is known as the **attempt mark**. You cannot get less than the attempt mark if you show **any correct step**, however small. For example, let us suppose that there is a 15-mark question about the volume of a cylindrical tank. If you write down the formula for the volume of a cylinder from the Mathematical Tables, then you will get 5 marks for doing this one correct step.

16. If you feel that you will not be able to solve a question completely, at least write down **one correct step** so that you will get the attempt mark. For example, let us suppose you are asked to solve the equation: $5^n = \frac{25^3}{\sqrt{125}}$ and you write $25 = 5^2$, then you will get one third of the marks for doing one step.

17. If you answer seven questions in a Maths exam, the examiner will correct all seven and award you the marks for your best six questions.

18. Answer the question which you like the most first. Then answer your next favourite. Avoid doing the questions in the order they appear on the exam paper. Suit yourself – it's your exam!

19. In Paper 2, you **must** answer at least five question from Section A and one from Section B. It would be disastrous to answer 6 from Section A and none from Section B as you would get zero marks for your sixth question.

20. Never leave the exam centre before the exam is over. Go over your work. Fill in explanations. Check for silly mistakes. There is always room for improvement. You have been preparing for this exam for a few years, so use all of the time at your disposal. Think of it this way: **extra time means extra marks**, if you use the extra time productively.

21. Mathematical Tables and graph paper are supplied by the superintendent in the exam hall. Ask for as many sheets of graph paper as you need.

22. After the exam, don't compare answers with your friends. This can be disconcerting if you find that you got wrong answers. Remember that it is the methods which count, not the answers.

CHECK-LIST FOR THE EXAMS

Here are some things to bring into your two Maths exams:

1. A **Mathematical Set.** You need a ruler and a compass (with pencil) for lines and circles. An eraser is handy in case you make a mistake on a graph or a diagram.
2. A **scientific calculator**. Make sure you remember how to do fractions, roots, scientific notation, sin, cos, and tan and their inverses, degrees and minutes and brackets.
3. Two or three **biros**. Colours are good for graphs.
4. A **highlighter pen** for highlighting the bits of the exam which you have done so far.
5. Any **food or drink**, which will help sustain you during these long and arduous tests, provided that the superintendent allows them. Maybe bring along a bottle of water and some chocolate (with the wrapper removed beforehand to avoid distracting other students with the noise of crinkling paper during the exam).

COMMON PITFALLS

FIVE DOS AND FIVE DON'TS

1. **DO** be careful with **minus signs**. About half of all mistakes which students make are with minus signs. For example if $x = -3$, then $12 - 2x = 12 - (-6) = 18$.
2. **DO** read each question **carefully** and answer precisely what you were asked.
3. **DO** give **reasons** for your answers: 'Since $m_1 \times m_2 = -1$, the lines are perpendicular.'
4. **DO** use **graph paper** for all graphs.
5. **DO** show all you work – **no roughwork**!

1. **DON'T** rush. Be careful, reasonably neat and work logically **down** the page.
2. **DON'T** use Tippex. Just **cross out mistakes** with a single line and get on with it!
3. **DON'T** leave blanks! Attempt **every part** of every question which you answer. Try to ensure that you get the **attempt mark** in each case.
4. **DON'T** leave before the full time is up. **Extra time means extra marks.**
5. **DON'T** panic. See the exam as an **opportunity** to show what you know.

REVISION TIMETABLE

Write down the date by which you want to be finished revising each chapter. Then put a tick in the 'Done' column when you have done the revision.

Chapter	Topic	Date for revision	Done ✓
1	Arithmetic		
2	Algebra		
3	Linear equations & inequalities		
4	Quadratic & cubic equations		
5	Powers & roots		
6	Functions & Graphs		
7	Co-ordinate geometry: the line		
8	The circle		
9	Complex Numbers		
10	Percentages, tax & interest		
11	Arranging, choosing & probability		
12	Statistics		
13	Length, area & volume		
14	Theorems & enlargements		
15	Trigonometry		
16	Sequences & series		
17	Calculus		
18	Option topic		

Chapter 1: Arithmetic

Exercise 1.B

1. 43 **2.** 23 **3.** 26 **4.** 6 **5.** 15 **6.** 20 **7.** 13 **8.** 13 **9.** 13 **10.** 10 **11.** 25 **12.** 11 **13.** 36 **14.** 8 **15.** 27 **16.** 3 **17.** 10 **18.** 100 **19.** 135 **20.** 26 **21.** 18 **22.** 7 **23.** 7 **24.** 16 **25.** 3 **26.** 8 **27.** 12 **28.** 16 **29.** 3 **30.** 16 **31.** 16 **32.** 25 **33.** 24 **34.** 26 **35.** 70 **36.** 12 **37.** 4 **38.** 32 **39.** 100 **40.** 201 **41.** 3 **42.** 120 **43.** 12 **44.** 6 **45.** 48 **46.** 14 **47.** 20 **48.** 13 **49.** 38 **50.** 82

Exercise 1.C

1. 2 **2.** 4 **3.** 4 **4.** 5 **5.** 10 **6.** $6\frac{11}{12}$ **7.** $7\frac{13}{20}$ **8.** $2\frac{1}{10}$ **9.** $8\frac{1}{8}$ **10.** $9\frac{1}{3}$ **11.** 3 **12.** 3 **13.** 3 **14.** 3 **15.** 3 **16.** 2 **17.** 5 **18.** 1 **19.** 2½ **20.** 3 **21.** 3 **22.** 4 **23.** 3 **24.** 2 **25.** 5

Exercise 1.D

9. €11 **10.** €4.50 **11.** €30 **12.** €210 **13.** €250 **14.** €8 **15.** 320 **16.** 20 **17.** €1.20

Exercise 1.E

13. 3.24 **14.** 16.402 **15.** 3.303 **16.** 3.2 **17.** 0.0385 **18.** 0.0078 **19.** 4100

Exercise 1.F

25. **(i)** $90 **(ii)** 250 **26.** €120 **27.** 110 **28.** €28 **29.** **(i)** 160 km **(ii)** 62.5 miles **30.** **(i)** 15.4 lbs **(ii)** 5 kg **31.** **(i)** 4 hr **(ii)** 22 lbs **32.** 9 km **33.** €32 : €16 : €6.40 **34.** €2.50 **35.** €135; €90; €75 **36.** $40 : $60 **37.** **(i)** €22.50 **(ii)** €170 **(iii)** €150 **38.** €35 **39.** 280

Revision Exercise 1.G

1. **(a)** –12 **(b)** 13 **(c)** €150 : €200

2. **(a)** 7 **(b)** **(i)** 0.077 **(ii)** 0.0769 **(c)** **(i)** 450 HKD **(ii)** $5.56

3. **(a)** 5 **(b)** €26; €34 **(c)** €600 : €200 : €100 **(d)** $\frac{1}{9}$

4. **(a)** **(i)** 2.65 **(ii)** 2.6 **(b)** 34½ **(c)** **(i)** 64 km **(ii)** 25 miles

5. **(a)** 17 **(b)** 12 **(c)** **(i)** €135 **(ii)** €3500

6. **(a)** 5 **(b)** $1\frac{1}{5}$ **(c)** €600 : €300 : €100

7. **(a)** 10½ **(b)** 1.143 **(c)** **(i)** 57 500 yen **(ii)** 109 euro

8. **(a)** **(i)** 53.170 **(ii)** 53.2 **(b)** 42 (c) €222

9. **(a)** 12 **(b)** 1 **(c)** €121, €88, €11

10. **(a)** –9 **(b)** $9\frac{7}{8}$ **(c)** **(i)** 30 **(ii)** 450, 50

Chapter 2: Algebra

Exercise 2.A

1. **(i)** 17 **(ii)** 20 **(iii)** –4 **(iv)** 9 **(v)** 14 **(vi)** 18 **(vii)** 45 **(viii)** 99 **(ix)** 91 **(x)** 28
2. **(i)** 7 **(ii)** 3 **(iii)** –3 **(iv)** 10 **(v)** 12 **(vi)** 50 **(vii)** 20 **(viii)** 29 **(ix)** 19 **(x)** 49
3. **(i)** 16 **(ii)** 24 **(iii)** 16 **(iv)** 96 **(v)** 100 **(vi)** 52 **(vii)** 8 **(viii)** 60 **(ix)** 60 **(x)** 60
4. **(i)** 1 **(ii)** –5 **(iii)** 5 **(iv)** –6 **(v)** 6 **(vi)** 0 **(vii)** –26 **(viii)** –8 **(ix)** 12 **(x)** –40
5. **(i)** –3 **(ii)** –7 **(iii)** 7 **(iv)** 12 **(v)** 12 **(vi)** 12 **(vii)** 0 **(viii)** 1 **(ix)** 4 **(x)** 12
6. **(i)** –3 **(ii)** –5 **(iii)** 0 **(iv)** 0 **(v)** 0 **(vi)** 9 **(vii)** 65 **(viii)** 23 **(ix)** –10 **(x)** 0

9. **(i)** –3 **(ii)** 1 **(iii)** 0 **(iv)** 2 **(v)** 10 **(vi)** –1 **(vii)** –11 **(viii)** 9 **(ix)** 27 **(x)** 81
10. 4 **11.** –6 **12.** 1.25 **13.** 2 **14.** ¾ **15.** 3 **16.** 1.304

Exercise 2.D

12. $8x + 9y$ **13.** $13m + 25n$ **14.** $15a - 27b + 6$ **15.** $11x^2 - 10x - 15$ **16.** $2t - 6k$ **17.** $2x - 8y$
18. $x + 26y - 4$ **19.** $5x^2 - 13x + 11$ **20.** $3x^2 - 23x$ **21.** $a + 5b$ **22.** $3a - 4b$ **23.** $-5a - 9b$ **24.** $5x + 6y - 2$
25. $9a^2 - 26b^2$ **26.** $5a - 22$ **27.** 11 **28.** $-ab$ **29.** $x^3 + x^2 + 5x$ **30.** $x^3 + 6x^2 - 99x$ **31.** 0

Exercise 2.E

21. $x^3 + 5x^2 + 6x$ **22.** $x^3 - 4x^2 - 5x$ **23.** $2x^3 + 12x^2 + 10x$ **24.** $x^3 + 2x^2 - x - 2$ **25.** $x^3 + 3x^2 + 3x + 1$
26. $x^3 - 8$ **27.** $8x^3 + 27$ **28.** $8x^3 - 36x^2 + 54x - 27$

Exercise 2.H

1. $x + 5$ **2.** $x + 3$ **3.** $x + 7$ **4.** $x + 2$ **5.** $x + 5$ **6.** $2x + 5$ **7.** $3x + 7$ **8.** $x + 3$ **9.** $2x + 5$ **10.** $x + 3$ **11.** $x - 4$
12. $x + 8$ **13.** $x - 10$ **14.** $x - 6$ **15.** $x - 8$ **16.** $5x - 3$ **17.** $3x + 4$ **18.** $5x - 2$ **19.** $3x - 2$ **20.** $2x - 1$
21. $x^2 + 2x + 3$ **22.** $x^2 + 3x + 7$ **23.** $x^2 + 2x + 5$ **24.** $2x^2 + x + 4$ **25.** $x^2 - 2x + 10$ **26.** $x^2 + 5x + 6$
27. $2x^2 - 4x + 7$ **28.** $x^2 + x - 3$ **29.** $x^2 + 3x - 3$ **30.** $x^2 - 3x + 1$ **31.** $5x^2 - 10x + 1$ **32.** $x^2 - 5x + 10$
33. $2x^2 + 3x - 5$ **34.** $12x^2 + 9x + 4$ **35.** $x^2 + x + 1$ **36.** $x^2 - 5x + 25$

Revision Exercise 2.I

1. **(a)** **(i)** 23 **(ii)** –29 **(iii)** 72 **(b)** $x^2 + 2x + 20$ **(c)** $2x + 9$
2. **(a)** **(i)** –30 **(ii)** 42 **(iii)** 90 **(iv)** 900 **(b)** **(i)** $6x^2 + 25x - 9$ **(ii)** $4x^2 + 36x + 81$ **(c)** $2x^2 - 11x + 6$
3. **(a)** **(i)** 15 **(ii)** 0 **(iii)** 9 **(iv)** 44 **(b)** $2x + 17$ **(c)** **(i)** 10 **(ii)** 4
4. **(a)** 0 **(b)** $12a$ **(c)** **(i)** 3 **(ii)** 16
5. **(a)** 0 **(b)** $2a^2 + 2$ **(c)** $2x^2 - 28x + 98$
6. **(a)** 2 **(b)** $20a$ **(c)** $x^3 + 30x^2 + 300x + 1000$
7. **(a)** –8 **(b)** **(i)** –4 **(ii)** 10 **(iii)** –40 **(iv)** –40 **(c)** $x + 4$
8. **(a)** –1 **(b)** **(i)** 25 **(ii)** 5; No **(c)** $x + 5$
9. **(a)** 4 **(b)** No **(c)** $x^2 + x + 5$
10. **(a)** **(i)** –10 **(ii)** 6 **(iii)** 4 **(b)** **(i)** $x^2 - 3x$ **(ii)** $18x^2 + 54$ **(iii)** $2a^5$ **(c)** **(i)** $x^2 - x - 1$ **(ii)** $9x^2 - 6x + 4$

Chapter 3: Linear Equations & Inequalities

Exercise 3.A

1. 3 **2.** 5 **3.** 6 **4.** 3 **5.** 6 **6.** 3 **7.** 8 **8.** 8 **9.** 9 **10.** –2 **11.** –3 **12.** –16 **13.** 8 **14.** 7 **15.** 4 **16.** 5 **17.** 4
18. 3 **19.** 9 **20.** 3 **21.** –3 **22.** 1 **23.** 3 **24.** 2 **25.** 6 **26.** –2 **27.** 1 **28.** –3 **29.** –1 **30.** –10 **31.** 2 **32.** –1
33. 2½ **34.** 1½ **35.** 3½ **36.** ¼ **37.** 2¼ **38.** – ⅓ **39.** 2½ **40.** ½ **41.** –4 **42.** –2 **43.** 7 **44.** –1 **45.** –2

Exercise 3.B

1. 2 **2.** 5 **3.** 7 **4.** 9 **5.** 11 **6.** 7 **7.** 10 **8.** 6 **9.** 9 **10.** 13 **11.** 6 **12.** 24 **13.** 12 **14.** 36 **15.** –1 **16.** 9
17. 10 **18.** 5 **19.** 14 **20.** –1 **21.** 8 **22.** 0

Exercise 3.C

14. $\frac{53 - x}{2}$ **15.** $\frac{1000 - x}{3}$ **16.** **(i)** xy **(ii)** $2x + 2y$ **17.** $\frac{3}{5}n - 200$ **18.** €$(z - nx - my)$

Exercise 3.D

1. 9 **2.** 28 **3.** 11 **4.** 24 **5.** 7 **6.** 41, 42 **7.** 6, 7 **8.** 9, 10, 11 **9.** 11 **10.** 70 **11.** 10, 12
12. 11, 13 **13.** 14, 17, 62 **14.** 15 **15.** 4 & 12 **16.** 5 **17.** 2, 18 **18.** 18 & 16 **19.** 14, 15, 16
20. 9, 3 **21.** 4 **22.** 9 **23.** 42

Exercise 3.E

1. (1, 2) **2.** (3, 1) **3.** (5, 3) **4.** (1, 4) **5.** (2, 7) **6.** (7, 3) **7.** (5, –1) **8.** (–2, 3) **9.** (1, –3) **10.** (–1, –2) **11.** (1, –1) **12.** (2½, 1) **13.** (1½, ½) **14.** (½, ½) **15.** (1, –2) **16.** (1, 0) **17.** (–1, 3) **18.** (4, 1) **19.** (4, 10) **20.** (14, 6) **21.** (2, 8) **22.** (7, 1.5)

Exercise 3.F

1. 9, 5 **2.** 28, 17 **3.** 11, 10 **4.** 3, 10 **5.** (10, 12) **6.** 16 cent, 20 cent **7.** 3 goals, 8 pts **8.** 3 & 7 **9.** 80, 20 **10.** 12, 5 **11.** 7, 3 **12.** 14 cent, 8 cent **13.** 30, 7 **14.** 45, 22

Exercise 3.H

1. {0, 1, 2, 3} **2.** {0, 1, 2, 3, 4, 5} **3.** {0, 1, 2, 3} **4.** {0, 1, 2, 3, 4, 5, 6} **5.** {0, 1, 2, 3, 4}
15. **(i)** $x \le 7$ **(ii)** $x \ge -1$ **(iii)** {–1, 0, 1, 2, 3, 4, 5, 6, 7}
16. **(i)** {..., 0, 1, 2, 3} **(ii)** {–2, –1, 0, ...} **(iii)** {–2, –1, 0, 1, 2, 3}

Exercise 3.I

1. $m = \frac{y-c}{x}$ **2.** $q = \frac{y+t}{p}$ **3.** $t = \frac{p}{v}$ **4.** $a = \frac{v-u}{t}$ **5.** $u = v - at$ **6.** $a = \frac{-by-c}{x}$

7. $x = \frac{z+2y}{8}$ **8.** $a = t-(n-1)d$ **9.** $d = \frac{t-a}{n-1}$ **10.** $n = \frac{t-a}{d}+1$ **11.** $r = \frac{A}{2\pi h}$

12. $h = \frac{A}{2\pi r} - r = \frac{A-2\pi r^2}{2\pi r}$ **13.** $t = \frac{2s-q}{6}$ **14.** $h = \frac{3V}{\pi r^2}$ **15.** $a = \frac{2(s-ut)}{t^2}$ **16.** $a = \frac{v^2-u^2}{2s}$

17. $u = \sqrt{v^2-2as}$ **18.** $s = \frac{v^2-u^2}{2a}$ **19.** $c = b - \frac{v(2-3a)}{u}$ **20.** **(i)** $h = \frac{V}{\pi r^2}$ **(ii)** $r = \sqrt{\frac{V}{\pi h}}$

21. **(i)** $a = \frac{3cx+b}{2}$ **(ii)** 34 **22.** **(i)** $x = \frac{k(a+b)+y}{3}$ **(ii)** $y = 3x - k(a+b)$ **23.** **(i)** $r = 1 - \frac{a}{s}$ **(ii)** ¾

Exercise 3.J

1. $x = \frac{c}{a-b}$ **2.** $x = \frac{c}{a+k}$ **3.** $q = \frac{c}{p-r}$ **4.** $r = \frac{c+1}{1-s}$ **5.** $b = \frac{c-a}{1-x}$ **6.** $a = \frac{b}{1-k}$ **7.** $a = \frac{2t}{2-c}$

8. $b = \frac{a}{c+3}$ **9.** $b = \frac{a-c}{c+1}$ **10.** **(i)** $p = \frac{2a}{b+2}$ **(ii)** 3 **11.** $l = \frac{sr+a}{r+s}$ **(ii)** $r = \frac{ls-a}{s-l}$ or $\frac{a-ls}{l-s}$ **(iii)** 57

Revision Exercise 3.K

1. **(a)** 38 **(b)** (3, 1) **(c)** 6, 7, 8

2. **(a)** 9 **(b)** **(i)** $x < 5$ **(ii)** $x > -4$ **(iii)** $-4 < x < 5$ **(c)** **(i)** $a = 5b + cd$ **(ii)** –13

3. **(a)** $x > 6$ **(b)** –5 **(c)** **(i)** $x = \frac{7y}{k-1}$ **(ii)** –7

4. **(a)** 13 **(b)** (3, –2) **(c)** 15, 17, 96

5. **(a)** 4 **(b)** **(i)** $x \le 5$ **(ii)** $x \le 2$ **(iii)** {3, 4, 5} **(c)** **(i)** $c = \frac{a-d}{d+5}$ **(ii)** –2

6. **(a)** 6 **(b)** (5, –2) **(c)** 4, 9

7. **(a)** $x < -6$ **(b)** (5, –2) **(c)** **(i)** $x = \frac{2y}{y-1}$ **(ii)** 6

8. **(b)** 13, 17 **(c)** $r = \sqrt[3]{\frac{3V}{4\pi}} = \frac{3}{2}$ when $V = \frac{99}{7}$

9. **(b)** $x = 5$ **(c)** 18, 6

10. **(a)** $x \le 1$ **(b)** –3, 11 **(c)** **(i)** $t = \frac{8x+7}{2-x}$ **(ii)** 107

Chapter 4: Quadratic & Cubic Equations

Exercise 4.B

1. $\frac{5x+17}{(x+1)(x+7)}$ **2.** $\frac{3x+16}{(x+5)(x+6)}$ **3.** $\frac{9x-39}{(x+1)(x-7)}$ **4.** $\frac{3x-22}{(x+10)(6x+6)}$ **5.** $\frac{4x-5}{(2x+1)(5x-1)}$

6. $\frac{-87}{(4x+1)(x-7)}$ **7.** $\frac{16}{(x-9)(x+7)}$ **8.** $\frac{2x+1}{(x-2)(x+2)(x+3)}$ **9.** $\frac{3x-4}{(x-3)(x+3)(x+2)}$

10. $\frac{2x-3}{(x-1)(x+1)(x-2)}$ **11.** $\frac{x+3}{(x-4)(x+2)}$ **12.** $\frac{x+3}{(x-3)(x+4)}$ **13.** $\frac{2x^2+x+11}{(x-2)(x+2)(x+5)}$

14. $\frac{2x^2-15x+27}{(x-6)(x+6)(x-5)}$

Exercise 4.C

1. $\frac{15}{(x-1)(x+1)}$ **2.** $\frac{30}{(x+7)(x-2)}$ **3.** $\frac{15}{x+1}$ **4.** $\frac{x-4}{x+1}$ **5.** $\frac{x-3}{x+2}$ **6.** $\frac{x-1}{x-2}$ **7.** $\frac{x-2}{2(x+1)}$ **8.** 1 **9.** $\frac{3}{5}$

10. $2x$ **11.** $\frac{x-1}{x-5}$ **12.** $\frac{x}{x-4}$ **13.** $\frac{x+1}{x-1}$ **14.** $\frac{1}{(x+1)(2x-9)}$ **15.** $\frac{x^2-4}{x^2-1}$ **16.** x^2-1

Exercise 4.D

1. –2, –5 **2.** –3, –5 **3.** 4, –2 **4.** 2, 10 **5.** –3, 2 **6.** 6, –3 **7.** –7, 3 **8.** 3.–3 **9.** 9, –9 **10.** 10, –10

11. 1½, –4 **12.** –3½, 4 **13.** 6, 3 **14.** $-2, \frac{1}{3}$ **15.** $\frac{7}{3}$, 2 **16.** 0, –5 **17.** $\frac{1}{2}, \frac{1}{3}$ **18.** $\frac{1}{2}, \frac{2}{5}$ **19.** 6, –1 **20.** 6, –5

21. –8, 3 **22.** ½, –4 **23.** 6, –6 **24.** 8, –9 **25.** $2, -\frac{5}{3}$ **26.** 0, 2 **27.** 4, 4 **28.** $1, -\frac{5}{3}$ **29.** $\frac{10}{7}, -\frac{10}{7}$ **30.** 2, –1

31. –5, 5 **32.** $\frac{2}{5}, -\frac{3}{4}$ **33.** $\frac{2}{3}, \frac{2}{3}$ **34.** –2, 8 **35.** 3, 3 **36.** $\frac{6}{5}, -\frac{7}{2}$ **37.** $\frac{1}{10}, \frac{1}{3}$ **38.** $-\frac{1}{15}, \frac{1}{2}$ **39.** –10, 100 **40.** $3, \frac{4}{3}$

Exercise 4.E

1. $\frac{-9 \pm \sqrt{41}}{4}$ **2.** $\frac{-2 \pm \sqrt{40}}{6}$ **3.** $\frac{8 \pm \sqrt{44}}{2}$ **4.** $\frac{2 \pm \sqrt{24}}{4}$ **5.** $\frac{-10 \pm \sqrt{96}}{2}$ **6.** $\frac{11 \pm \sqrt{177}}{4}$ **7.** $\frac{-12 \pm \sqrt{104}}{2}$

8. $\frac{1 \pm \sqrt{177}}{8}$ **9.** $\frac{-1 \pm \sqrt{21}}{10}$ **10.** $\frac{3 \pm \sqrt{409}}{20}$ **11.** 1.4, –3.4 **12.** 11.6, 0.4 **13.** 2.7, –3.7 **14.** 6.2, –3.2

15. 0.4, –1.4 **16.** 1.3, 0.3 **17.** 1.1, –0.9 **18.** 1.7, –6.7 **19.** 1.4, –2.4 **20.** 8.6, 1.4

Exercise 4.F

1. 8, –7 **2.** $1, \frac{2}{5}$ **3.** 5, –2 **4.** $1, \frac{8}{3}$ **5.** –3, 2 **6.** 4, –2 **7.** 1½, 5 **8.** $6, \frac{2}{3}$ **9.** 3, –2 **10.** $5, -\frac{5}{3}$ **11.** $5, \frac{5}{6}$

12. 5½, –2½ **13.** 12, 1 **14.** 1.37, –0.37 **15.** 2.732, –0.732

Exercise 4.G

1. (3, 2), (–2, –3) **2.** (5, 1), (0, –4) **3.** (2, 4), (–4, –2) **4.** (3, 4), (–4, –3) **5.** (5, 5), (–7, –7)
6. (1, 2), (2, 1) **7.** (–1, –5), (2, –2) **8.** (4, 1), (–1, –4) **9.** (2, 1), (–2, –1) **10.** (–9, –5), (3, 1)
11. (1, 0), (0, 1) **12.** (3, 4), (4, 3) **13.** (7, 2), (4, 3½) **14.** (5, 3), (–1½, –10) **15.** (5, 3), (–4, –1½)
16. (3, –1), $\left(-\frac{11}{3}, \frac{7}{3}\right)$ **17.** (1, 1), (0.2, 1.4) **18.** (–1, –1), (5, 3) **19.** (4, –3) **20.** (–1, 1), $\left(\frac{26}{19}, -\frac{11}{19}\right)$

Exercise 4.H

1. (5, 6) **2.** (4, 7) or (–7, –4) **3.** (12, 8) or (8, 12) **4.** (7, –2) **5.** (2, 5) **6.** (7, 8) **7.** (6, 9) **8.** 6 × 10
9. 3, 4, 5 or –5, –4, –3 **10.** (6, 8) **11.** $\left(\frac{5}{2}, \frac{2}{5}\right)$ **12.** 3 **13.** 8 **14.** 10 **15.** 16 **16.** 9 & 10

Exercise 4.I

1. $x^2 - 8x + 12 = 0$ **2.** $x^2 - 6x + 5 = 0$ **3.** $x^2 - 9x - 22 = 0$ **4.** $x^2 - 6x - 40 = 0$ **5.** $x^2 + 2x - 35 = 0$ **6.** $x^2 + 7x + 12 = 0$ **7.** $2x^2 - 7x + 3 = 0$ **8.** $4x^2 - 5x + 1 = 0$ **9.** $2x^2 + 3x - 9 = 0$ **10.** $2x^2 - 5x - 25 = 0$ **11.** $3x^2 + 10x + 8 = 0$ **12.** $10x^2 + 7x + 1 = 0$ **13.** –17, 70 **14.** 3, 0 **15.** –11, 12 **16.** –6, 9 **17.** 8, 16 **18.** –20, 100 **19.** 36 **20.** 25

Exercise 4.J

1. 1, 2, –5 **2.** 2, –1, –½ **3.** 1, –1, 3 **4.** 2, –2, –5 **5.** 1, –4, ½ **6.** 2, 5, –7 **7.** 2, –2, $-\frac{1}{3}$ **8.** 2, 2, $\frac{1}{3}$

9. 1, –1, –¼ **10.** –2, –2 **11.** –½, –2 **12.** –1, –1 **13.** $\frac{1}{2}, -\frac{1}{3}$ **14.** ½, –½

Revision Exercise 4.K

1. **(a)** 11, –10 **(b)** (1, 4), (7, 2) **(c)** –½, –3 **2.** **(b)** (3, 7), (7, 3) **(c)** 8, –1

3. **(a)** $(4x - 3)(3x + 4)$ **(b)** –2½, –2 **(c)** 3, 4

4. **(a)** $(2x + 1)(x - 4)$; –½, 4 **(b)** $k = -11$, Root = $-\frac{10}{7}$ **(ii)** $\frac{2(x+3)}{x+5}$ **(c)** 4, 5

5. **(a)** $\frac{4}{5}, -\frac{1}{2}$ **(b)** (3, –1), $\left(-\frac{13}{5}, \frac{9}{5}\right)$ **(c)** $\frac{1}{3}, \frac{1}{2}$ **6.** **(a)** 3, –6 **(b)** $p = 5$, $q = -24$ **(c)** $k = 6$; Roots: 3, –1

7. **(b)** 13, 6 **(c)** (–1, 5), (3.4, –3.8); 124, –15.568

8. **(a)** **(i)** 10, –10 **(ii)** 7, –2 **(b)** 6 × 5 **(c)** 3, $\frac{1}{5}$

9. **(a)** $(2x - 7)(x + 3)$ **(i)** 3½, –3 **(ii)** 3½, –3, 0 **(b)** $\frac{1 - x^2}{x}$; ¼, –4

(c) **(i)** $x^2 - 20x + 100 = 0$ **(ii)** Roots = 7, 7; $k = 14$ **10.** **(a)** –1.8, 3.8 **(b)** $\frac{4 - x^2}{x^2}$; $\pm\frac{1}{2}$ **(c)** (2, –3)

Chapter 5: Powers & roots

Exercise 5.B

1. 3 **2.** 2 **3.** 5 **4.** 2 **5.** 2 **6.** 2½ **7.** 14 **8.** 15 **9.** 7½ **10.** 5 **11.** 2½ **12.** ½ **13.** 1½ **14.** $1\frac{2}{3}$ **15.** ¾ **16.** 2¼

17. ¾ **18.** 10½ **19.** –3, 2 **20.** 1, 2 **21.** $x = 4¼$ **22.** $x = 4½$ **23.** $x = 7$ **24.** $x = 1\frac{5}{8}$

Exercise 5.C

5. 8 **6.** 45 **7.** 40 **8.** 200 **9.** 6 **10.** 10 **11.** 4 **12.** 3 **13.** 5 **14.** 2

Exercise 5.D

11. $7\sqrt{2}$ **12.** $5\sqrt{3}$ **13.** $7\sqrt{5}$ **14.** $n = 5$ **15.** $n = 11$ **16.** $k = 6$ **17.** $\sqrt{3}$ **18.** $\sqrt{5}$ **19.** $\sqrt{7}$ **20.** $\sqrt{7}$ **21.** $\sqrt{2}$ **22.** $2 \pm \sqrt{3}$ **23.** $6 \pm \sqrt{2}$ **24.** $1 \pm \sqrt{7}$ **25.** $-3 \pm \sqrt{5}$

Exercise 5.E

1. 25 **2.** 100 **3.** 9 **4.** 10 **5.** 40 **6.** 5 **7.** 5 **8.** 8 **9.** 10 **10.** 11 **11.** 8 **12.** 2 **13.** ±12 **14.** ±10 **15.** ±5

16. $x = y^2$ **17.** $x = y^2 - a$ **18.** $x = c^2 + b$ **19.** $x = \frac{p^2 + y}{2}$ **20.** $x = (b - a)^2$ **21.** $x = y^2z^2 + 1$

22. $x = \frac{mghT^2}{4\pi^2}$

Exercise 5.G

1. 3410 **2.** 57 800 **3.** 630 000 **4.** 4200 **5.** 214.1 **6.** 902 000 **7.** 750 000 000 000 **8.** 3000 **9.** 21.86
10. 0.000 771 **11.** 9 **12.** 2000 **13.** 5.3×10^2 **14.** 6.31×10^4 **15.** 6.51×10^{17} **16.** 4×10^7
17. 6.42×10^{-1} **18.** -2.26×10^{-4} **19.** 1.1×10^5 **20.** 2×10^{-5} **21.** **(i)** 31 **(ii)** 3.1×10^1
22. **(i)** 0.0103 **(ii)** 1.03×10^{-2} **23.** **(i)** 9.185×10^{-17} **(ii)** 6×10^{26} **24.** 6.054×10^{24}
25. **(i)** 1.472×10^{10} **(ii)** 5.3728×10^{12} **26.** 3×10^8 m/s **27.** 1.778×10^{-6} **28.** 7.18×10^{-5}

Revision Exercise 5.H

1. **(a)** 5 **(b)** **(i)** 3^2 **(ii)** $3^{\frac{1}{2}}$ **(iii)** $x = 1\frac{1}{2}$ **(c)** $n = 6$ **2.** **(a)** $\frac{1}{8}$ **(b)** **(i)** 2^7 **(ii)** $2^{\frac{1}{2}}$ **(iii)** $x = 2\frac{3}{4}$ **(c)** $x = \frac{z^2 + y}{2}$
3. **(a)** $\frac{1}{8} = 1.25 \times 10^{-1}$ **(b)** 920 **(c)** 1.04×10^{-2}
4. **(a)** $\frac{3}{2}$ **(b)** **(i)** 0.002 **(ii)** 2×10^{-3} **(c)** **(i)** p^{10} **(ii)** p^{24} **(iii)** $p^{1.5}$
5. **(a)** $\frac{9}{2}$ **(b)** **(i)** 7^3 **(ii)** $7^{\frac{1}{2}}$; $x = \frac{1}{4}$ **(c)** $g = \frac{4\pi^2 l}{T^2} = 9.9$
6. **(a)** **(i)** 0.0000116 **(ii)** 1.16×10^{-5} **(b)** **(i)** 10^2 **(ii)** $10^{1\frac{1}{2}}$; $x = \frac{1}{2}$ **(c)** $x - \frac{4}{x}$; $x = 4$
7. **(a)** 3.3×10^{-4} **(b)** 1100 **(c)** $y = \frac{4x - 25z^2}{3} = 4$ **8.** **(a)** $\frac{9}{100}$ **(b)** **(i)** 63 **(ii)** 3969 **(c)** $\frac{3 \pm \sqrt{33}}{2}$; 3, –6
9. **(a)** $\frac{27}{8}$ **(b)** $x^{1.25}$ **(c)** $x = 2$ **10.** **(a)** 3.006×10^{-26} **(b)** **(i)** 0.00274 **(ii)** 2.74×10^{-3} **(c)** $b = -2$; $c = -10$

CHAPTER 6: FUNCTIONS AND GRAPHS

Exercise 6.A

7. **(i)** 3 **(ii)** 1 **(iii)** 2½ **8.** **(i)** –1½ **(ii)** 4 **(iii)** 6 **9.** **(i)** 0 **(ii)** 0 **(iii)** $k = -1$ **10.** $k = 8$ **11.** $a = 2$ **12.** $k = -7$
13. **(i)** 22 **(ii)** 14 **(iii)** 41; No **14.** 12 **15.** 4, –3 **16.** **(i)** 32 **(ii)** 8 **17.** **(i)** 38 **(ii)** $3x + 11$ **(iii)** 5
18. **(i)** –11 **(ii)** $4x + 5$ **(iii)** 8 **19.** **(i)** 6 **(ii)** 11 **20.** **(i)** 19 **(ii)** 12 **(iv)** 5 **21.** **(i)** 5 **(ii)** 3, –2
22. $a = 7, b = 1$ **23.** $a = 1, b = -6$ **24.** $a = -2\frac{1}{2}, b = 8\frac{1}{2}$ **25.** **(i)** $a = -1, b = -6$ **(ii)** –6
26. **(i)** $a = 1, b = -4$ **(ii)** Both $= x^2 - 4$ **27.** **(i)** $a = 2, b = 3$ **(ii)** $k = -7$ **28.** **(i)** $p = -21, q = 10$, **(ii)** $n = -1$

Exercise 6.C

1. **(i)** 2.9 **(ii)** –1.7 **2.** **(i)** –4.6 **(ii)** 1.5 **(iii)** $0 < x < 3$ **3.** (1.5, 2) **4.** **(i)** 8 **(ii)** 1.7 **(iii)** 15 **(iv)** $t = 5$
5. **(ii)** 115 mins **(iii)** 4.3 kg **(iv)** $m < 2$ **6.** **(ii)** 64 **(iii)** 38 **(iv)** $52 \leq F \leq 59$
7. **(ii)** 435 **(iii)** 5.4 kg **(iv)** $2.1 \leq m \leq 3.3$ **8.** **(iii)** 25 **(iv)** 58 **(v)** $32 \leq F \leq 58$

Exercise 6.D

1. **(i)** –4.6 **(ii)** –1.4, 3.4 **(iii)** $-1.4 \leq x \leq 3.4$ **(iv)** –6 **2.** **(i)** 3.3 **(ii)** 1, 3
3. **(i)** 4.3 **(ii)** 1.7, 4.3 **4.** **(i)** 2.7 **(ii)** –1.4 **(iii)** –0.4, 3.4
5. **(i)** –2.3 **(ii)** –3.2 **(iii)** –3.3, 2.3 **6.** **(i)** –4 **(ii)** –1.8, 2.8 **(iii)** –2.5, 3.5
7. **(i)** –1.3, 2.8 **(ii)** –0.5, 2 **(iii)** $-1.3 \leq x \leq 2.8$ **(iv)** –8.1 at $x = 0.75$
8. **(i)** –1.6, 2.6 **(ii)** $-1.6 \leq x \leq 2.6$ **(iii)** –0.6, 1.6 **(iv)** 4.25
9. **(i)** –2, 1.5 **(ii)** –2.7, 2.2 **(iii)** $x \leq -2$ or $x \geq 1.5$
10. **(i)** –0.7, 1.7 **(ii)** –1.8, 2.8 **(iii)** $0 < x < 1$ **(iv)** –4.8 at $x = 0.5$
11. **(i)** 7.5 **(ii)** –2.2, 0.6 **(iii)** $-2.3 < x < 0.7$ **(iv)** –2.6
12. **(ii)** –1.7, 1.2 **(ii)** $x < -1.7$ or $x > 1.2$ **(iii)** 4.1 **(iv)** $x = -1.4, 0.9$ **(v)** $n = 5$
13. **(i)** –2.5 **(ii)** –2.1, 0.3 **(iii)** –2.2, 0.9 **(iv)** $-2.2 < x < 0.9$
14. **(i)** 7.25 **(ii)** $x = -1.5$ **(iii)** 3.25, 3.25 **(iv)** –5, 1
15. **(a)** –0.2, 6.2 **(b)** **(i)** –0.2, 6.2 **(ii)** $x < -0.2, x > 6.2$
16. **(a)** –0.7, 1.1 **(b)** **(i)** –0.7, 1.1 **(ii)** $-0.7 < x < 1.1$
17. **(i)** 15 km **(ii)** 5.17 p.m. **(iii)** 7.3 km

Exercise 6.E

1. **(i)** –2, –½, 2 **(ii)** –1.7, –0.7, 2.2 **2.** **(i)** –3, –2, 1 **(ii)** $x < -3$ and $-2 < x < 1$ **(iii)** $-3 < x < -2$
3. **(i)** –1.3, 0.2, 3.1 **(ii)** –1, –0.2, 3.3 **(iii)** –2, 2
4. **(i)** –3, –1, 1 **(ii)** $x < -3$ and $0.15 < x < 1$ **(iii)** –3.3, 0, 0.3 **(iv)** 5.5
5. **(i)** –3.7, 0.5, 3.2 **(ii)** $-3.7 < x < -2$ and $x > 3.2$ **(iii)** $-3.5 \le x \le 0$ or $x \ge 3.5$
6. **(i)** 3 **(ii)** –1, 1, 3 **(iii)** –1.2 **7.** **(i)** 2 **(ii)** –1, 0, 4 **(iii)** –2, 2, 3 **8.** **(b)** 0.4, –1.5 **9.** **(i)** 2.4 **(ii)** –2.7
10. **(i)** 1.9 **(ii)** –2, 1, 2 **11.** –2.65, 0, 2.65; $\sqrt{7} = 2.65$ **12.** **(i)** 3 **(ii)** 1 **(iii)** 2 **(iv)** 1; $k < 1$
13. **(i)** $0.35 < x < 2$ **(ii)** –2.2, 0, 2.2; $\sqrt{5} = 2.2$ **(iii)** –2.4, –0.2, 2.5 **14.** **(i)** $0.6 < x < 3.4$ **(ii)** 1, 3.5

Exercise 6.F

2. $1 < x < 3$ **3.** **(i)** 2.7 **(ii)** $1 < x < 2$ **4.** **(i)** 0.6 **(ii)** $x > 4$ **5.** **(i)** 4 **(ii)** 0 **(v)** $x = 2, 5$ **6.** **(i)** $\frac{4}{3}$ **(iii)** $k = -9$
7. **(i)** $x = 3, 5$ **(ii)** $-3 < x < 4$ and $x > 5$

Revision Exercise 6.G

1. **(a)** **(i)** –2 **(ii)** 0.4 **(b)** **(i)** $\frac{7}{2}$ **(ii)** $a = -2, b = 5$ **(c)** $-½ < x < 1$

2. **(a)** $k = -25$ **(b)** **(i)** $a = 2, b = -3$ **(ii)** $p = 5$ **(c)** **(i)** $x = 0, 3$ **(ii)** $x > 3$

3. **(b)** $b = 3, c = -5, k = -2$ **(c)** **(i)** 3.6 **(ii)** $4 < x < 5$

4. **(a)** **(i)** $2, -\frac{1}{7}$ **(ii)** $-\frac{2}{3}$ **(b)** **(iii)** 2.2 **(c)** **(i)** 2 **5.** **(a)** 2.7 **(b)** **(i)** $-2 < x < 4$ **(ii)** 2.6

6. **(ii)** $-1 < x < 1$ **(iv)** –1.4, 0, 1.4 **(v)** $x = 0, \pm\sqrt{2}$

7. **(a)** **(i)** 0.4 **(ii)** $k = 2$ **(iii)** $\frac{1}{x(x+1)}$; $x = 4$ **(b)** **(i)** 3.75 m at 10.45 a.m. **(ii)** 9 a.m. and 12.25 p.m. **(iii)** 20 m **(iv)** 4 hrs

8. **(a)** {–1, 1, 7} **(b)** **(i)** $a = -7, b = 6$ **(ii)** $p = (-3, 0), q = (2, 0)$ **(c)** 3.1 **9.** **(a)** 2.5 **(b)** 0.8 **(c)** **(i)** 4, –3 **(ii)** $x = 4$ **10.** **(a)** **(i)** 150 **(ii)** 9 **(b)** **(i)** –0.4 **(c)** **(i)** –2.45, 0, 2.45; $\sqrt{6} \approx 2.45$

CHAPTER 7: CO–ORDINATE GEOMETRY OF THE LINE

Exercise 7.A

1. $\sqrt{13}$ **2.** 5 **3.** 10 **4.** $\sqrt{34}$ **5.** $\sqrt{104}$ **6.** $\sqrt{61}$ **7.** $\sqrt{50}$ **8.** $\sqrt{8}$ **9.** 13 **10.** $\sqrt{2}$ **11.** 5 **12.** 3
13. 5 **14.** $\sqrt{8}$ **15.** $\sqrt{32}$ **16.** $\sqrt{72}$ **17.** 10 **18.** 17 **19.** $\sqrt{13}$ **20.** $\sqrt{2}$ **21.** (7, –4) [$\sqrt{65} > \sqrt{61}$]
22. (6, 1) **30.** **(i)** $\sqrt{65}$ **(ii)** 0, 16 **31.** 12, –8 **32.** 7, –5 **33.** 2, –2 **34.** –9, 1

Exercise 7.B

1. (3, 8) **2.** (7, 3) **3.** (3, 4) **4.** (1, 3) **5.** (–3, 3) **6.** (–8, –3) **7.** (–1, 0) **8.** (–1½, 3½) **9.** (–2½, –½)
10. (1, 2½) **11.** (2½, 2) **12.** (5, 5) **13.** (5, –2) **14.** (–2, 0) **15.** **(i)** Both = (1, –1) **18.** **(i)** $m = (-5, 1)$
19. **(i)** $m = (-2, 7)$; $n = (6, -8)$ **(ii)** 17 **20.** **(i)** (3, –3) **(ii)** 5 **21.** $x = 8$; $y = 12$
22. $x = 2$; $y = 3$ **23.** $x = 0$; $y = -5$

Exercise 7.C

1. $\frac{2}{3}$ **2.** $\frac{6}{5}$ **3.** 5 **4.** 1 **5.** ½ **6.** 1 **7.** 8 **8.** $-\frac{1}{3}$ **9.** ½ **10.** 1 **11.** $-\frac{1}{3}$ **12.** –7 **13.** 3 **14.** –2

23. not collinear **24.** collinear **25.** **(i)** –¾ **(ii)** (3, 8) **27.** 1 **28.** 6 **29.** $\frac{3}{2}$ **30.** 4 **31.** 3, 2

Exercise 7.D

31. Yes **32.** Yes **33.** No **34.** $k = 7$ **35.** $k = -10$ **36.** $t = 16$ **37.** Yes **38.** Yes **39.** No **40.** Yes **41.** $k = 3$ **42.** $k = 6$ **43.** $k = -2$ **44.** $k = -4$ **45.** (5, 1) **46.** (3, –1) **47.** (1, –6) **48.** $k = 7$; $t = -14$ **49.** (0, –3.8) **50.** **(ii)** ½ **(iii)** Yes **(iv)** (5, –½) **(v)** No

Exercise 7.E

11. $3x - y = 1$ **12.** $x - y = 5$ **13.** $2x - y = 8$ **14.** $x + y = 4$ **15.** $x - y = -15$ **16.** $3x + y = 5$

17. $4x - y = 1$ **18.** $2x + y = 0$ **19.** $5x - y = 1$ **20.** $4x + y = 1$ **21.** $x - 2y = -9$ **22.** $x + 2y = 0$

23. $3x + 4y = 0$ **24.** $3x - 7y = -30$ **25.** $7x + 11y = -36$ **26.** **(i)** 2 **(ii)** $2x - y = 1$

27. **(i)** ½ **(ii)** $x - 2y = -1$ **28.** $5x - 6y = 14$ **29.** $x + 3y = 23$ **30.** $5x - 3y = 1$

31. **(i)** $\frac{1}{3}$ **(ii)** $x - 3y = 0$ **32.** **(i)** –1 **(ii)** $x - y = 3$ **33.** **(i)** $\frac{3}{2}$ **(ii)** $3x - 2y = 5$

34. **(i)** $\frac{7}{4}$ **(ii)** $7x - 4y = 26$ **(iii)** $4x + 7y = 52$ **35.** **(i)** $2x + y = 8$ **(ii)** (5, –2)

36. **(i)** $-\frac{3}{2}$; $3x + 2y = 7$ **(ii)** $2x - 3y = 9$ **(iii)** (3, –1) **37.** **(i)** $2x + 7y = 5$ **(ii)** (–1, 1)

38. **(i)** $2x + y = 10$ **(ii)** $x - 2y = 0$ **(iii)** (4, 2) **39.** $2x - y = -3$ **40.** $3x + 4y = 3$ **41.** **(ii)** $x + 2y = 7$

Exercise 7.F

1. **(i)** (6, 5) **(ii)** (4, 3) **(iii)** (6, 7) **(iv)** (4, 4) **(v)** (–2, 3) **(vi)** (3, 2) **(vii)** (2, 9) **(viii)** (3, –1) **(ix)** (7, –12) **(x)** (3, –4) **2.** (9, 3) **3.** **(i)** (3, 8) **(ii)** (–4, 6) **(iii)** (–2, 3) **4.** **(i)** (–4, –1) **(ii)** (–3, –2) **(iii)** (1, –3) **(iv)** (–4, 0) **(v)** (5, 2) **5.** (5, 4) **6.** (7, 7) **7.** (0, 6) **8.** (10, 2) **9.** (–1, 5) **10.** **(i)** (4, –2) **(ii)** (3, –1) **(iii)** (1, –3) **(iv)** (0, –5) **(v)** (–2, 3) **(vi)** (–3, –1) **(vii)** (3, 3) **(viii)** (–5, –1) **(ix)** (2, 0) **(x)** (–4, 0) **11.** **(i)** (–5, 1) **(ii)** (–2, 3) **(iii)** (–3, 2) **(iv)** (–4, 0) **(v)** (2, 2) **(vi)** (6, 5) **(vii)** (2, –1) **(viii)** (4, 1) **(ix)** (0, 5) **(x)** (0, –2) **12.** **(i)** (3, –2) **(ii)** (–3, 2) **13.** (6, –5) **14.** (4, 0) **15.** **(i)** (3, 1) **(ii)** (3, –1) **(iii)** (0, 0) **16.** **(i)** (2, 10) **(ii)** (–2, 4) **(iii)** (2, –4) **17.** $x + y = 7$ **18.** $3x - y = -6$ **19.** $4x + y = 4$ **20.** $x - 2y = 9$ **21.** $3x + 4y = -12$ **22.** $y = -3x$

Exercise 7.G

1. 22 **2.** 8 **3.** 4 **4.** 6 **5.** 3½ **6.** 8 **7.** 11 **8.** 8½ **9.** 13 **10.** 15 **11.** **(i)** $m = (4, 3)$ **12.** 16 **13.** 33½ **14.** ±3 **15.** ±2 **16.** $x = 7$ **17.** $k = 4$ **18.** 19, 1

Revision Exercise 7.H

1. **(i)** ¾ **(ii)** $3x - 4y = 11$ **(iii)** 17 **(iv)** $\sqrt{53}$ **(v)** (2, 3)

3. **(a)** $x + 4y = 0$ **(b)** **(i)** (2, 0) **(v)** –4; $4x + y + 1 = 0$

4. **(ii)** $\frac{4}{3}$ **(iii)** $3x + 4y = 2$ **(iv)** (2, –1) **(v)** Both = 5 **5.** **(a)** $k = 2$ **(b)** Area = 19½

6. **(a)** $2x - 5y = 32$; Yes **(b)** **(i)** –1 **(ii)** $x + y = 3$ **(iii)** $r(3, 0)$ **(iv)** 3 : 1

7. **(a)** 29 **(b)** **(i)** (3, 2) **(ii)** $\frac{14}{3}$ **(iii)** No **(c)** 3, 7 **8.** **(i)** $4x + 5y = 20$ **(ii)** $5x - 4y = 0$

(iii) $\left(\frac{80}{41}, \frac{100}{41}\right)$ **(iv)** No **(v)** $\frac{16}{25}$ **9.** **(a)** $3x - y = 16$ **10.** **(i)** –½ **(iii)** $2x - y = 7$ **(iv)** (5, 3) **(v)** 10

Chapter 8: The Circle

Exercise 8.B

4. On **5.** Outside **6.** Inside **7.** Outside **8.** On **9.** Inside **10.** On **11.** **(ii)** Inside **(iii)** ± 11
12. **(ii)** Outside **(iii)** ± 7 **13.** **(ii)** $t = \pm 8$ **(iii)** 7 **14.** **(ii)** 3, –7 **(iii)** 7 **15.** **(i)** $x^2 + y^2 = 6.25$ **(ii)** ± 2
17. **(ii)** (29, 0), (–29, 0) **(iii)** ± 20 **18.** ± 1.5 **19.** **(i)** $\pm\frac{5}{3}$ **(ii)** $\left(0, \frac{13}{3}\right), \left(0, -\frac{13}{3}\right)$ **(iii)** 4 **20.** **(i)** 5

Exercise 8.C

1. $x^2 + y^2 = 25$ **2.** $x^2 + y^2 = 29$ **3.** $(x-2)^2 + (y-1)^2 = 13$ **4.** $(x+2)^2 + y^2 = 25$
5. $(x+3)^2 + (y-3)^2 = 53$ **6.** $(x-3)^2 + (y-3)^2 = 18$ **7.** $(x-1)^2 + (y-1)^2 = 13$
8. $(x-5)^2 + (y-2)^2 = 4$ **9.** $(x+3)^2 + (y-6)^2 = 25$
10. **(i)** $(x-2)^2 + (y-2)^2 = 8$ **(ii)** $(x-2)^2 + (y-2)^2 = 4$ **(iii)** 2 : 1
11. **(i)** (7, –4) **(iii)** $(x-4)^2 + (y+2)^2 = 13$ **12.** **(i)** (5, –12), (0, 0) **(ii)** 13 **(iv)** 5

Exercise 8.D

1. **(ii)** $(x-6)^2 + (y-4)^2 = 9$ **2.** **(ii)** $(x+3)^2 + y^2 = 1$ **3.** **(iii)** $(x+3)^2 + (y+5)^2 = 4$
4. **(a)** $x^2 + y^2 = 10$ **(b)** $(x-6)^2 + (y+1)^2 = 10$ **5.** **(iii)** $(x-3)^2 + (y-5)^2 = 81$
6. $(x+6)^2 + (y+4)^2 = 20$ **7.** **(iii)** $(x-4)^2 + (y+8)^2 = 10$ **8.** **(ii)** $(x+2)^2 + (y-5)^2 = 18$
9. **(a)** $(x-1.5)^2 + (y-2)^2 = 6.25$ **(b)** $(x+1.5)^2 + (y+2)^2 = 6.25$ **(c)** $x^2 + y^2 = 25$
10. **(i)** $(x+6)^2 + y^2 = 4$ **(ii)** $r = 4, 8$

Exercise 8.E

1. (3, 1), (1, 3) **2.** (3, 2), (–2, –3) **3.** (1, 3), (–3, –1) **4.** (–1, 5), (3.4, –3.8) **5.** (–3, 0), (1.8, 2.4)
6. (–3, 1), (3.16, 0.12) **7.** (–2, 4) **8.** (1, –1) **9.** **(ii)** $\sqrt{20}$ **10.** **(ii)** (–2, 1) **11.** (1½, 1½)
12. **(iv)** $x + 4y + 17 = 0$

Exercise 8.F

1. **(ii)** $3x + y = 10$ **2.** **(ii)** $3x - 2y = 13$ **3.** $2x - y = -10$ **4.** $2x + y + 15 = 0$
5. **(ii)** (–4, –3) **(iii)** $4x + 3y = 25$ **(iv)** $4x + 3y = -25$ **6.** **(ii)** $3x + 4y = 0$ **7.** **(ii)** $y = 3, y = -3$
8. **(ii)** $x = 10, x = -2$ **(iii)** 12 units
9. **(ii)** $x^2 + y^2 = 17$ **(iii)** $x - 4y + 17 = 0$ **(iv)** $x - 4y = 0$ **(v)** (4, 1) and (–4, –1)
10. $2x - y = 5$

Revision Exercise 8.G

1. **(iii)** (–3, –4) **(iv)** $3x + 4y = 25$ **(v)** $(x-7)^2 + (y+2)^2 = 25$
2. **(a)** (13, 0), (–3, 0) **(b)** (–3, 4), (4, –3) **(c)** (–1, 11)
3. **(ii)** (–2, 4) **(iii)** $(x+4)^2 + (y-8)^2 = 20$ **(iv)** (0, 6), (0, 10)
4. **(i)** (0,0) **(ii)** 13 **(iii)** $x^2 + y^2 = 169$ **(iv)** $5x - 12y + 169 = 0$ **(v)** (8, –4)
5. **(ii)** (0, 3), (–2.4, –1.8) **(iii)** $(x-9)^2 + y^2 = 9$
6. **(i)** $\sqrt{26}$ **(ii)** $x^2 + y^2 = 26$ **(iii)** $5x - y + 26 = 0$ **(iv)** $5x - y - 26 = 0$ **(v)** $(x+2.5)^2 + (y-0.5)^2 = 6.5$
7. **(iv)** $3x + 4y = 0$ **(v)** (–8, 6), (8, –6)
8. **(a)** $x^2 + y^2 = 34$; $\sqrt{128}$ **(b)** (6, –3) **(c)** $(x-7)^2 + (y-4)^2 = 16$
9. **(a)** (1, –3). Yes **(b)** $(x-5)^2 + (y+5)^2 = 65$; $(x+5)^2 + (y+5)^2 = 65$; $n = 4$ or 6.
10. **(ii)** ± 5 **(iii)** 6 **(iv)** $(0, -\frac{50}{7})$, (50, 0) **(v)** Area Δoab is greater

CHAPTER 9: COMPLEX NUMBERS

Exercise 9.B

1. $-2 \pm 3i$ **2.** $1 \pm 2i$ **3.** $1 \pm 3i$ **4.** $4 \pm i$ **5.** $-3 \pm 4i$ **6.** $-7 \pm i$ **7.** $6 \pm 2i$ **8.** $5 \pm 3i$ **9.** $1 \pm i$ **10.** $\pm 2i$
11. $2 \pm i$ **12.** $4 \pm 3i$ **13.** $-1 \pm 4i$ **14.** $-2 \pm 6i$ **15.** $0 \pm 4i$ **16.** $0 \pm 5i$ **17.** $1.5 \pm 2i$ **18.** $\frac{1}{3} \pm \frac{2}{3}i$
19. $-1 \pm i$ **20.** $3 \pm i$

Exercise 9.C

1.	**(i)** $9 + 6i$	**(ii)** $5 + 4i$	**(iii)** $25 + 17i$	**(iv)** $8 + 7i$	**(v)** $9 - 6i$
2.	**(i)** $8 - 2i$	**(ii)** $2 + 6i$	**(iii)** $14 - 10i$	**(iv)** $-5 + 24i$	**(v)** $8 + 2i$
3.	**(i)** $7i$	**(ii)** $-4 + i$	**(iii)** $7 + 0i$	**(iv)** $3 + i$	**(v)** $1 - 5i$
4.	**(i)** $4 + 5i$	**(ii)** $4 - 5i$	**(iii)** $1 + 5i$	**(iv)** $4 + 2i$	**(v)** $5 - 5i$
5.	**(i)** $2 - 3i$	**(ii)** $2 + 3i$	**(iii)** $1 - i$	**(iv)** $4 + 0i$	**(v)** $-1 - 3i$
6.	**(i)** $-6 + i$	**(ii)** $0 - 2i$	**(iii)** $-7 + 2i$	**(iv)** $-10 + i$	**(v)** $11 + 3i$
7.	**(i)** $3 + 2i$	**(ii)** $3 - 2i$	**(iii)** $3 - 2i$; Yes		
8.	**(i)** $-1 + i$	**(ii)** $-1 - i$	**(iii)** $-1 - i$; Yes		
9.	**(i)** $3 + 7i$	**(ii)** $3 - 7i$	**(iii)** $3 - 7i$; Yes		
10.	**(i)** $1 - 6i$	**(ii)** $1 + 6i$	**(iii)** $1 + 6i$; Yes		

Exercise 9.D

1. $41 + 11i$ **2.** $-18 + 13i$ **3.** $-15 + 16i$ **4.** $7 + 2i$ **5.** 53 **6.** 13 **7.** $5 - 5i$ **8.** 5 **9.** 104 **10.** $-12 + 6i$
11. ½ **12.** 2 **13.** 8 **14.** 7 **15.** 88 **16.** $6 + 17i$ **17.** $-8 - 32i$ **18.** $-5 + 12i$ **19.** $35 + 12i$ **20.** $-3 - 4i$
21. **(i)** $18 - 12i$ **(ii)** $5 - 12i$ **(iii)** $0 + 0i$ **22.** **(i)** $-1 + i$ **(ii)** $0 + 2i$ **(iii)** -2
23. $5 + 5i$, $2 + 5i$, $5 - 5i$ **24.** **(i)** $5 + 8i$ **(ii)** $14 + 5i$ **25.** **(i)** 5 **(ii)** $3 + 4i$ **(iii)** $0 + 0i$
26. **(i)** 10 **(ii)** $4 - 3i$ **(iii)** -10 **27.** **(i)** $0 + 2i$ **(ii)** $-2 + 2i$ **(iii)** -4 **30.** -8

Exercise 9.E

1. $3 - i$ **2.** $3 - 2i$ **3.** $1 + 3i$ **4.** $1 - 2i$ **5.** $2 + i$ **6.** $1 - 3i$ **7.** $3 + 3i$ **8.** $5 - i$ **9.** $4 - 3i$ **10.** $3 + 4i$
11. $\frac{1}{2} - \frac{1}{2}i$ **12.** $\frac{7}{10} - \frac{1}{10}i$ **13.** $-\frac{3}{5} + \frac{11}{5}i$ **14.** $2 - \frac{1}{2}i$ **15.** $-4\frac{1}{2} - \frac{1}{2}i$ **16.** $\frac{1}{2} + 3\frac{1}{2}i$ **17.** $-0.8 + 0.6i$
18. $-2 + 0i$ **19.** Both = $1 - i$. True **20.** Both = $2 - 3i$. True

Exercise 9.F

1. 10 **2.** 5 **3.** $\sqrt{5}$ **4.** $\sqrt{8}$ **5.** 10 **6.** $\sqrt{10}$ **7.** $\sqrt{29}$ **8.** 13 **9.** $\sqrt{2}$ **10.** $\sqrt{109}$ **11.** 4 **12.** 3
13. 7 **14.** $\sqrt{\frac{1}{2}}$ **15.** $\frac{5}{4}$ **16.** ± 5 **17.** ± 6 **19.** ± 3 **21.** ± 5 **22.** $\sqrt{2}$ **26.** 13 **27.** ± 5
28. $x^2 + y^2 = 25$ **29.** 0 **30.** ± 8

Exercise 9.G

1. 6, 4 **2.** 5, 1 **3.** –4, 3 **4.** 5, 3 **5.** 2, –1 **6.** 1, 4 **7.** –5, 3 **8.** 3, –4 **9.** 5, 3 **10.** 3½, –5½
11. $a = 3, b = 2$ **12.** 2, 1 **13.** 1, –1 **14.** 4, –1 **15.** 7, 1 **16.** $s = -3, t = 2$ **17.** 3, 1 **18.** $-3, -\frac{4}{3}$
19. $x = 8, y = -6$ **20.** $a = -2, b = 5$ **21.** –6, 10 **22.** 2, 26 **23.** 2, –2 **24.** –32, 25 **25.** $p = 2, q = -1$
26. $x = 1, y = -2$ **27.** 5, 3 **28.** $t = 2$ **29.** $\alpha = -3, \beta = 5$ **30.** $3 - i$

Revision Exercise 9.H

1. **(a)** $67 + 13i$ **(b)** $u = 2, v = -3$ **2.** **(a)** **(i)** $-10 - 2i$ **(ii)** $1 + i$ **(iii)** $-1 - 2i$ **(b)** $4 \pm 3i$
3. $k = -3$ **4.** **(iv)** $p = -\frac{4}{3}$; $q = \frac{2}{3}$ **5.** **(a)** $11 - 17i$ **(b)** 5, –5 **(c)** $0 - i$; $t = 1$; $k = 3$
6. **(a)** $4 - 2i$, $2 - 2i$, $2 + 4i$ **(b)** $u = 2, v = -3$; $k = \pm 5$ **(c)** $a = 14$; $b = 50$
7. **(b)** $5 \pm i$ **8.** **(b)** –3, –4; $1 + i$; $\sqrt{2}$ **9.** **(b)** $\frac{1}{2} + \frac{5}{2}i$ **(c)** 2, 2

Chapter 10: Percentages, tax and interest

Exercise 10.A

3. €198 **4.** €22.80 **5.** 34 cents **6.** €18 **7.** 6090 **8.** (i) 30% (ii) 60% (iii) 10% **9.** 80% **10.** 15%
11. 49% **12.** 30 seats **13.** (i) 8 hours 24 mins (ii) 15 hr 36 mins **14.** 500.5 ml **15.** €112.50
16. 15% **17.** 62 400 forint **18.** (i) 40 km/hr (ii) 87% **19.** 4680 **20.** (i) 37½% (ii) €10.98 (iii) €75

Exercise 10.B

1. (i) €12 440 (ii) €37 560 **2.** €6.60 **3.** (i) €980 (ii) €65 **4.** €45 200 **5.** (i) €6240 (ii) €600 (iii) No tax. **6.** (i) €45 (ii) €725 **7.** (i) €28 560 (ii) 6.1% **8.** (i) €19 600 (ii) 10.2%
9. (i) €1200 (ii) 21% **10.** (i) €1188 (ii) 15% **11.** (i) €36 000 (ii) €29 000
12. (i) €45 000 (ii) €33 000

Exercise 10.C

1. €41 **2.** €23820.32 **3.** €889 **4.** €514.15 **5.** €940.90 **6.** €25 937 **7.** €46.39 **8.** The first
9. (i) €8670 (ii) €7369.50 **10.** €143.36 **11.** €1679.24 **12.** €358 **13.** (i) 4% (ii) €625
14. $X > Y$ **15.** 2% **16.** $r = 5, A = 1600$ **17.** €659 **18.** 11½% **19.** 12% **20.** 10.4%

Exercise 10.D

1. €770 **2.** €152.32 **3.** €337.46 **4.** €21 **5.** €2350.54 **6.** €1141.37 **7.** €90.59
8. €10 152 **9.** €173 **10.** €59 **11.** €325 **12.** (i) €410.26 (ii) €369.95 **13.** €1750; 12½%
14. €2000 **15.** €500; €450 **16.** €321.69 **17.** (i) €7140 (ii) 10% **18.** 4%
19. (i) €119.10 (ii) 6% **20.** (i) 21% (ii) 26%

Exercise 10.E

1. 5% **2.** 20% **3.** 12½% **4.** (i) $\frac{1}{10}$ (ii) 10% **5.** (i) 0.28 (ii) 28% **6.** 25% **7.** 7½% **8.** 2%
9. (i) $\frac{1}{5}$ (ii) 20% **10.** (ii) **11.** (iii) **12.** (iii) **13.** (i) 4.7% (ii) 3.3% (iii) 0.5%
14. (i) 4.48% (ii) 3.61% (iii) 0.78% (iv) 13.04% **15.** 5% **16.** 9.9% **17.** (i) 2% (ii) 2½% (iii) $2.\dot{2}$%
18. (i) 0.4% (ii) 0.37% (iii) 10% **19.** (i) 4.5% (ii) 0.051% (iii) 0.040% **20.** (i) $\frac{1}{10}$ (ii) 10%

Revision Exercise 10.F

1. (a) 6¼% (b) €3382.26 (c) €46 370.93 **2.** (a) 9% (ii) €416 (c) (i) €104.60 (ii) €25.80
3. (a) €9826 (b) 4158; 1% (c) (i) 5 (ii) €2315.25 **4.** (a) 45% (b) 6¼% (c) €31 000
5. (a) 28.125% (b) (i) 2% (ii) 1% (c) 2 ; 1 500 000 **6.** (a) 1.94% (b) 25%; €91.875; €9095.625
7. (a) €1677 (b) 4% (c) €2500 **8.** (a) (ii) (b) 6% (c) €61.51
9. (a) 7.7% (b)(i) 0.42% (ii) 0.045% (c) (i) €5834.19 (ii) €8000
10. (a) 48% (b) (i) €40 000 (ii) 5.8% (c) €416

Chapter 11: Arrangements, choices & probability

Exercise 11.A

1. 18 **2.** 15 **3.** 200 **4.** 18 **5.** 650 **6.** 24 **7.** 720 **8.** (i) 362 880 (ii) 40 320 (iii) 322 560
9. (i) 720 (ii) 120 (iii) 360 (iv) 144 **10.** (i) 40 320 (ii) 720 (iii) 4320 (iv) 14 400 (v) 720
11. (i) 362 880 (ii) 5040 (iii) 100 800 (iv) 60 480 (v) 2880 **12.** 120
13. (i) 24 (ii) 18 (iii) 6 (iv) 6 (v) 18 **14.** (i) 120 (ii) 24 (iii) 6
15. (i) 24 (ii) 64 **16.** (i) 24 (ii) 256 **17.** (i) 18 (ii) 192 **18.** (i) 5040 (ii) 720 (iii) 1440 (iv) 3600
19. (i) 720 (ii) 240 (iii) 480 **20.** (i) 48 (ii) 36 **21.** 9000 **22.** (i) 5040 (ii) 504
23. (i) 720 (ii) 36 **24.** (i) 39 916 800 (ii) 86 400 (iii) 86 400
25. (i) 30 (ii) 12 (iii) 9 **26.** (i) No (ii) No (iii) No **27.** (i) 30 (ii) 126 (iii) 120 **28.** 10
29. 72 **30.** $k = 20$ **31.** (i) $n + 1$ (ii) n **32.** 4 **34.** (i) 5040 (ii) 144 (iii) 720

Exercise 11.B

9. 792 **10.** 78 **11.** 190 **12.** **(i)** 15 **(ii)** 10 **(iii)** 5 **13.** **(i)** 35 **(ii)** 15 **(iii)** 20 **(iv)** 5 **14.** 78 **15.** 136 **16.** 462 **17.** **(i)** 70 **(ii)** 35 **(iii)** 15 **(iv)** 20 **18.** 5 245 786 **19.** **(i)** 84 **(ii)** 28 **(iii)** 56 **(iv)** 30 **20.** 45 **21.** 220 **22.** 2½ million

Exercise 11.C

1. $\frac{1}{2}$ **2.** **(i)** $\frac{1}{6}$ **(ii)** $\frac{1}{2}$ **(iii)** $\frac{1}{3}$ **(iv)** $\frac{2}{3}$ **(v)** $\frac{1}{3}$ **3.** **(i)** $\frac{1}{10}$ **(ii)** $\frac{2}{5}$ **(iii)** $\frac{3}{10}$ **(iv)** $\frac{2}{5}$ **(v)** $\frac{3}{5}$

4. **(i)** $\frac{4}{11}$ **(ii)** $\frac{2}{11}$ **(iii)** $\frac{1}{11}$ **(iv)** $\frac{4}{11}$ **(v)** $\frac{7}{11}$ **5.** **(i)** $\frac{1}{4}$ **(ii)** $\frac{3}{4}$ **6.** **(i)** 10 **(ii)** 20 **(iii)** 30

7. **(i)** $\frac{1}{3}$ **(ii)** $\frac{4}{9}$ **8.** **(i)** $\frac{1}{13}$ **(ii)** $\frac{1}{4}$ **(iii)** $\frac{1}{2}$ **(iv)** $\frac{3}{4}$ **(v)** $\frac{4}{13}$ **9.** **(i)** $\frac{1}{2}$ **(ii)** $\frac{3}{10}$ **(iii)** $\frac{4}{5}$ **(iv)** $\frac{1}{2}$ **(v)** $\frac{7}{10}$

10. **(i)** $\frac{1}{7}$ **(ii)** $\frac{6}{7}$ **(iii)** $\frac{2}{7}$ **(iv)** $\frac{5}{7}$ **(v)** $\frac{2}{7}$ **11.** **(i)** $\frac{1}{36}$ **(ii)** $\frac{1}{9}$ **(iii)** $\frac{1}{6}$ **(iv)** $\frac{11}{36}$ **(v)** $\frac{1}{6}$

12. **(i)** $\frac{1}{12}$ **(ii)** $\frac{1}{4}$ **(iii)** $\frac{1}{3}$ **13.** **(i)** $\frac{1}{10}$ **(ii)** $\frac{6}{25}$ **(iii)** $\frac{13}{50}$ **(iv)** $\frac{18}{25}$ **(v)** $\frac{1}{10}$

14. **(i)** $\frac{1}{9}$ **(ii)** $\frac{4}{9}$ **(iii)** $\frac{25}{99}$ **(iv)** $\frac{58}{99}$ **15.** **(i)** $\frac{2}{21}$ **(ii)** $\frac{6}{7}$ **(iii)** $\frac{10}{21}$ **(iv)** $\frac{11}{21}$ **(v)** $\frac{2}{7}$

16. **(i)** $\frac{1}{12}$ **(ii)** $\frac{1}{4}$ **(iii)** $\frac{1}{3}$ **17.** **(i)** $\frac{1}{6}$ **(ii)** $\frac{1}{3}$ **(iii)** $\frac{2}{3}$ **(iv)** $\frac{1}{2}$ **(v)** $\frac{1}{3}$

18. **(i)** 20 **(ii)** 40 **(iii)** 220 **(iv)** 140 **19.** **(i)** $\frac{1}{8}$ **(ii)** $\frac{3}{8}$ **(iii)** $\frac{7}{8}$ **(iv)** $\frac{1}{2}$ **(v)** $\frac{3}{8}$

20. **(i)** $\frac{3}{10}$ **(ii)** $\frac{7}{10}$ **(iii)** $\frac{3}{20}$ **(iv)** $\frac{13}{20}$ **21.** **(i)** 120 **(ii)** 48 **(iii)** $\frac{2}{5}$

22. **(i)** 720 **(ii)** 48 **(iii)** $\frac{1}{15}$ **23.** **(i)** 66 **(ii)** 35 **(iii)** $\frac{35}{66}$

24. **(i)** 560 **(ii)** 270 **(iii)** $\frac{27}{56}$ **25.** $\frac{10}{21}$ **26.** **(i)** $\frac{3}{7}$ **(ii)** $\frac{4}{7}$ **(iii)** $\frac{2}{7}$ **27.** $\frac{10}{21}$ **28.** $\frac{1}{12}$ **29.** $\frac{9}{19}$ **30.** $\frac{1}{5}$

Exercise 11.D

1. **(i)** ¼ **(ii)** ¾ **2.** **(i)** $\frac{25}{102}$ **(ii)** $\frac{77}{102}$ **3.** $\frac{1}{216}$ **4.** **(i)** $\frac{1}{144}$ **(ii)** $\frac{1}{12}$ **(iii)** $\frac{11}{12}$ **5.** **(i)** $\frac{5}{18}$ **(ii)** $\frac{1}{6}$ **(iii)** $\frac{5}{6}$

6. **(i)** $\frac{2}{15}$ **(ii)** $\frac{1}{3}$ **(iii)** $\frac{2}{3}$ **7.** **(i)** $\frac{3}{11}$ **(ii)** $\frac{6}{11}$ **8.** **(i)** $\frac{16}{25}$ **(ii)** $\frac{1}{25}$ **(iii)** $\frac{24}{25}$ **9.** **(i)** $\frac{3}{8}$ **(ii)** $\frac{1}{8}$ **(iii)** $\frac{7}{8}$

10. $\frac{1}{10}$ **11.** (i) $\frac{1}{25}$ **(ii)** $\frac{19}{50}$ **(iii)** $\frac{31}{50}$ **12.** **(i)** $\frac{121}{400}$ **(ii)** $\frac{161}{400}$

Revision Exercise 11.E

1. **(a)** 720; 240 **(b)** **(i)** 210 **(ii)** 84 **(iii)** 126 **(c)** **(i)** $\frac{3}{7}$ **(ii)** $\frac{2}{7}$ **(iii)** $\frac{5}{7}$

2. **(a)** **(i)** $\frac{2}{5}$ **(ii)** $\frac{3}{5}$ **(iii)** $\frac{2}{3}$ **(b)** **(i)** 720 **(ii)** 24 **(c)** 96; 18

3. **(a)** 15 **(b)** 720 **(i)**120 **(ii)** 240 **(iii)** 288 **(c)** **(i)** ¼ **(ii)** $\frac{1}{169}$ **(iii)** $\frac{1}{8}$

4. **(a)** **(i)** $\frac{3}{8}$ **(ii)** $\frac{5}{8}$ **(iii)** $\frac{7}{12}$ **(b)** **(i)** 210 **(ii)** 126 **(c)** $\frac{2}{7}$

5. **(a)** **(i)** ¼ **(ii)** ½ **(b)** **(i)** $\frac{1}{4}$ **(ii)** $\frac{7}{18}$ **(iii)** $\frac{11}{18}$ **(c)** **(i)** 1365 **(ii)** 588 **(iii)** 1050

6. **(a)** **(i)** $\frac{2}{3}$ **(ii)** $\frac{1}{4}$ **(iii)** $\frac{5}{24}$ **(b)** 24 **(i)** 6 **(ii)** 12 **(c)** **(i)** $\frac{1}{9}$ **(ii)** $\frac{5}{18}$

7. **(a)** **(i)** No **(ii)** Yes **(b)** **(i)**1140 **(ii)** 528 **(iii)** $\frac{44}{95}$ **(c)** **(i)** $\frac{1}{16}$ **(ii)** $\frac{15}{16}$

8. **(a)** **(i)** $\frac{1}{12}$ **(ii)** $\frac{1}{4}$ **(iii)** $\frac{1}{3}$ **(b)** 40 320 **(i)** 5040 **(ii)** 15120 **(iii)** 720 **(iv)** 4320 **(c)** $\frac{2}{65}$

9. **(a)** **(i)** $\frac{3}{8}$ **(ii)** $\frac{1}{4}$ **(iii)** $\frac{1}{8}$ **(b)(i)** 362 880 **(ii)** 2880 **(iii)** 0.008 **(c)** 30 times

10. **(a)** 343 **(b)** 420 **(c)** **(i)** $\frac{1}{30}$ **(ii)** $\frac{1}{10}$ **(iii)** $\frac{1}{5}$

Chapter 12: Statistics

Exercise 12.A

1. 5, 4, 4 **2.** 2, 2, 2 **3.** 4, 4.5, 5 **4.** 5 **5.** 7.95 **6.** 9.8, 9 **7.** 3.5, 3 **8.** 7 **9.** 0.4 **10.** 3 **11.** 8 **12.** 12 **13.** 9 **14.** 31 **15.** **(i)** $x = 2$ **(ii)** 7 **(iii)** 5 **16.** 23 **17.** 138 cm **18.**5 mm per day **19.** €261 **20.** 3392

Exercise 12.B

1. **(ii)** 3 **2.** **(i)** 7 **3.** **(ii)** 2.1 **4.** **(i)** 5.3 **5.** **(i)** 2.6 **6.** **(ii)** 2 **(iv)** 33 people **7.** **(ii)** 2.2 **(iii)** 65%
8. **(ii)** 6.5 **(iii)** 48% **9.** **(ii)** €16 **10.** **(i)** 41.05 **(ii)** 69% **11.** **(iv)** 3.6 **12.** **(i)** 4.7 mins
13. **(ii)** 50 kg **(iii)** 60 kg **14.** **(i)** 71.1% **15.** **(i)** 10 **16.** 3 **17.** **(i)** 5 **18.** **(i)** 5 **19.** **(iii)** $60\frac{2}{3}$ **(iv)** 1%
20. **(iii)** 33 **(iv)** 3%

Exercise 12.C

1. 3.9 cent **2.** 108.25 **3.** 3.9 **4.** 11 cent **5.** 102.9 **6.** **(i)** 9.6 cent **(ii)** 10 cent
7. **(i)** Alice **(ii)** Bernard **8.** Year 2 **9.** **(i)** €12 **(ii)** €10 **10.** $k = 5$

Exercise 12.D

4. **(ii)** 42.8 **8.** **(ii)** 43 **9.** **(ii)** 50 **(iii)** 52.9 **10.** **(ii)** 84 **(iii)** $33\frac{1}{3}$% **11.** **(ii)** €1124 **(iii)** €11.24
12. **(ii)** 32 acres

Exercise 12.E

1. **(iii)** 53 **2.** **(c)** **(i)** 46 **(ii)** 63 **(iii)** 78 **(iv)** 32 **3.** **(iii)** 40 **(iv)** 19.5
4. **(c)** **(i)** €3.40 **(ii)** €5 **(iii)** €6.80 **(iv)** €3.40 **5.** **(i)** €16.50 **(ii)** €15 **(iii)** 10
6. **(c)** **(i)** 2.50 **(ii)** 425 **(iii)** 40 mins **7.** **(b)** **(i)** 47 **(ii)** 18 **(c)** 50 **8.** **(b)** **(i)** 6.5 km **(ii)** 29 **(iii)** No

Exercise 12.F

1. 7; 1.87 **2.** **(ii)** 2.1; 3.9 **3.** 3; 2.6 **4.** **(i)** 7 **(ii)** 5 **(iii)** 5 **(iv)** 1.9 **6.** 3.16; 0.08 **7.** **(ii)** 6.5; 1.9
8. 3.2; 0.059 **9.** **(i)** 20 **(ii)** 8 **10.** **(i)** 5; 2.74

Exercise 12.G

1. 1.26 **2.** **(ii)** 1.4 **(iii)** 60% **3.** **(ii)** 1.58 **4.** **(i)** 2; 1.1 **(ii)** 16 **5.** 10; 4 **6.** **(i)** 70 **(ii)** 27
7. **(i)** 7.9 **(ii)** 0.7 **8.** 282 cent; 111 cent

Revision Exercise 12.H

1. **(ii)** 1.55, 1 **(iii)** 16 **2.** **(i)** 30 **(ii)** 60 **(iii)** 8.46 **(iv)** 200 **3.** **(ii)** €58.18 **(iii)** €62.72 **(iv)** 8%
4. **(iii)** 21 **(iv)** 3.8 **5.** **(a)** **(i)** 10 **(ii)** 7 **(iii)** 11 **(iv)** 3.6 **(b)** 6 **6.** **(a)** **(i)** S_1 **(ii)** S_2 **(b)** **(i)** 111 **(iii)** 105
7. **(b)** **(ii)** 10; 5.9 **8.** **(b)** **(i)** €14 000 **(iv)** 14; 240 **9.** **(a)** 32 **(b)** 1.5 **(c)** **(ii)** 0932 **(iii)** 40
10. **(a)** 4 **(b)** 10; 5.3 **(i)** 20 **(ii)** 8

CHAPTER 13: LENGTH, AREA & VOLUME

Exercise 13.A

1. **(i)** 102 cm **(ii)** 630 cm^2 **2.** **(i)** 66 m **(ii)** 200 m^2 **3.** **(i)** 12 m **(ii)** 38 m^2 **4.** **(i)** 3 m **(ii)** 5 m **5.** **(i)** 5 m **(ii)** 13 m **6.** 1600 m^2 **7.** 600 cm^2 **8.** €207 **9.** **(ii)** 6 **10.** 5.8 × 6.8 **11.** 42 **12.** The first **13.** 24 **14.** **(ii)** 2 × 15 **15.** **(i)** 10 **(ii)** 14.14 **16.** 7; 84 **18.** **(i)** 6 **(ii)** 15 **(iii)** 84 **19.** **(i)** 3 **(ii)** 47.6 **(iii)** €33.32 **20.** **(i)** 8 **(ii)** 29

Exercise 13.B

1. **(i)** 154 **(ii)** 308 **(iii)** 616 **(iv)** 924 **2.** **(i)** 78.5; 35.7 **(ii)** 157; 55.7 **(iii)** 9.42; 12.28 **(iv)** 4.71; 8.71 **3.** **(i)** 48 **(ii)** 10½ **(iii)** 22 **(iv)** 33 **4.** **(a)** Outer region **(b)** **(i)** 10π **(ii)** 10π **5.** **(i)** $\frac{1}{20}$ **(ii)** 298.3 **7.** **(i)** 88 m^2 **(ii)** €1518 **8.** 28.5 **10.** **(i)** 400 m **(ii)** 406 m **(iii)** 6 m and 12 m

Exercise 13.C

1. 24π **2.** 80π ; 40π **3.** 75π **4.** 15π **5.** 36π **6.** **(i)** 4.5π **(ii)** 9π **7.** 6 m^3 **8.** 120 m^3 **9.** 154 cm^3 **10.** 19404 cm^3 **11.** 628 cm^3 **12.** 385 cm^3; 297 cm^2 **13.** 16 cm^3 **14.** 15 m^3 **15.** **(i)** 77 m^2 **(ii)** 3080 m^3 **16.** **(i)** 15 m^2 **(ii)** 120 m^3 **17.** 167 cm^3 **18.** 250π **19.** **(ii)** 4500π **(iii)** 6750π **20.** **(i)** 0.54 m^3 **(ii)** €47.52

Exercise 13.D

1. **(ii)** $\frac{32\pi}{3}$ **2.** **(i)** 10 cm **(ii)** 264π **3.** $5338\frac{2}{3}$ m^3 **4.** **(i)** 288π **(ii)** 96 cm **5.** 6 cm **6.** **(a)** 36π **(b)** **(ii)** 162π **(iii)** $\frac{2}{3}$ **7.** ¾ **8.** **(i)** 308 cm^3, 38.5 cm^3 **(ii)** 8 : 1 **(iii)** 539 cm^3 **9.** **(i)** 144π cm^3 **(ii)** 4 cm **(iii)** 10 cm; More. **10.** **(i)** 3 **(ii)** 16π **(iii)** 10 cm **11.** **(i)** 2 m **(ii)** 18 m **(iii)** 42π **(iv)** 4 m **12.** 24 m **13.** **(i)** 81π **(ii)** 9 **14.** **(i)** 122.5π **(ii)** 6 **(iii)** 110.25π; 9 cm **15.** 280 **16.** **(i)** 528 **(ii)** 1.9

Exercise 13.E

1. 4 : 1 **2.** 12 : 1 **3.** The second **4.** **(i)** 27 : 1 **(ii)** 2 : 1 **5.** C **6.** 1 : 4 **7.** 8 : 1 **8.** 2 cm **9.** ¼ cm **10.** 50 seconds **11.** 21 cm **12.** **(i)** $\frac{9\pi}{4}$ cm^3 **(ii)** 1½ cm **(iii)** 40 **13.** 800 seconds **14.** 100 cm/s **15.** **(i)** $\frac{1}{8}$ cm **(ii)** $\frac{3}{2}$ cm

Exercise 13.F

1. 692 **2.** 1860 **3.** 35500 **4.** 2420 **5.** **(i)** 5760 **(ii)** 1360 **(iii)** $39\frac{1}{3}$ **(iv)** 95.8 **6.** **(i)** 6.8 **(ii)** 11.76 **7.** 4 **8.** 15 **9.** 4 **10.** 15 **11.** 85 000 km^2

Exercise 13.G

1. **(a)** 117.75 **(b)** **(i)** 55 566 **(ii)** 4851 **(iii)** 29 106 **2.** **(a)** The first **(b)** 1100 **(c)** **(i)** 8 **(ii)** 320π **3.** **(a)** 60 **(b)** **(i)** 60.75π **(ii)** 4.5 cm **(iii)** 32 **4.** **(a)** **(i)** 2320 **(ii)** 16 240 **(b)** 10.5 **5.** **(a)** 14.13 cm^2; 16.71 cm **(b)** **(i)** 480 **(ii)** 36π **(iii)** 96π **6.** **(a)** 15 **(b)** 5 **(c)** 4 cm **7.** **(a)** 35% **(b)** The latter **(c)** **(i)** 18π **(ii)** 4.5 **8.** **(b)** 144π; 50%

Chapter 14: Plane Geometry: Theorems & Enlargements

Exercise 14.A

1. (b) (i) 30° **(ii)** 57° **(iii)** 100° **(iv)** 36° **2. (b) (i)** 122° **(ii)** 131° **(iii)** 45° **(iv)** 66°
4. (b) Area = 10 **(ii)** Area = 6 **(iii)** Area = 6.6 **(iv)** $x = 5$, $y = 7$; Area = 28
5. (c) 1.4 **6. (b)** 3.3; 6.4 **7. (b) (i)** 48; 14 **(ii)** 15; 8 **(iii)** $x = \sqrt{125}$; $y = 5$ **(iv)** $x = 3$; $y = 4$
8. (b) (i) Yes **(ii)** No **(iii)** Yes **(iv)** Yes **9. (b) (i)** 5.6 **(ii)** 10 **(iii)** 12 **(iv)** 4 **11. (e) (i)** $x = 125$

Exercise 14.B

7. (iv) Yes **(v)** $|\angle b'a'c'| = 90°$ **9. (b) (i)** 9.5 **(ii)** 5 **(d) (i)** 38 **(ii)** 10

Exercise 14.C

6. (ii) 2.5 **(iii)** 4 **(iv)** 1.2, 1.6 **(v)** 25 : 4 **10. (i)** 3.5 **(ii)** 5.25 **(iii)** 1.4 **(iv)** 49 : 4

Revision Exercise 14.D

2. (a) (i) 68° **(ii)** 22° **(c) (i)** 10 **(ii)** 6.6 **(iii)** 32.4 **3. (a)** 5.20 **(c) (i)** 1.25 **(ii)** 0.75 **(iii)** 4 : 5 **(iv)** 25 : 16
4. (a) (i) 76° **(ii)** 128° **(c) (i)** 2.5 **(ii)** 5.4 **(iii)** 2 : 3 **(iv)** 3.36 **5. (c) (i)** 3 **(ii)** 6 **(iii)** 4 **(iv)** 0.36
6. (a) 9π **(c) (i)** 4½ **(ii)** 2 : 9 **(iii)** 4 : 81 **(iv)** 19½ **7. (a)** 12 **(c) (i)** 8.5 **(iii)** 5.625 **(iv)** 8.4375
8. (b) Yes **(c)** $x = 4$ **10. (d) (i)** (0, 1) **(ii)** 4 **(iii)** (12, 17)

Chapter 15: Trigonometry

Exercise 15.A

1. 92° 28’ **2.** 83° 18’ **3.** 50° 53’ **4.** 67° 19’ **5.** 56° 58’

Exercise 15.B

1. 18 **2.** 62 **3.** 27 **4.** 4 **5.** 9 **6.** 9.1 **7.** 19.8° **8.** 4 **9.** 21.8° **10.** 30 **11.** 12, 12 **12.** 9, 10
13. 20, 14 **14.** 50, 35 **15.** 4.5, 5 **16.** 24, 30 **17.** 35, 45 **18.** 14, 28 **19.** 10, 15 **20.** 22, 25
21. 4.54 m **22.** 192 cm **23.** 13° **24. (i)** 16 m **(ii)** 18 m

Exercise 15.C

7. $\text{Cos } A = \frac{4}{5}$; $\sin A = \frac{3}{5}$ **8.** $\text{Sin } A = \frac{5}{13}$; $\tan A = \frac{5}{12}$ **9.** $\text{Cos } A = \frac{8}{17}$; $\tan A = \frac{15}{8}$

10. $\text{Sin } A = \frac{7}{25}$; $\tan A = \frac{7}{24}$ **11.** $\text{Cos } A = \frac{3}{4}$; $\sin A = \frac{\sqrt{7}}{4}$ **12.** $\text{Cos } A = \frac{1}{\sqrt{10}}$; $\tan A = 3$

13. $\text{Sin } A = \frac{2}{3}$; $\tan A = \frac{2}{\sqrt{5}}$ **14.** $\text{Cos } A = \frac{1}{\sqrt{5}}$; $\sin A = \frac{2}{\sqrt{5}}$ **15.** $\text{Cos } A = \frac{36}{85}$; $\tan A = \frac{77}{36}$

16. $\text{Cos } A + \sin A = \frac{1}{\sqrt{17}} + \frac{4}{\sqrt{17}} = \frac{5}{\sqrt{17}}$ **17.** $\text{Sin } A = \frac{\sqrt{15}}{4}$; $\tan A = \sqrt{15}$; $\theta = 75½°$

Exercise 15.D

1. (b) 5 **2. (b)** 8 **3. (b)** 6 **4.** $h = 6$; 30 **5. (i)** 7 **(ii)** 7 **(iii)** 24½ **6.** $2\sqrt{3}, 2$ **7.** 1 **8.** 4 **9.** $\frac{13}{3}$

Exercise 15.E

1. $\frac{\sqrt{3}+1}{2\sqrt{2}}$ **2.** $\frac{\sqrt{3}+1}{2\sqrt{2}}$ **3.** $\frac{\sqrt{3}-1}{2\sqrt{2}}$ **4.** $\frac{\sqrt{3}+1}{2\sqrt{2}}$ **5.** $\frac{1-\sqrt{3}}{2\sqrt{2}}$ **6.** $\frac{\sqrt{3}-1}{2\sqrt{2}}$ **7. (i)** $\frac{4}{5}$ **(ii)** $\frac{12}{13}$ **(iii)** $\frac{56}{63}$

8. (i) $\frac{3}{5}$ **(ii)** $\frac{8}{17}$ **(iii)** $\frac{36}{85}$ **9. (i)** $\frac{4}{5}$ **(ii)** $\frac{20}{29}$ **(iii)** $\frac{143}{145}$ **10.** $\frac{4}{5}$ **11.** $\frac{-360}{481}$ **12.** $\frac{12}{13}$

13. (i) $\frac{2}{3}$ **(ii)** $\frac{3}{4}$ **(iii)** $\frac{3\sqrt{5}-2\sqrt{7}}{12}$ **14. (i)** $\frac{3}{5}$ **(ii)** $\frac{24}{25}$

Exercise 15.F

2. (iii) –1 **7. (iii)** 0.75 **8. (iii)** $-\sqrt{3}$

Exercise 15.G

1. (i) $\frac{1}{\sqrt{2}}$ **(ii)** –1 **(iii)** $\frac{\sqrt{3}}{2}$ **(iv)** $-\frac{1}{2}$ **(v)** $-\sqrt{3}$ **(vi)** $-\frac{1}{2}$ **(vii)** $-\frac{\sqrt{3}}{2}$ **(viii)** 1 **(ix)** $-\frac{1}{\sqrt{2}}$ **(x)** $\frac{1}{2}$
2. (i) 20°, 160° **(ii)** 35°, 325° **(iii)** 40°, 220° **(iv)** 170°, 190° **(v)** 202°, 338° **(vi)** 122°, 302°
3. (i) 45°, 225° **(ii)** 210°, 330° **(iii)** 150°, 210° **(iv)** 120°, 300° **(v)** 45°, 135° **(vi)** 45°, 315° **(vii)** 135°, 315° **(viii)** 60°, 120° **(ix)** 120°, 240° **(x)** 60°, 240°
4. (i) 24°, 156° **(ii)** 41°, 319° **(iii)** 117°, 297° **(iv)** 134°, 226° **(v)** 222°, 318° **(vii)** 74°, 254° **(vii)** 0°, 180°, 360° **(viii)** 90°, 270° **(ix)** 180° **(x)** 0°, 180°, 360°
5. (a) 217° **(b)** 337°; $\tan\theta = -\frac{5}{12}$ **(c)** 90° **6.** 106°, $\cos\theta = -\frac{7}{25}$

Exercise 15.H

1. (i) 15 **(ii)** 16 **(iii)** 384 **(iv)** 230 **(v)** 75 **2. (i)** 30° **(ii)** 53° **(iii)** 68° **(iv)** 37° **(v)** 82°
3. (i) $\sqrt{21}$ **(ii)** $\sqrt{65}$ **(iii)** $\sqrt{7}$ **(iv)** $\sqrt{184}$ **(v)** $\sqrt{15}$ **4. (i)** 60° **(ii)** 120° **(iii)** 41° **(iv)** 17° **(v)** 90°
5. (i) 5.3 **(ii)** 3.3 **6.** 79; 130 **7.** 34° **8. (i)** 24 **(ii)** 18.45 **9. (i)** 12 **(ii)** 117°
10. $a = 5.14$, $B = 48.6°$, $C = 91.2°$ **11.** 21 **12.** 80 km

Exercise 15.I

1. (i) 30 **(ii)** 32 **(iii)** 9 **(iv)** 23 **2. (i)** 0.8 **(ii)** 24 **3. (a)** 50° **(b)** 105 mm **(c)** 30°
4. (i) 83° **(ii)** 10 **5.** 400 **6.** 24 **7. (i)** 7.66 **(ii)** 12.31; $|wz| = 3.21$ **8.** 420

Revision Exercise 15.J

1. (a) $A = 30°$; No **(b)** 9.25 **(c) (i)** $\frac{5}{13}$ **(ii)** $\frac{12}{13}$ **(iii)** $\frac{120}{169}$
2. (a) 120°, 240° **(b) (i)** 7.4 **(ii)** 6.3 **(c) (i)** 48° **(ii)** 26.8
3. (a) $\frac{119}{101}$ **(b)** 104½° **(c) (i)** 15 **(ii)** 337 **4. (a)** 33°, 213° **(b)** $\frac{63}{65}$ **(c) (i)** 21 **(ii)** 28°
5. (a) $x = 15$, $A = 49°$ **(b) (i)** $\frac{12}{37}$ **(ii)** $A = 19°$ **(c)** 191°, 349°
6. (a) 41° 41' **(b) (i)** $\frac{8}{17}$ **(ii)** $\frac{240}{289}$ **(c)** $A = 54°$, $B = 81°$, $b = 39$ **7. (b)** 396 m **(c)** $\frac{28}{53}$
8. (a) $A = 45°$, $B = 75°$ **(b) (i)** 40 m **(ii)** 60; 1736 m²
9. (a) 72°; No **(b)** 330°, $-\frac{1}{\sqrt{3}}$ **(c) (i)** 6.5 **(ii)** 90° **10. (a)** 135° **(c)** $\frac{1-\sqrt{3}}{2\sqrt{2}}$

CHAPTER 16: SEQUENCES & SERIES

Exercise 16.A

7. 4 **8.** 3 **9.** **(i)** 7 **(ii)** –3 **(iii)** 14 **10.** **(i)** 7 **(ii)** –4 **(iii)** 7, 3

Exercise 16.B

1. 45 **2.** 49 **3.** 121 **4.** 293 **5.** 39 **6.** 68 **7.** –23 **8.** 880 **9.** 277 **10.** –183 **11.** $2n + 1$ **12.** $6n + 1$
13. $8n - 5$; T_{20} **14.** $37 - 6n$; T_7 **15.** $4n + 1$; T_{36} **16.** 35 **17.** 46 **18.** 15 **19.** 21
20. 59 **21.** **(ii)** $d = 7, a = 4$ **22.** **(ii)** $a = 2; d = 6$ **(iii)** 596 **23.** $a = -7, d = 9$ **24.** $a = 190; d = -9$
25. **(i)** $a = 16; d = -5$ **(ii)** $b = 6, c = 1$ **26.** **(ii)** $a = 7, d = 4$ **27.** **(ii)** $a = 2, d = 3$ **(iii)** 149
28. $a = 40, d = -7$ **29.** $T_1 = 3, T_{20} = 31.5$ **30.** 3997

Exercise 16.C

1. 650 **2.** 2700 **3.** 366 **4.** 275 **5.** 945 **6.** –2220 **7.** –32800 **8.** 8670 **9.** 3240 **10.** 900
11. **(i)** –77 **(ii)** –175 **12.** 40; 1640 **13.** 33; 1683 **14.** 14; 287 **15.** 14; 735 **16.** **(i)** 280 **(ii)** 1160
(iii) 880 **17.** **(i)** 737 **(ii)** 4785 **(iii)** 1968 **(iv)** 396 **(v)** 5201.5 **18.** **(ii)** $a = 3, d = 2$ **19.** **(ii)** $a = 2, d = 3$
20. **(ii)** 900 **(iii)** 14 **(iv)** 32 **21.** 10 **22.** 11, 12 **23.** **(ii)** 1275 **(iii)** 21 **24.** **(ii)** $a = 4, d = 2$
25. **(ii)** $a = 2, d = 2$ **(iii)** 62 **26.** **(i)** 120 **(ii)** 99 **(iii)** 21 **27.** **(i)** 160 **(ii)** 187 **(iii)** 27
28. **(i)** $a = 3$ **(ii)** $d = 4$ **(iii)** 39 **29.** **(iii)** 59 **30.** $a = 3, d = 6$ **31.** **(ii)** 505 **32.** 3

Exercise 16.D

3. **(i)** 96 **(ii)** 3584 **(iii)** 2916 **(iv)** 49152 **(v)** 9375 **(vi)** 4 **(vii)** 11264 **(viii)** 2048 **(ix)** 1.728
(x) 1.4641 **4.** **(iii)** 128 **5.** 583.9 **6.** 68.72 **7.** 37.25 **8.** 83.886 **9.** 47684 **10.** 213.6
11. **(i)** $\frac{2}{3}$ (ii) $\frac{16}{243}$ **12.** $5(2^{n-1})$ **13.** **(i)** $\frac{1}{3}$ **(ii)** 18, 6 **(iii)** $162\left(\frac{1}{3}\right)^{n-1}$ **14.** **(i)** 6, 12 **(ii)** 384
15. **(i)** ±15 **(ii)** 3645 **16.** **(i)** 5 **(ii)** 2, 2 **(iii)** 4096 **17.** **(i)** 9 **(ii)** 13112
18. **(i)** 4, –1½ **(ii)** 1, 4, 16, 64 or –4½, –1½, –½, $-\frac{1}{6}$ **19.** 2 **20.** 2, 3 **21.** **(i)** 2, 5 **(ii)** 1250
23. 14, 56; $T_n = 14(2^{n-1})$ **24.** **(ii)** 2 **(iii)** Greater **25.** **(ii)** 0.015625 **(iii)** 3×10^{-6}
26. **(i)** 4, –5 **(ii)** 3, 12, 48 or 3, –15, 75

Exercise 16.E

1. 765 **2.** 3906 **3.** 2555 **4.** 198.6 **5.** 59048 **6.** 9.487 **7.** 3099 **8.** $\frac{121}{162}$ **9.** **(i)** 2 **(ii)** 3584 **(iii)** 7161
10. **(i)** 0.8 **(ii)** 32 **(iii)** 239 **11.** **(i)** ½ **(ii)** $\frac{1}{512}$ **(iii)** $\frac{511}{512}$ **12.** **(ii)** 2 **(iii)** 4094 **13.** **(i)** 4, 2, 1 **(ii)** ½
(iii) $7\frac{7}{8}$ **14.** **(ii)** $24(½)^{n-1}$ **(iii)** $48(1 - (½)^n)$ **(iv)** 48 **15.** **(i)** 0.75, 4 **(ii)** 16777215.75
16. **(i)** $a = 4, c = 36, d = 108$ **(ii)** 26244 **(iii)** 39364

Revision Exercise 16.F

1. **(a)** 64 **(b)** 18.5 **(c)** 165; 407 **2.** **(a)** 109, 1040 **(b)** **(i)** $\frac{7}{3}$ **(ii)** 5, $\frac{1}{3}$
3. **(a)** 35; 1925 **(b)** **(i)** 0.75 **(ii)** 2.25 **(iii)** 12.2 **4.** **(a)** 200 **(b)** **(i)** 0.25 **(ii)** 287.93 **(iii)** 0.07
5. **(a)** –81, –806 **(b)** **(i)** $2(3)^{n-1}$ **(ii)** $3^n - 1$
6. **(a)** **(i)** 66 **(ii)** 2047 **(b)** **(i)** $a = 4, d = 2$ **(ii)** $2n + 2$ **(iii)** 499th
7. **(a)** $d = -6; -66$ **(b)** **(i)** 2 **(ii)** 2^{n-2} **(iii)** 31.5 **(c)** 8, 2 **8.** **(a)** 28, 2842 **(b)** 1134 **(c)** 300
9. **(a)** 499.6 **(b)** $a = 3, d = 2$; 3, 5, 7, 9 **(c)** **(ii)** 4, 5 **10.** **(a)** **(i)** 2 **(ii)** 3 **(iii)** 610 **(b)** $x = 4, 0; T_4 = 125$ or 1

Chapter 17: Calculus

Exercise 17.A

1. $2x+2; 8$ **2.** $2x+3; 3$ **3.** $2x+7; 11$ **4.** **(i)** $2x-2$ **(ii)** 4 **5.** **(i)** $6x-2$ **(iii)** 10 **6.** $4x-10$ **7.** $4x+2; 6$
8. $-2x; -4$ **9.** $6-2x; 2; 2x-y+5=0$ **10.** **(i)** $-6x$ **(ii)** -6 **(iii)** $6x+y=4$
11. $-2-2x; -4; 4x+y=11$ **12.** 0

Exercise 17.B

15. $\frac{1}{2\sqrt{x}}$ **16.** $2x+15$ **17.** $12x^3-1$ **18.** $3x^2-11$ **19.** $10t+50$ **20.** $3t^2+4t-1$ **21.** $2\pi r+2\pi$ **22.** 17
23. -3 **24.** **(i)** $10x-2$ **(ii)** 8 **25.** **(i)** $2x-12$ **(ii)** -6 **(iii)** $6x+y=1$ **28.** **(i)** $3x^2-12x+10$ **(ii)** -2
29. **(i)** $8x-26$ **(ii)** -2 **(iii)** $2x+y=13$ **30.** $x+y=7$

Exercise 17.C

2. (3,2) **3.** (3, 7) **4.** (5, –24) **5.** (4, 19) **6.** (2, –9) **7.** **(i)** $x-y=3$ **(ii)** (3, 0) **9.** (1, –3), (–1, 1)
11. **(i)** 2, –2 **(ii)** $2x-y=5$ or $2x+y=-1$ **(iii)** No **(iv)** (1, –3) **12.** (0,1)

Exercise 17.D

1. $30x+26$ **2.** $42x-1$ **3.** $15x^2+4x+5$ **4.** $40x-6$ **5.** $6x^2+6x-4$ **6.** 11 **7.** 34 **8.** 58
9. **(i)** 0 **(ii)** 4 **(iii)** –4 **10.** **(i)** $12x-14$ **(ii)** $12x-14$ **11.** **(i)** $3x^2-1$ **(ii)** 2 **12.** –96

Exercise 17.E

1. $-\frac{7}{(2x+1)^2}$ **2.** $\frac{13}{(x+3)^2}$ **3.** $\frac{5}{(4x-1)^2}$ **4.** $\frac{1-x^2}{(1+x^2)^2}$ **5.** $\frac{-2x^2-2x+4}{(x^2+2)^2}$ **6.** $\frac{-4}{(4x+3)^2}$ **7.** $\frac{-1}{(x-1)^2}$
8. $\frac{-1}{x^2}$ **9.** $\frac{30x^2}{(1-x^3)^2}$ **10.** $\frac{-2x-2}{(x^2+2x-1)^2}$ **11.** $-\frac{7}{9}$ **12.** –3 **13.** ¾ **14.** –½; $x+2y=4$ **16.** $x=-5, 1$
17. **(i)** $\frac{1}{(x-1)^2}$ **(ii)** (2, –1), (0,1) **20.** 9

Exercise 17.F

1. $15(3x+1)^4$ **2.** $8x(x^2+7)^3$ **3.** $24(8x+3)^2$ **4.** $6x^2(x^3+2)$ **5.** $7(x^2+x-4)^6(2x+1)$
6. $40x(x^2-1)^{19}$ **7.** $20(2x+3)^9$ **8.** $2(x^3+2x^2-x+1)(3x^2+4x-1)$ **9.** $8(x^2+7x-6)^7(2x+7)$
10. $45x^4(x^5+1)^8$ **11.** 14 **12.** 12 **13.** 225 **14.** 864 **16.** 25 **17.** 200; $200x-y=199$
18. **(i)** $\frac{2}{(x+1)^2}$ **(ii)** $3\left(\frac{x-1}{x+1}\right)^2\left(\frac{2}{(x+1)^2}\right)$ **19.** **(i)** $\frac{x^2+8x}{(x+4)^2}$ **(ii)** $2\left(\frac{x^2}{x+4}\right)\left(\frac{x^2+8x}{(x+4)^2}\right)$
20. **(i)** $1-\frac{1}{x^2}$ **(ii)** $4\left(\frac{1}{x}+x\right)^3\left(1-\frac{1}{x^2}\right)$ **(iii)** $\frac{1}{2}\left(\frac{1}{x}+x\right)^{-1/2}\left(1-\frac{1}{x^2}\right)$

Exercise 17.G

1. (2, 6) **2.** (3, 8) **3.** (1, 3) **4.** (4, 17) **5.** (5, 28) **6.** (2, –11) **7.** 25 **8.** 4 **9.** **(i)** $b=-4, c=5$ **(ii)** (2, 1)
10. **(i)** (–2, 5) **(iii)** No **11.** Max (–2, 16); Min (2, –16) **12.** Max (–1, 3); Min (2, –24)
13. Max (–1, 3); Min (1, –1) **14.** Max (–2, 54); Min (3, –71) **15.** Min (–1, 2); Max (5, 110)
16. Max (1, 4); Min (–1, 0) **17.** **(i)** $a=1, b=-27$ **(ii)** (3, –54), (–3, 54)
18. **(i)** $y=3x-24$ **(ii)** $A=3x^2-24x$ **(iii)** –48 **19.** **(i)** $a=2, b=-4$ **(ii)** $0, \frac{4}{3}$ **(iii)** (2, 0), $\left(-\frac{2}{3}, \frac{64}{27}\right)$
20. **(i)** $\frac{5}{3}, -\frac{1}{3}$ **(ii)** 7; $7x-y=13$ **(iii)** $63x-9y=139$

Exercise 17.H

1. **(i)** $x > 7$ **2.** $x < 4.5$ **3.** **(i)** 4 m **(ii)** 9 m **(ii)** $2t$ m/s **(iv)** 8 m/s
4. **(i)** 8 m **(ii)** 12.5 m **(iii)** 4.5 m **(iv)** t m/s **(v)** 7 m/s
5. **(i)** 35 m **(ii)** 60 m **(iii)** $40 - 10t$ m/s **(iv)** 10 m/s **(iv)** $t = 4$ **(vi)** 80 m
6. **(i)** 48 m **(ii)** $20 - 4t$ m/s **(iii)** 4 m/s **(iv)** 20 m/s **(v)** $t = 5$ **(vi)** 50 m
7. **(i)** $-\frac{600}{p^2}$ **(ii)** -1.5 **10.** **(i)** $-\frac{2000}{r^3}$ **(ii)** -2
11. **(i)** 1600 m **(ii)** $200 - 8t$ m/s **(iii)** 120 m/s **(iv)** 200 m/s **(v)** $t = 25$ **(vi)** 2500 m **(vii)** 8 m/s²
12. **(i)** 2 m **(ii)** 5 m/s **(iii)** 8 m/s² **(iv)** $\frac{1}{3}$, 1 **(v)** $\frac{2}{3}$
13. **(i)** 96 m **(ii)** 108 m **(iii)** 12 m **(iv)** $\frac{144}{(t+1)^2}$ **(v)** 16 m/s **(vi)** $t = 5$ **(vii)** $t > 11$
14. **(i)** 48 m/s; 178 m/s **(ii)** $a = 3t^2 - 8t + 4$ m/s² **(iii)** $t = \frac{2}{3}$, 2

Revision Exercise 17.I

1. **(a)** $2x$ **(b)** **(i)** 2 **(ii)** $12x + 7$ **(iii)** $6(2x + 1)^2$ **(c)** -2; $2x + y + 3 = 0$
2. **(a)** $2x - 5$; 2.5 **(b)** $\frac{20}{(3x+7)^2}$; 1¼ **(c)** **(i)** 20 **(ii)** $25 - 10t$ **(iii)** 10 **(iv)** 2.5, 31.25
3. **(a)** $2x + 4$ **(b)** **(i)** $15x^2$ **(ii)** $-25x^4 + 15x^2 - 22x$ **(iii)** $60x^2(5x^3 + 11)^3$
4. **(a)** $4x - 12$; $x < 3$ **(b)** $\frac{36}{(x+3)^2}$; 3, -9 **(c)** **(i)** 84 **(ii)** $\pm 8t$ **(iii)** ± 28 **(iv)** 5
5. **(a)** $-2x$ **(b)** **(i)** $5 - 2x - 6x^2$ **(ii)** $\frac{2x^2 - 2x + 2}{(1-x^2)^2}$ **(iii)** $-10x(1 - x^2)^4$ **(c)** Max $(-2, 42)$; min $(2, -22)$
6. **(a)** **(i)** 5, -4 **(ii)** 5 **(b)** **(i)** $2x + \frac{2}{x^3}$ **(ii)** $4\left(x^2 - \frac{1}{x^2}\right)^3\left(2x + \frac{2}{x^3}\right)$ **(c)** **(i)** 12 m/s **(iii)** 36 m **(iii)** 3 m/s².
7. **(a)** 5 **(c)** $(1, -4)$ **8.** $-32(1 - 4x)^7$; 32 **(b)** $\frac{3x^2 + 14x + 15}{(3x+7)^2}$; $-\frac{5}{3}$, -3 **(c)** **(i)** $4\pi r^2$ (ii) 100π
9. **(a)** **(i)** $-1 - 2x - 3x^2$ **(ii)** $2(1 - x - x^2 - x^3)(-1 - 2x - 3x^2)$ **(iii)** $\frac{-1 - 2x - 3x^2}{2\sqrt{1 - x - x^2 - x^3}}$
(b) $3\left(1 - \frac{1}{x}\right)^2\left(\frac{1}{x^2}\right)$; 12 **(c)** **(i)** (0,0), (2, 4) **(ii)** -9 **(iii)** (3, 0)
10. **(a)** $6 - 10x$ **(b)** **(i)** $100 - 9t^2$ **(ii)** 43.75 **(iii)** $t = \frac{10}{3}$ **(iv)** -54 m/s² **(c)** **(i)** $a = 2$, $b = 5$ **(ii)** -1, -4

CHAPTER 18: LINEAR PROGRAMMING

Exercise 18.C

1. At (6, 0) **2.** –10 **3.** 7½ **4.** 23 **5.** **(iii)** (160, 72) **6.** **(ii)** 50 **7.** **(c)** **(i)** 25 **(ii)** 21
10. **(ii)** $x - 3y \geq 0, y \geq 0, x + 3y \leq 6$ **11.** **(iii)** 13 **12.** **(iii)** 0

Exercise 18.D

1. (1, 4) **2.** (6, 36) **3.** (6, 3) **4.** €14 000, €20 000; (30, 16) **5.** 50 caravans; (20, 48)
6. **(i)** 5 **(ii)** (6, 2) **(iii)** (0, 5) **7.** €2232 **8.** €6000

Revision Exercise 18.E

1. **(ii)** At (0, 3) **2.** **(iv)** (24, 12) **3.** **(b)** (5, 0) **4.** **(b)** 20 of A, 30 of B **5.** **(b)** 4 taxis, 4 mini-buses
6. **(b)** **(ii)** 14 of P **(iii)** (30, 0) **7.** **(b)** Profit = $30x + 15y$; Max = €450 **8.** **(a)** **(iii)** At (5,3)
9. **(b)** **(ii)** 6 shops, 20 offices : €6200 **(iii)** 14 shops, 0 offices : 112 jobs.
10. **(a)** **(ii)** At (0, 6) **(b)** **(ii)** 65 cent

CHAPTER 19: FURTHER SEQUENCES & SERIES & THE BINOMIAL THEOREM

Exercise 19.A

1. **(iii)** 165 cent **(iv)** €27.75 **2.** **(iii)** 720 **3.** **(iii)** 120 cm **(iv)** 121 m **4.** 231 **5.** **(iii)** 407 km
6. 97% 7. **(i)** €121.55 **(ii)** €452.56 **8.** €2662 **9.** **(i)** 80 **(ii)** 605 **10.** **(i)** 16 777 216 **(ii)** 225
11. **(iii)** €20 971.52 **(iv)** €83 886.08 **12.** **(i)** 43 **(ii)** 383 **13.** **(i)** €6655 **(ii)** €18 205 **(iii)** €117 610
14. €396.14 **15.** €4200 **16.** €200 000 **17.** **(i)** 8.32 **(ii)** 9.75 **(iii)** 11.9 **(iv)** 21.5 **18.** €4000

Exercise 19.B

1. **(i)** $\frac{3}{8}$ **(ii)** 2 **(iii)** 320 **(iv)** 135 **(v)** $\frac{5}{8}$ **(vi)** $\frac{2}{3}$ **(vii)** $\frac{8}{15}$ **(viii)** 10 **(ix)** $1111\frac{1}{9}$ **(x)** $\frac{1}{6}$ **2.** **(ii)** $\frac{1}{9}$ **(iii)** $\frac{28}{9}$

3. **(a)** $\frac{2}{3}$ **(b)** **(i)** $\frac{8}{9}$ **(ii)** $\frac{1}{15}$ **(iii)** $\frac{2}{9}$ **(iv)** $\frac{1}{10}$ **4.** **(i)** 31.75 **(ii)** 32 **5.** 0.0004 **6.** $\frac{1}{3}$ **7.** 8, ½

8. **(ii)** $r = \frac{1}{3}$, $a = 162$ **(iii)** 243 **9.** $\frac{7}{33}$ **10.** **(i)** $\frac{19}{90}$
11. **(ii)** €728.20 **(iii)** €875 **12.** **(iii)** 79.375 m **(iv)** 80 m

13. **(ii)** $\frac{1}{2 - 2x}$ **(iii)** ¾ **(iv)** ½ **(v)** $0 < x < 1$ **14.** $\frac{1}{30}$ **(i)** $\frac{2}{15}$ **(ii)** $\frac{62}{15}$ **(iii)** $\frac{3}{10}$

15. **(i)** $\frac{1}{45}$ **(ii)** $\frac{3}{11}$ **(iii)** $\frac{5}{18}$ **(iv)** $\frac{7}{3}$ **(v)** $\frac{23}{1500}$

Exercise 19.C

1. $1 + 6x + 15x^2 + 20x^3 + 15x^4 + 6x^5 + x^6$ **2.** $1 + 7x + 21x^2 + 35x^3 + 35x^4 + 21x^5 + 7x^6 + x^7$
3. $1 + 2x + x^2$ **4.** $1 - 4x + 6x^2 - 4x^3 + x^4$ **5.** $1 - 5x + 10x^2 - 10x^3 + 5x^4 - x^5$
6. **(i)** $1 + 5x + 10x^2 + 10x^3 + 5x^4 + x^5$ **7.** **(i)** $1 + 3x + 3x^2 + x^3$ **8.** **(i)** $1 + 4x + 6x^2 + 4x^3 + x^4$
11. $601 + 205\sqrt{10}$ **14.** $1 - 3x + 3x^2 - x^3$; Both = –1 **16.** $1 + 7x + 21x^2$

Revision Exercise 19.D

1. **(a)** **(i)** €1.95 **(ii)** €36.75 **(b)** 6 **2.** **(a)** $\frac{2}{9}$ **(c)** 245 760

3. **(a)** **(i)** $\frac{4}{5}$ **(ii)** $\frac{8}{15}$ **(iii)** $\frac{25}{6}$ **(b)** **(i)** €334.56 **(ii)** €1493.83 **4.** **(c)** €462 **5.** **(a)** 1092 m **(b)** 6

6. **(a)** $\frac{1}{9}$ **(i)** $\frac{1}{90}$ **(ii)** $\frac{100}{9}$ **(b)** **(i)** €3934.30 **(ii)** €29 567.20

7. **(a)** **(iii)** 6074 **(iv)** 6250 **(b)** **(i)** €13 113 **(ii)** €1220 **8.** **(a)** **(i)** 38 **(ii)** 50

9. **(a)** $r = \frac{1}{3}$ $(a = 6)$ or $r = \frac{2}{3}$ $(a = 3)$ **(b)** **(i)** $\frac{2}{11}$ **(ii)** $\frac{17}{90}$ **(iii)** $\frac{7}{990}$

10. **(b)** €1450 **(c)** **(ii)** $\frac{1}{2-4x}$ **(iii)** $\frac{3}{2}$ **(iv)** $\frac{1}{5}$ **(v)** $0 < x < ½$

Chapter 20: Vectors

Exercise 20.D

1. **(i)** $\vec{x} + \vec{z}$ **(ii)** $\vec{x} + ½\vec{z}$ **(iii)** $\vec{z} + ½\vec{x}$ **(iv)** $\vec{z} - \vec{x}$ **2.** **(i)** $\vec{p} + \vec{r}$ **(ii)** $½\vec{p} + ½\vec{r}$

(iii) $½\vec{p} + ½\vec{r}$ **(iv)** $\vec{r} - \vec{p}$ **3.** **(i)** $½\vec{a} + ½\vec{b}$ **(ii)** $¼\vec{a}$ **(iii)** $\frac{2}{3}\vec{b}$ **(iv)** $¼\vec{a} + ½\vec{b}$

4. **(i)** $\vec{x} = ½\vec{a} + ½\vec{b}$ **(ii)** $\vec{y} = ½\vec{a} + ½\vec{c}$ **(iii)** $\vec{z} = ½\vec{b} + ½\vec{c}$

5. **(i)** $½\vec{a} + ½\vec{c}$ **(ii)** $\vec{b} - ½\vec{a} - ½\vec{c}$ **(iii)** $\frac{1}{3}\left(\vec{b} - \frac{1}{2}\vec{a} - \frac{1}{2}\vec{c}\right)$ **(iv)** $\frac{1}{3}\vec{a} + \frac{1}{3}\vec{b} + \frac{1}{3}\vec{c}$ **6.** $p = ¾$; $m = -1$, $n = 1½$

Exercise 20.E

3. **(i)** $11\vec{i} + 2\vec{j}$ **(ii)** $5\vec{i} - \vec{j}$ **(iii)** $-\vec{i} + 3\vec{j}$ **4.** **(i)** $4\vec{i} - 6\vec{j}$ **(ii)** $22\vec{j}$ **(iii)** $-2\vec{i} - 8\vec{j}$

5. **(i)** (4, 3) **(ii)** (7, –2) **(iii)** (–1, 4) **(iv)** (3, –7) **(v)** (3, 4) **6.** $l = 2$, $k = -1$

7. **(i)** $6\vec{i} - 6\vec{j}$ **(ii)** $t = ½$, $k = 2$ **8.** **(ii)** $k = 4$ **9.** **(i)** $2\vec{i} + 8\vec{j}$ **(ii)** $\vec{i} + 4\vec{j}$ **10.** $10\vec{i} - 3\vec{j}$

11. **(i)** $-15\vec{i} + 8\vec{j}$ **(ii)** $-25\vec{i} + 10\vec{j}$

Exercise 20.F

1. **(i)** $\sqrt{52}$ **(ii)** $\sqrt{5}$ **(iii)** $\sqrt{34}$ **(iv)** $\sqrt{68}$ **(v)** $\sqrt{2}$ **(vi)** 4 **(vii)** 6 **(viii)** $\sqrt{2}$ **(ix)** 13 **(x)** $\sqrt{10}$

3. Yes **4.** ±10 **5.** ±7 **6.** **(i)** $3\vec{i} + 4\vec{j}$ **(ii)** 5 **7.** 10 **8.** **(i)** $\sqrt{5}$, $\sqrt{10}$, 5

10. **(i)** $2\vec{i} + \vec{j}$ **(ii)** $10\vec{i} - 5\vec{j}$ **(iii)** $10\vec{i} + 5\vec{j}$ **11.** **(iii)** $k = -2$, $t = -3$ **(iv)** No

Exercise 20.G

1. **(i)** 36 **(ii)** 62 **(iii)** 50 **(iv)** –2 **(v)** 36 **(vi)** –7 **(vii)** 0 **(viii)** 38 **(ix)** 8 **(x)** –42

2. **(i)** 9 **(ii)** 7 **(iii)** 16; Yes **3.** **(i)** –2 **(ii)** –24 **(iii)** 22; Yes **5.** **(i)** 8 **(ii)** –1.6 **(iii)** 6.6

6. **(i)** 3 **(ii)** –1.5 **(iii)** –2 **7.** **(i)** $8\vec{i} + 8\vec{j}$ **(ii)** 8 **(iii)** 136 **8.** **(i)** $4\vec{i} + 4\vec{j}$ **(ii)** –4

9. **(i)** $2\vec{i} + 10\vec{j}$ **(ii)** 26 **10.** 155

Exercise 20.H

2. Yes **4.** Not ⊥ **5.** $k = 9$ **6.** Yes, perpendicular **7.** Not perpendicular

8. $\vec{pq} = 4\vec{i} + (k-1)\vec{j}$; $k = 33$ **10.** **(i)** 16° **(ii)** 45° **(iii)** 53° **(iv)** 157° **(v)** 90°

Exercise 20.I

4. **(iii)** Yes **5.** **(i)** $-7\vec{i} + 2\vec{j}$; $-11\vec{i} + 0\vec{j}$ **(ii)** No

Revision Exercise 20.J

1. **(b)** **(i)** $\vec{a} + \vec{c}$ **(ii)** $\vec{a} + \frac{1}{2}\vec{c}$ **(iii)** $\frac{1}{2}\vec{c} - \vec{a}$ **(c)** **(i)** $3\vec{i} - 4\vec{j}$ **(ii)** 5 **(iii)** 14 **(iv)** $-4\vec{i} - 3\vec{j}$

2. **(b)** **(i)** $6\vec{i} - 3\vec{j}$ **(ii)** $\sqrt{45}$ **(iii)** 1 **(iv)** $3\vec{i} + 6\vec{j}$ **(v)** Yes **(c)** **(i)** $\frac{1}{2}\vec{b}$ **(ii)** $\vec{a} - \frac{1}{2}\vec{b}$ **(iii)** $\frac{1}{3}\vec{a} - \frac{1}{6}\vec{b}$ **(iv)** $\frac{1}{3}\vec{a} + \frac{1}{3}\vec{b}$

3. **(b)(i)** $\vec{a} + \vec{c}$ **(ii)** $\frac{1}{2}\vec{a} + \vec{c}$ **(iii)** $\vec{c} - \frac{1}{2}\vec{a}$ **(c)** **(ii)** $\sqrt{72}$ or 8.485 **(iv)** 13 **(v)** $4\vec{i} - 2\vec{j}$

4. **(b)** **(i)** $2\vec{a}$ **(ii)** $\vec{a} + \frac{1}{2}\vec{c}$ **(iii)** $\vec{a} - \frac{1}{2}\vec{c}$ **(iv)** $2\vec{a} - \vec{c}$; 10; 16

5. **(b)** **(ii)** $9\vec{i} + 2\vec{j}$ **(iii)** $3\vec{i} + \vec{j}$

6. **(b)** **(ii)** $\sqrt{68}$ or 8.246 **(v)** $m = 3, n = -1$

7. **(a)** **(i)** $\vec{a} + \vec{c}$ **(ii)** $\frac{2}{5}\vec{a}$ **(iii)** $-\frac{3}{5}\vec{a} - \vec{c}$ **(iv)** $-\frac{1}{5}\vec{a} - \vec{c}$ **(b)** **(ii)** 10 **(iii)** $m = 2, t = 10$ **(iv)** Not ⊥

8. **(b)** **(i)** $8\vec{i} + 16\vec{j}$, $-4\vec{i} + 3\vec{j}$, $-12\vec{i} + 5\vec{j}$ **(iii)** 63 **(iv)** No **(v)** Yes

9. **(b)** **(i)** $-4\vec{i} - 4\vec{j}$; $8\vec{i} - 6\vec{j}$ **(iv)** 98° **10.** **(b)** **(i)** 0 **(ii)** No **(iii)** 16° **(iv)** Yes

CHAPTER 21: FURTHER THEOREMS

Exercise 21.A

2. **(i)** (98, 65) **(ii)** (108, 30) **(iii)** (30, 20) **(iv)** (58, 116) **3.** 18° **4.** **(i)** 100° **(ii)** 50°; 10° **5.** **(i)** 136° **(ii)** 110°

Exercise 21.B

1. **(i)** 33° **(ii)** 90° **(iii)** 57° **2.** 5 **6.** 5; 8 **7.** **(i)** 60° **(ii)** 30° **(iii)** 90° **(iv)** 30°; 30°, 60°

Exercise 21.C

1. **(i)** 8 **(ii)** 6 **(iii)** 5 **(iv)** 15 **(v)** 6 **(vi)** 8 **(vii)** 5 **(viii)** 4 **(ix)** 10 **(x)** 1.6 **2.** 6 **3.** 4 **4.** $\sqrt{18}$ **5.** 8 **6.** 6 **7.** 2.2 **8.** **(i)** 4 **(ii)** 10 **(iii)** 5

Exercise 21.D

1. **(i)** 72° **(ii)** 67° **2.** **(a)** **(i)** 30° **(ii)** 90° **3.** **(i)** 75° **(ii)** 75° **(iii)** 75° **4.** **(i)** 60° **(ii)** 110° **(iii)** 35° **6.** 70°; 55°

Revision Exercise 21.E

2. **(b)** **(i)** 80° **(ii)** 40° **3.** **(b)** $\sqrt{3}r$ **4.** **(b)** 7.2 **5.** **(b)** 6 **6.** **(b)** 3, 6, 4 **7.** **(b)** **(i)** 65° **(ii)** 25° **(iii)** 25°